Evaluation Guide for Merrill Geometry

Merrill Geometry provides a comprehensive course in high school geometry. *Merrill Geometry* was high school teacher developed and written. This text provides every opportunity for student success.

To further strengthen the presentation of the text material, many special features have been included. To examine selected examples of the features of *Merrill Geometry*, please turn to the following pages.

(pp. 38, 449)   **Student Annotations** help students to identify important concepts as they study.

(pp. 79, 287)   **Highlighting** in color helps identify important concepts.

(pp. 245, 344)   **Mini Reviews** and **Cumulative Reviews** help students maintain skills introduced in previous chapters.

(pp. 178–181)   **Review and Test** material provided in the *Vocabulary, Chapter Summary, Chapter Review,* and *Chapter Test* enables students to review and evaluate their progress.

(pp. 532–548)   The **Logo Appendix** at the back of the text provides a short course in Logo programming.

(pp. 432–433)   **Standardized Test Practice Questions** help students prepare for college entrance tests.

Special features appear periodically to provide interesting and useful extra topics.

(pp. 13, 129)   **Applications** pages provide insights into the uses of geometry in everyday life from a variety of disciplines.

(pp. 145, 330)   **Problem Solving** pages illustrate helpful strategies for solving problems.

(pp. 87, 210)   **Topics in Geometry** provide information concerning different approaches to geometry.

(pp. 155, 334)   **Using Calculators** features instruct students in using a calculator.

(pp. 171, 497)   **Statistics That Shape Your Life** introduce students to statistical concepts with interesting graphs.

(pp. 199, 442)   **Excursions in Geometry** topics include glimpses into the development and uses of geometry as well as enrichment concepts.

(pp. 4, 165)   **Algebra Review** features help students to maintain and use algebraic concepts.

(pp. 93, 122)   **Annotations** in the Teacher Annotated Edition give an objective for each lesson, teaching suggestions, answers to problems, and suggested daily assignments.

(pp. 549–566)   **Diagnostic Skills Review** provides a comprehensive review of algebraic skills.

(pp. 568–579)   **Postulates and Theorems** list provides students with a concise listing of the postulates and theorems used in the text.

Teacher Guide and Tests
for
Geometry

Authors
Foster • Cummins • Yunker

Merrill Publishing Company
A Bell & Howell Company
Columbus, Ohio
Toronto • London • Sydney

Contents

Permission is granted to teachers of *Merrill Geometry* to reproduce and use the tests in this Teacher Guide entirely or in part.

ISBN 0-675-05843-0

Published by
Merrill Publishing Co.
A Bell & Howell Company
Columbus, Ohio 43216

Printed in the United States of America

Merrill
Geometry

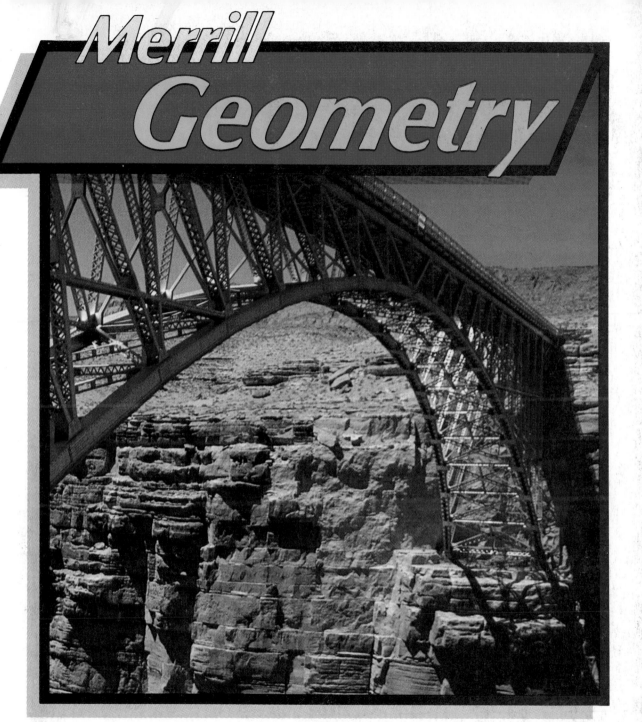

Foster • Cummins • Yunker

Merrill Publishing Company
A Bell & Howell Company
Columbus, Ohio

Toronto • London • Sydney

Authors

Alan G. Foster is chairman of the Mathematics Department at Addison Trail High School, Addison, Illinois. He has taught mathematics courses at every level of the high school curriculum. Mr. Foster obtained his B.S. degree from Illinois State University and his M.A. degree in mathematics from the University of Illinois. Mr. Foster is active in professional organizations at local, state, and national levels, frequently speaking or conducting workshops. He is past president of the Illinois Council of Teachers of Mathematics. Mr. Foster is a recipient of the Illinois Council of Teachers of Mathematics T. E. Rine Award for outstanding service and leadership to mathematics education. He is a co-author of *Merrill Algebra One* and *Merrill Algebra Two*.

Jerry J. Cummins is the Director of Management Information Services for Proviso Township High Schools, Maywood and Hillside, Illinois. He served as Mathematics Department Chairman in the district for 18 years. Mr. Cummins obtained his B.S. degree in mathematics education and his M.S. degree in educational administration and supervision from Southern Illinois University. He also holds an M.S. degree in mathematics education from the University of Oregon. Mr. Cummins has spoken on mathematics at the local, state, and national levels. Mr. Cummins received an Illinois State Presidential Award for Excellence in Teaching of Mathematics in 1984. He is a co-author of Merrill's *Programming in BASIC*.

Lee E. Yunker is chairman of the Mathematics Department at West Chicago Community High School, West Chicago, Illinois. Mr. Yunker obtained his B.S. degree from Elmhurst College and his M.Ed. degree in mathematics from the University of Illinois. Mr. Yunker is very active in professional mathematics organizations for which he frequently speaks or conducts workshops. Currently, Mr. Yunker is editor for the *Student Math Notes* for the National Council of Teachers of Mathematics and is on the Board of Directors of the National Council of Supervisors of Mathematics. He received an Illinois State Presidential Award for Excellence in Teaching of Mathematics in 1985. Mr. Yunker is a co-author of *Merrill Advanced Mathematical Concepts*.

ISBN 0-675-05842-2

Published by
Merrill Publishing Company
A Bell & Howell Company
Columbus, Ohio 43216

Printed in the United States of America

Consultants

John W. Kenelly
Department of Mathematical Sciences
Clemson University
Clemson, South Carolina

Margaret J. Kenney
Assistant to the Director
  Mathematics Institute
Boston College
Chestnut Hill, Massachusetts

Reviewers

John Bisbikis
Program Administrator, Mathematics
Reavis High School
Burbank, Illinois

Michael G. Bolduc
Mathematics Teacher
Nashua High School
Nashua, New Hampshire

Beverly G. Everett
Mathematics Department Chairperson
Terry Parker High School
Jacksonville, Florida

Sandra L. Giuliani
Mathematics Teacher
Stonewall Jackson High School
Manassas, Virginia

Carol Hermann
Mathematics/Computer Teacher
Athens High School
Troy, Michigan

Mary Beth Johnson
Mathematics Teacher
Plantation High School
Plantation, Florida

Wandaline K. Perelli
Mathematics Teacher
Lowell High School
San Francisco, California

Jerry W. Shannon
Mathematics Department Chairperson
Red Bank High School
Chattanooga, Tennessee

Julia M. Snellgroves
Instructional Specialist/Teacher
Douglas Byrd High School
Fayetteville, North Carolina

James R. Raines
Mathematics Teacher
Woodbridge High School
Woodbridge, Virginia

Joyce Fielder White
Mathematics Department Chairperson
Campbell High School
Smyrna, Georgia

Staff

Editorial:

Project Editor: Susan H. Danko; *Editors:* Nancy E. Dawson, Donald T. Porzio; *Photo Editor:* David T. Dennison; *Production Editor:* Kimberly Munsie

Art:

Book Designer: Larry W. Collins; *Project Artist:* Lewis H. Bolen; *Artist:* Karen Martino; *Illustrators:* Jim Shough, Don Robison

Photo Credits

Preface

Merrill Geometry was developed by experienced high school teachers for the classroom. The goals of the text are to develop proficiency with geometric skills and to apply the understanding of geometric concepts to real-life situations. This text promotes success, improves logical reasoning, and provides a complete course in high school geometry. To achieve these goals, the following strategies are used.

Build upon a Solid Foundation. Geometric concepts are introduced intuitively by drawing upon students' past experience with geometry in real life. Students learn to organize their ideas and gradually are led to the concept of geometric proof. Once the needed background is provided, students can progress successfully.

Utilize Sound Pedagogy. *Merrill Geometry* covers in logical sequence all topics generally presented at this level. Concepts are introduced when they are needed. Each concept presented is then used within that lesson and in later lessons.

Facilitate Learning. An appropriate reading level has been maintained throughout the text. Furthermore, many photographs, illustrations, charts, graphs, and tables provide visual aids for the concepts and skills presented. Hence, students are able to read and learn with increased understanding.

Use Relevant Real-Life Applications. Applications are provided not only for practice but also to aid understanding of how concepts are used.

Merrill Geometry offers a variety of useful aids for the student.

Student Annotations	Helps students identify important concepts as they study.
Selected Answers	Allows students to check their progress as they work. These answers are provided at the back of the text.
Mini Review	Provides students with a quick review of skills and concepts taught previously.
Vocabulary	Enables students to focus on increasing their mathematical vocabulary.
Chapter Summary	Provides students with a listing of major concepts presented within the chapter.
Chapter Review	Permits students to review each chapter by working sample problems from each lesson.
Chapter Test	Enables students to check their own progress.
Cumulative Review	Helps students maintain and reinforce geometric concepts.
Standardized Test Practice Questions	Helps students to become familiar with types of questions that appear on standardized tests.

The following special features, which appear periodically throughout the text, provide interesting and useful extra topics.

Applications	Provides insights into the uses of geometry in everyday life from a variety of disciplines.
Using Calculators	Instructs students in using a calculator. The use of the calculator is related to concepts that are taught within the chapter.
Problem Solving	Illustrates several helpful strategies for solving geometric problems.
Topics in Geometry	Provides information concerning different approaches to geometry such as topology and elliptic geometry.
Algebra Review	Helps students maintain and use algebraic concepts.
Statistics That Shape Your Life	Introduces statistical concepts with interesting graphs.
Excursions in Geometry	Enlivens and helps maintain student interest by providing interesting side trips. Topics are varied and include glimpses into the development and uses of geometry as well as enrichment concepts, history, and puzzles.

The textbook contains an appendix on **Logo** that provides instruction in writing programs using the Terrapin™ Logo language. This feature can be taught as a unit or interspersed throughout the year.

The **Diagnostic Skills Review** at the back of the text provides review exercises to help students maintain algebraic skills.

The **Postulates and Theorems List** provides students with a concise listing of the postulates and theorems used in the text.

The **Glossary** provides students with a list of the important mathematical terms used in the text.

Students will find the practical, straightforward approach of *Merrill Geometry* both interesting and easy to understand. Teachers will find that the careful sequencing of topics and thorough mathematical treatment of essential ideas provide an effective course in high school geometry.

Terrapin™ Logo is a trademark of Terrapin, Inc., 222 Third St., Cambridge, Massachusetts 02142 (617) 492-8816

Table of Contents

1   Points, Lines, and Planes

2   Measure

3 Angles and Perpendiculars _____

Lessons

Angles and Measure

Perpendiculars

Review and Testing

Applications and Extensions

4 Congruent Triangles _____

Lessons

Introduction to Triangles

Congruence and Triangles

Review and Testing

Applications and Extensions

5 Triangle Inequalities

6 Parallels

7 Polygons

8 Similarity

9 Right Triangles ────────────────────

Lessons

Review and Testing

Applications and Extensions

Technology

10 Circles and Spheres ────────────────

Lessons

Review and Testing

Applications and Extensions

11   Area and Volume

12   Coordinates

13   Loci and Constructions

14   Transformations

Appendix: Logo

CHAPTER 1

Points, Lines, and Planes

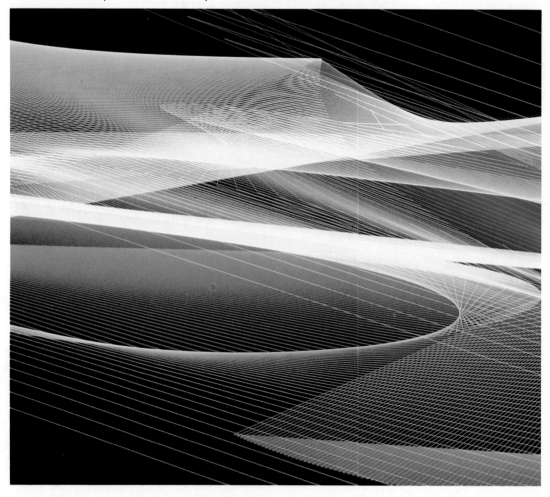

Computer graphics is the process of displaying output in the form of graphs, diagrams, or pictures. Every image is made by a pattern of dots on the screen. A dot on the computer screen is similar to the concept of a point in geometry.

1-1 Points, Lines, and Planes

Objectives: Recognize and identify models for points, lines, and planes.

One of the most important features of a computer graphics screen is its resolution, or the fineness of the detail, it can display. In low resolution graphics, the screen might be partitioned into a grid of 1600 dots. In high resolution graphics, the same screen might be partitioned into a grid of 240,000 dots. Certainly these dots are smaller and more numerous than the dots used in low resolution graphics. As the resolution increases, the dots decrease in size until they suggest the idea of a point in geometry.

Points, lines, and **planes** are the basic terms in geometry. These three terms are not defined but they are used to define other terms and to describe problems.

Physical models of the concepts, including intersecting lines and planes, enhance discussion.

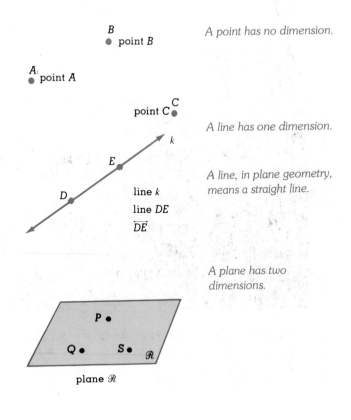

A location on a map or a pinhole suggests the idea of a point. Points are represented by dots and named by capital letters. You can think of a point as an exact location in space.

A point has no dimension.

A flight path or a straight series of dots on a computer screen suggests the idea of a line. Lines extend indefinitely and have no thickness or width. Lines are represented by double arrows and are named by lowercase letters. A line also can be named using double arrows over capital letters representing two points on the line. For example, the figure at the right can be named as line k, line DE, or $\overleftrightarrow{DE}$.

A line has one dimension.

A line, in plane geometry, means a straight line.

A flat map or a flat computer screen itself suggests the idea of a plane. A plane extends indefinitely in all directions and has no thickness. Planes are represented by four-sided figures and are named by capital script letters. Planes also can be named by using three points of the plane that are not on the same line. The figure at the right is plane $\mathcal{R}$ or plane P, Q, S.

A plane has two dimensions.

Two lines, two planes, or lines and planes **intersect** if they have points in common. For example, the two lines below intersect at point E.

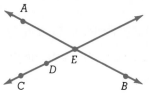

$\overleftrightarrow{AB}$ intersects $\overleftrightarrow{CD}$ at E.
The intersection of $\overleftrightarrow{AB}$
and $\overleftrightarrow{CD}$ is E.

Examples

1 **Find the intersection of plane $\mathcal{A}$ and plane $\mathcal{B}$.**

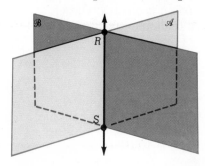

Plane $\mathcal{A}$ and plane $\mathcal{B}$ have $\overleftrightarrow{RS}$ in common. Their intersection is $\overleftrightarrow{RS}$.

2 **Find the intersection of plane $\mathcal{A}$ and $\overleftrightarrow{TR}$.**

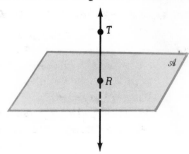

Plane $\mathcal{A}$ and $\overleftrightarrow{TR}$ have point R in common. Their intersection is point R.

In the figure at the right, all the points of $\overleftrightarrow{AB}$ are also points of $\mathcal{M}$. We say $\overleftrightarrow{AB}$ is in $\mathcal{M}$, or $\mathcal{M}$ **contains** $\overleftrightarrow{AB}$. Also, A **lies on** $\overleftrightarrow{AB}$ and is in $\mathcal{M}$. Alternatively, both $\overleftrightarrow{AB}$ and $\mathcal{M}$ contain A.

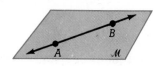

Lines contain points.   Points lie on lines and are in planes.
Planes contain points and lines.   Lines are in planes.

In geometry, points, lines, and planes are represented by figures or diagrams. These are labeled to help visualize the relationships between the points, lines, and planes.

Examples

3 Draw and label a diagram to show $\overleftrightarrow{AB}$ and $\overleftrightarrow{CD}$ intersecting at P.

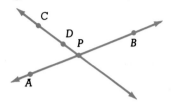

4 Draw and label a digram to show plane $\mathcal{N}$ contains m but not S.

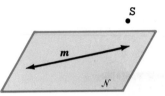

In the Assignment Guide
EN: refers to Enriched Course
AV: refers to Average Course
FD: refers to Fundamental Course

EN: 1–13 odd, 1–27 odd, 28–32; **AV:** 1–13 odd, 1–30; **FD:** 1–14, 1–21 odd;

Exploratory Exercises

ALL LEVELS: Algebra Review

Determine whether each of the following suggests a point, a line, or a plane.

1. corner of a box
2. side of a box
3. meeting of a wall and ceiling of a room
4. wall of a room
5. parking lot
6. guitar string
7. vapor trail of an airplane
8. grain of salt
9. ceiling of a room
10. clothesline
11. period at the end of a sentence
12. star in the sky
13. laser beam
14. small town on a map

Written Exercises

For Exercises 1–12, see students' work.

Draw and label a diagram to show each of the following relationships.

1. Plane $\mathcal{L}$ and $\overleftrightarrow{CD}$ intersect at P.
2. ℓ and m intersect at R.
3. $\overleftrightarrow{RS}$ and plane $\mathcal{M}$ do *not* intersect.
4. $\overrightarrow{PQ}$, $\overleftrightarrow{RS}$, and plane $\mathcal{N}$ intersect at T.
5. Plane $\mathcal{L}$, plane $\mathcal{M}$, and plane $\mathcal{N}$ intersect at P.
6. Plane $\mathcal{M}$, plane $\mathcal{N}$, and plane $\mathcal{L}$ do *not* intersect.
7. P lies on $\overleftrightarrow{AB}$.
8. $\overleftrightarrow{AB}$ contains R.
9. t contains Q and R, but does *not* contain P and S.
10. A, B, and C lie on m but D does *not* lie on m.
11. Plane $\mathcal{M}$ contains n and R.
12. t contains P and lies in plane $\mathcal{N}$.

For Exercises 13–21, see the Teacher Guide.

Use the figure for each of the following.

13. Write another name for $\overleftrightarrow{AB}$.

14. Write another name for ℓ.

15. What points do $\overleftrightarrow{AD}$ and $\overleftrightarrow{BC}$ have in common?

16. What points do $\overleftrightarrow{AB}$ and m have in common?

17. Name two points that lie on $\overleftrightarrow{AD}$.

18. Name two points that lie on p.

19. Write three other names for n.

20. Write three other names for $\overleftrightarrow{BC}$.

21. Write three names for the plane that contains all the points and lines represented in the figure.

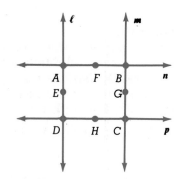

Exercises 13–21

Use the figure for each of the following.

22. Write another name for plane $\mathcal{A}$.

23. What points do line m and plane $\mathcal{A}$ have in common?

24. Name a point *not* in plane $\mathcal{B}$.

25. Name a point *not* in plane $\mathcal{A}$.

26. Name all points common to plane $\mathcal{A}$ and plane $\mathcal{B}$.

27. What points do lines m and n have in common?

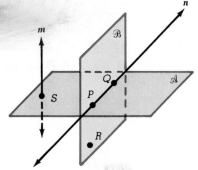

Exercises 22–27

Answer the following.

28. Suppose P and Q are two points. How many lines can contain both P and Q?

29. Suppose P and Q are two points. How many planes can contain both P and Q?

30. Suppose P, Q, and R are three points *not* on the same line. How many lines can be drawn so that each line contains two of the points?

31. Think about a board or a piece of stiff cardboard. What is the *minimum* number of legs needed to support it in a fixed position?

32. Why does a tripod stand firm on uneven ground?

Algebra Review

1. Express 0.00000253 in scientific notation. 2.53×10^{-6}

Solve.

2. Les is 6 years younger than twice Jim's age. The sum of their ages is 30. What are their ages?   Les, 18 yr Jim, 12 yr

Simplify.

3. $x(2x + 5) - 7(x^2 + 3x - 2)$

4. $(2y^2 + 5y - 3) + (7y^2 - 8y + 9)$

5. $(2y + 5)(3y - 7)$ $6y^2 + y - 35$

3. $-5x^2 - 16x + 14$ 4. $9y^2 - 3y + 6$

The Algebra Review provides an opportunity for continuous review.

1-2 Definitions

Objectives: Recognize collinear and coplanar points; recognize the characteristics of a good definition.

To define a word, you use **undefined** terms or terms that have previously been defined. The basic terms of geometry—**point, line, and plane**—are undefined. They are used as building blocks in the construction of other terms of geometry.

An undefined term is a word that has a meaning that is readily understood.

The following definitions are based on points, lines, and planes.

Points are collinear if and only if they lie on the same line.	*Definition of Collinear Points*
Points are coplanar if and only if they lie in the same plane.	*Definition of Coplanar Points*

A model of a tetrahedron can enhance classroom discussion.

Examples

1 **In the figure, are points A, E, and D collinear?**

Since points A, E, and D lie on $\overleftrightarrow{AD}$, they are collinear.

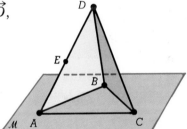

2 **In the figure above, are points A, B, C, and D coplanar?**

Points A, B, and C lie in plane $\mathcal{M}$, but point D does *not* lie in plane $\mathcal{M}$. Thus, the four points are *not* coplanar.

Definitions must be written very carefully. The following guidelines will help you write good definitions.

1. Name the term being defined. 2. Use only undefined terms or previously defined terms. 3. Identify the set to which the term belongs. 4. State the properties that distinguish the term from others in the set. 5. Make it reversible. 6. Make it concise.	*Guidelines for a Definition*

Points are collinear if and only if they lie on the same line. Notice that this definition satisfies all the guidelines of a good definition.

1. The term being defined is *collinear*.	*Name the term being defined.*
2. The definition uses *points* and *lines*. These terms are undefined.	*Use only undefined terms or previously defined terms.*
3. Collinear points belong to the set of *points*.	*Identify the set to which the term belongs.*
4. Collinear points *lie on the same line*. Some sets of points do *not* lie on the same line.	*State the properties which distinguish the term from others in the set.*
5. If points are collinear, then they lie on the same line. If points lie on the same line, then they are collinear. Notice how "points are collinear" and "lie on the same line" are reversed. Studying conditional statements will help students learn to reverse statements.	*Make it reversible.*
6. Points are collinear if and only if they lie on the same line. Notice this statement contains as few words as possible.	*Make it concise.*

Example

3 **Noncollinear points are points that are *not* collinear. Write a good definition for noncollinear points without using the word collinear.**

The term being defined is *noncollinear* points.	*Name the term being defined.*
Use only *points* and *line*.	*Use only undefined terms or previously defined terms.*
Noncollinear points belong to the set of *points*.	*Identify the set to which the term belongs.*
Some sets of points do *not* lie on the same line. Collinear points *lie on the same line*.	*State the properties that distinguish the term from others in its set.*
If points are noncollinear, then they do *not* lie on the same line. If points do *not* lie on the same line, then they are noncollinear.	*Make it reversible.*
Points are noncollinear if and only if they do *not* lie on the same line. Reversing statements will be further developed in the next lesson.	*Make it concise.*

Example

4 The statement "they lie in the same plane" is *not* a good definition. Tell why. Assume the terms in the statement are previously defined.

The statement does *not* satisfy guidelines **1, 3,** and **5.**

1. It does *not* name the term being defined.
3. It does *not* identify the set to which the term belongs.
5. It is *not* reversible.

EN: 1–11 odd, 1–31 odd, 33–36; **AV:** 1–11 odd, 1–29 odd; **FD:** 1–12, 1–17, p. 4, 22–27

Exploratory Exercises

Use the figure to determine whether each of the following is *true* or *false.*

1. A, B, and C are collinear.
2. A, B, and C are coplanar.
3. E, F, G, and H are coplanar.
4. A, F, E, and G are coplanar.
5. B, J, and E are coplanar.
6. B, J, and C are coplanar.
7. H, G, and D are collinear.
8. B, J, and C are collinear.
9. B, J, H, and G are coplanar.
10. B, J, H, and G are collinear.
11. G and H are collinear.
12. K and D are collinear.

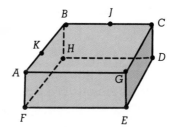

Exercises 1–12

Written Exercises

Use the figure to identify each of the following sets of points as collinear or non-collinear.

1. F, G, E
2. A, J, E
3. B, F, A
4. H, B, A
5. C, J, E
6. K, G, C
7. F, D, B
8. J, K, E

Points are noncoplanar if and only if they do *not* lie in the same plane. Use the figure to identify each of the following sets of points as coplanar or noncoplanar.

9. A, H, E, D
10. F, B, G, C
11. E, J, C, D
12. F, A, D, J
13. F, G, K, D
14. G, F, C, D

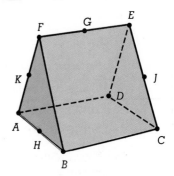

Exercises 1–14

Use the figure below to complete the following exercises.

15. Name ten lines.
16. Name seven planes.
17. Name four noncoplanar points.
18. Name the intersection of $\overleftrightarrow{BD}$ and $\overleftrightarrow{CD}$.
19. Name the intersection of plane A, E, B and plane A, C, D.
20. What points do plane A, E, C and $\overleftrightarrow{AE}$ have in common?
21. Name the intersection of plane A, E, B and $\overleftrightarrow{ED}$.
22. Name the intersection of plane A, E, C, plane E, C, D, and plane A, B, D. C

Plane A, D, E; Plane A, B, E; Plane B, E, D; Plane D, E, C; Plane A, E, C; Plane A, B, C

A, B, D, E; B, C, D, E; A, C, D, E

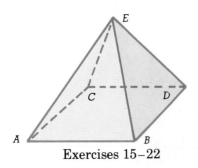

Exercises 15–22

For Exercises 23–32, see the Teacher Guide.

Determine whether each of the following statements is a good definition. If *not*, tell why. Assume the terms in each statement are previously defined.

23. Skew lines are lines that are *not* coplanar.
24. A bedroom is a room where people sleep.
25. A person who lives in Detroit lives in Michigan.
26. A triangle is a polygon having three sides and three angles.
27. A diagonal of a quadrilateral separates the quadrilateral into two triangles.
28. Coinciding lines are lines that have all their points in common.
29. Points are noncoplanar points if and only if they do *not* lie in the same plane.
30. Points are collinear points if and only if they lie on the same line.

For each of the following, write your own definition. State how the definition satisfies the guidelines of a good definition.

31. reversible
32. concise

Challenge Exercises

Use the following sequence of definitions to answer the questions.

(i) **Points are costellar if and only if they are contravariant.**
(ii) **Points are contravariant if and only if they are semidiffused.**
(iii) **Points are semidiffused if and only if they are costellar.**

33. To what set does costellar belong?
34. What are the undefined terms being used to define contravariant?
35. What properties distinguish semidiffused points from the other points?
36. Have costellar, contravariant, and semidiffused been defined? Explain.

1-3 Conditional Statements

Objective: Write statements in "if-then" or "if and only if" form.

In the previous lesson, part of the definition for collinear points was written in the following way.

If points are collinear, then they lie on the same line.

This statement has two parts. One part begins with *if* and the other part begins with *then*. An if-then statement is called a **conditional statement.** The statement in the photo below is a conditional statement with *then* omitted.

If you want a healthy cat, then start with a healthy kitten.

If you want a healthy cat, start with a healthy kitten.

Conditional statements are written in many different ways, but all conditional statements can be written in **if-then** form. For example, *all* of the following statements can be written as: *If you are a genius, then you are left-handed.*

All geniuses are left-handed.
You are left-handed if you are a genius.
You are a genius only if you are left-handed.
Being a genius implies you are left-handed.
You are left-handed when you are a genius.

You may want to emphasize how *all, if, only if, implies,* and *when* are used in these conditional statements.

Example

1 **Rewrite the following conditional statement in if-then form.**

There is at least one plane that contains a line and a point *not* on the line.

If there is a line and a point *not* on the line, *then* there is at least one plane that contains them.

Sometimes a conditional statement is written "if p, then q." The part following *if* is called the **hypothesis.** It tells what is given or to be *assumed*. The part following *then* is called the **conclusion.** It tells the *result*, or what is believed to follow from the assumption. Another way of reading "if p, then q" is "p implies q."

The hypothesis is p.
The conclusion is q.

Conditional   If there is a line and a point *not* on the line, then there is at least one plane that contains them.

Hypothesis   there is a line and a point *not* on the line

Conclusion   there is at least one plane that contains them

Conditional statements may be true or false. Consider this example. Suppose a city tax law states "If a person earns $1000 or more, then that person must file a tax return." There are four possibilities.

Some students may find truth tables interesting.

Earned $1000 or more?	Filed tax return?	Law satisfied?
yes	yes	yes
yes	no	no
no	yes	yes
no	no	yes

p	q	$p \rightarrow q$
T	T	T
T	F	F
F	T	T
F	F	T

The only way that the law is *not* satisfied is if a person does earn $1000 or more and does *not* file a tax return. Similarly, the only way a conditional statement is false is if the hypothesis is true and the conclusion is false.

Given a conditional statement, a new statement can be formed by interchanging the hypothesis and conclusion. This new statement is called the **converse** of the conditional.

p	q	$q \rightarrow p$
T	T	T
T	F	T
F	T	F
F	F	T

Statement   If it is raining, then there are clouds in the sky.

Converse   If there are clouds in the sky, then it is raining.

As the above example shows, the converse of a true statement may *not* be true.

Example

2   **Write the converse of the following true conditional statement. Is the converse a true statement?**

   If three points lie on the same line, then they are collinear.

   Converse   If three points are collinear, then they lie on the same line.

   Yes, the converse is a true statement in this case.

A statement in **if and only if** form can be written as two conditional statements.

Two planes are parallel *if and only if* they do *not* intersect.

If and only if may be represented by iff.

means

If two planes are parallel, then they do *not* intersect,

and

if two planes do *not* intersect, then they are parallel.

Statements that can be written in *if and only if* form are called **biconditional statements.** All definitions are biconditional statements because they are reversible.

Not all reversible statements are definitions.

Example

3 Rewrite the following pair of statements as a single statement in *if and only if* form.

If two lines are skew, then they do *not* intersect and are *not* in the same plane.

If two lines *do not* intersect and are *not* in the same plane, then they are skew.

Two lines are skew if and only if they do *not* intersect and are *not* in the same plane.

EN: 2–14 even, 2–34 even; **AV:** 2–14 even, 1–29 odd, 32; **FD:** 2–14 even, 1–23 odd, p. 8, 23–29 odd

Exploratory Exercises

The hypothesis is underlined, and the conclusion is circled.

Identify the hypothesis and conclusion for each of the following.

1. If <u>it rains</u>, then (the grass gets wet.)

2. If <u>a triangle has a right angle</u>, then (it is a right triangle.)

3. If <u>you live in Texas</u>, then (you are an American.)

4. If <u>you ride a bicycle</u>, then (you have strong legs.)

5. If <u>two lines are perpendicular</u>, then (the two lines intersect.)

6. If <u>$3x = 12$</u>, then (x = 4.)

7. If <u>n is even</u>, then (n² is even.)

8. If <u>a number is rational</u>, then (it is real.)

9. If <u>an animal is a chimpanzee</u>, then (it is a mammal.)

10. If <u>you practice hard</u>, then (you will make the team.)

11. All <u>birds</u> can (fly.)

12. All lawyers are (college graduates.)

13. <u>We will go skiing</u> only if (it snows.)

14. (You will do well in school) if <u>you study.</u>

Written Exercises

For Exercises 1–12, see the Teacher Guide.

Rewrite each conditional statement in if-then form. Then write the converse of each.

1. Parallel lines do *not* intersect.
2. A square is *not* a triangle.
3. A square is a rectangle.
4. All integers are real numbers.
5. $x < 0$ implies $5x > 6x$.
6. $2n + 1 = 5$ implies $n = 2$.
7. When it rains it pours.
8. If you want a new account, phone for it.
9. Two intersecting lines are contained in exactly one plane.
10. Two angles are congruent when they are vertical angles.
11. Where there is smoke, there is fire.
12. Show me a genius and I'll show you a scholar.

Remind students that conditional statements are not necessarily in if-then form.

Determine whether each of the following is a conditional statement. Write *yes* or *no*. Determine if each is *true*, *false*, or *neither*. Be prepared to justify your answer.

13. If it is blue, then it is *not* green. yes; true
14. If it is *not* green, then it is blue. yes; false
15. When animals are hungry, they eat.
16. A person who is crying is *not* happy. yes; neither
17. Be home by twelve o'clock. no; neither
18. Define collinear points. no; neither
19. Every line contains at least two points.
20. Sugar is *not* always white. yes; true

15. yes; neither   19. yes; true

Give an example for each of the following. Answers will vary. See the Teacher Guide.

21. A conditional and its converse that are both true
22. A conditional and its converse that are both false
23. A true conditional statement whose converse is false
24. A false conditional statement whose converse is true

For Exercises 25–34, see the Teacher Guide.

Rewrite each of the following statements as two if-then statements, one of which is the converse of the other.

25. Points are collinear if and only if they lie on the same line.
26. Points are coplanar if and only if they lie in the same plane.
27. Two segments are congruent if and only if they have the same measure.
28. Two angles are congruent if and only if they have the same measure.
29. Two angles are supplementary if and only if the sum of their degree measures is 180.
30. Two angles are complementary if and only if the sum of their degree measures is 90.

Rewrite the following pairs of statements as single statements using *if and only if*.

31. If two lines are perpendicular, then they intersect at right angles.

    If two lines intersect at right angles, then they are perpendicular.

32. In a plane, if two lines do *not* intersect, then they are parallel.

    In a plane, if two lines are parallel, then they do *not* intersect.

33. If two lines are intersected by a transversal so that alternate interior angles are congruent, then the lines are parallel.

    If two lines are parallel and intersected by a transversal, then the alternate interior angles are congruent.

34. If two lines are parallel and intersected by a transversal, then the corresponding angles are congruent.

    If two lines are intersected by a transversal so that corresponding angles are congruent, then the lines are parallel.

Applications in Law

Terry Muir wants to study to become a lawyer. A lawyer must be able to organize information in a logical order and arrive at valid conclusions.

Terry has studied if-then statements in geometry. She knows that if the hypothesis of a true if-then statement occurs, then the conclusion follows.

This is called the **Rule of Detachment.**

Example   **Consider each of the following to be a true statement:**

S-1 It is raining if and only if the humidity is 100%.
S-2 I am happy if the sun is shining.
S-3 If the grass is wet, then the trees are wet.
S-4 I am happy only if it is raining.
S-5 If the trees are wet, then the temperature is *not* below 32°F.
S-6 The humidity is 100% if and only if I am *not* comfortable.
S-7 If the temperature is *not* below 32°F, then the water does not freeze.
S-8 If the trees are wet, then the flowers are wet.
S-9 The flowers are wet if and only if the humidity is 100%.

You may want to have students assign a variable to each of the simple sentences and rewrite each statement in symbolic form.

Suppose *the trees are wet* is a valid hypothesis. What conclusions can be reached?

S-5 states *if the trees are wet, then the temperature is not below 32°F*. Since *the trees are wet* is a valid hypothesis, *the temperature is not below 32°F* is a valid conclusion. This conclusion can then be used as a valid hypothesis for S-7. The conclusion from this statement is *the water does not freeze*.

Notice that S-8 also uses *the trees are wet* as the hypothesis. This statement will lead to other valid conclusions.

Exercises   For Exercises 1–6, see the Teacher Guide.

Using the statements in the Example above, state as many valid conclusions as you can for each of the given hypotheses.

1. The trees are wet.   2. It is raining.
3. The water does not freeze.   4. The sun is shining.

Show that each of the following statements is a true statement.

5. If the sun is shining, then it is raining.   6. If the trees are wet, I am not comfortable.

1-4 Postulates

Objectives: Identify and use the basic postulates about points, lines, and planes.

In order to play a game, you must know the rules. In order to study geometry, you must know the **postulates.**

The rules, or postulates, of geometry tell how different sets of points are related. Postulates are statements that are accepted as true.

The first postulate relates points and lines. It guarantees that P and Q, for example, always determine a line.

Through any two points there is exactly one line.	*Postulate 1-1*

The next postulate relates points and planes.

Point out that "exactly one" means at least one and no more than one.

Through any three points *not* on the same line there is exactly one plane.	*Postulate 1-2*

Examples

1 **Given four points with no three collinear, how many lines can be drawn that contain any two of them?**

For every two points there is exactly one line. Thus, for four points there are at most six lines that can be drawn.

In the figure, $\overleftrightarrow{AB}$, $\overleftrightarrow{BC}$, $\overleftrightarrow{CD}$, $\overleftrightarrow{AD}$, $\overleftrightarrow{BD}$, and $\overleftrightarrow{AC}$ can be drawn.

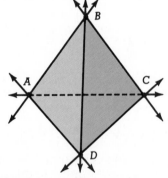

2 **Given four noncoplanar points with no three collinear, how many planes can be drawn that contain any three of them?**

For every three points *not* on the same line there is exactly one plane. Each face of the pyramid in the figure represents a plane containing three of the four points. The figure shows that there are, at most, four planes that can be drawn through the four points taken three at a time. The planes formed are the planes containing the following sets of points.

H, E, G G, E, F E, F, H F, G, H

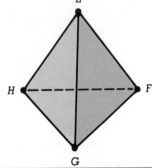

These postulates state the minimum number of points on a line and in a plane.

A line contains at least two points.	*Postulate 1-3*
A plane contains at least three points *not* on the same line.	*Postulate 1-4*

This postulate relates points, lines, and planes.

If two points lie in a plane, then the entire line containing those two points lies in that plane.	*Postulate 1-5*

Example
3 Suppose three noncollinear points, *A*, *B*, and *C*, lie on the same plane. How many lines can be drawn containing any two of the points? Name the lines.

There are three lines that can be drawn. They are $\overleftrightarrow{AB}$, $\overleftrightarrow{BC}$, and $\overleftrightarrow{AC}$.

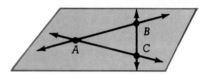

This postulate relates lines and planes.

If two planes intersect, then their intersection is a line.	*Postulate 1-6*

Example
4 Suppose plane $\mathcal{M}$ contains noncollinear points *A*, *C*, and *E*. Suppose plane $\mathcal{N}$ contains noncollinear points *A*, *C*, and *D*. Name the intersection of the two planes.

The intersection of planes $\mathcal{N}$ and $\mathcal{M}$ is $\overleftrightarrow{AC}$.

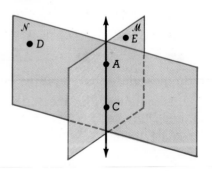

Exploratory Exercises

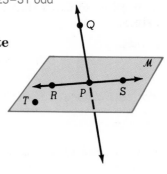

For each of the following statements, name the postulate that explains the relationship. Use the figures.

1. Exactly one line contains Q and P. Post.
2. The entire line containing R and S lies in plane $\mathcal{M}$. Post.
3. There are at least three points in plane $\mathcal{M}$. Post.
4. There are at least two points on $\overleftrightarrow{QP}$. Post.
5. The intersection of plane $\mathcal{M}$ and the plane determined by Q, P, and R is $\overleftrightarrow{RP}$. Post.

Exercises 1–5

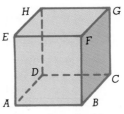

6. Exactly one line contains A and B. Post.
7. There are at least two points on $\overleftrightarrow{AC}$. Post.
8. Exactly one plane contains E, H, and B. Post.
9. The entire line containing F and C lies in the plane determined by G, C, and B. Post.
10. B and H lie on exactly one line. Post.

Exercises 6–10

Written Exercises

In the figure P, Q, and R are collinear. Points P and S lie in plane $\mathcal{M}$. Points R and T lie in plane $\mathcal{N}$. Determine whether each of the following statements is *true* or *false*.

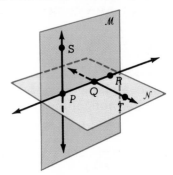

1. P, Q, and R lie in plane $\mathcal{N}$.
2. P, Q, and R lie in plane $\mathcal{M}$.
3. $\overleftrightarrow{PS}$ does *not* lie in plane $\mathcal{M}$.
4. Q lies in plane $\mathcal{M}$.
5. P, Q, R, and S are coplanar.
6. Q does *not* lie in plane $\mathcal{M}$.
7. Q, R, and T are collinear.
8. P, Q, S, and T are coplanar.
9. Plane $\mathcal{M}$ and plane $\mathcal{N}$ intersect in $\overleftrightarrow{PR}$.
10. $\overleftrightarrow{QT}$ lies in plane $\mathcal{N}$. true

11. Post. 12. Post. 13. Post.

Exercises 1–10

Name the postulate that explains each relationship.

11. If $\overleftrightarrow{AB}$ is contained in plane $\mathcal{M}$, there is at least one more point on $\mathcal{M}$ that is *not* on $\overleftrightarrow{AB}$.
12. If C and D are on line ℓ and C and D are on line m, then ℓ and m must be the same line.
13. If X and Y lie in plane $\mathcal{M}$, there are no points on $\overleftrightarrow{XY}$ that are not contained in plane $\mathcal{M}$.
14. If A, B, and C are contained in plane $\mathcal{M}$ and A, B, and D are contained in plane $\mathcal{N}$, then $\overleftrightarrow{AB}$ is the intersection of planes $\mathcal{M}$ and $\mathcal{N}$. Post.

The main emphasis of Exercises 15–22 is to reinforce the concept that three noncollinear points, or a line and a point not on the line, determine a plane.

State the number of lines that can be drawn that contain the given sets of points taken two at a time.

15. two points
16. three collinear points
17. three noncollinear points
18. five points, *no* three of which are collinear
19. four points, three of which are collinear
20. the intersection of two planes
21. six points, *no* three of which are collinear
22. four points, *no* three of which are collinear

State the number of planes that can be drawn that contain the given sets of points taken three at a time. For Exercises 25-26, see the Teacher Guide.

23. three noncollinear points
24. three collinear points
25. four points, three of which are collinear
26. five points, no three of which are collinear

Statistics That Shape Your Life

The chart below is a calorie expenditure chart. It lists several different activities and the number of calories that each activity burns off per minute. To use this chart, find the column closest to your weight. Multiply the number of calories in that column by the number of minutes you spend on an activity. For example, if you weigh 130 pounds and play tennis for 45 minutes, you will burn off 6.4 × 45, or 288 calories.

How can you find the number of calories you burn off if you weigh 145 pounds and play tennis for 45 minutes? Since there is no calorie listing for 145, but there are listings for 130 and 150, you must use a method of estimation called **interpolation.**

$$20\left[15\left[\begin{array}{cc} \textbf{Weight} & \textbf{Calories per minute} \\ 130 & 6.4 \\ 145 & \text{unknown} \\ 150 & 7.4 \end{array}\right] x\right] 1.0$$

$$\frac{15}{20} = \frac{x}{1.0}$$

$$x \approx 0.8$$

You would burn off about 6.4 + 0.8, or 7.2 calories per minute.

How fast you burn off calories

Activity	Weight (in pounds)					
	110	130	150	170	190	203
	Calories per minute					
Badminton	4.9	5.7	6.6	7.5	8.3	8.9
Basketball	6.9	8.1	9.4	10.6	11.9	12.7
Canoeing (leisurely)	2.2	2.6	3.0	3.4	3.8	4.0
Playing cards	1.3	1.5	1.7	1.9	2.2	2.3
Croquet	3.0	3.5	4.0	4.5	5.1	5.4
Cycling (5.5 mph)	3.2	3.8	4.4	4.9	5.5	5.9
Dancing (active)	5.2	6.1	7.0	7.9	8.9	9.5
Eating	1.2	1.4	1.6	1.8	2.0	2.1
Fishing	3.1	3.7	4.2	4.8	5.3	5.7
Football	6.6	7.8	9.0	10.2	11.4	12.1
Mowing lawn	5.6	6.6	7.6	8.6	9.6	10.3
Planting seedlings	3.5	4.1	4.8	5.4	6.0	6.4
Resting	1.1	1.3	1.5	1.7	1.9	2.0
Tennis	5.5	6.4	7.4	8.4	9.4	10.0
Volleyball	2.5	3.0	3.4	3.9	4.3	4.6
Walking	4.1	4.8	5.6	6.3	7.1	7.5

Exercises

1. What is the best activity for burning off calories? basketball
2. If you weigh 180 pounds and mow the lawn, how many calories per minute will you burn off? 9.1 calories
3. Jim plays football for 1 hour and Brenda leads 2 hours of aerobic dancing. If Jim weighs 150 pounds and Brenda weighs 110 pounds, who burns off more calories? Brenda

1-5 Theorems

Can you always believe what you see? Consider the following diagram. If you extend the drawing of line ℓ, will it intersect point X, Y, or Z? You might be surprised with the result.

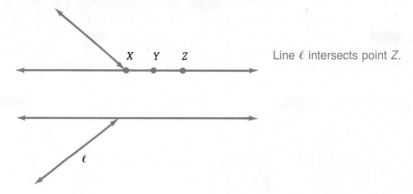

Line ℓ intersects point Z.

This diagram is obviously misleading. But the results should convince you *not* to rely solely on a diagram to prove an argument.

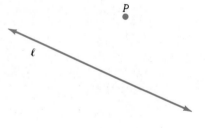

The figure at the right shows a line ℓ and a point P not on the line. How many planes can contain both point P and line ℓ? The following argument uses the *postulates* from the previous lesson to lead to a conclusion.

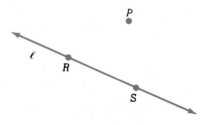

According to Postulate 1-3, a line contains at least two points. The points are labeled R and S. So, there are at least three points, P, R, and S, *not* on the same line.

According to Postulate 1-2 through any three points *not* on the same line there is exactly one plane.

According to Postulate 1-5, if two points lie in a plane, then the entire line containing them lies in that plane. So there is at least one plane containing P and ℓ.

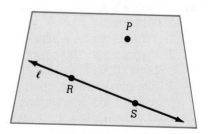

Physical models are most helpful in concept development.

Are you convinced?

Not everyone has the same idea of what is convincing. Some arguments are more convincing than others. Geometry uses a system of reasoning that many people find convincing. It is called **deductive reasoning.** In order to establish a statement in a deductive system, you must show that the statement is a logical consequence of some previously established statements. These statements must also have been previously established, and so on. Eventually, you will arrive at some statements that are so basic they are accepted as true. In geometry, undefined terms, definitions, and postulates are accepted as true.

Undefined terms are basic terms with which other terms are defined.

Definitions are explanations of how words are to be used.

Postulates are statements that describe fundamental properties of the basic terms.

This information is not proven.

The information from undefined terms, definitions, and postulates is used to find new information, written as a theorem. **Theorems** are statements that must be proved before they can be accepted. Theorems may be conditional or biconditional statements.

For example, the argument on the previous page leads to the following statement. Theorems may be written in "if-then" or "if and only if" form.

If there is a line and a point *not* on the line, then there is exactly one plane that contains them.	*Theorem 1-1*

This statement must be proved. To prove a theorem, start with the *hypothesis*. Then use postulates, definitions, and previously proved theorems to reach the *conclusion*.

Different postulates can lead to different conclusions.

Example

1 **For Theorem 1-1, state the hypothesis and the conclusion.**

Theorem 1-1 states, *if there is a line and a point not on the line, then there is exactly one plane that contains them.*

The hypothesis, the part following *if*, states there is a line and a point *not* on the line.

The conclusion, the part following *then*, states there is exactly one plane that contains them.

It is important to organize the information in a proof in a logical manner. **Formal proofs** usually have five main parts.

1. Statement of the theorem
2. The given information
3. The prove statement
4. A diagram
5. The proof with statements and reasons

Formal proofs can be written in the form shown below.

Theorem: Write out the theorem to be proven.

Given: Write the information given in the hypothesis of the theorem. Use the names for the terms from the diagram.

Prove: Write the conclusion of the theorem. Use the names from the diagram.

> A diagram may be provided for the given statements. It should picture the information in the hypothesis of the theorem. Label the diagram with names to be used in the proof.

Proof:

STATEMENTS	REASONS
1. Write a list of numbered statements arranged in 2. order so that they lead to the conclusion. Each 3. statement must be justified by a reason.	1. Write a list of numbered reasons that go with the 2. statements on the left. Reasons used can be given 3. information, definitions, postulates, or theorems.

You cannot use the theorem itself or any statement not already proved as a reason in a proof.

Example

2 **For Theorem 1-1, state the given. Then draw a diagram to illustrate the given.**

Theorem 1-1 states, *if there is a line and a point not on the line, then there is exactly one plane that contains them.* The hypothesis, the part following *if*, states there is a line and a point *not* on the line. Name the line ℓ and the point P.

Given: P *not* on ℓ

Diagram:

Names other than P and ℓ may be used.

Exploratory Exercises
ALL LEVELS: Mini Review

Answer each of the following exercises about formal proofs.
1. theorem, given, prove statement, diagram, and proof with statements and reasons

1. Name the five main parts of a proof.

2. What information is in the *given* statement? information in the ▬▬▬

3. What information is in the *prove* statement? information in the ▬▬▬

4. What does the diagram illustrate? the diagram illustrates the ▬▬▬

5. Should a theorem be stated? Write *yes* or *no*. ▬

6. Must a diagram be shown? Write *yes* or *no*. ▬

7. Must the given be stated? ▬

8. Must the *prove* statement be stated? ▬

9. Name the headings for the two columns in a *proof*. statements, reasons

10. What is the purpose of the statements? 10. to show logically how the hypothesis leads to the conclusion

11. What is the purpose of the reasons? to justify each statement

12. What can be used as reasons? 12. the given, postulates already stated, definitions already made, theorems already proved

State the hypothesis for each of the following theorems or postulates.

13. If two lines intersect, then exactly one plane contains both lines.

14. If two lines intersect, then they intersect in exactly one point.

15. If a line and a plane intersect, and the plane does *not* contain the line, then their intersection is a point.

16. If four points are collinear, then they are coplanar.

The answers to Exercises 13–20 are underlined.

State the conclusion for the following theorems or postulates.

17. If three points are noncollinear, then there is exactly one plane that contains them.

18. If two points are in a plane, then the line containing the two points is in the plane.

19. If two distinct planes intersect, then their intersection is a line.

20. If four points are collinear, then there is exactly one line that contains them.

Written Exercises

State the given and the prove statement for each of the following theorems. Use labels from a diagram you draw. For Exercises 1–4, see the Teacher Guide.

1. If two lines intersect, then exactly one plane contains both lines.

2. If two lines intersect, then they intersect in exactly one point.

3. If a line and a plane intersect, and the plane does *not* contain the line, then their intersection is a point.

4. If four points are collinear, then they are coplanar.

For Exercises 5–14, see students' work.

Draw and label a diagram to illustrate each of the following given statements.

5. **Given:** line ℓ and point P *not* on ℓ

6. **Given:** points A, B, and C *not* on the same line

7. **Given:** line m intersecting line n

8. **Given:** line m contained in plane $\mathcal{P}$

9. **Given:** point R *not* in plane $\mathcal{M}$

10. **Given:** coplanar lines m and n point P on line m

Draw and label a diagram to illustrate the hypothesis for each of the following theorems.

11. If three points are noncollinear, then there is exactly one plane that contains them.

12. If two points are in a plane, then the line containing the two points is in the plane.

13. If two distinct planes intersect, then their intersection is a line.

14. If four points are collinear, then there is exactly one line that contains them.

The following diagrams are taken from proofs. State the given for each diagram.

For Exercises 15–23, see the Teacher Guide.

15.

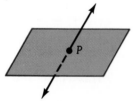

16.

17.

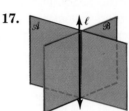

18.

19.

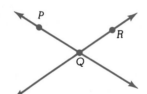

20.

21.

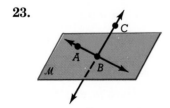

22.

23.

mini-review

1-1 **1.** Draw and label a diagram that shows that ℓ contains A and B but does not contain C and D.

1-4 **2.** If M and N are two points, how many lines can contain M and N?

1-2 **3.** Draw and label a diagram that shows four noncoplanar points.

1-3 **4.** Name the hypothesis and conclusion of this statement: If you live in Pittsburgh, then you live in Pennsylvania.

1-3 **5.** Write this statement in if-then form: An odd number is not divisible by 2.

The Mini Review provides an opportunity for continuous review.

1-6 Writing Proofs

Objectives: Plan and develop formal proofs.

A formal proof is a summary. It does *not* show the thinking and planning done to make a logical argument. The following suggestions will help you write a formal proof.

1. **Write out the theorem.**
2. **Draw a diagram.**
3. **Write the given and the prove statement.**
4. **Plan the proof.**
5. **Write the proof.**

Procedure for Writing Formal Proofs

Theorem: If there is a line and a point *not* on the line, then there is at least one plane that contains them.

Write out the theorem.

This information helps students define the problem.

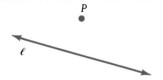

Draw a diagram.

Diagrams help students see possible relationships.

Given: line ℓ and point P *not* on ℓ
Prove: At least one plane contains ℓ and P.

Write the given and the prove statement.

Review the definitions, postulates, and theorems already proven that relate to the theorem.

Plan the proof.

Postulate 1-2: Through any three points *not* on the same line, there is exactly one plane.

Postulate 1-3: A line contains at least two points.

Postulate 1-5: If two points lie in a plane, then the entire line containing those two points lies in that plane.

Arrange the ideas in logical order. Start with the given and end with the prove statement.

line ℓ and point P *not* on ℓ
ℓ contains 2 points, say R and S.
There are 3 noncollinear points, namely R, S, and P.
Exactly one plane contains R, S, and P.
R and S lie in a plane, so ℓ lies in the plane.
ℓ and P lie in at least one plane.

List the statements with the reasons.

Write the proof.

The theorem is proved in Example 1.

Example

1   **Write a formal proof for the following theorem.**

This example can be used as a basis for discussion of formal proofs.

Theorem: If there is a line and a point *not* on the line, then there is at least one plane that contains them.

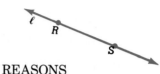

Given: line ℓ and point P *not* on ℓ

Prove: At least one plane contains ℓ and P.

Proof:

STATEMENTS	REASONS
1. line ℓ and point P *not* on ℓ	1. Given
2. points R and S on ℓ	2. A line contains at least two points. (Postulate 1-3)
3. P, S, and R are noncollinear.	3. Definition of Noncollinear Points
4. Exactly one plane contains R, S, and P.	4. Through any three points *not* on the same line there is exactly one plane. (Postulate 1-2)
5. At least one plane contains ℓ and P.	5. If two points lie in a plane, then the entire line containing those two points lies in that plane. (Postulate 1-5)

The following theorem relates lines and planes.

If two lines intersect, then exactly one plane contains both lines.	***Theorem 1-2***

Example

2   **Plan a proof to show that at least one plane contains two intersecting lines.**

This example can be used to discuss planning a proof.

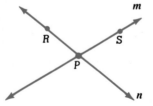

This plan assumes that P, R, and S are noncollinear.

The lines m and n intersect in P. Thus, by Postulate 1-3, m and n both contain two points. By Postulate 1-3, there are three points, namely P, R, and S. Then, by Postulate 1-2, exactly one plane contains P, R, and S. Finally, Postulate 1-5 says that the plane contains both m and n.

Exploratory Exercises

Name the postulates or theorems you have learned that have the same hypothesis as each of the following theorems. If you have *not* learned any, write *none*.

1. If two lines intersect, then exactly one plane contains both lines.

2. If two planes intersect, then their intersection contains at least two points.

3. A plane contains at least three lines.

4. If two lines intersect, then their intersection contains one point.

5. Through any three points *not* on the same line, there are exactly three lines.

6. Through four collinear points, there is exactly one line.

7–12. For each of the theorems in Exercises 1–6, name the postulates or theorems you have learned that have the same conclusion. If you have *not* learned any, write *none*.

1. Theorem ▆ 2. Post. ▆ 3. Post. ▆ 4. Theorem ▆ 5. Post. ▆ 6. ▆

7. Theorem ▆ 8. ▆ 9. ▆ 10. ▆ 11. ▆ 12. Post. ▆

Written Exercises

For each of the following, fill in the blank with a reason. Use a definition, a postulate, or a proven theorem.

1. S and Q are points.
There is exactly one line through S and Q.
Given
Post. ▆

2. Q and R are points.
There is exactly one line containing Q and R.
Given
Post. ▆

3. Q, S, and R are noncollinear points.
There is exactly one plane containing Q, S, and R.
Given
Post. ▆

4. P, Q, and R are noncollinear.
There is only one plane containing P, Q, and R.
Given
Post. ▆

5. Q and R lie in $\mathcal{L}$.
$\overleftrightarrow{QR}$ lies in $\mathcal{L}$.
Given
Post. ▆

6. P is *not* on m.
There is only one plane containing P and m.
Given
Theorem ▆

7. S is *not* on m.
Exactly one plane contains S and m.
Given
Theorem ▆

8. S, P, and Q lie on ℓ.
S, P, and Q are collinear. definition of ▆
Given

9. S and R lie on m.
P does *not* lie on m.
S, R, and P are noncollinear. definition of ▆
Postulate 1-1
Given

10. P does *not* lie on ℓ.
A and B lie on ℓ.
A, B, and P are coplanar. Theorem 1-1; Post. 1-2; definition of ▆
Given
Given

For each of the following, fill in the blank with a statement that follows from the stated reason.

11. ℓ and m intersect.
_____
Exactly one plane contains ℓ and m.
Given
If two lines intersect, then exactly one plane contains both lines. (Theorem 1-2)

12. P, Q, and R are noncollinear.
_____
There is exactly one plane through P, Q, and R.
Given
Through any three points *not* on the same line, there is exactly one plane. (Postulate 1-2)

13. $\mathcal{M}$ and $\mathcal{N}$ intersect.
The intersection of $\mathcal{M}$ and $\mathcal{N}$ is a line.

Given
If two planes intersect, then their intersection is a line. (Postulate 1-6)

14. $\mathcal{L}$ is a plane.
P, Q, and R are noncollinear points.

Given
A plane contains at least three points *not* on the same line. (Postulate 1-4)

15. ℓ is a line.
ℓ contains at least 2 points.

Given
A line contains at least two points. (Postulate 1-3)

16. P and Q are two points.
There is exactly one line through P and Q.

Given
Through any two points there is exactly one line. (Postulate 1-1)

17. ℓ is a line and P is a point *not* on ℓ.
Exactly one plane contains ℓ and P.

Given

If there is a line and a point *not* on the line, then there is exactly one plane that contains them. (Theorem 1-1)

18. R and S lie in $\mathcal{R}$.
$\overleftrightarrow{RS}$ lies in $\mathcal{R}$.

Given
If two points lie in a plane, then the entire line containing those two points lies in that plane. (Postulate 1-5)

For each of the following theorems, name the given, the prove statement, and draw a diagram you would use in a formal proof. For Exercises 19–22, see the Teacher Guide.

19. If two planes intersect, then their intersection contains at least two points.

20. If two lines intersect, then at least one plane contains both lines.

21. Two intersecting lines contain at least three points.

22. A plane contains at least three lines.

23. Complete the reasons for the incomplete proof that follows.

Theorem: If two planes intersect, then their intersection contains at least two points.

Given: $\mathcal{M}$ and $\mathcal{N}$ intersect.

Prove: The intersection of $\mathcal{M}$ and $\mathcal{N}$ contains points A and B.

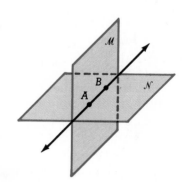

Proof:

STATEMENTS	REASONS
1. $\mathcal{M}$ and $\mathcal{N}$ intersect.	**1.** Given
2. The intersection of $\mathcal{M}$ and $\mathcal{N}$ is line ℓ.	**2.** Post. 1-6
3. Line ℓ contains points A and B.	**3.** Post. 1-3

Point, *line*, and *plane* are undefined terms of geometry. The postulates of geometry describe the fundamental properties of these terms. *Different* geometries can be made by changing the undefined terms and postulates.

A miniature geometry can be created by changing the interpretation of *point*, *line*, and *plane*.

Postulate 1 For every two points, there is exactly one line that contains them.

Postulate 2 If a line contains two distinct points of a plane, it is contained in the plane.

Postulate 3 For any three points, there is at least one plane containing them. For any three noncollinear points, there is exactly one plane containing them.

Postulate 4 If two distinct planes intersect, then their intersection is a line.

Postulate 5 Every line contains at least two points, every plane contains at least three noncollinear points, and space contains exactly four noncoplanar points.

The following three-dimensional figure is one model for the miniature geometry.

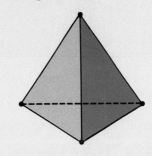

Each dot represents a point.
Each edge represents a line.
Each surface represents a plane.

Emphasize that in this geometry, space contains exactly four points.

Check this model against each postulate.

Using Postulates 1–5, the following theorems can be proven.

Theorem 1 If two lines intersect, the intersection contains exactly one point.

Theorem 2 A line and a point *not* on that line are contained in exactly one plane.

Theorem 3 Every line contains exactly two points.

Theorem 4 Every plane contains exactly three points.

Theorem 5 Every plane contains exactly three lines.

Exercises

Answer each of the following.

1. How many points are in the geometry?
2. How many lines are in the geometry?
3. How many planes are in the geometry?
4. Name the postulates or theorems that justify the conclusions of Theorem 5.

1. 4 by Postulate 5   2. 6 by Postulate 5 and Theorem 3   3. 4 by Postulate 5 and Theorem 4
4. Theorem 4, Postulate 5, Postulate 1

1-7 Inverses and Contrapositives

Objective: Write inverses and contrapositives of conditional statements.

A statement that is formed by denying another statement is called a **negation**.

The truth table for negation is as follows.

Sentence   The moon revolves around the earth.

Negation   The moon does not revolve around the earth.

p	$\sim p$
T	F
F	T

Sentence   Three points are noncollinear.

Negation   Three points are collinear.

If p represents a sentence, $\sim p$ represents the negation.

If a statement is true, then its negation is false. If a statement is false, then its negation is true.

A statement and its negation cannot both be true, nor can they both be false at the same time.

The negation of a statement may be written several ways. Some times a statement may *appear* to be the negation of another, when it is *not*.

Example

1 **Name which statements are negations of the following statement.**

The point is on the line.

a. No point is on the line.
b. The point is *not* on the line.
c. The line is *not* the point.
d. The line does *not* contain the point.
e. The point is *not* the line.

Only **b** and **d** are negations of the given statement.

Recall that a statement written in if-then form is called a conditional statement. The converse of a conditional statement is formed by interchanging the hypothesis and the conclusion. Two other types of statements, the inverse and the contrapositive, are related to the conditional statement.

Given a conditional statement, its **inverse** can be formed by *negating* both the hypothesis and conclusion.

Statement	If a figure is a square, then the figure is a rectangle.	Statement: $p \rightarrow q$
Inverse	If a figure is *not* a square, then the figure is *not* a rectangle.	Inverse: $\sim p \rightarrow \sim q$

As the example shows, the inverse of a true statement may *not* be true. A figure may *not* be a square but could be a rectangle.

Conditional statements also have **contrapositives.** A contrapositive statement is formed by interchanging the hypothesis and conclusion, and negating both.

Statement	If a figure is a square, then the figure is a rectangle.	Statement: $p \rightarrow q$
Contrapositive	If a figure is *not* a rectangle, then the figure is *not* a square.	Contrapositive: $\sim q \rightarrow \sim p$

The contrapositive of a true statement is *always* a true statement. The contrapositive of a false statement is *always* a false statement.

Example

2 **Write the inverse and contrapositive of the following true statement. Determine whether they are true.**

If two points lie in a plane, then the entire line containing the points lies in that plane.

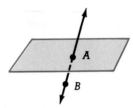

Inverse   If two points do *not* lie in a plane, then the entire line containing the points does *not* lie in the plane.

In this case, the inverse is true.   *Note points A and B on the figure.*

Contrapositive   If one entire line containing two points does *not* lie in a plane, then the two points do *not* both lie in the plane.

The contrapositive of a true statement is *always* true.

Exploratory Exercises

For Exercises 1–12, see the Teacher Guide.

State the negation for each of the following.

1. A figure is a triangle.
2. Two points lie in a plane.
3. Three points are collinear.
4. A figure is a polygon.
5. $\mathcal{M}$ intersects $\mathcal{N}$.
6. $\overleftrightarrow{AB}$ does *not* intersect $\mathcal{M}$.
7. ℓ does *not* lie in $\mathcal{M}$.
8. ℓ intersects t.
9. P, Q, and R are noncoplanar.
10. A, B, and C are noncollinear.
11. Two points lie in different planes.
12. Two lines are in distinct planes.

Written Exercises

Determine whether each sentence is a negation of the given sentence. Write *yes* or *no*.

$$-1 \text{ is a real number.}$$

1. yes if limited to the complex number system, otherwise no
1. -1 is an imaginary number.
2. -1 is really a number.
3. 1 is a real number.
4. -1 is *not* really a number.
5. -1 is *not* a real number.
6. -1 is a rational number.

$$\text{A triangle has four sides.}$$

7. A triangle has three sides.
8. A triangle does *not* have sides.
9. A triangle has *no* sides.
10. A triangle does *not* have four sides.
11. Four triangles have sides.
12. A triangle has foresight.

$$\text{Tomorrow it will rain.}$$

13. It will *not* rain tomorrow.
14. Tomorrow it won't rain.
15. Tomorrow the sun will shine.
16. It will *not* rain today.
17. Tomorrow it will *not* rain.
18. Today it will rain.

$$A \text{ and } B \text{ are on a line.}$$

19. A and B are in a plane.
20. A and B are *not* on a line.
21. A and B are *not* in a plane.
22. A and B exist.
23. A and B are points.
24. A and B do *not* exist.

For Exercises 25–42, see the Teacher Guide.

Write the inverse and the contrapositive for each of the following statements.

25. If it rains, then the grass gets wet.
26. If $3x = 12$, then $x = 4$.
27. If you live in Texas, then you are an American.
28. If you ride a bicycle, then you have strong legs.
29. If two lines are perpendicular, then the two lines intersect.
30. If a triangle has a right angle, then it is a right triangle.
31. If n is even, then n^2 is even.
32. If a number is rational, then it is real.
33. If an animal is a chimpanzee, then it is a mammal.
34. If you practice hard, then you will make the team.

35. Parallel lines do *not* intersect.

36. A square is *not* a triangle.

37. A square is a rectangle.

38. Integers are real numbers.

39. $x < 0$ implies $5x > 6x$.

40. $2n + 1 = 5$ implies $n = 2$.

For Exercises 35–40, students should write the inverse and contrapositive in "if-then" form.

For each of the following, write the inverse, converse, and contrapositive of the statement.

41. If today is Friday, then it is *not* Sunday.

42. If you want a job, then learn how a computer works.

Using Calculators —————————————— Basic Functions

Some calculators differ in the functions they perform. Most calculators have the following keys and functions.

Key	Name	Function
$+/-$	Change Sign	changes the sign of the number
x^2	Square	calculates the square of the number
$\sqrt{x}$	Square Root	calculates the square root of the number
$1/x$	Reciprocal	calculates the reciprocal of the number

First enter the number and then press the appropriate key.

A calculator can be used to evaluate expressions. It is best to use a calculator that evaluates expressions in the algebraic mode. That is, the algebraic order of operations should hold when the calculator performs any sequence of operations.

Example Evaluate $7 + 3 \div 5 + 5^2$.

ENTER:	7	$+$	3	$\div$	5	$+$	5	x^2	$=$		
DISPLAY:	7	7	3	3	5	7.6	5	25	32.6		

The answer is 32.6.

If your calculator does not use the algebraic order of operations, your answer will be different. In such cases, read the manual for your calculator and adapt the order of entry accordingly.

Exercises

Use the calculator to evaluate each expression.

1. $6 \cdot 2 - 4 \cdot 2$ 4

2. $42 - 54 \div 6$ 33

3. $24 \div 6 - 3^2 \div 3$ 1

4. $6 \cdot 3 \div 9 - 1$ 1

5. $-24 \div 6 - 3^2 \div 3$ −7

6. $13 - 4(17)^2 + \sqrt{0.978}$ −1142.0111

Additional practice in evaluating expressions can be found on page 558 of the Diagnostic Skills Review.

Vocabulary

points (1)
lines (1)
planes (1)
intersect (2)
undefined terms (5)
collinear points (5)
coplanar points (5)
noncollinear points (6)
noncoplanar points (7)
conditional statements (9)
if-then form (9)

hypothesis (10)
conclusion (10)
converse (10)
if and only if form (11)
biconditional statements (11)
postulates (14)
theorems (19)
formal proofs (20)
negation (28)
inverse (29)
contrapositive (29)

Chapter Summary

1. Points have *no* dimensions. (1)

2. Lines extend indefinitely and have *no* thickness or width. (1)

3. A plane extends indefinitely in all directions and has *no* thickness. (1)

4. Two lines, two planes, or lines and planes, intersect if they have points in common. (2)

5. Guidelines for a Definition: (5)
    1. Name the term being defined.
    2. Use only undefined terms or previously defined terms.
    3. Identify the set to which the term belongs.
    4. State the properties that distinguish the term from others in the set.
    5. Make it reversible.
    6. Make it concise.

6. All conditional statements can be written in *if-then* form and may be true or false. (9)

7. The converse of a conditional statement is formed by interchanging the hypothesis and conclusion. (10)

8. Postulate 1-1: Through any two points there is exactly one line. (14)

9. Postulate 1-2: Through any three points *not* on the same line there is exactly one plane. (14)

10. Postulate 1-3: A line contains at least two points. (15)

11. Postulate 1-4: A plane contains at least three points *not* on the same line. (15)

12. Postulate 1-5:   If two points lie in a plane, then the entire line containing those two points lies in that plane.   (15)

13. Postulate 1-6:   If two planes intersect, then their intersection is a line. (15)

14. Theorem 1-1:   If there is a line and a point *not* on the line, then there is exactly one plane that contains them.   (19)

15. Formal proofs have five main parts, namely, the statement of the *theorem*, the *given* information, the *prove* statement, a *diagram*, and the *proof* with statements and reasons.   (20)

16. Procedure for Writing Formal Proofs: (23)
    1. Write out the theorem.
    2. Draw a diagram.
    3. Write the given and the prove statement.
    4. Plan the proof.
    5. Write the proof.

17. Theorem 1-2:   If two lines intersect, then exactly one plane contains both lines.   (24)

18. A statement that is formed by denying another statement is called a negation.   (28)

19. The inverse of a conditional statement is formed by negating both the hypothesis and conclusion.   (29)

20. The contrapositive of a conditional statement is formed by interchanging the hypothesis and conclusion, and negating both.   (29)

Chapter Review

1-1   **Draw and label a diagram to show each of the following.** See students' work.

   1. ℓ intersects $\mathcal{M}$ at A.
   2. A and B lie on ℓ, but C does *not*.
   3. P does *not* lie on m.
   4. P does *not* lie in $\mathcal{M}$.

1-2   **Answer each of the following.** For Exercises 5–12, see the Teacher Guide.

   5. Noncoplanar points are points that are *not* coplanar. Write a good definition for noncoplanar points without using the word coplanar.
   6. They do *not* intersect is *not* a good definition. Explain why.

1-3   **Rewrite each of the following conditional statements in if-then form. Identify the hypothesis and the conclusion.**

   7. An angle is a right angle when it has a degree measure of 90.
   8. A triangle is isosceles if it has at least two sides with the same length.

   9–10. Write the converse for each statement in Exercises 7 and 8.

   Rewrite each of the following biconditional statements in *if and only if* form.

   11. Skew lines are lines that are *not* coplanar.
   12. Concurrent lines are lines that have only one point in common.

1-4   **Answer each of the following.**

13. Suppose a set of points consists of a plane and a line *not* in the plane. State the minimum number of points in the set. 4, If the line intersects the plane, then 3 points determine the plane plus 1 point outside the plane can be paired with one of the 3 points of the plane to determine the line.

14. Suppose two different planes both contain *A* and *B*. Describe the intersection of the planes. $\overleftrightarrow{AB}$

1-5   **Draw and label a diagram to illustrate each of the following given statements.**

15. Given: ℓ and $\mathscr{A}$ do *not* intersect.

16. Given: *A*, *B*, and *C* are noncollinear.

17. Given: *p* and *q* intersect at *A*.

18. Given: $\mathscr{L}$ and *m* intersect at *R*.

For Exercises 15–18, see students' work.

1-6   **Use the proof below to answer the questions that follow.**

Theorem: If there is a line and a point *not* on the line, then there is at least one plane that contains them.

Given: ℓ and point *P* *not* on ℓ

Prove: At least one plane contains ℓ and *P*.

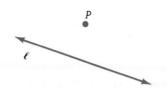

Proof:

STATEMENTS	REASONS
1. ℓ and point *P* *not* on ℓ.	1. Given
2. *R* and *S* on ℓ.	2. A line contains at least two points. (Postulate 1–3)
3. *P*, *S*, and *R* are noncollinear.	3. Definition of Noncollinear Points
4. At least one plane contains *R*, *S*, and *P*.	4. _____
5. _____	5. If two points lie in a plane, then the entire line containing those two points lies in that plane. (Postulate 1–5)

19. Complete Reason **4** in the above proof. Post. 1-2

20. Complete Statement **5** in the above proof. At least one plane contains ℓ and P.

For Exercises 21–25, see the Teacher Guide.

1-7   **Write the inverse and contrapositive for each of the following statements.**

21. If it is green, then it is *not* yellow.

22. When the sun shines, the sky is blue.

23. If $2x = 8$, then $x = 4$.

24. If two points exist, then a line exists.

25. Write the inverse, converse, and contrapositive of the statement. "If the month is May, then it is *not* June." Determine whether the statements are *true* or *false*. Assume the original statement to be true.

Chapter Test

Draw and label a diagram to illustrate each of the following relationships.

For Exercises 1–8, see students' work.

1. P lies in $\mathcal{M}$.

2. P, Q, and R are coplanar.

3. ℓ and m intersect at S.

4. p intersects $\mathcal{M}$ at A.

5. $\mathcal{L}$ does not contain A or B.

6. $\mathcal{M}$ and $\mathcal{N}$ intersect.

7. A, B, and C are collinear.

8. m contains A but not B.

Rewrite each of the following conditional statements in if-then form. Identify the hypothesis and conclusion. For Exercises 9–27, see the Teacher Guide.

9. You are 16 years old only if you can drive a car.

10. When a number is an integer, it is a real number.

11. A triangle is equilateral when it has three sides with the same measure.

12. An angle is not obtuse if it is a right angle.

Rewrite each of the following statements as two if-then statements.

13. I will not go to the game if and only if it rains.

14. Points lie in the same plane if and only if they are coplanar.

Write the converse for each of the following statements.

15. A triangle is isosceles when it has two sides with the same measure.

16. When a number is rational it is a fraction.

17. An angle is not acute if it is an obtuse angle.

18. You are 18 years old only if you have graduated from high school.

Write the inverse and contrapositive of each of the following statements.

19. If two lines intersect, then they are *not* parallel.

20. If it snows, then the ground is white.

21. If points are collinear, then they lie on the same line.

22. If you ride a bicycle, then you have strong legs.

State the theorem, definition, or postulate that justifies each statement.

23. If A and B are two points, then m is the only line through A and B.

24. If m is a line and G is a point *not* on m, then $\mathcal{N}$ is the only plane that contains m and G.

Write the given, the prove statement, and draw a diagram for each of the following statements.

25. If two lines intersect, then at least one plane contains both lines.

26. Two intersecting lines contain at least three points.

27. There is at least one plane that contains a line and a point *not* on the line.

CHAPTER 2

Measure

Measurement is important in many facets of our lives. In order to determine placement in Olympic competitions, accurate measurements must be made.

In this chapter you will study the importance of measure and measurement in geometry.

2-1 Number Lines

Objectives: State the coordinates of points on the number line, convert fractions to decimals, and vice versa.

A point has *no* size or shape. However, it does have position. Just as a capital letter is used to name a point, a numeral is used to name the *position* of the point.

The following figure is a **number line.** Some points on the line and their corresponding numerals are shown. These represent some of the numbers in the set of **whole numbers.**

The whole numbers without zero make up the natural numbers.

Negative numbers are used to name points to the left of zero. The following number line shows some of the numerals from the set of **integers.** Notice that each positive integer can be paired with a negative integer, which is its opposite.

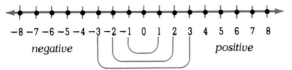

Remind students that the arrows mean the numbers continue indefinitely in both the positive and negative directions.

Many numbers can be expressed in the form $\frac{a}{b}$, where a and b denote integers and b is *not* zero. Any number of this type is called a **rational number.** The following number line shows some points and their corresponding rational numbers.

Every rational number can be written in decimal form as well as in fractional form. To change a fraction to a decimal, divide the numerator by the denominator. *You may want to encourage students to use calculators.*

Examples

1 Change $\frac{5}{8}$ to a decimal.

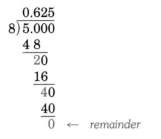

The decimal form of $\frac{5}{8}$ is 0.625.

2 Change $1\frac{3}{4}$ to a decimal.

$1\frac{3}{4} = \frac{7}{4}$ *Express $1\frac{3}{4}$ as an improper fraction.*

$$
\begin{array}{r}
1.75 \\
4)\overline{7.00} \\
\underline{4} \\
3\,0 \\
\underline{2\,8} \\
20 \\
\underline{20} \\
0 \leftarrow \text{ remainder}
\end{array}
$$

Now divide.

The decimal form of $1\frac{3}{4}$ is 1.75.

Notice that the division process in Examples **1** and **2** stops or terminates when a remainder of 0 occurs. The resulting decimal quotient in these cases is called a **terminating decimal.**

A decimal in which a digit or a group of digits repeat is called a **repeating decimal.**

To terminate, the rational number must be in simplest form and the denominator must have factors of only 2 and/or 5.

Example

3 Change $\frac{1}{3}$ to a decimal.

$$
\begin{array}{r}
0.333\ldots \\
3\overline{)1.000} \\
\underline{9} \\
10 \\
\underline{9} \\
10 \\
\underline{9} \\
1 \quad \leftarrow \ \text{remainder}
\end{array}
$$

Notice that the same remainder, 1, repeats. Thus, the same quotient digit, 3, repeats.

Additional practice can be found on page 556 of the Diagnostic Skills Review.

The decimal form of $\frac{1}{3}$ is 0.333. . .

A repeating decimal can be indicated by placing a *bar* over the digit or digits that repeat. Thus, 0.333 . . . can be written as $0.\overline{3}$.

You can change a three-digit repeating decimal to a fraction by the following method.

Example

4 Change $0.\overline{345}$ to a fraction.

Let $x = 0.\overline{345}$

By definition $0.\overline{345}$ means 0.345345. . .

Multiply both sides by 1000.

Why is 1000 chosen?

$$
\begin{array}{r}
1000\,x = 345.\overline{345} \\
x = \ \ \ 0.\overline{345} \\
\hline
999\,x = 345
\end{array}
$$

Subtract the original equation.

$$\frac{999}{999}\,x = \frac{345}{999}$$

Divide both sides by 999.

$$x = \frac{345}{999}$$

Change $\frac{345}{999}$ to simplest form.

$$x = \frac{115}{333}$$

The fractional form of $0.\overline{345}$ is $\frac{115}{333}$.

Some decimals are nonterminating and nonrepeating. For example, the decimal 1.020020002 . . . is nonterminating and nonrepeating. Nonterminating, nonrepeating decimals represent **irrational numbers.** Another example of an irrational number is the decimal approximation of $\sqrt{13}$.

$$\sqrt{13} \approx 3.6055512 \ldots$$

The square root of any prime number is an irrational number.

Perhaps the most famous nonterminating, nonrepeating decimal is the approximation for π.

$$\pi \approx 3.14159265358979323846264338 \ldots$$

Taken together, the rational numbers and irrational numbers make up the set of **real numbers.** Each point on a number line can be named by a real number.

Unless otherwise stated, the word number means real number.

Each real number corresponds to exactly one point on a number line. Each point on a number line corresponds to exactly one real number.	*Postulate 2-1* *Number Line* *Postulate*

The number assigned to a point on a number line is called the **coordinate** of the point. On the number line below, the coordinate of A is -7. The coordinate of B is 2.

EN: 2–24 even, 3, 6, 9, . . . 36, 37–44; **AV:** 1–25 odd, 1–44; **FD:** 1–25, 1–34

Exploratory Exercises

State the coordinate of each of the following points on the number lines below.

1. H 1
2. F −1
3. B −8
4. E −2
5. G 0
6. A −10
7. J 5
8. K 7
9. C −6
10. I 3

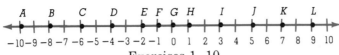

Exercises 1–10

11. N $-\frac{5}{3}$
12. S $\frac{1}{3}$
13. Q $-\frac{4}{3}$
14. V 1
15. M
16. P −3
17. R $-\frac{2}{3}$
18. X $\frac{7}{3}$
19. W $\frac{5}{3}$
20. T $\frac{2}{3}$

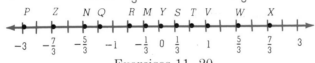

Exercises 11–20

Estimate the value of each fraction as a decimal to the nearest tenth.

21. $\frac{7}{10}$ 0.7
22. $\frac{3}{7}$ 0.4
23. $\frac{5}{12}$ 0.4
24. $\frac{2}{9}$ 0.2
25. $\frac{15}{17}$ 0.9

Written Exercises

For Exercises 1–12, change each fraction or mixed numeral to decimal form. Express your answers as terminating or repeating decimals only.

1. $\frac{3}{10}$ ■

2. $\frac{1}{4}$ ■

3. $-\frac{4}{5}$ ■

4. $-\frac{3}{7}$ $-0.\overline{428571}$

5. $\frac{4}{12}$ ■

6. $-\frac{5}{6}$ ■

7. $-4\frac{3}{8}$ ■

8. $2\frac{2}{3}$ ■

9. $5\frac{2}{9}$ ■

10. $3 + \left(-\frac{2}{3}\right)$ ■

11. $-5 + \frac{3}{8}$ ■

12. $-2 + \frac{1}{9}$ ■

Change each repeating decimal to a fraction in simplest form.

13. $0.\overline{7}$ ●

14. $0.\overline{23}$ ■

15. $0.\overline{5}$ ■

16. $0.3\overline{27}$ ■

17. $0.\overline{524}$ $\frac{524}{999}$

18. $0.\overline{231}$ $\frac{77}{333}$

19. $1.\overline{2}$ $\frac{11}{9}$

20. $4.2\overline{6}$ $\frac{64}{15}$

21. $2.\overline{36}$ $\frac{26}{11}$

22. $6.0\overline{2}$ $\frac{596}{99}$

23. $1.\overline{26}$ $\frac{125}{99}$

24. $1.\overline{162}$ $\frac{43}{37}$

Draw a number line from -12 to 14. Indicate the approximate position of each of the following points by labeling each point with the appropriate letters. See the Teacher Guide.

25. A is $\sqrt{126}$.

26. B is $-\sqrt{111}$.

27. C is $\sqrt{3}$.

28. D is $\sqrt{175}$.

Complete the following chart. Write *yes* or *no*.

	Number	$\frac{\pi}{2}$	-13	0.07	$-11\frac{2}{3}$	$0.6\overline{6}$	π	$\sqrt{3}$	$\frac{5}{4}$	$1.74\overline{21}$	0
29.	Natural Number	No	No	No	No	No	No	No	No	No	No
30.	Whole Number	No	No	No	No	No	No	No	No	No	Yes
31.	Integer	No	Yes	No	No	No	No	No	No	No	Yes
32.	Rational Number	No	Yes	Yes	Yes	Yes	No	No	Yes	Yes	Yes
33.	Irrational Number	Yes	No	No	No	No	Yes	Yes	No	No	No
34.	Real Number	Yes	Yes	Yes	Yes	Yes	Yes	Yes	Yes	Yes	Yes

Determine whether each statement is *true* or *false*. If it is false, give an example that supports your answer.

35. All whole numbers are integers. True

36. All integers are whole numbers. False. -5 is an integer but not a whole number.

37. No whole numbers are natural numbers. False. 2 is a natural number and a whole number.

38. A number is a real number if it is a rational number. True

39. If a number is *not* a real number, then it is *not* an irrational number. True.

40. When a number is a whole number, then it is a rational number. True

41. A number is a rational number if it is a natural number. True.

42. No irrational numbers are whole numbers. True.

43. If a number is *not* a natural number, then it is a rational number. False. π is not a natural number and is not a rational number.

44. If a number is positive, then it is a natural number. False. $\frac{1}{2}$ is positive and not a natural number.

2-2 Distance

Mile markers placed beside the road help motorists determine the **distance** they have traveled. If these same mile markers were changed to kilometer marks, would the distance traveled by a motorist be altered?

The positive number chosen by the Ruler Postulate determines the unit of measure.

> **The points on any line can be paired with the real numbers so that, given any two points *P* and *Q* on the line, *P* corresponds to zero, and *Q* corresponds to a positive number.**

Postulate 2-2
Ruler Postulate

When a measurement is made, a number called the **measure** is associated with a unit, called the **unit of measure.**

Suppose you measure the width of a window, first using 1 inch as the unit and then using 1 centimeter as the unit. Although the width of the window remains the same, the measures, units, and measurements differ.

A measurement always has two parts, a number and a unit.

A line that has a specific ordered assignment of numbers to points is called a number line.

The window is 25 inches wide.

The window is 63.5 centimeters wide.

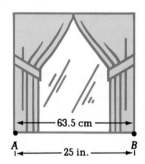

The measure is 25.
The unit of measure is 1 inch.
The measurement is 25 inches.

The measure is 63.5.
The unit of measure is 1 centimeter.
The measurement is 63.5 centimeters.

Given a certain unit of measure, the measure of the distance between two points is unique.

Emphasize that the measure is a *unique positive* number.

For any two points on a line and a given unit of measure, there is a unique positive number called the measure of the distance between the two points.	*Postulate 2-3* *Distance Postulate*

The unit of measure is not always stated. If no units are stated, you can assume that the same unit is used for all measurements.

Suppose you want to find the measure of the distance between A and B on the number line below.

On a number line, the markings are placed at equal intervals apart.

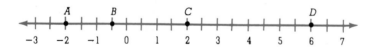

To find the measure of the distance, first identify the coordinates of A and B. Then, find the absolute value of the difference of the coordinates.

Use the Exploratory Exercises to help review absolute value.

$$|5 - 1| = |4| \qquad \text{or} \qquad |1 - 5| = |-4|$$
$$= 4 \qquad\qquad\qquad\qquad\quad = 4$$

Finding the distance from A to B or from B to A results in the same measure.

The measure of the distance between A and B is 4. To indicate this measure, write AB. Thus, in the example above, $AB = 4$.

When expressions are written AB, CD, etc., they always represent numerical values.

Example

1 Find CD, CB, AB, and AC.

The markings are placed at equal intervals.

$$CD = |6 - 2|$$
$$= |4| \text{ or } 4$$

$$CB = \left|-\frac{1}{2} - 2\right|$$
$$= \left|-2\frac{1}{2}\right| \text{ or } 2\frac{1}{2}$$

Since CD = DC, either $|2 - 6|$ or $|6 - 2|$ can be used to find CD. List the other ways to find CB, AB, and AC.

$$AB = \left|-\frac{1}{2} - (-2)\right|$$
$$= \left|1\frac{1}{2}\right| \text{ or } 1\frac{1}{2}$$

$$AC = |2 - (-2)|$$
$$= |4| \text{ or } 4$$

Example

2 Find PQ, QR, PS, and RS.

$$PQ = |7.2 - 2.5| \qquad QR = |7.7 - 7.2|$$
$$= |4.7| \text{ or } 4.7 \qquad = |0.5| \text{ or } 0.5$$

$$PS = |8.4 - 2.5| \qquad RS = |8.4 - 7.7|$$
$$= |5.9| \text{ or } 5.9 \qquad = |0.7| \text{ or } 0.7$$

Remind students that the Distance Postulate states that the measure of the distance between any two points is unique.

The symbol RR represents the distance from point R to point R. Thus, $RR = 0$. For example, if the coordinate of R is 5, then $RR = |5 - 5|$ or 0.

EN: 3, 6, 9, . . . , 36, 2–60 even; AV: 2–36 even, 2–52 even; FD: 1–36, 1–43 odd, p. 40, 36–44 even;

Exploratory Exercises

ALL LEVELS: Algebra Review

State the absolute value for each of the following.

1. 12 12
2. -33 33
3. 30 30
4. 90 90
5. $\frac{1}{4}$ $\frac{1}{4}$

6. -15 15
7. -2.3 2.3
8. 11 11
9. -7 7
10. -0.01 0.01

11. -3 3
12. -61 61
13. $7\frac{1}{2}$ $7\frac{1}{2}$
14. 39 39
15. 89 89

16. $-12\frac{7}{8}$ $12\frac{7}{8}$
17. 97 97
18. -52 52
19. -58 58
20. 10.02 10.02

Identify each of the following statements as *true* or *false*.

21. $AB = 3$

22. $BA = -3$

23. $CD = DC$

24. $BB = 0$

25. $CA = BD$

26. $CD = -2$

27. $BA = AD$

28. $AC = CA$

29. $QR = \left| \frac{5}{2} - \frac{3}{2} \right|$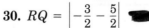

30. $RQ = \left| -\frac{3}{2} - \frac{5}{2} \right|$

31. $ST = \left| 0 - \frac{3}{2} \right|$

32. $RT = -\left| \frac{3}{2} - \left(-\frac{3}{2} \right) \right|$

33. $-ST = -SR$

34. $SQ = -\frac{5}{2}$

35. $TQ = 2$

36. $QT = 1$

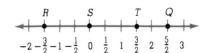

Exercises 21–28

Exercises 29–36

Additional practice with absolute value can be found on page 562 of the Diagnostic Skills Review.

Written Exercises

Find each difference.

1. $28 - 19$ 9
2. $4 - 7$ −3
3. $0 - 12$ −12
4. $-78 - (-19)$ −59
5. $24 - 42$ −18
6. $-27 - 42$ −69
7. $-59 - 38$ −97
8. $0 - (-35)$ 35
9. $-77 - 76$ −153
10. $-99 - 29$ −128
11. $-6 - (-17)$ 11
12. $-41 - (-36)$ −5
13. $-17 - (-23)$ 6
14. $-115 - (-28)$ −87
15. $-9 - (-12)$ 3
16. $-101 - (-101)$ 0

Find each value.

17. $|2 - (-2)|$ 4
18. $|0 - (-6)|$ 6
19. $|-2 - (-5)|$ 3
20. $\left|6\frac{1}{3} - 8\frac{2}{3}\right|$ $2\frac{1}{3}$
21. $|5 - (-4)|$ 9
22. $|-5.4 - 7.8|$ 13.2
23. $|3.6 - 9.2|$ 5.6
24. $|7.7 - (-7.2)|$ 14.9
25. $\left|-2\frac{2}{3} - 2\frac{1}{6}\right|$
26. $\left|9\frac{3}{5} - (-6)\right|$
27. $\left|-5\frac{1}{4} - \left(-2\frac{1}{2}\right)\right|$
28. $\left|9 - \left(-2\frac{3}{4}\right)\right|$

Use the number line below to find each measure.

29. AB
30. CD
31. DA
32. AE
33. BE
34. BC
35. AC
36. BD
37. AA
38. EC
39. ED
40. AD
41. CC
42. DC
43. CA

Number line: points A (at −1.5 region), B (at 0 region), C, D, E marked between −3 and 3, with fractional gradations $-\frac{8}{3}, -\frac{5}{2}, -\frac{7}{3}$ near −2; $-\frac{5}{3}, -\frac{8}{5}... $; $\frac{1}{3}, \frac{1}{2}, \frac{2}{3}$; $\frac{4}{3}, \frac{3}{2}, \frac{5}{3}$; $\frac{7}{3}, \frac{5}{2}, \frac{8}{3}$.

Use the ruler to find each measure.

44. PQ
45. RS
46. SP
47. PT
48. QT
49. QR
50. PR
51. QS
52. SS
53. TR
54. TS
55. PS
56. RR
57. SR
58. RP

Ruler marked in centimeters (cm), 0 to 13, with points P, Q, R, S near 2–3 and T near 5.

Given a number line marked in units, answer each of the following.

59. Beginning at coordinate −3, move to the left 2 units then to the right 6 units. What is the coordinate of the new position?   1

60. Beginning at coordinate 8, move to the right 6 units then to the left 10 units. What is the coordinate of the new position?   4

61. Beginning at coordinate −9, move to coordinate 5 then to coordinate −1. What is the total distance you have traveled?   20

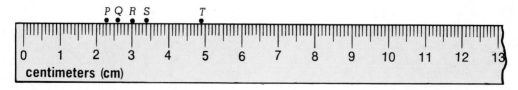

Algebra Review

Solve.

1. $5x + 7 = 8x - 21$
2. $|x + 3| = 12$ $x =$ or
3. $|3x - 4| = 19$ $x =$ or
4. $\frac{x}{4} - 1 = -\frac{5}{2}$ $x =$
5. $7 \geq \frac{3x + 7}{7}$

Topics in Geometry

A set is a collection of things called *elements* or members that have been grouped together. The members of a set could be people, points, or almost anything. A Venn diagram is often used to show the relationships among sets.

Example 1 **Draw a Venn diagram to show the relationship between the following sets.**

Set *S* is the set of seniors attending South High School.
Set *F* is the set of freshmen attending South High School.

Since a student cannot be a senior and a freshman at the same time, the sets, represented by circles, do not overlap.

S and F are mutually exclusive or disjoint sets.

Example 2 **Draw a Venn diagram to show the relationship between the following sets.**

Set *X* is the set of all four legged animals.
Set *Y* is the set of all horses.

Since every member of the set of horses has four legs, set *Y* is completely contained in set *X*.

Since Y is completely contained in X, Y is a subset of X.

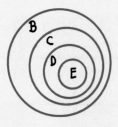

Exercises

The Venn diagram at the left shows the relationship among subsets of the real numbers. Match each set of numbers with the letter for that set in the diagram.

1. integers *C*   2. whole numbers *D*
3. rational numbers *B* 4. natural numbers *E*
5. irrational numbers *A*

For converse statements for Exercises 6–11, see the Teacher Guide.

From the diagram, determine if the following statements are *true* or *false*. Then, state the converse of the statement and indicate if the converse is *true* or *false*.

6. If a number is a natural number, then it is a real number. True

7. If a number is an irrational number, it is not a rational number. True

8. An integer cannot be a rational number. False

9. A whole number is a natural number. False

10. If *x* is a member of the natural numbers, then *x* is a member of the rational numbers. True

11. Irrational numbers are not real numbers. False

2-3 Segments

Objectives: Recognize the properties of segments and the relationships of betweenness and midpoints.

Look at the figure at the right. Point Q is between P and R. Points W, X, Y, and Z are *not* between P and R. In geometry, **between** is defined in the following way.

Unless stated otherwise, betweenness and collinearity of points may be assumed if they are given in a diagram.

Emphasize what can and cannot be assumed from a diagram.

A point Q is between points P and R if and only if each of the following conditions hold. 1. P, Q, and R are collinear. 2. $PQ + QR = PR$	*Definition of Between*

Example

1 Show that Z is *not* between P and R in the figure below.

$$PZ + ZR \overset{?}{=} PR$$
$$|-2 - 5| + |5 - 2| \overset{?}{=} |-2 - 2|$$
$$7 + 3 \overset{?}{=} 4$$
$$10 \neq 4$$

Thus, $PZ + ZR \neq PR$.

Since the three points do *not* satisfy condition 2 of the definition of between, Z is *not* between P and R.

The part of the line below that includes points A and B and all the points between them is called a **segment.** Points A and B are called the **endpoints** of the segment.

Segment AB can be written $\overline{AB}$ or $\overline{BA}$.

$\overline{AB}$ refers to a set of points. AB represents a number, the length of $\overline{AB}$.

The **length** of a segment is the distance between the two endpoints of the segment. The **midpoint** of a segment separates it into two segments of equal length.

Remind students that there are two requirements for a point to be a midpoint.

A point M is the midpoint of a segment, $\overline{PQ}$, if and only if M is between P and Q, and $PM = MQ$.	*Definition of Midpoint*

2 **Find the coordinate of the midpoint of $\overline{AB}$.**

Compute AB.

$$AB = |5 - (-3)| = 8$$

The midpoint will be halfway between endpoints A and B or 4 units from each. Th coordinate of the midpoint of $\overline{AB}$ must be 1. To check, find the length of the segmen between -3 and 1 and the length of the segment between 1 and 5. Since both segmen have a length of 4, the coordinate of the midpoint of $\overline{AB}$ is 1.

3 **Show that M is the midpoint of $\overline{PQ}$.**

There are two conditions to be met.

1. Show that M is between P and Q.
Assume from the figure that all three points are collinear.

$$PM + MQ \stackrel{?}{=} PQ$$
$$|-5 - (-1)| + |-1 - 3| \stackrel{?}{=} |-5 - 3|$$
$$|-4| + |-4| \stackrel{?}{=} |-8|$$
$$8 = 8$$

2. Show that $PM = MQ$.

$$PM \stackrel{?}{=} MQ$$
$$|-5 - (-1)| \stackrel{?}{=} |-1 - 3|$$
$$|-4| \stackrel{?}{=} |-4|$$
$$4 = 4$$

Since both conditions are met, M is the midpoint of $\overline{PQ}$.

Because the Distance Postulate states the distance between two points is unique, the midpoint of a segment must also be unique.

If a segment is given, then it has exactly one midpoint.	*Theorem 2-1*

Exploratory Exercises

ALL LEVELS: Mini Review

Use the number line below to state the absolute value relation used to find the measure of each segment. For Exercises 1–10, see the Teacher Guide.

1. $\overline{AD}$	2. $\overline{BF}$	3. $\overline{AG}$	4. $\overline{EB}$	5. $\overline{FE}$
6. $\overline{CG}$	7. $\overline{FA}$	8. $\overline{CB}$	9. $\overline{BD}$	10. $\overline{AE}$

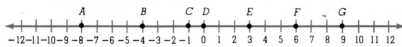

Using the number line above, estimate the coordinate of the midpoint of each of the following segments.

11. $\overline{AB}$	12. $\overline{GF}$	13. $\overline{DG}$	14. $\overline{CD}$	15. $\overline{CF}$
16. $\overline{BC}$	17. $\overline{BE}$	18. $\overline{DA}$	19. $\overline{EC}$	20. $\overline{AG}$

Written Exercises

Use the number line below to find the length of each of the following segments.

1. $\overline{CD}$	2. $\overline{BF}$	3. $\overline{AG}$	4. $\overline{EB}$	5. $\overline{BA}$
6. $\overline{CG}$	7. $\overline{FE}$	8. $\overline{GA}$	9. $\overline{AD}$	10. $\overline{BE}$
11. $\overline{CF}$	12. $\overline{FG}$	13. $\overline{FA}$	14. $\overline{CB}$	15. $\overline{BD}$
16. $\overline{AE}$	17. $\overline{EF}$	18. $\overline{CE}$	19. $\overline{BG}$	20. $\overline{EG}$

For Exercises 21–42, see the Teacher Guide.

Use the number line below to answer each of the following.

21. Show that T is *not* between R and S.
22. Show that Q is *not* between V and R.
23. Show that N is *not* the midpoint of $\overline{PS}$.
24. Show that R is *not* the midpoint of $\overline{PS}$.
25. Show that Q is the midpoint of $\overline{PS}$.
26. Show that S is the midpoint of $\overline{QV}$.
27. Find the coordinate of the midpoint of $\overline{PT}$.
28. Find the coordinate of the midpoint of $\overline{NS}$.
29. Show that $NP + PQ = NQ$.
30. Show that $QT - QS = ST$.
31. Show that $RV - ST = RS + TV$.
32. Show that $QR + RS + ST = QT$.
33. Find the coordinate of the midpoint of $\overline{NT}$.
34. Show that $QR + RS = ST + TV$.

For each of the following, draw a diagram to illustrate the given. Then apply definitions, postulates, or theorems to show each of the following.

35. **Given:** A has coordinate -2.
    B has coordinate 5.
    M has coordinate 1.5.
    M is between A and B.
    Show: M is the midpoint of $\overline{AB}$.

36. **Given:** T has coordinate -9.
    R has coordinate -6.
    S has coordinate -3.
    R is between T and S.
    Show: R is the midpoint of $\overline{TS}$.

37. Given: A, B, and C are collinear.
  $AB = 3$
  $AC = 5$
  $BC = 2$
  Show: B is between A and C.

38. Given: P, Q, and R are collinear.
  $RQ = 6.5$
  $PQ = 2.3$
  Q is between P and R.
  Show: $PR = 8.8$

39. Given: N is the midpoint of $\overline{AB}$.
  $AB = 4.5$

  Show: $NB = 2.25$

40. Given: M is the midpoint of $\overline{PQ}$.
  $MQ = 7\frac{1}{2}$

  Show: $PM = 7\frac{1}{2}$

41. Given: A has coordinate -3.
  B has coordinate 0.
  C has coordinate 2.
  D has coordinate 3.
  Show: C is *not* the midpoint of $\overline{AD}$.

42. Given: E, F, and H are collinear.
  $EH = 14$
  $EF = 8$
  $FH = 6$
  Show: F is between E and H.

Answer each of the following. $A = $ ■ or $A = $ ■

$Q = $ ■ or $Q = $ ■

43. The coordinate of B is -5 and $AB = 6$. Find the two possible coordinates of A.

44. The coordinate of P is 3 and $PQ = 5$. Find the two possible coordinates of Q.

45. The coordinate of B is -5 and $AB = 6$. Find the two possible coordinates of the midpoint of $\overline{AB}$. $M = $ ■ or $M = $ ■

46. The coordinate of P is 3 and $PQ = 5$. Find the two possible coordinates of the midpoint of $\overline{PQ}$. $M = $ ■ or $M = $ ■

47. The coordinate of X is -7 and the coordinate of the midpoint of $\overline{XY}$ is -1. Find the coordinate of Y. $Y = $ ■

48. The coordinate of X is $-\frac{13}{5}$ and the coordinate of Y is $\frac{3\pi}{4}$. Find the coordinate of the midpoint of $\overline{XY}$. $M = $ ■

Challenge Exercises

For each of the following, draw a figure that satisfies the given conditions.

49. a. $DE = EF$
  b. E is *not* the midpoint of $\overline{DF}$.

50. a. Points V, W, X, Y, and Z are collinear.
  b. $WY = YX$
  c. V is between Y and Z.
  d. X is next to V.
  e. V is *not* between X and Z.

For Exercises 49–50, see students' work.

Find the coordinate of the midpoint of $\overline{AB}$ if the coordinates for A and B are given as follows.

51. $A = \frac{1}{4}$ and $B = \frac{7}{16}$ ■

52. $A = \frac{3}{8}$ and $B = \frac{5}{24}$ ■

53. Suppose A, B, and C are collinear with B between A and C. Find AB if $BC = \frac{2}{3}(AC)$ and $BC = 52$. ■

mini-review

See the Teacher Guide.

1. State the contrapositive of: If three points lie on a line, then they are collinear.

2. Name the type of statement that can be written in "if and only if" form.

3. State the two conditions that must be met for Q to be between points P and R.

4. If K is the midpoint of $\overline{JL}$, write an equation to state the relationship between JK and JL.

5. Explain the difference between $\overline{AB}$ and AB.

2-4 Properties of the Real Number System

Objectives: Recognize properties of real numbers, and apply formal proofs to equation solving.

In arithmetic you have assumed the following properties of equality. Some classes may need a thorough review of these properties.

For any number a, $a = a$.	*Postulate 2-4* **Reflexive Property** *of Equality*
For any numbers a and b, if $a = b$, then $b = a$.	*Postulate 2-5* **Symmetric Property** *of Equality*
For any numbers a, b, and c, if $a = b$ and $b = c$, then $a = c$.	*Postulate 2-6* **Transitive Property** *of Equality*

These properties can be applied to measures since measures are real numbers.

Example

1 Prove for P, Q, R, and T in that order on a line, if $PQ = QR$ and $PQ = RT$, then $RT = QR$.

Given: $PQ = QR$
$PQ = RT$
Prove: $RT = QR$

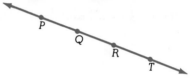

Proof:

STATEMENTS	REASONS
1. $PQ = RT$	1. Given
2. $RT = PQ$	2. Symmetric Property of Equality (Postulate 2-5)
3. $PQ = QR$	3. Given
4. $RT = QR$	4. Transitive Property of Equality (Postulate 2-6)

In longer geometric proofs, statements having the reflexive, symmetric, and transitive properties as reasons may be combined.

The following properties of equality are used to solve equations. Simple algebraic examples applying each of these properties may be helpful.

For any numbers a, b, and c, if $a = b$, then $a + c = b + c$ and $a - c = b - c$.	*Postulate 2-7* **Addition and Subtraction** *Properties of Equality*
For any numbers a, b, and c, if $a = b$, then $a \cdot c = b \cdot c$ and if c is *not* zero, then $\frac{a}{c} = \frac{b}{c}$.	*Postulate 2-8* **Multiplication and** *Division Properties of* **Equality**

For any numbers a and b, if $a = b$, then a may be replaced by b.	*Postulate 2-9* **Substitution Property** *of Equality*

The chart below summarizes properties of addition and multiplication of real numbers.

Property	For any numbers a, b, and c		
	Addition	**Multiplication**	
Commutative	$a + b = b + a$	$a \cdot b = b \cdot a$	*Order Change* — *Postulate 2-10*
Associative	$(a + b) + c = a + (b + c)$	$(a \cdot b) \cdot c = a \cdot (b \cdot c)$	*Regrouping* *Postulate 2-11*
Identity	$a + 0 = a = 0 + a$	$a \cdot 1 = a = 1 \cdot a$	*Postulate 2-12*
Inverse	*opposite* $(2 = -2)$ $a + (-a) = 0 = (-a) + a$	If a is *not* zero, then $a \cdot \dfrac{1}{a} = 1 = \dfrac{1}{a} \cdot a$.	*Reciprocal* *Postulate 2-13*
Distributive Property of Multiplication over Addition: $a(b + c) = ab + ac$ and $(b + c)a = ba + ca$			*Postulate 2-14*

A review of operations with signed numbers can be most helpful.

Example

2 Prove that if $5x - 7 = 23$, then $x = 6$.

Given: $5x - 7 = 23$
Prove: $x = 6$

Proof:

STATEMENTS	REASONS
1. $5x - 7 = 23$	1. Given
2. $5x - 7 + 7 = 23 + 7$	2. Addition Property of Equality (Postulate 2-7)
3. $5x + 0 = 30$ *Notice that $5x - 7 + 7$ can be grouped as $5x + [(-7) + 7]$.*	3. Associative Property of Addition (Postulate 2-11), Inverse Property of Addition (Postulate 2-13), and Substitution Property of Equality (Postulate 2-9)
4. $5x = 30$	4. Identity Property of Addition (Postulate 2-12)
5. $\dfrac{5x}{5} = \dfrac{30}{5}$	5. Division Property of Equality (Postulate 2-8)
6. $1x = \dfrac{30}{5}$	6. Inverse Property of Multiplication (Postulate 2-13)
7. $x = 6$	7. Substitution Property of Equality (Postulate 2-9), and Identity Property of Multiplication (Postulate 2-12)

When referring to algebraic properties, postulate numbers may be omitted. Notice in the following proof that some steps contain more than one statement or reason.

Example

3 **Prove that if** $6(a + 5) + 10a = -2$, **then** $a = -2$.

Several proofs of this type should be done to improve skills in step-by-step reasoning.

Given: $6(a + 5) + 10a = -2$
Prove: $a = -2$
Proof:

STATEMENTS	REASONS
1. $6(a + 5) + 10a = -2$	1. Given
2. $6a + 30 + 10a = -2$	2. Distributive Property of Multiplication over Addition
3. $16a + 30 = -2$	3. Commutative and Associative Properties of Equality, Distributive Property of Multiplication over Addition, and Substitution Property of Equality
4. $16a = -32$	4. Subtraction and Substitution Properties of Equality
5. $\dfrac{16a}{16} = \dfrac{-32}{16}$	5. Division Property of Equality
6. $1a = -\dfrac{32}{16}$	6. Inverse Property of Multiplication
7. $a = -2$	7. Substitution Property of Equality

The Substitution Property of Equality often is called Substitution.

EN: 1–20, 1–11; **AV:** 1–20, 1–11; **FD:** 1–20, 1–8, p. 49, 43–47 odd

Exploratory Exercises

State the property shown in each of the following.

1. $3 + (2 + 3) = 3 + (2 + 3)$

2. If $x - 7 = 11$, then $x = 18$.

3. $\dfrac{12}{17} \cdot \dfrac{17}{12} = 1$

4. $9(x - 3y) = 9x - 27y$

5. If $5 + 7 = 7 + 5$, then $7 + 5 = 5 + 7$.

6. If $8 = 6 + 2$ and $6 + 2 = 5 + 3$, then $8 = 5 + 3$.

7. $5 \cdot 1 = 5$

8. $2 \cdot 3 = 3 \cdot 2$

9. $2(5 \cdot 7) = (2 \cdot 5)7$

10. $2x^2 - 34x + 36 = 2(x^2 - 17x + 18)$

11. $(-35) + 0 = -35$

12. If $\frac{1}{4}x = 7$, then $x = 28$.

13. $x + (2 + y) = x + (y + 2)$

14. $17 + (-17) = 0$

15. If $48 = 16x$, then $3 = x$.

16. If $t + 7 = 6 + 7$, then $t = 6$.

17. If $2 + 2 = 4$, then $6 + (2 + 2) = 6 + 4$.

18. If $AB = BC$, then $AB + EF = BC + EF$.

19. $(-\sqrt{2} + \sqrt{5}) + 3\sqrt{5} = -\sqrt{2} + (\sqrt{5} + 3\sqrt{5})$

20. If $PQ = QR$ and $QR = ST$, then $PQ = ST$.

In some cases more than one property was applied. Accept answers that indicate the implied steps that may have been omitted.

Written Exercises

State the property that justifies each step.

1. (1) $-4x = 16$ (1) Given

    (2) $x = -4$ (2)

2. (1) $9x = -\dfrac{3}{2}$ (1) Given

    (2) $\dfrac{1}{9}(9x) = \dfrac{1}{9}\left(-\dfrac{3}{2}\right)$ (2)

    (3) $1x = -\dfrac{1}{6}$ (3)

3. (1) $\dfrac{x}{6} + 3 = 12$ (1) Given

    (2) $\dfrac{x}{6} = 9$ (2)

    (3) $x = 54$ (3)

4. (1) $2(x - 4) = 40$ (1) Given

    (2) $2x - 8 = 40$ (2)

    (3) $2x = 48$ (3)

5. (1) $AB + BD = AD$ (1) Given
    (2) $BC + CD = BD$ (2) Given
    (3) $AB + BC + CD = AD$ (3)

6. (1) $AM + MB = AB$ (1) Given
    (2) $AM = MB$ (2) Given
    (3) $2AM = AB$ (3)

Complete each proof.

7.   **Given:** $\dfrac{3}{4}x = \dfrac{1}{3}$

     Prove: $x = \dfrac{4}{9}$

     Proof:

STATEMENTS	REASONS
1. $\dfrac{3}{4}x = \dfrac{1}{3}$	1. Given
2. $\dfrac{4}{3} \cdot \dfrac{3}{4}x = \dfrac{4}{3} \cdot \dfrac{1}{3}$	2. 
3. $1x = \dfrac{4}{9}$	3.
4. $x = \dfrac{4}{9}$	4.

8.   **Given:** $4 - 7x = 25$
     Prove: $x = -3$

     Proof:

STATEMENTS	REASONS
1. $4 - 7x = 25$	1. Given
2. $-4 + 4 - 7x = -4 + 25$	2. 
3. $0 - 7x = 21$	3.
4. $-7x = 21$	4.
5. $\dfrac{-7x}{-7} = \dfrac{21}{-7}$	5.
6. $1x = \dfrac{21}{-7}$	6.
7. $x = -3$	7.

9. **Given:** $AB = CD$
  Prove: $AC = BD$

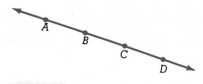

Proof:

STATEMENTS	REASONS
1. $AB = CD$	1. Given
2. $AB + BC = CD + BC$	2. ▬▬▬▬▬▬
3. $AB + BC = AC$	3. ▬▬▬▬▬▬
$CD + BC = BD$	
4. $AC = BD$	4. ▬▬▬▬▬▬

10. **Given:** $PM = MS$
  M is the midpoint of $\overline{PQ}$.
  Prove: $MS = MQ$

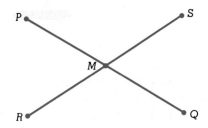

Proof:

STATEMENTS	REASONS
1. $PM = MS$	1. Given
2. M is the midpoint of $\overline{PQ}$.	2. Given
3. $PM = MQ$	3. ▬▬▬▬▬▬
4. $MS = MQ$	4. ▬▬▬▬▬▬

11. **Given:** $MB = MQ$
  M is between A and B.
  Prove: $AB = AM + MQ$

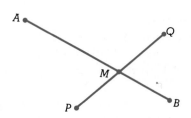

Proof:

STATEMENTS	REASONS
1. $MB = MQ$	1. Given
2. $AB = AM + MB$	2. ▬▬▬▬▬▬
3. $AB = AM + MQ$	3. ▬▬▬▬▬▬

Applications in Carpentry   **Total Probable Error**

Jerry Dillon is a carpenter. His job varies daily from cutting and nailing pieces of wood together to constructing a flight of stairs from blueprint specifications. In either case, his responsibilities include measuring accurately. However, all measurements involve errors. Errors may occur because of human mistakes or flaws in the measuring instruments. To plan for these types of errors, Jerry estimates the **total probable error.** The total probable error is based upon the error in one measurement and the total number of measurements to be made.

Jerry uses the following formula.

$$T = E\sqrt{n}$$

T is the total probable error.
E is the error in one measurement.
n is the number of measurements.

Example Jerry is determining the amount of wood he will need to put baseboards in a family room. Suppose the tape measure Jerry uses is 0.005 centimeters shorter than the standard. To measure the perimeter of the family room, he uses the tape 16 times. A maximum error of 0.4 centimeters is allowed. Find the total probable error and tell whether or not it is within the maximum.

$$\begin{aligned} T &= E\sqrt{n} \\ &= (0.005)(\sqrt{16}) \\ &= (0.005)(4) \\ &= 0.02 \end{aligned}$$

E is 0.005.
n is 16.

Encourage students to use calculators.

The total probable error is 0.02 centimeters, which is within the 0.40 centimeter maximum.

Exercises

For each of the following, find the total probable error and determine whether it is within the maximum.

1. A 100-foot long tape is 0.02 feet longer than standard. The tape will be used 49 times. A maximum error of 0.19 feet is allowed. *T = 0.14; within the maximum*

2. A worker makes consistent errors of 1.3 millimeters each time for 81 times. A maximum error of 15 millimeters is allowed. *T = 11.7; within the maximum*

3. One end of a tape is held 1.5 centimeters too low. This error occurs consistently 25 times. A maximum error of 4 centimeters is allowed. *T = 7.5; not within the maximum*

4. A tape measure is consistently held 2 feet too high. The tape is used 49 times. A maximum error of 5 feet is allowed. *T = 14; not within the maximum*

5. A machine makes consistent errors of 1.3 millimeters each time for 300 times. A maximum error of 15 millimeters is allowed. *T ≈ 22.516; not within the maximum*

6. A machine makes consistent errors of 0.4 millimeters each time for 5000 times. A maximum error of 30 millimeters is allowed. *T ≈ 28.28; within the maximum*

2-5 Congruent Segments

Objectives: Recognize theorems and properties of congruence and use congruence of segments in $\overline{PQ}$ and $\overline{RS}$ below are congruent because they are both 4 units.   geometric proofs.

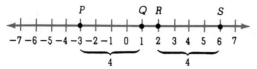

Two segments are congruent if and only if they have exactly the same length.	*Definition of Congruent Segments*

The symbol $\cong$ means *congruent* or *is congruent to*. In the example above, $\overline{PQ} \cong \overline{RS}$ means $\overline{PQ}$ is congruent to $\overline{RS}$.

Since congruence of segments is related to measure, the following theorems hold.

Point out the relationship between congruent segments and the measure of segments.

Congruence of segments is reflexive.	*Theorem 2-2*
Congruence of segments is symmetric.	*Theorem 2-3*
Congruence of segments is transitive.	*Theorem 2-4*

You may want to present Construction 1 on page 475 at this time.

The proofs of these theorems are similar. The proof of Theorem 2-3 is shown below.

Example

1 **Prove that congruence of segments is symmetric.**

Given: $\overline{PQ} \cong \overline{RS}$
Prove: $\overline{RS} \cong \overline{PQ}$

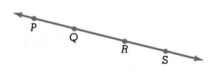

Proof:

STATEMENTS	REASONS
1. $\overline{PQ} \cong \overline{RS}$	1. Given
2. $PQ = RS$	2. Definition of Congruent Segments
3. $RS = PQ$	3. Symmetric Property of Equality (Postulate 2-5)
4. $\overline{RS} \cong \overline{PQ}$	4. Definition of Congruent Segments

The midpoint of a segment separates a segment into two segments of equal length. The Midpoint Theorem extends this relationship to congruence.

| If M is midpoint of $\overline{PQ}$, then $\overline{PM} \cong \overline{MQ}$. | *Theorem 2-5* *Midpoint Theorem* |

Example

2 **Prove Theorem 2-5.**

Given: M is the midpoint of $\overline{PQ}$.
Prove: $\overline{PM} \cong \overline{MQ}$

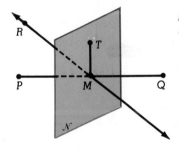

Proof:

STATEMENTS	REASONS
1. M is the midpoint of $\overline{PQ}$.	1. Given
2. $PM = MQ$	2. Definition of Midpoint
3. $\overline{PM} \cong \overline{MQ}$	3. Definition of Congruent Segments

Any point, segment, ray, line, or plane that intersects a segment at its midpoint is said to be a **segment bisector**.

$\overline{TM}$ is a bisector of $\overline{PQ}$.
$\overleftrightarrow{RM}$ is a bisector of $\overline{PQ}$.
$\mathcal{N}$ is a bisector of $\overline{PQ}$.
$\overrightarrow{MR}$ is a bisector of $\overline{PQ}$.
Point M is a bisector of $\overline{PQ}$.

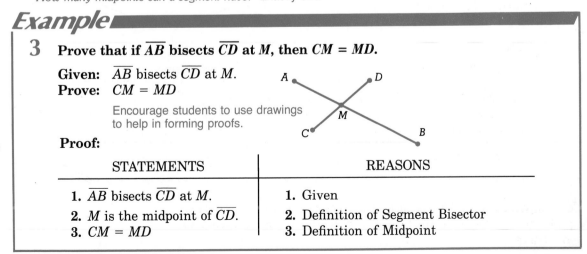

M is the midpoint of $\overline{PQ}$.

How many bisectors can a segment have? Infinitely many
How many midpoints can a segment have? Exactly one

Example

3 **Prove that if $\overline{AB}$ bisects $\overline{CD}$ at M, then $CM = MD$.**

Given: $\overline{AB}$ bisects $\overline{CD}$ at M.
Prove: $CM = MD$

Encourage students to use drawings
to help in forming proofs.

Proof:

STATEMENTS	REASONS
1. $\overline{AB}$ bisects $\overline{CD}$ at M.	1. Given
2. M is the midpoint of $\overline{CD}$.	2. Definition of Segment Bisector
3. $CM = MD$	3. Definition of Midpoint

If $\overline{PQ}$ is bisected at point M, then $\overline{PM} \cong \overline{MQ}$.	**Theorem 2-6** **Bisector Theorem**

A segment bisector must contain the midpoint of the segment.

EN: 2–8 even, 1–19 odd, 20–32 even, 33–38; **AV:** 1–8, 2–38 even; **FD:** 1–8, 1–32, p. 54, 9–11

Exploratory Exercises

State the property shown in each of the following.

1. $\overline{RS} \cong \overline{RS}$

2. If $\overline{RS} \cong \overline{PQ}$ and $\overline{PQ} \cong \overline{TV}$, then $\overline{RS} \cong \overline{TV}$.

3. If $\overline{PQ} \cong \overline{RS}$, then $\overline{RS} \cong \overline{PQ}$.

4. $\overline{PQ} \cong \overline{PQ}$

5. If $\overline{AB} \cong \overline{CD}$ and $\overline{CD} \cong \overline{EF}$, then $\overline{AB} \cong \overline{EF}$.

6. If $\overline{AB} \cong \overline{BC}$ and $\overline{BC} \cong \overline{CD}$, then $\overline{AB} \cong \overline{CD}$.

7. If $\overline{RX} \cong \overline{PQ}$ and $\overline{PQ} \cong \overline{TR}$, then $\overline{RX} \cong \overline{TR}$.

8. If $\overline{AB} \cong \overline{BC}$, then $\overline{BC} \cong \overline{AB}$.

Written Exercises

Use the drawing below to identify each of the following statements as *true* or *false*.

1. $\overrightarrow{PS}$ bisects $\overline{BC}$.

2. D is the midpoint of $\overline{CE}$.

3. $\overline{AB} \cong \overline{CD}$

4. $\overline{BQ} \cong \overline{CE}$

5. $\overline{AQ} \cong \overline{QD}$

6. $\overrightarrow{RP}$ bisects $\overline{AD}$.

7. Q is the midpoint of $\overline{BC}$.

8. $\overline{BC} \cong \overline{QE}$

9. C bisects $\overline{EQ}$.

10. $\overline{BQ} \cong \overline{QC}$

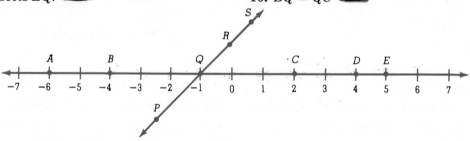

Answer each of the following. For Exercises 11–20, see the Teacher Guide.

11. Give a definition of midpoint.

12. Give a definition for bisects.

13. State the hypothesis and conclusion of Theorem 2-5: If M is the midpoint of $\overline{PQ}$, then $\overline{PM} \cong \overline{MQ}$.

14. Write the converse of Theorem 2-5 and determine if it is *true* or *false*. If false, give a counterexample.

15. State the hypothesis and conclusion of Theorem 2-6: If $\overline{PQ}$ is bisected at point M, then $\overline{PM} \cong \overline{MQ}$.

16. Draw and label a diagram to illustrate the hypothesis of Theorem 2-6.

17. Using the figure in Exercise **16,** state the given and prove for a proof of Theorem 2-6.

18. Write a definition of midpoint based on congruence.

19. Give a plan for a proof of Theorem 2-6.

20. Write a formal proof for Theorem 2-6.

For Exercises 21–26, copy and complete the table below. P, Q, and M are points on a number line. M is the midpoint of $\overline{PQ}$. More than one correct answer may be possible.

	coordinates			PQ	MQ
	P	Q	M		
21.	-5	5	▮	▮	▮
22.	7	▮	20	▮	▮
23.	▮	▮	3	10	▮
24.	▮	-3	▮	8	▮
25.	$\frac{1}{3}$	$\frac{3}{4}$	▮	▮	▮
26.	▮	▮	-1	▮	3.4

For Exercises 27–30, M is the midpoint of $\overline{AB}$, N is the midpoint of $\overline{MB}$, $\overline{CD}$ bisects $\overline{AM}$ at P, and Q is the midpoint of $\overline{AP}$. Emphasize the necessity of a labeled figure.

27. If $AB = 12$, find QN. ▮

28. If $AN = 18$, find AB. ▮

29. If $PN = 14$, find QM. ▮

30. If $AQ = 2.7$, find PN. ▮

Identify each of the following statements as *true* or *false*. If the statement is false, tell why.

31. If $AB = BC$, then B is the midpoint of $\overline{AC}$. ▮

32. If $\overline{AB} \cong \overline{BC}$, then ℓ bisects $\overline{AC}$ at B. ▮
For Exercises 31 and 32, A, B, and C must be collinear.

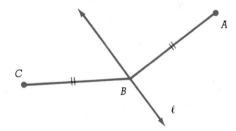

Exercises 31 and 32

For Exercises 33–36, see the Teacher Guide.

Prove each of the following statements.

33. Congruence of segments is reflexive.

34. Congruence of segments is transitive.

35. If M is between P and Q, and $\overline{PM} \cong \overline{MQ}$, then M is the midpoint of $\overline{PQ}$.

36. If $\overline{LP}$ bisects $\overline{RS}$ at M, then $\overline{RM} \cong \overline{MS}$.

Complete each proof.

37. **Given:** B is the midpoint of $\overline{AC}$.

    Prove: $AB = \frac{1}{2}AC$

    Proof:

STATEMENTS	REASONS
1. B is the midpoint of $\overline{AC}$.	1. Given
2. $AB = BC$	2. ▮
3. $AB + BC = AC$	3. ▮
4. $AB + AB = AC$	4. ▮
5. $2AB = AC$	5. ▮
6. $AB = \frac{1}{2}AC$	6. ▮

38. **Given:** $EF = GH$
Prove: $EG = FH$

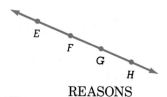

Proof:

STATEMENTS	REASONS
1. $EF = GH$	1. ▬▬▬▬
2. $EF + FG = FG + GH$	2. ~~Addition Property of Equality~~
3. $EG = EF + FG$	3. ~~Definition of Between~~
4. $FH = FG + GH$	4. ~~Definition of Between~~
5. $EG = FH$	5. ▬▬▬▬

Statistics That Shape Your Life

Over the past few decades there have been rapid changes in computers and their usage. There are very few areas of our lives, if any, that are not affected in one way or another by computers. The computer is no longer available to just large corporations. The availability of smaller, inexpensive microcomputer systems has made them practical for use in homes, schools, and small businesses.

Office computer users, by age

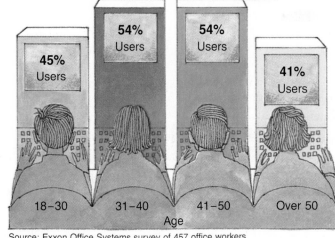

The graph reflects the use of computers in an office of 457 workers. The office workers have been divided according to age with a percentage of users designated for each age category.

Source: Exxon Office Systems survey of 457 office workers
Copyright, 1985 USA Today. Reprinted with permission.

Exercises

1. Why is the sum of percentages in the groups 31–40 and 41–50 greater than 100%? Each group is distinct.

2. Which of the following ratios would be reasonable for calculating the percentage of users in the "over 50" category? Why?

   a. $\frac{37}{90}$ **b.** $\frac{187}{457}$ a.; There could not be 457 in the over 50 group since the total in all groups is 457.

3. Why do you think the smallest percentage of office computer users is the over 50 group? Answers will vary. Older group may be management; older group may not be as eager or willing to be retrained.

2-6 Properties of Inequalities

Objectives: Use inequality symbols, and use inequality postulates in proofs.

Segments are congruent if they have the same length. Segment lengths may also be compared in other ways.

CD equals AB.   EF is less than AB.   GH is greater than AB.

AB, CD, EF, and *GH* each represent numerical values.

An equation or inequality can be used to describe each situation.

$$CD = AB \qquad\qquad EF < AB \qquad\qquad GH > AB$$

Remind students that $6 > 4$ is equivalent to $4 < 6$.

For any two numbers a and b, exactly one of the following statements is true. $$a < b \qquad a = b \qquad a > b$$	*Postulate 2-15* *Comparison Property*

The symbols $\neq$, $\leq$, and $\geq$ also can be used when comparing numbers. For example, $x \leq y$ means $x < y$ or $x = y$.

The symbol $\neq$ means $<$ or $>$. For many computers the symbol $<>$ is used to mean $\neq$.

Operating with the same number on both sides of an inequality may or may *not* affect its truth value. The following properties state how the truth value is affected.

For any numbers a, b, and c: 1. If $a > b$, then $a + c > b + c$ and $a - c > b - c$. 2. If $a < b$, then $a + c < b + c$ and $a - c < b - c$.	*Postulate 2-16* *Addition and Subtraction Properties of Inequality*
For any numbers a, b, and c: 1. If $c > 0$ and $a < b$, then $ac < bc$ and $\dfrac{a}{c} < \dfrac{b}{c}$. 2. If $c > 0$ and $a > b$, then $ac > bc$ and $\dfrac{a}{c} > \dfrac{b}{c}$. 3. If $c < 0$ and $a < b$, then $ac > bc$ and $\dfrac{a}{c} > \dfrac{b}{c}$. 4. If $c < 0$ and $a > b$, then $ac < bc$ and $\dfrac{a}{c} < \dfrac{b}{c}$.	*Postulate 2-17* *Multiplication and Division Properties of Inequality* *Notice in 3 and 4, $c < 0$.*

Emphasize that multiplying or dividing by a negative number reverses the inequality symbol.

For any numbers a, b, and c,

1. If $a < b$ and $b < c$, then $a < c$.
2. If $a > b$ and $b > c$, then $a > c$.

Postulate 2-18 Transitive Property of Inequality

Examples

1 **Prove that if $3x > 9x + 6$, then $x < -1$.**

Additional practice with inequalities can be found on page 560 of the Diagnostic Skills Review.

Given: $3x > 9x + 6$
Prove: $x < -1$

Proof:

STATEMENTS	REASONS
1. $3x > 9x + 6$	**1.** Given
2. $-6x > 6$	**2.** Subtraction Property of Inequality (Postulate 2-16), Substitution (Postulate 2-9)
3. $x < -1$	**3.** Division Property of Inequality (Postulate 2-17), Substitution (Postulate 2-9)

2 **Two segments, $\overline{PQ}$ and $\overline{RS}$, intersect at point T so that $\overline{RT}$ is congruent to $\overline{TQ}$. If PQ is greater than RS, prove that $PT > TS$.**

Given: $\overline{RT} \cong \overline{TQ}$
$PQ > RS$
Prove: $PT > TS$

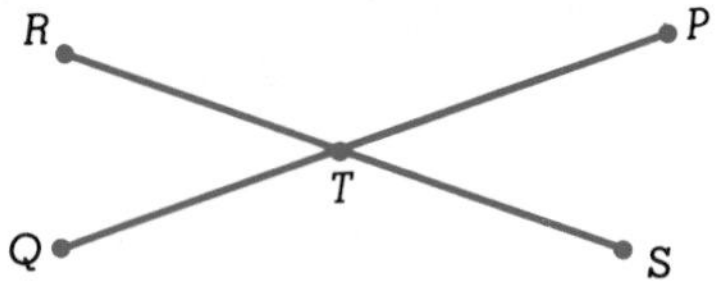

Proof:

STATEMENTS	REASONS
1. $PQ > RS$	**1.** Given
2. $RS = RT + TS$ $PQ = PT + TQ$	**2.** Definition of Between
3. $\overline{RT} \cong \overline{TQ}$	**3.** Given
4. $RT = TQ$	**4.** Definition of Congruent Segments
5. $PQ = PT + RT$	**5.** Substitution Property of Equality (Postulate 2-9)
6. $PT + RT > RT + TS$	**6.** Substitution Property of Equality (Postulate 2-9)
7. $PT > TS$	**7.** Subtraction Property of Inequality (Postulate 2-16), Substitution of Equality (Postulate 2-9)

Exploratory Exercises

Replace each ▦ with <, >, or = to make each sentence true.

1. 2 ▦ 6

2. 7 ▦ 15

3. 6 ▦ 2

4. −5 ▦ −1

5. −1 ▦ −6

6. 0.01 ▦ 0.001

7. 2 + 3 ▦ 4 + 1

8. $3\frac{1}{2} + 1$ ▦ $3\frac{1}{2}$

9. 1.25 ▦ 1.253

10. −5 + 4 ▦ 2 + (−3)

11. $2\frac{1}{4} - 3$ ▦ $2\frac{1}{4}$

12. $2\frac{1}{4} - 3$ ▦ 3

Written Exercises

Complete the table below. For each inequality listed in the sentence column, perform the indicated operation on both members of the inequality.

	Sentences	Add −12	Subtract 7	Subtract −3	Multiply by $-\frac{1}{4}$	Divide by 3	Divide by −2
1.	15 > 12	3 > 0	8 > 5	18 > 15	$-\frac{15}{4} < -3$	5 > 4	$-\frac{15}{2} < -6$
2.	3 < 4	−9 < −8	−4 < −3	6 < 7	$-\frac{3}{4} > -1$	$1 < \frac{4}{3}$	$-\frac{3}{2} > -2$
3.	−10 < −6	−22 < −18	−17 < −13	−7 < −3	$\frac{5}{2} > \frac{3}{2}$	$-\frac{10}{3} < -2$	5 > 3
4.	10 > 6	−2 > −6	3 > −1	13 > 9	$-\frac{5}{2} < -\frac{3}{2}$	$\frac{10}{3} > 2$	−5 < −3

Use the number line below. Replace each ▦ with <, >, or = to make each sentence true.

5. *QR* ▦ *ST*

6. *PS* ▦ *QV*

7. *PQ* ▦ *TV*

8. *PS* ▦ *RV*

9. *RT* ▦ *QS*

10. *PV* ▦ *RS*

11. *PT* ▦ *QV*

12. *PR* ▦ *RV*

13. *PQ* ▦ *QS*

14. *RS* ▦ *TV*

15. *SV* ▦ *PR*

16. *PS* ▦ *QT*

State the property of inequality that justifies each step.

17. (1) $x + 7 < 21$ (1) Given
      (2) $x < 14$ (2) _____

18. (1) $9 > p - 21$ (1) Given
      (2) $30 > p$ (2) _____

19. (1) $7r < -4.9$ (1) Given
      (2) $r < -0.7$ (2) _____

20. (1) $\frac{t}{3} > 21$ (1) Given
      (2) $t > 63$ (2) _____

21. (1) $10p - 14 < 8p - 17$ (1) Given
      (2) $10p < 8p + (-3)$ (2) _____
      (3) $2p < -3$ (3) _____
      (4) $p < -\frac{3}{2}$ (4) _____

22. (1) $-5(y + 5) > 5(y - 1)$ (1) Given
      (2) $-5y + (-25) > 5y + (-5)$ (2) Distributive
      (3) $-5y > 5y + 20$ (3) _____
      (4) $-10y > 20$ (4) _____
      (5) $y < -2$ (5) _____

Solve each of the following inequalities.

23. $3x + 7 > 43$ $x >$

24. $2t - 9 < 21$ $t <$

25. $11 - 5y < -77$ $y >$ ___ or $y >$ ___

26. $8 - 3x < 44$ $x >$

27. $9(x + 2) < 72$ $x <$

28. $5(5z - 3) > 60$ $z >$

29. $8c - (c - 5) < c + 17$ $c <$

30. $-\dfrac{d}{4} - 5 < 23$ $d >$

31. $4x - 13 > 2.7x + 13$ $x >$

32. $3y - 2(8y - 11) > 5 - (2y + 6)$ $y <$

33. Suppose P, Q, R, and S are collinear points with Q between P and R, and R between Q and S. Also, $\overline{PQ}$ is congruent to $\overline{RS}$, and QR is less than RS. Write an equation or inequality that relates PQ and QR.

34. Suppose A, B, C, and D are collinear points with B between A and C, and C between B and D. Also, $\overline{AB}$ is congruent to $\overline{CD}$, and BC is greater than CD. Write an equation or inequality that relates BD and AC.

35. If $AB < CD$ and $CD < EF$, how are AB and EF related? $AB < EF$ by the ___ Property of Inequality.

36. If $PQ > RS$ and $RS > TV$, how are PQ and TV related? $PQ > TV$ by the ___ Property of Inequality.

37. Suppose A, B, and C are collinear points and $AB > AC$. Which of the following could *not* be true?
   a. Point C is between A and B.
   b. Point B is between A and C.
   c. Point A is between B and C.

38. Suppose X, Y, and Z are collinear points and $XY = YZ$. Which of the following could be true?
   a. Point X is between Y and Z.
   b. Point Y is between X and Z.
   c. Point Z is between X and Y.

Challenge Exercises

Complete the following proof.

39. **Given:** $ST < PQ$
  M is the midpoint of $\overline{ST}$
  N is the midpoint of $\overline{PQ}$.

Prove: $SM < PN$

Proof:

STATEMENTS	REASONS
1. $ST < PQ$	1. ___
2. $SM + MT = ST$ $PN + NQ = PQ$	2. ___
3. $SM + MT < PN + NQ$	3. ___
4. M is the midpoint of $\overline{ST}$. N is the midpoint of $\overline{PQ}$.	4. ___
5. $SM = MT$ $PN = NQ$	5. ___
6. $2SM < 2PN$	6. ___
7. $SM < PN$	7. ___

Vocabulary

Chapter Summary

1. Numbers that can be written in the form $\frac{a}{b}$, where a and b are integers and b is *not* zero, are called *rational numbers*. Nonterminating, nonrepeating decimals represent *irrational numbers*. Taken together, the rational numbers and irrational numbers make up the *real numbers*.   (37–39)

2. Number Line Postulate (Postulate 2-1): Each real number corresponds to exactly one point on a number line. Each point on a number line corresponds to exactly one real number.   (39)

3. A number assigned to a point on a number line is called the coordinate of the point.   (39)

4. Ruler Postulate (Postulate 2-2): The points on any line can be paired with the real numbers so that, given any two points P and Q on the line, P corresponds to zero, and Q corresponds to a positive number.   (41)

5. Distance Postulate (Postulate 2-3): For any two points on a line and a given unit of measure, there is a unique positive number called the measure of the distance between two points.   (42)

6. To find the measure of the distance between two points on a number line, find the absolute value of the difference of their coordinates.   (42)

7. Definition of Between: A point Q is between points P and R if and only if each of the following conditions hold.
   1. P, Q, and R are collinear.
   2. $PQ + QR = PR$ (46)

8. Definition of Midpoint: A point M is the midpoint of a segment, $\overline{PQ}$, if and only if M is between P and Q, and $PM = MQ$.   (46)

9. Theorem 2-1: If a segment is given, then it has exactly one midpoint.   (47)

10. Properties of equality: (50–51)

		For any numbers a, b, and c
Postulate 2-4	Reflexive	$a = a$
Postulate 2-5	Symmetric	If $a = b$, then $b = a$.
Postulate 2-6	Transitive	If $a = b$ and $b = c$, then $a = c$.
Postulate 2-7	Addition and Subtraction	If $a = b$, then $a + c = b + c$, and $a - c = b - c$.
Postulate 2-8	Multiplication and Division	If $a = b$, then $a \cdot c = b \cdot c$, and if c is not zero, $\dfrac{a}{c} = \dfrac{b}{c}$.
Postulate 2-9	Substitution	If $a = b$, then a may be replaced by b.

11. Properties of operations: (51)

		For any numbers a, b, and c	
	Property	Addition	Multiplication
Postulate 2-10	Commutative	$a + b = b + a$	$a \cdot b = b \cdot a$
Postulate 2-11	Associative	$(a + b) + c = a + (b + c)$	$(a \cdot b) \cdot c = a \cdot (b \cdot c)$
Postulate 2-12	Identity	$a + 0 = a = 0 + a$	$a \cdot 1 = a = 1 \cdot a$
Postulate 2-13	Inverse	$a + (-a) = 0 = -a + a$	If a is not zero, then $a \cdot \dfrac{1}{a} = 1 = \dfrac{1}{a} \cdot a$.
Postulate 2-14	Distributive Property of Multiplication over Addition: $a(b + c) = ab + ac$ and $(b + c)a = ba + ca$		

12. Definition of Congruent Segments: Two segments are congruent segments if and only if they have exactly the same length. (56)

13. Theorem 2-2: Congruence of segments is reflexive. (56)

14. Theorem 2-3: Congruence of segments is symmetric. (56)

15. Theorem 2-4: Congruence of segments is transitive. (56)

16. Midpoint Theorem (Theorem 2-5): If M is the midpoint of $\overline{PQ}$, then $\overline{PM} \cong \overline{MQ}$. (57)

17. Bisector Theorem (Theorem 2-6): If $\overline{PQ}$ is bisected at point M, then $\overline{PM} \cong \overline{MQ}$. (58)

18. Properties of inequality: (61–62)

		For any numbers a, b, and c
Postulate 2-15	Comparison	$a < b$, or $a = b$, or $a > b$
Postulate 2-16	Addition and Subtraction	**1.** If $a > b$, then $a + c > b + c$ and $a - c > b - c$. **2.** If $a < b$, then $a + c < b + c$ and $a - c < b - c$.
Postulate 2-17	Multiplication and Division	**1.** If $c > 0$ and $a < b$, then $ac < bc$ and $\frac{a}{c} < \frac{b}{c}$. **2.** If $c > 0$ and $a > b$, then $ac > bc$ and $\frac{a}{c} > \frac{b}{c}$. **3.** If $c < 0$ and $a < b$, then $ac > bc$ and $\frac{a}{c} > \frac{b}{c}$. **4.** If $c < 0$ and $a > b$, then $ac < bc$ and $\frac{a}{c} < \frac{b}{c}$.
Postulate 2-18	Transitive	**1.** If $a < b$ and $b < c$, then $a < c$. **2.** If $a > b$ and $b > c$, then $a > c$.

Chapter Review

2-1   **State the coordinates of each of the following points on the number line.**

1. A **2.** B **3.** C **4.** D

Change each fraction or mixed numeral to a terminating or repeating decimal.

5. $\frac{7}{10}$ **6.** $-1\frac{2}{5}$ **7.** $-\frac{2}{3}$ **8.** $2\frac{1}{6}$

Change each decimal to a fraction in simplest form.

9. $0.\overline{3}$ **10.** $1.\overline{4}$ **11.** $0.\overline{12}$ **12.** $6.2\overline{5}$

2-2   **Use the number line below to find each measure.**

13. PQ **14.** QR **15.** PT **16.** SQ

17. PS **18.** QT **19.** SR **20.** RT

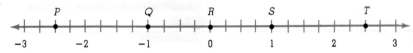

2-3   **Use the number line below to answer each of the following.**

21. Show that Q is between P and R.   **22.** Show that Q is *not* between R and T.

23. Show that S is *not* the midpoint of Q and T.   **24.** Show that R is the midpoint of P and T.

For Exercises 21–24, see the Teacher Guide.

2-4 **Complete each sentence so it is an example of the indicated property.**

25. Associative ($\times$) $8(5 \cdot 7) = $ _____

26. Distributive $-3(x - 2y) = $ _____

27. Commutative ($+$) $AB + BC = $ _____

28. Transitive ($=$)   If $g + 2 = f - 3$ and $f - 3 = t + 7$, then _____ $= t + 7$

29. Symmetric ($=$)   If $PM = MQ$, then _____

30. Substitution   If $x + y = 14$ and $x = 5$, then _____

Indicate the property represented by each sentence.

31. $-8 + 8 = 0$ ~~inverse~~

32. $\sqrt{2} + 0 = \sqrt{2}$ ~~identity~~

33. $\dfrac{5}{4}\left(\dfrac{4}{5}\right) = 1$ ~~inverse~~

34. $184 = 184$ ~~reflexive~~

35. $(3)(6) = (6)(3)$ ~~commutative~~

36. $97 \cdot 1 = 97$ ~~identity~~

2-5 **Supply the reasons for the following proof.**

37. **Given:** M is between P and Q.
           $\overline{PM} \cong \overline{MQ}$
     Prove: M is the midpoint of $\overline{PQ}$.

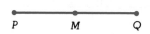

     Proof:

STATEMENTS	REASONS
1. M is between P and Q.	1. ~~Given~~
2. $\overline{PM} \cong \overline{MQ}$	2. ~~Given~~
3. $PM = MQ$	3. ~~Definition of congruent segments~~
4. M is the midpoint of $\overline{PQ}$.	4. ~~Definition of midpoint~~

For $\overline{AB}$, if A and B have coordinates -7 and 5 respectively, find the following.

38. AB ▪

39. coordinate of midpoint M ▪

40. MB ▪

2-6 **Solve each of the following.**

41. $9(x + 2) < 72$ ▪

42. $-\dfrac{1}{4}m > 19$ ▪

43. $2r - 2.1 < -8.7 + r$ ▪

Supply the reasons for the following proof.

44. **Given:** $\overline{PQ}$ bisects $\overline{AB}$ at M.
           $MQ > AM$
     Prove: $MQ > MB$

     Proof:

STATEMENTS	REASONS
1. $\overline{PQ}$ bisects $\overline{AB}$ at M.	1. ▪
2. $\overline{AM} \cong \overline{MB}$	2. ▪
3. $AM = MB$	3. ▪
4. $MQ > AM$	4. ▪
5. $MQ > MB$	5. ▪

Chapter Test

Change each fraction or mixed numeral to decimal form.

1. $\frac{1}{8}$

2. $2\frac{3}{10}$

3. $-\frac{17}{20}$

Change each decimal to a fraction or mixed numeral in simplest form.

4. $0.\overline{9}$

5. -1.3

6. $-8.0\overline{6}$

Use the number line below to find the following.

7. DE

8. AC

9. AE

Refer to the number line above to complete the following.

10. Show E is between D and F.

11. Show C is not the midpoint of $\overline{AD}$.

For Exercises 10 and 11, see the Teacher Guide.

Select the best answer for the following.

12. All rational numbers are also:
    a. natural numbers   **b.** real numbers   c. integers   d. whole numbers

13. AB represents:
    a. a number   b. 2 points   c. a line   d. a line segment

14. Point Q is between M and P if and only if Q, M, and P are collinear and:
    a. $MQ = QP$ b. $MP + PQ = MQ$ **c.** $MQ + PQ = MP$ d. $QM + MP = QP$

15. The coordinate of A is 4 and AB is 3. The possible coordinate(s) of the midpoint of the line segment whose endpoints are A and B is (are):
    a. 1   b. 2   c. 1 and 7   **d.** $2\frac{1}{2}$ and $5\frac{1}{2}$

16. If $a > b$ and $c < 0$, then:
    a. $ac < bc$ and $a + c < b + c$
    b. $ac > bc$ and $a + c > b + c$
    c. $ac < bc$ and $a + c > b + c$
    d. $ac > bc$ and $a + c < b + c$

Supply the given, prove, and complete the proof for the following statement.

17. If B is between A and C and $\overline{AB} \cong \overline{CD}$, then $CD + BC = AC$.

Given: _____

Prove: _____

Proof:

STATEMENTS	REASONS
1. B is between A and C.	1.
2. $AB + BC = AC$	2.
3.	3. Given
4. $AB = CD$	4.
5.	5. Substitution

The test questions on these two pages deal with algebraic and geometric concepts. Read each problem carefully and select the best answer.

> 1. Many problems can be solved without much calculating if the basic mathematical concepts are understood. Always look carefully at what is asked, and think of possible shortcuts for solving the problem.
>
> 2. Check your solutions by substituting values for the variables.

1. In the figure, if $AD = 50$, $CD = 12$, and B is the midpoint of $\overline{AC}$, then $BC =$ ___?___ .

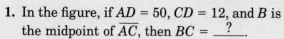

   (A) 12   (B) 18

   (C) 19   (D) 38

2. If $x < 12$ and $y < 18$, then which of the following must be true?

   (A) $x < y$ (B) $y < x$ (C) $y - x = 6$ (D) $x + y < 30$

3. In a stack of sweaters, a green one is the ninth sweater from the one on the top, and the ninth sweater from the one on the bottom. How many sweaters are there?

   (A) 9   (B) 17   (C) 18   (D) 19

4. If $x + 5 = \frac{1}{3}(3x - 5)$, then x is ___?___ .

   (A) 5   (B) 0   (C) any real number   (D) no real number

5. If $b = 2x + 3$, then $4x - 6 =$ ___?___ .

   (A) $2b$ (B) $2b - 9$ (C) $2b - 12$ (D) 0

6. What is another name for $\frac{1}{2}$ of $\frac{x}{2}$?

   (A) $\frac{1}{4}x$ (B) $\frac{1 + x}{4}$ (C) $\frac{1x}{2}$ (D) $\frac{1 + x}{2}$

7. What is the value of

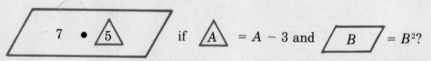

   (A) 35   (B) 98   (C) 196   (D) 343

8. On a true-false test of 158 questions, 14 more of the answers are true than false. What part of the test questions are false?

   (A) $\frac{36}{43}$ (B) $\frac{36}{79}$ (C) $\frac{43}{79}$ (D) $\frac{43}{158}$

9. What is 35% of $\frac{2}{5}$?

   (A) 0.14   (B) 0.875   (C) 1.14   (D) 14

10. The graphs show sales of TV sets by a company. What percent of total sales was Model *B* color? (Round to the nearest percent.)

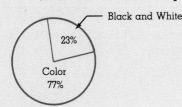
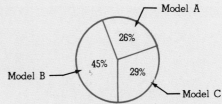

Percent of TV sets   **Percent of Models of Color Sets**

   (A) 32%   (B) 35%   (C) 45%   (D) 77%

11. 40% of 120 is one-third of what number?

   (A) 40   (B) 48   (C) 120   (D) 144

12. If a cake is cut with 15 straight cuts from the center, how many pieces of cake will result?

   (A) 14   (B) 15   (C) 16   (D) 28

13. How many integers between 325 and 400, inclusive, are divisible by 4?

   (A) 19   (B) 18   (C) 20   (D) 24

14. What values of x and y satisfy the following system of equations?
$$3x + y = 10$$
$$x = y + 6$$

   (A) $x = 4, y = 2$ (B) $x = 4, y = -2$
   (C) $x = -4, y = 2$ (D) $x = -4, y = -2$

15. A rectangle is five times as long as it is wide. Its perimeter is 96 feet. What is its length?

   (A) 12 ft   (B) 16 ft   (C) 40 ft   (D) 48 ft

16. What is the average of $2b - 4$, $b + 5$, and $3b + 8$?

   (A) $b + 3$ (B) $2b$ (C) $2b + 3$ (D) $6b + 9$

17. The length of $\overline{ST}$ is ___?___ .

   (A) $4\frac{1}{2}$ (B) 5   (C) $5\frac{1}{2}$ (D) 6

18. $8(916) + 916 =$
   (A) $3(916) + 4(916)$ (B) $4(916) + 3(916)$
   (C) $5(916) + 4(916)$ (D) $6(916) + 4(916)$

CHAPTER 3

Angles and Perpendiculars

Satellites are vital components of domestic and international telecommunication systems. Television signals in the form of electromagnetic waves are transmitted to a satellite. The signal is then relayed to a ground antenna, making it possible for millions of people to see the same communication at the same time. The electromagnetic wave is similar to the concept of a ray in geometry.

3-1 Rays and Angles

Objectives: Name and identify the parts of an angle.

A television signal that is transmitted to a satellite is a model of a ray. In geometry, a **ray** is a never-ending straight path in one direction.

A ray is part of a line and it has one endpoint. To name a ray, name the endpoint first and then name any other point on the ray.

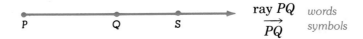

ray PQ *words*

$\overrightarrow{PQ}$ *symbols*

$\overrightarrow{PQ}$ is a ray if and only if it is the set of points $\overline{PQ}$ and all points S for which Q is between P and S.	*Definition of Ray*

Any point on a line determines two rays on that line. The point is the endpoint of the two rays that head in opposite directions.

Opposite rays have a common endpoint.

$\overrightarrow{PQ}$ and $\overrightarrow{PR}$ are **opposite rays.**

$\overrightarrow{PQ}$ and $\overrightarrow{PR}$ are opposite rays if and only if P is between Q and R.	*Definition of Opposite Rays*

A figure is an angle if and only if it consists of two noncollinear rays with a common endpoint.	*Definition of Angle*

The two rays that form an angle are called the **sides** of the angle. The common endpoint is called the **vertex** of the angle. The hands of the clocks below show several angles.

The plural of vertex is vertices.

Angles can be named in several ways using letters or numbers. When three letters are used to name an angle, the letter naming the vertex is between the other two letters.

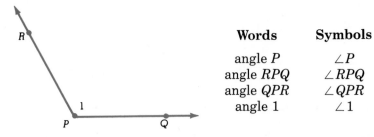

Words	**Symbols**
angle P	$\angle P$
angle RPQ	$\angle RPQ$
angle QPR	$\angle QPR$
angle 1	$\angle 1$

Use Example 1 to show that a single letter may be inadequate for naming an angle.

Example

1 Draw two angles that have a common side. Label the angles and name the common side.

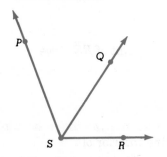

$\angle PSQ$ and $\angle QSR$ have side $\overrightarrow{SQ}$ in common.

Notice that these angles cannot be named by giving the vertex only.

An angle separates a plane into three distinct parts. The parts are the **interior** of the angle, the **exterior** of the angle, and the angle itself. In the figure below, any point in the green part of the plane is in the interior of ∠*P*. Any point in the yellow part of the plane is in the exterior of ∠*P*. The angle itself is shown in black.

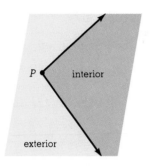

Neither the interior nor the exterior of an angle contains the angle.

A point is in the interior of an angle if it is between any two points, one on each side of the angle. Neither of these points can be the vertex of the angle. In the diagram at the right, *R* is in the interior of ∠*P*.

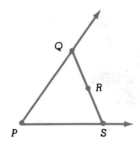

In baseball, a ball is fair if it is hit between the baselines.

EN: 2–16 even, 2–30 even; **AV:** 1–16, 1–24; **FD:** 1–16, 1–20

Exploratory Exercises

Determine whether each of the following is *true* or *false*.

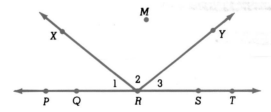

1. $\overrightarrow{RT}$ and $\overrightarrow{RS}$ name the same ray. true

2. $\overrightarrow{QT}$ and $\overrightarrow{TQ}$ name the same ray. false

3. *T* is the endpoint of $\overrightarrow{RT}$. false

4. *S* is the endpoint of $\overrightarrow{RS}$. false

5. $\overrightarrow{QS}$ and $\overrightarrow{QP}$ have the same endpoint. true

6. $\overrightarrow{RT}$ and $\overrightarrow{RQ}$ have the same endpoint. true

7. *R* lies on $\overrightarrow{SQ}$. true

8. *S* lies on $\overrightarrow{RQ}$. false

9. $\overrightarrow{RT}$ and $\overrightarrow{QP}$ are opposite rays. false

10. $\overrightarrow{SR}$ and $\overrightarrow{ST}$ are opposite rays. true

11. ∠*PRX* and ∠*XRP* name the same angle. true

12. ∠*YRS* and ∠3 name the same angle. true

13. *S* is in the interior of ∠*QRX*. false

14. *M* is in the interior of ∠*YRX*. true

15. *R* is the vertex of ∠3. true

16. *R* is the vertex of ∠1. true

Written Exercises

Answer each question.

1. How many endpoints does a ray have? ▆▆

2. What point is the endpoint of $\overrightarrow{PR}$? ▆

3. What is the intersection of two opposite rays? ▆▆▆▆

4. If two rays have the same endpoint, are they opposite rays? ▆▆▆▆

5. Suppose $\overrightarrow{PQ}$ and $\overrightarrow{PR}$ are opposite rays on a number line. The coordinate of P is 0. The coordinate of R is 10. Is the coordinate of Q positive or negative? ▆▆▆

6. Suppose $\overrightarrow{AB}$ and $\overrightarrow{AC}$ are opposite rays on a number line. The coordinate of A is 0. The coordinate of C is -4. What is the set of possible coordinates for B? ▆▆▆▆

For each of the following, draw $\overrightarrow{PQ}$ and $\overrightarrow{RS}$ so that the given conditions are satisfied.

7. $\overrightarrow{PQ}$ and $\overrightarrow{RS}$ intersect, but $\overline{PQ}$ and $\overline{RS}$ do *not* intersect.

8. $\overrightarrow{PQ}$ and $\overrightarrow{RS}$ intersect at point P, but $\overline{PQ}$ and $\overline{RS}$ do *not* intersect.

9. $\overrightarrow{PQ}$ and $\overrightarrow{RS}$ intersect at point Q, but $\overline{PQ}$ and $\overline{RS}$ do *not* intersect.

10. P, Q, R, and S are collinear, but $\overrightarrow{PQ}$ and $\overrightarrow{RS}$ do *not* intersect.

For Exercises 7–10, see students' work.

Use the figures to answer each of the following.

11. Give another name for $\angle 1$. $\angle$▆▆ or $\angle$▆▆

12. Name the vertex of $\angle TQR$. ▆

13. Name the vertex of $\angle 3$. ▆

14. Name the sides of $\angle PQT$. ▆▆

15. Name the sides of $\angle 2$. ▆

16. Name the common side of $\angle 1$ and $\angle 2$. ▆

17. Name all angles with $\overrightarrow{QV}$ as a side.

18. Name a point that lies on $\angle 4$. ▆▆

19. Name a point in the interior of $\angle TQR$. ▆

20. Name a point in the exterior of $\angle 2$. ▆▆

▆▆ ▆▆▆▆

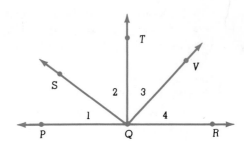

Exercises 11–20

21. Name the angles with point B as their vertex. ▆▆

22. What is another name for $\angle BAD$?

23. The interiors of $\angle ABD$ and $\angle DBC$ are both common to the interior of what angle? ▆▆

24. Name a pair of opposite rays. ▆▆

▆▆

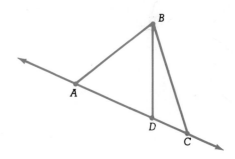

Exercises 21–24

For Exercises 25–30, see students' work.

For each of the following, draw two angles so that the given conditions are satisfied.

25. Two angles intersect in a point.

26. Two angles intersect in a segment.

27. Two angles intersect in a ray.

28. Two angles intersect in two points.

29. Two angles intersect in four points.

30. The vertex of one angle lies in the interior of the other angle and vice versa.

3-2 Measuring Angles

Objective: Measure angles with a protractor.

Surveys are required during the planning and construction of highways, buildings, bridges, tunnels, and so on. Surveyors must make accurate measurements of angles. Angles are often measured in units called **degrees.**

Other units of measure for angles include the radian and the grad.

For every angle there is a unique positive number between 0 and 180 called the degree measure of the angle.	*Postulate 3-1* *Angle Measure* *Postulate*

A **protractor** is used to find the *degree measure* of a given angle.

Place the center point of the protractor on the vertex of the angle. Line up the mark labeled 0 on either scale with one side of the angle. Then read the scale where it falls on the other side of the angle.

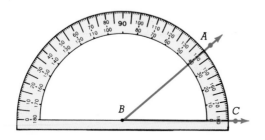

The two scales make it convenient to measure angles in different positions.

The degree measure of angle ABC is 40.   words

$$m \angle ABC = 40$$ symbols

A line separates a plane into two regions called **half planes.** In the figure at the right, $\overleftrightarrow{QT}$ separates the plane into two half planes and is called the **edge** of each half plane. The ray QT is the side of two angles, each measuring 40 degrees (40°). The Protractor Postulate guarantees that in each half plane, there is only one 40° angle having $\overrightarrow{QT}$ as a side. The edge is not part of either half plane.

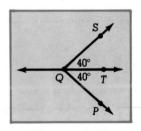

Given a ray on the edge of a half plane, for every positive number *r* between 0 and 180 there is exactly one ray in the half plane such that the degree measure of the angle formed by the two rays is *r*.

Postulate 3-2
Protractor Postulate

Together, the Angle Measure Postulate and the Protractor Postulate establish a one-to-one correspondence between angles and the real numbers between 0 and 180.

Examples

1 **Find the degree measure for each numbered angle.**

Measure each angle with a protractor.
$m \angle 1 = 30$ $m \angle 2 = 95$
$m \angle 3 = 18$ $m \angle 4 = 37$

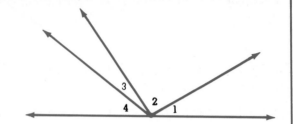

2 **Use a protractor to draw an angle having a degree measure of 65.**

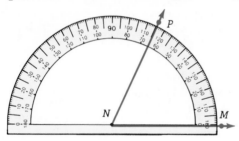

1. Draw $\overrightarrow{NM}$.
2. Place the center point of the protractor on *N* and line up the mark labeled zero with the ray.
3. Locate and draw point *P* at the mark labeled 65.
4. Draw $\overrightarrow{NP}$.

In the diagram, $\angle PQR$ and $\angle SQV$ are **congruent angles** because they both have a degree measure of 50.

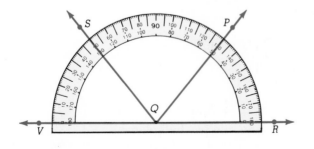

Angle PQR is congruent to angle SQV.   words

$\angle PQR \cong \angle SQV$ symbols

| Two angles are congruent if and only if they have the same measurement. | *Definition of Congruent Angles* |

Congruence of angles is related to equality of numbers. Therefore, the following theorem can be stated.

Students will prove Theorem 3-1 in Written Exercises 27–29 on page 81.

| Congruence of angles is reflexive, symmetric, and transitive. | *Theorem 3-1* |

Have students state this theorem in if-then form using angle notation.

The parts of this theorem parallel the theorems about congruence of segments.

In the figure below, $\angle PQR$ and $\angle RQS$ are **adjacent angles.**

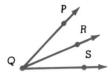

Angle PQS and angle RQS are not adjacent angles.

| Two angles in the same plane are adjacent if and only if they have a common side and a common vertex, but no interior points in common. | *Definition of Adjacent Angles* |

"No interior points in common" means the interiors of the angles cannot overlap.

Measures of adjacent angles can be added to find measures of other angles. For example, in the figure below $m \angle PQS$ is 110 and $m \angle PQR + m \angle RQS$ is 80 + 30 or 110.

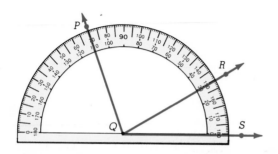

| If R is in the interior of $\angle PQS$, then $m \angle PQR + m \angle RQS = m \angle PQS$. | *Postulate 3-3 Angle Addition Postulate* |

Compare this postulate to the Definition of Between on page 46.

Example

3 In the figure, $m \angle PTR = 130$ and $m \angle PTQ = 40$. Find $m \angle QTR$.

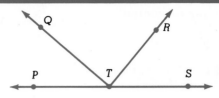

$m \angle PTQ + m \angle QTR = m \angle PTR$	*Angle Addition Postulate*
$40 + m \angle QTR = 130$	*Substitution*
$m \angle QTR = 90$	*Subtraction Property of Equality*

EN: 2–10 even, 11–14, 2–34 even, 36, 37; **AV:** 1–13 odd, 1–35 odd, 36;

Exploratory Exercises

FD: 1–14, 3, 6, 9, 13, 15–27 odd, p. 76, 21–24

Find the degree measure for each of the following angles.

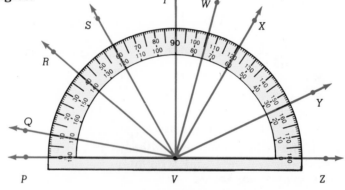

1. $\angle QVZ$ 170
2. $\angle RVZ$ 140
3. $\angle SVZ$ 120
4. $\angle TVZ$ 90
5. $\angle WVZ$ 75
6. $\angle XVZ$ 60
7. $\angle YVZ$ 25
8. $\angle QVP$ 10
9. $\angle SVP$ 60
10. $\angle RVW$ 65

Estimate the degree measure for each of the following angles.

11.  30

12.  120

13. 75

14.  55

Written Exercises

For Exercises 1–8, see students' work.

Use a protractor to draw angles having the following degree measures.

1. 45	2. 60	3. 144	4. 135
5. 75	6. 29	7. 179	8. 120

Use the figure to complete each of the following.

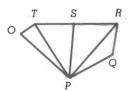

9. $m \angle OPS = m \angle OPT +$ ___
10. $m \angle SRQ =$ ___ $+$ ___
11. $m \angle TPQ - m \angle SPR =$ ___ $+ m \angle$ ___
12. ___ $- m \angle SPR = m \angle OPS$
13. $m \angle TPQ =$ ___ $+$ ___ $+$ ___

80 *Angles and Perpendiculars*

Use the information given in each of the following to find the value of x.

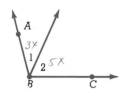
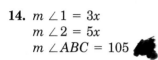

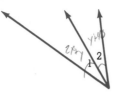

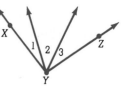
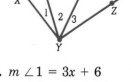

14. $m \angle 1 = 3x$
$m \angle 2 = 5x$
$m \angle ABC = 105$

15. $m \angle 1 = 2x + y$
$m \angle 2 = y + 40$
$\angle 1 \cong \angle 2$

16. $m \angle 1 = 3x + 6$
$m \angle 2 = 2x + 18$
$m \angle 3 = 7x + 6$
$m \angle XYZ = 18x$

Determine whether each of the following is *true* or *false*.

17. $\angle A \cong \angle A$

18. If $\angle A \cong \angle B$, then $m \angle A = m \angle B$.

19. If $\angle B \cong \angle C$ and $\angle C \cong \angle A$, then $\angle B \cong \angle A$.

20. If $\angle P \cong \angle Q$ and $m \angle P = 30$, then $m \angle Q = 30$.

21. If $m \angle ABC = 50$ and $m \angle CBD = 50$, then $\angle ABC \cong \angle CBD$.

22. Angle congruence is transitive.

23. If $\angle BMA \cong \angle XYZ$, then $\angle XYZ \cong \angle BMA$.

24. Angle congruence is reflexive.

25. If $\angle A \cong \angle P$ and $\angle P \cong \angle Z$ and $m \angle A = 40$, then $m \angle Z = 80$.

26. Angle congruence is *not* symmetric.

For Exercises 27–29, see Teacher Guide.

27. Prove that angle congruence is reflexive.

28. Prove that angle congruence is symmetric.

29. Prove that angle congruence is transitive.

Students should not use a protractor for Exercises 30–35.
The figure contains lines ℓ, m, and n. The sum of the degree measures for all of the angles in the figure is 360. If $\angle 1 \cong \angle 5$, $\angle 6 \cong \angle 2$, $\angle 2 \cong \angle 3$, $\angle 1 \cong \angle 4$, $m \angle 7 = m \angle 3 + m \angle 4$, and $m \angle 3 = 30$, find the degree measures for each of the following angles.

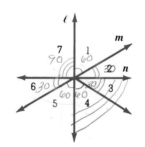

30. $\angle 2$

31. $\angle 6$

32. $\angle 4$

33. $\angle 1$

34. $\angle 5$

35. $\angle 7$

Review solving simultaneous equations before assigning Challenge Exercises.

Challenge Exercises

Use the information given in each of the following to find the values of x and y.

36.

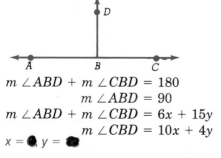

$m \angle ABD + m \angle CBD = 180$
$m \angle ABD = 90$
$m \angle ABD + m \angle CBD = 6x + 15y$
$m \angle CBD = 10x + 4y$
$x = \blacksquare, y = \blacksquare$

37.

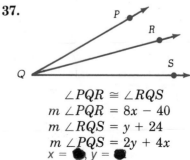

$\angle PQR \cong \angle RQS$
$m \angle PQR = 8x - 40$
$m \angle RQS = y + 24$
$m \angle PQS = 2y + 4x$
$x = \blacksquare, y = \blacksquare$

3-3 Pairs of Angles

Objective: Determine if a pair of angles is complementary or supplementary.

Pairs of angles can be related by the sum of their measures.

Two angles are supplementary if and only if the sum of their degree measures is 180.	*Definition of Supplementary Angles*

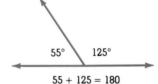

Each angle is called a supplement of the other.

$125 + 55 = 180$ $55 + 125 = 180$

Two angles are complementary if and only if the sum of their degree measures is 90.	*Definition of Complementary Angles*

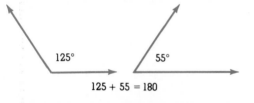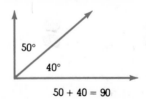

Each angle is called a complement of the other.

$50 + 40 = 90$ $50 + 40 = 90$

Two angles form a linear pair if and only if they are adjacent and their noncommon sides are opposite rays.	*Definition of Linear Pair*

Note that the Definition of Linear Pair and related theorems can be used in situations involving lines.

    In the figure at the right, $\angle 1$ and $\angle 2$ are a linear pair because they are adjacent and $\overrightarrow{YX}$ and $\overrightarrow{YZ}$ are opposite rays.

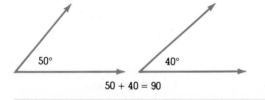

If two angles form a linear pair, then they are supplementary angles.	Postulate 3-4 Supplement Postulate

Since linear pairs form supplementary angles, the sum of their degree measures is 180.

Suppose $\angle A$ is a supplement of $\angle B$. Also, suppose $\angle C$ is a supplement of $\angle B$. If $m\angle B = 40$, what can you say about $m\angle A$ and $m\angle C$?

They both have a degree measure of 140.

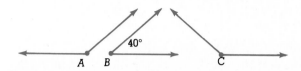

If two angles are supplementary to the same angle, then they are congruent.	Theorem 3-2

Examples

1 Suppose $\angle A$ and $\angle B$ are supplementary to $\angle C$. If $m\angle C = 25$, find the degree measures of $\angle A$ and $\angle B$.

$m\angle A + m\angle C = 180$ — *Definition of Supplementary Angles*
$m\angle A + 25 = 180$ — *Substitute 25 for $m\angle C$.*
$m\angle A = 180 - 25$ or 155 — *Subtraction Property of Equality*

$m\angle B + m\angle C = 180$ — *Definition of Supplementary Angles*
$m\angle B + 25 = 180$ — *Substitute 25 for $m\angle C$.*
$m\angle B = 180 - 25$ or 155 — *Subtraction Property of Equality*

$\angle A$ and $\angle B$ each have a degree measure of 155.

2 Prove Theorem 3-2.

Given: $\angle A$ is a supplement of $\angle B$.
$\angle C$ is a supplement of $\angle B$.
Prove: $\angle A \cong \angle C$

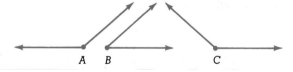

Proof:

STATEMENTS	REASONS
1. $\angle A$ is a supplement of $\angle B$. $\angle C$ is a supplement of $\angle B$.	**1.** Given
2. $m\angle A + m\angle B = 180$ $m\angle C + m\angle B = 180$	**2.** Definition of Supplementary Angles
3. $m\angle A + m\angle B =$ $m\angle C + m\angle B$	**3.** Substitution (Postulate 2-9)
4. $m\angle A = m\angle C$	**4.** Subtraction Property of Equality (Postulate 2-7)
5. $\angle A \cong \angle C$	**5.** Definition of Congruent Angles

Suppose two angles are supplementary to two congruent angles. The figure below shows two linear pairs. The 60 degree angles are congruent. What can you say about ∠1 and ∠2?

You may want to present Construction 2 on page 476 with this lesson.

They are congruent.

If two angles are supplementary to two congruent angles, then the two angles are congruent to each other.

Theorem 3-3

Example

3 **Prove Theorem 3-3.**

Given: ∠A is a supplement of ∠B.
 　　　　∠C is a supplement of ∠D.
 　　　　∠B ≅ ∠D

Prove: ∠A ≅ ∠C

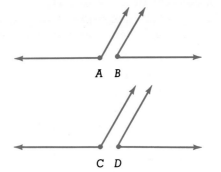

Proof:

STATEMENTS	REASONS
1. ∠A is a supplement of ∠B. ∠C is a supplement of ∠D.	1. Given
2. $m \angle A + m \angle B = 180$ $m \angle C + m \angle D = 180$	2. Definition of Supplementary Angles
3. $m \angle A + m \angle B = m \angle C + m \angle D$	3. Substitution (Postulate 2-9)
4. ∠B ≅ ∠D	4. Given
5. $m \angle B = m \angle D$	5. Definition of Congruent Angles
6. $m \angle A + m \angle B = m \angle C + m \angle B$	6. Substitution (Postulate 2-9)
7. $m \angle A = m \angle C$	7. Subtraction Property of Equality (Postulate 2-7)
8. ∠A ≅ ∠C	8. Definition of Congruent Angles

Theorems similar to those about supplementary angles can be proven for complementary angles.

Students will prove Theorems 3-4 and 3-5 in Written Exercises 13 and 14, page 86.

If two angles are complementary to the same angle, then they are congruent to each other.	*Theorem 3-4*
If two angles are complementary to two congruent angles, then the two angles are congruent to each other.	*Theorem 3-5*

The relationships between complementary and supplementary angles can be expressed algebraically. Consider this example.

Example

4 The degree measure of an angle is 50 more than its complement. Find the degree measure of the angle and its complement.

Let x = the degree measure of the angle.
$x - 50$ = the degree measure of the complement.

$$x + x - 50 = 90 \qquad \textit{Definition of complementary angles}$$
$$2x - 50 = 90$$
$$2x = 140$$
$$x = 70 \qquad \textit{The degree measure of the angle is 70.}$$
$$x - 50 = 20 \qquad \textit{The degree measure of the complement is 20.}$$

EN: 2, 3, 5, 8, 2–18 even; **AV:** 1–7 odd, 1–17 odd, 12, 14; **FD:** 1–8, 1–13 odd, p. 81, 16, 29

Exploratory Exercises   **ALL LEVELS:** Algebra Review

Use the following theorem to answer Exercises 1–8. See the Teacher Guide.

If two sides of adjacent angles lie on a line, then the angles are supplementary.

1. State the hypothesis of the theorem.
   same

2. Draw and label a diagram to illustrate the hypothesis of the theorem.

3. State the given that goes with your diagram for a proof of the theorem.

4. State the conclusion of the theorem.

5. State the prove statement that goes with your diagram for a proof of the theorem.

6. Give another name for two adjacent angles that lie on a line. *Linear Pair*

7. State the theorem or postulate from this lesson that is about adjacent angles and lines. *Post. 3-4*

8. Give a plan for a proof of the theorem.

Written Exercises

In the figure, the following pairs of angles are complementary: ∠1 and ∠2, ∠3 and ∠4, ∠5 and ∠6, ∠7 and ∠8. If $m\angle 1 = 45$, $m\angle 3 = 30$, $\angle 5 \cong \angle 6$, and $m\angle 8 = 10$, find the degree measure for each of the following.

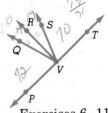

1. ∠2
2. ∠4
3. ∠7
4. ∠6
5. ∠5

Exercises 1–5

In the figure $\angle QVR \cong \angle RVS$, $m\angle PVQ = 72$, $m\angle TVS = 70$, and $\overrightarrow{VP}$ and $\overrightarrow{VT}$ are opposite rays.

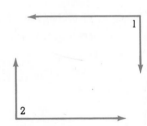

6. Find $m\angle QVS$.
7. Find $m\angle QVR$.
8. Find $m\angle PVR$.
9. Find $m\angle TVR$.
10. Find $m\angle PVS$.
11. Find $m\angle TVQ$.

Exercises 6–11

For Exercises 12–14, see the Teacher Guide.

12. Complete the statements and reasons for the following proof.

> **Theorem:** If two angles are congruent and supplementary, then they each have a degree measure of 90.
> **Given:** ∠1 ≅ ∠2
> ∠1 and ∠2 are supplementary.
> **Prove:** $m\angle 1 = m\angle 2 = 90$

Prove each theorem.

13. If two angles are complementary to the same angle, then they are congruent to each other. (Theorem 3-4)

14. If two angles are complementary to two congruent angles, then the two angles are congruent to each other. (Theorem 3-5)

Solve.

15. The degree measure of an angle is one-third the measure of its supplement. Find the measure of the angle.

16. The degree measure of an angle is one-fourth the measure of its complement. Find the measure of the angle.

17. The degree measure of one of two complementary angles is 6 more than twice the other angle. Find the degree measure of each angle.

18. The degree measure of one of two supplementary angles is 5 less than 4 times the other angle. Find the degree measure of each angle.

Algebra Review

Solve.

1. $5(8 - 2n) = 4n - 2$
2. $5x + 7 = 28 + 2x$

3. Find three consecutive odd integers whose sum is 93.

4. Four times a number decreased by twice the number is 100. Find the number.

5. Twice a number increased by 20 is 62. Find the number.

One way to present a proof is to write it in flow proof form. The following example is a flow proof for Theorem 3-2.

Given: $\angle A$ is a supplement of $\angle B$.
$\angle C$ is a supplement of $\angle B$.
Prove: $\angle A \cong \angle C$

Flow Proof:

$\underline{\angle A \text{ is supplement of } \angle B.} \xrightarrow{1} m\angle A + m\angle B = 180 \Big\}\xrightarrow{2} m\angle A + m\angle B = m\angle C + m\angle B \xrightarrow{3}$
$\underline{\angle C \text{ is supplement of } \angle B.} \xrightarrow{1} m\angle C + m\angle B = 180$
$\xrightarrow{3} m\angle A = m\angle C \xrightarrow{4} \angle A \cong \angle C$

1. Definition of Supplementary Angles
2. Substitution
3. Subtraction Property of Equality
4. Definition of Congruent Angles

A flow proof organizes a series of statements in logical order, starting with given statements that are underlined. The arrows show the order the statements should follow.

The numbers above the arrows refer to the reasons that allow the statements to be made. The reasons are written below the proof. For example, if $\angle A$ is the supplement of $\angle B$ then the definition of supplementary angles implies that $m\angle A + m\angle B = 180$.

Exercises

Answer the questions below about the following flow proof.

Given: $\angle A$ is a supplement of $\angle B$.
$\angle C$ is a supplement of $\angle D$.
$\angle B \cong \angle D$
Prove: $\angle A \cong \angle C$

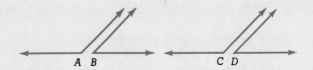

Flow Proof: For Exercises 3–10, see the Teacher Guide.

$\underline{\angle A \text{ is supplement of } \angle B.} \xrightarrow{1} m\angle A + m\angle B = 180 \Big\} \xrightarrow{2} m\angle A + m\angle B = m\angle C + m\angle D \Big] 2$
$\underline{\angle C \text{ is supplement of } \angle D.} \xrightarrow{1} m\angle C + m\angle D = 180$
$\angle B \cong \angle D \xrightarrow{3} m\angle B = m\angle D$
$\xrightarrow{2} m\angle A + m\angle B = m\angle C + m\angle B \xrightarrow{4} m\angle A = m\angle C \xrightarrow{3} \angle A \cong \angle C$

1. Draw the symbol that is used to show that one statement follows from another. $\rightarrow$
2. Draw the symbol used to show that two or more statements imply another. $\}\rightarrow$
3. Write the statements that imply $m\angle A + m\angle B = m\angle C + m\angle B$.
4. Write the reason for arrow 1.
5. Write the reason for arrow 2.
6. Why do two arrows have a 2 above them?
7. Write the reason for arrow 3.
8. Why do two arrows have a 3 above them?
9. Write the reason for arrow 4.
10. Write a flow proof for Theorem 3-4.

3-4 Right Angles

Objectives: Classify acute and obtuse angles according to their measure; use properties of angles in proofs.

Angles can be classified according to their measures.

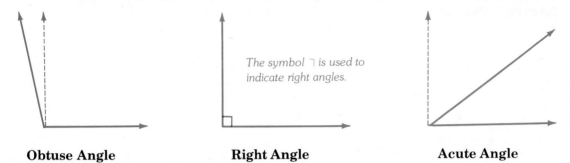

| Obtuse Angle | Right Angle | Acute Angle |

The symbol ⌐ is used to indicate right angles.

| A right angle is an angle whose degree measure is 90. An acute angle is one whose degree measure is less than 90. An obtuse angle is one whose degree measure is greater than 90. | *Definition of Right, Acute, and Obtuse Angles* |

Have students write these definitions in "if and only if" form.

All right angles are congruent because they have the same measure.

Students will prove Theorems 3-6, 3-7, and 3-8 in the Written Exercises.

| If two angles are right angles, then the angles are congruent. | *Theorem 3-6* |

Suppose two angles form a linear pair and one of them is a right angle. In the figure at the right, $\angle 1$ is a right angle.

$m \angle 1 + m \angle 2 = 180$ *The angles in a linear pair are supplementary.*

$m \angle 1 = 90$ *$\angle 1$ is a right angle.*

$90 + m \angle 2 = 180$ *Substitution*

$m \angle 2 = 90$ *Subtraction Property of Equality*

This reasoning shows that $\angle 2$ is also a right angle.

| If one angle in a linear pair is a right angle, then the other angle is also a right angle. | *Theorem 3-7* |

To prove the following theorem, use substitution and the fact that congruent angles have the same measure.

| If two angles are congruent and supplementary, then each angle is a right angle. | *Theorem 3-8* |

The proof of the following theorem is based on Theorem 3-7.

| If two intersecting lines form one right angle, then they form four right angles. | *Theorem 3-9* |

1 **Prove Theorem 3-9.**

Given: Two intersecting lines forming $\angle 1$, $\angle 2$, $\angle 3$, and $\angle 4$.
$\angle 1$ is a right angle.

Prove: $\angle 2$, $\angle 3$, and $\angle 4$ are right angles.

Proof:

STATEMENTS	REASONS
1. Two intersecting lines forming $\angle 1$, $\angle 2$, $\angle 3$, and $\angle 4$.	1. Given
2. $\angle 1$ and $\angle 2$ form a linear pair. $\angle 1$ and $\angle 4$ form a linear pair.	2. Definition of Linear Pair
3. $\angle 1$ is a right angle.	3. Given
4. $\angle 2$ is a right angle. $\angle 4$ is a right angle.	4. If one angle in a linear pair is a right angle, then the other angle is also a right angle. (Theorem 3-7)
5. $\angle 3$ and $\angle 4$ form a linear pair.	5. Definition of Linear Pair
6. $\angle 3$ is a right angle.	6. Theorem 3-7

| Two angles are vertical if and only if they are two nonadjacent angles formed by two intersecting lines. | *Definition of Vertical Angles* |

In the figure at the right, two pairs of vertical angles are formed.

$\angle 1$ and $\angle 3$ are vertical angles.
$\angle 2$ and $\angle 4$ are vertical angles.

Notice that $\angle 1$ and $\angle 2$, $\angle 2$ and $\angle 3$, $\angle 3$ and $\angle 4$, and $\angle 4$ and $\angle 1$ form linear pairs.

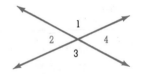

| If two angles are vertical, then they are congruent. | *Theorem 3-10* |

Students will prove Theorem 3-10 in Written Exercise 5.

Exploratory Exercises

Classify angles with each of the following degree measures as either acute, right, or obtuse, or none of these.

1. 61 acute   **2.** 174 obtuse   **3.** 31 acute   **4.** 260 none of these

5. 96 obtuse   **6.** 3 acute   **7.** 90 right   **8.** 105 obtuse

9. 89 acute   **10.** 0 none of these   **11.** 180 none of these   **12.** 94 obtuse

For Exercises 13–18, see the Teacher Guide.

State the hypothesis and conclusion for a proof of each of the following theorems.

13. An angle with a degree measure of 90 and a right angle are congruent.

14. If two angles are vertical angles, then the angles are congruent.

15. If two angles are right angles, then the angles are supplementary.

16. If two angles are congruent and supplementary, then each angle is a right angle.

17. If one angle in a linear pair is a right angle, then the other angle also is a right angle.

18. If two angles are right angles, then the angles are congruent.

Written Exercises

Write whether each of the following angles appears to be acute, right, or obtuse.

1.    **2.**   **3.**    **4.**

Complete the reasons for each of the following proofs.

5. Theorem 3-10: If two angles are vertical, then they are congruent.

    Given: ∠1 and ∠2 are vertical angles.

    Prove: ∠1 ≅ ∠2

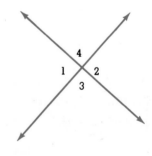

    Proof:

STATEMENTS	REASONS
1. ∠1 and ∠2 are vertical angles.	1. _____
2. ∠1 and ∠4 form a linear pair. ∠2 and ∠4 form a linear pair.	2. _____ of Linear Pair
3. ∠1 and ∠4 are supplementary. ∠2 and ∠4 are supplementary.	3. Supplement Postulate
4. ∠1 ≅ ∠2	4. Theorem _____

6. Theorem 3-8: If two angles are congruent and supplementary, then each angle is a right angle.

Given: $\angle 1 \cong \angle 2$
$\angle 1$ and $\angle 2$ are supplementary.

Prove: $\angle 1$ is a right angle.
$\angle 2$ is a right angle.

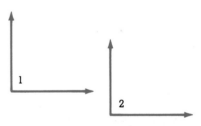

Proof:

STATEMENTS	REASONS
1. $\angle 1$ and $\angle 2$ are supplementary.	1. ~~Given~~
2. $m\angle 1 + m\angle 2 = 180$	2. ~~Definition of Supplementary Angles~~
3. $\angle 1 \cong \angle 2$	3. ~~Given~~
4. $m\angle 1 = m\angle 2$	4. ~~Definition of Congruent Angles~~
5. $m\angle 1 + m\angle 1 = 180$	5. ~~Substitution~~
6. $2(m\angle 1) = 180$	6. ~~Distributive~~
7. $m\angle 1 = 90$	7. ~~Division Property of Equality~~
8. $m\angle 2 = 90$	8. ~~Substitution~~
9. $\angle 1$ is a right angle. $\angle 2$ is a right angle.	9. ~~Definition of Right Angle~~

Use the information given in each of the following figures to find the value of x.

7.

$2x$ $x + 43$

8.

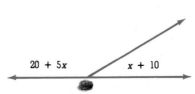

$20 + 5x$ $x + 10$

9.

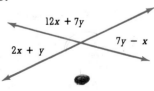

$12x + 7y$ $7y - x$
$2x + y$

Prove each of the following. For Exercises 10–16, see the Teacher Guide.

10. Given: $\angle 2 \cong \angle 6$
   Prove: $\angle 3 \cong \angle 7$

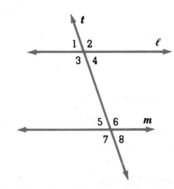

Exercise 10

11. Given: ∠A and ∠C are complementary.

$\angle 1 \cong \angle C$

$\angle 2 \cong \angle A$

Prove: ∠ABC is a right angle.

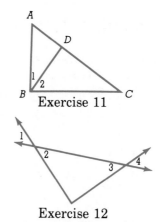
Exercise 11

12. Given: ∠2 and ∠3 are complementary.

Prove: ∠1 and ∠4 are complementary.

Exercise 12

Prove each of the following.

13. An angle with a degree measure of 90 and a right angle are congruent.

14. If two angles are right angles, then the angles are supplementary.

15. If one angle in a linear pair is a right angle, then the other angle is also a right angle. (Theorem 3-7)

16. If two angles are right angles, then the angles are congruent. (Theorem 3-6)

Statistics That Shape Your Life

In recent years there has been a dramatic increase in the number of home satellite dishes sold in the United States. This trend is charted in the graph below. By studying the information in the graph, it is possible to make predictions of future sales of satellite dishes based on past sales.

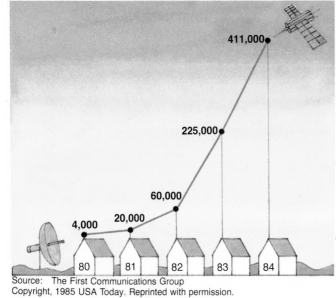

Source: The First Communications Group
Copyright, 1985 USA Today. Reprinted with permission.

Exercises

1. How might the trend in satellite dish sales during the past five years be explained? Cost has decreased; Increase in satellite channels.

2. Find the percentage increase in sales from 1983 to 1984. $82\frac{2}{3}$%

3. Using the same percentage increase from 1983 to 1984, predict the number of sales from 1984 to 1985. 750,760

4. In what areas of the country would you expect to find highest percentage of the population buying satellite dishes? Why? Rural areas. Lack of available cable service.

3-5 Perpendiculars

Objectives: Recognize and use properties and theorems of perpendicular lines.

The weather vane provides an example of **perpendicular lines.**
The north-south line is perpendicular to the east-west line.

> **Two lines are perpendicular if and only if they intersect to form a right angle.**

*Definition of
Perpendicular Lines*

Emphasize the two conditional statements that can be derived from this biconditional.

The symbol ⊥ means *is perpendicular to.* In the figure below, the two lines are perpendicular.

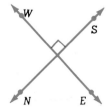

$\overleftrightarrow{NS}$ is perpendicular to $\overleftrightarrow{EW}$.   *words*
$\overleftrightarrow{NS} \perp \overleftrightarrow{EW}$ *symbols*

Parts of lines are perpendicular to each other if they intersect and if the lines containing them are perpendicular. For example, a ray can be perpendicular to a segment. In the figure below, $\overrightarrow{RS} \perp \overline{PQ}$.

*The same term, perpendicular, and the
same symbol, ⊥, are used for lines,
segments, and rays.*

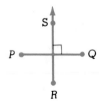

Recall that when two intersecting lines form one right angle, they form four right angles. This information leads to the theorem that follows.

If two lines are perpendicular, then they form four right angles.	*Theorem 3-11*

A given line may have many lines perpendicular to it. In a plane, through any given point on the line, there is exactly one line perpendicular to the given line. In space, there may be infinitely many lines perpendicular to the given line through the given point.

You may want to present Construction 4 on page 479 and Construction 6 on page 480 with this lesson.

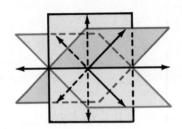

There is one line perpendicular for each plane that contains the given line.

If a point is on a line in a given plane, then there is exactly one line in that plane perpendicular to the given line at the given point.	*Theorem 3-12*

Exactly one means at least one and no more than one.

Theorems 3-13 and 3-14 are converses of one another. Thus, one test for perpendicular lines is congruent adjacent angles.

If two lines are perpendicular, then they form congruent adjacent angles.	*Theorem 3-13*
If two intersecting lines form congruent adjacent angles, then they are perpendicular.	*Theorem 3-14*

Example

1 **Prove Theorem 3-13.**

Given: $\overleftrightarrow{PQ} \perp \overleftrightarrow{QR}$

Prove: $\angle PQR \cong \angle RQS$
$\angle PQR \cong \angle PQT$
$\angle TQS \cong \angle RQS$
$\angle TQS \cong \angle PQT$

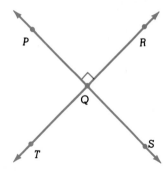

Proof:

STATEMENTS	REASONS
1. $\overleftrightarrow{PQ} \perp \overleftrightarrow{QR}$	1. Given
2. $\overleftrightarrow{PQ}$ and $\overleftrightarrow{QR}$ form a right angle.	2. Definition of Perpendicular Lines
3. $\overleftrightarrow{PQ}$ and $\overleftrightarrow{QR}$ form four right angles, $\angle PQR$, $\angle RQS$, $\angle TQS$, and $\angle PQT$.	3. If two intersecting lines form one right angle, then they form four right angles. (Theorem 3-9)
4. $\angle PQR \cong \angle RQS$ $\angle PQR \cong \angle PQT$ $\angle TQS \cong \angle RQS$ $\angle TQS \cong \angle PQT$	4. If two angles are right angles, then the angles are congruent. (Theorem 3-6)

EN: 3, 6, 9, . . . 18, 3–7; **AV:** 1–19 odd, 1, 2, 5–7; **FD:** 1–20, 1, 2, 6, p. 92, 11, 14; **ALL LEVELS:** Mini Review

Exploratory Exercises

In the figure, $\overleftrightarrow{AB} \perp \overleftrightarrow{FE}$, $\overleftrightarrow{AE} \perp \overleftrightarrow{GC}$, and C is the midpoint of $\overline{AE}$. Determine whether each of the following is *true* or *false*.

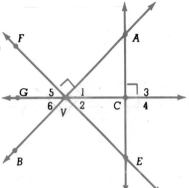

1. $\overleftrightarrow{BV} \perp \overleftrightarrow{VB}$ false

2. $\overleftrightarrow{GV} \perp \overleftrightarrow{AE}$ true

3. $m \angle 1 + m \angle 2 = 90$ true

4. $\overline{AC} \cong \overline{CE}$ true

5. $\overline{AC} \perp \overleftrightarrow{GC}$ true

6. $m \angle BVE = 90$ true

7. $\angle 3 \cong \angle 4$ true

8. $m \angle 3 + m \angle 4 = 180$ true

9. $m \angle AVF = 90$ true

10. $\overleftrightarrow{VB} \perp \overline{VA}$ false

11. $m \angle 4 = m \angle 1 + m \angle 2$ true

12. $\angle 2$ and $\angle 6$ are complementary. true

13. $\angle FVB$ and $\angle 4$ are complementary. false

14. $\angle GVA$ is a right angle. false

15. $\angle 6 \cong \angle 1$ true

16. $\overrightarrow{AE} \perp \overleftrightarrow{FV}$ false

17. $m \angle 1 + m \angle 5 = 90$ true

18. $\angle 4 \cong \angle 1$ false

19. $\angle 6$ and $\angle 3$ are supplementary. false

20. $\angle AVE$ and $\angle BVF$ are supplementary. true

Written Exercises

1. Complete the reasons for the following proof.

Theorem: If two intersecting lines form two congruent adjacent angles, then they are perpendicular.

Given: ℓ and m intersect.
  $\angle 1 \cong \angle 2$

Prove: $\ell \perp m$

Proof:

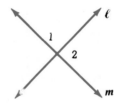

STATEMENTS	REASONS
1. $\angle 1$ and $\angle 2$ form a linear pair.	1. Definition of linear pair
2. $\angle 1$ and $\angle 2$ are supplementary.	2. Supplement Postulate
3. $m \angle 1 + m \angle 2 = 180$	3. Definition of Supplementary Angles
4. $\angle 1 \cong \angle 2$	4.
5. $m \angle 1 = m \angle 2$	5.
6. $m \angle 1 + m \angle 1 = 180$	6.
7. $2(m \angle 1) = 180$	7.
8. $m \angle 1 = 90$	8. Division Property of Equality
9. $\angle 1$ is a right angle.	9. Definition of right angle
10. $\ell \perp m$	10.

Prove each of the following. For Exercises 2–5, see the Teacher Guide.

2. If two lines are perpendicular, then they form four right angles. (Theorem 3-11)

3. If the noncommon sides of two adjacent acute angles are perpendicular, then the angles are complementary.

4. Given: $\angle YXZ$ and $\angle YZX$ are complementary.
  $\angle 1 \cong \angle YZX$
  $\angle 2 \cong \angle YXZ$
Prove: $\overleftrightarrow{XY} \perp \overleftrightarrow{YZ}$

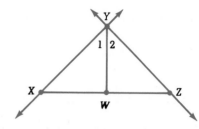

Exercise 4

5. Given: $\overline{AB} \perp \overline{AD}$
  $\overline{BC} \perp \overline{CD}$
  $\angle 2 \cong \angle 4$
Prove: $\angle 1 \cong \angle 3$

Exercise 5

Solve each of the following problems.

6. Given: $\overline{AC} \perp \overline{BC}$

$m \angle APC = 7x + 3$

$m \angle BPC = 16y$

$m \angle ACP = 3x + 2y$

$m \angle BCP = 3x + 4y$

Find $m \angle BPC$.

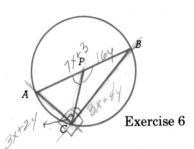

Exercise 6

7. Given: $\overleftrightarrow{AB} \perp \overleftrightarrow{MN}$ at T

$\mathcal{S}$ contains $\overleftrightarrow{MN}$

$m \angle MTB = 2x + 6y$

$m \angle ATN = 4x + 3y$

$m \angle BTN = \frac{8}{3}x + 5y$

Find the values of x and y.

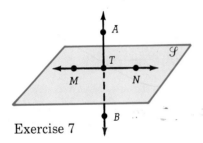

Exercise 7

mini-review

1. Four noncoplanar points, taken three at a time, determine at most how many planes? •

2. Name the five parts of a formal proof.

Use the information in the diagram below to answer each of the following questions.

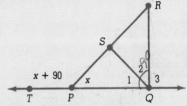

3. If $\angle TPS$ and $\angle SPQ$ form a linear pair, find the degree measure of these angles. •, •

4. If $\angle 1$ and $\angle 2$ are complementary, find the degree measure of $\angle 3$. •

5. If S is the midpoint of $\overline{PR}$, $PS = 2y - 4$, and $PR = 18$, find y. •

Excursions in Geometry _____ Angles

Each of the figures below show noncollinear rays with a common endpoint. Count the number of angles in each figure.

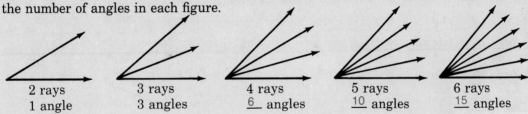

2 rays	3 rays	4 rays	5 rays	6 rays
1 angle	3 angles	6 angles	10 angles	15 angles

Do you see a pattern? Try to predict the number of angles that are formed by 7 rays. 21

If n is the number of rays, $\frac{n(n-1)}{2}$ is the number of angles.

3-6　Perpendicular Planes

Objectives: Recognize and use properties of perpendicular planes.

A line is perpendicular to a plane if and only if the given line is perpendicular to every line in the plane that intersects it.	*Definition of a Line Perpendicular to a Plane*

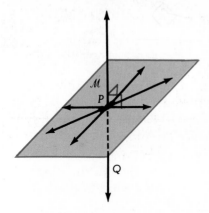

$\overleftrightarrow{PQ} \perp \mathcal{M}$ because it is perpendicular to every line in $\mathcal{M}$ that intersects $\overleftrightarrow{PQ}$. Parts of lines are perpendicular to a plane if and only if they intersect the plane and are contained on a line that is perpendicular to the plane. For example, $\overline{PQ} \perp \mathcal{M}$.

A plane is perpendicular to a line if and only if every line in the plane that intersects the given line is perpendicular to it.	*Definition of a Plane Perpendicular to a Line*

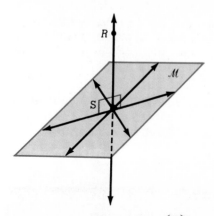

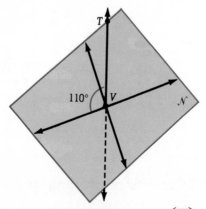

$\mathcal{M}$ is perpendicular to $\overleftrightarrow{RS}$.　　$\mathcal{N}$ is not perpendicular to $\overleftrightarrow{TV}$.

If a line is perpendicular to two intersecting lines at their point of intersection, then it is perpendicular to the plane that contains the two lines.	*Theorem 3-15*

　Just as lines can be perpendicular to lines, planes can be perpendicular to planes. Most walls meet at right angles and provide a model for perpendicular planes.

When the flaps on the wing of an airplane are up or down, they form an angle with the wing. Considered in cross section, this situation can be described using an angle. Considered in space, this situation can be described using another geometric figure called a **dihedral angle.**

Fold a sheet of paper once. The result is a model of a dihedral angle.

An angle is dihedral if and only if it consists of two noncoplanar half planes with a common edge.

Definition of Dihedral Angle

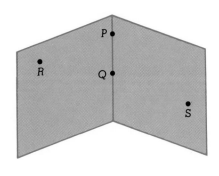

Each half plane in a dihedral angle is called a **face.** A dihedral angle is usually named by its edge and a point on each face. For example, the dihedral angle at the left is $\angle R\text{-}\overleftrightarrow{PQ}\text{-}S$.

It may be useful to have students construct models of dihedral angles. For example, use small pieces of transparencies that have been taped together to indicate the faces and edge of the angle.

Example

1 **Name all eight dihedral angles.**

angles formed by bottom edges	angles formed by side edges
$\angle T\text{-}\overleftrightarrow{PQ}\text{-}S$	$\angle S\text{-}\overleftrightarrow{TP}\text{-}Q$
$\angle T\text{-}\overleftrightarrow{QR}\text{-}S$	$\angle P\text{-}\overleftrightarrow{TQ}\text{-}R$
$\angle T\text{-}\overleftrightarrow{SR}\text{-}Q$	$\angle Q\text{-}\overleftrightarrow{TR}\text{-}S$
$\angle T\text{-}\overleftrightarrow{SP}\text{-}Q$	$\angle R\text{-}\overleftrightarrow{TS}\text{-}P$

The cross section of a dihedral angle is an angle. Geometrically, the cross section is the intersection of a plane and the dihedral angle. The plane intersects the edge of the dihedral angle in a single point. The following figures show two different cross sections.

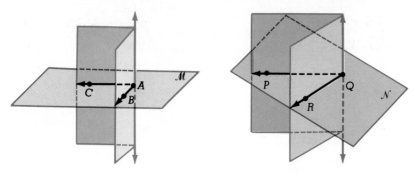

A **plane angle** of a dihedral angle is the intersection of the dihedral angle and a plane perpendicular to its edge. All the plane angles of a given dihedral angle have the same measure. Thus, the measure of a dihedral angle is defined to be the measure of any of its plane angles.

$\angle BAC$ is a plane angle.
$\angle RQP$ is not a plane angle.

A dihedral angle is a right dihedral angle if and only if its plane angles are right angles.	*Definition of Right Dihedral Angle*

Just as perpendicular lines form right angles, perpendicular planes form right dihedral angles.

Two planes are perpendicular if and only if they intersect to form a right dihedral angle.	*Theorem 3-16*

Exploratory Exercises

In the figure, $\overline{PQ} \perp \overline{QR}$, $\overline{PQ} \perp \overline{QS}$, and $\overline{QS} \perp \overline{QR}$.

1. Name the dihedral angle with edge $\overleftrightarrow{PQ}$.
2. Name the dihedral angle with edge $\overleftrightarrow{QS}$.
3. Name the dihedral angle with edge $\overleftrightarrow{QR}$.
4. Name the dihedral angle with edge $\overleftrightarrow{PS}$.
5. Name the dihedral angle with edge $\overleftrightarrow{SR}$.
6. Name the dihedral angle with edge $\overleftrightarrow{PR}$
7. Name a plane angle for $\angle P\text{-}\overleftrightarrow{SQ}\text{-}R$.
8. Name a plane angle for $\angle S\text{-}\overleftrightarrow{PQ}\text{-}R$.
9. Name a plane angle for $\angle P\text{-}\overleftrightarrow{QR}\text{-}S$.

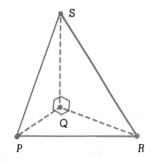

Written Exercises

In the figure at the right, $\mathcal{M} \perp \mathcal{L}$ and $\mathcal{L} \perp \mathcal{N}$.

1. Name two dihedral angles.
2. Name a plane angle for $\angle S\text{-}\overleftrightarrow{YQ}\text{-}Z$.
3. Name a plane angle for $\angle R\text{-}\overleftrightarrow{XZ}\text{-}W$.
4. $\overline{SR} \perp \overline{RX}$. Write *yes* or *no*.
5. $\overline{PQ} \perp \overline{QT}$. Write *yes* or *no*.
6. $\overline{RX} \perp \overline{TV}$. Write *yes* or *no*.
7. $\overline{QT} \perp \overline{XW}$. Write *yes* or *no*.

For Exercises 8–12, see students' work.

Draw a diagram to show each of the following.

8. Three dihedral angles with a common edge.

9. Two intersecting planes forming four right dihedral angles.

10. A dihedral angle with three plane angles shown.

11. A line intersecting both faces of a dihedral angle at different points.

12. Two dihedral angles that intersect in one line.

Answer the following.

13. How many dihedral angles are shown in the figure at the right?

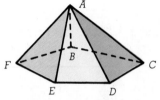

Prove each of the following. For Exercises 14–15, see the Teacher Guide.

14. Prove that if a line is perpendicular to a plane, then any plane containing that line is perpendicular to the plane.

15. Prove that if two planes intersect to form a right dihedral angle, then the planes are perpendicular.

Applications in Physics

The sun is a source of huge quantities of electromagnetic energy. The sun's energy reaches the earth through light waves.

Light travels in a straight line. For example, when the air contains many dust particles, the path of light can be seen. The light forms a "beam" that consists of a very large number of individual waves traveling together in a straight line. Rays can be used to represent the direction of the light waves.

A beam of light is composed of rays traveling in the same direction. Using ray diagrams in studying light is called **ray optics.**

When a ray of light falls on the surface of an object, the light may be reflected. Light that is reflected bounces off an object much as a billiard ball bounces back from the edge of a billiard table. When a ray of light strikes a reflecting object, such as a mirror, it makes an angle with an imaginary line that is normal (perpendicular) to the mirror. The angle is called the angle of incidence. The ray that is reflected from the mirror also makes an angle with the normal line. This angle is called the angle of reflection. The incident ray, the reflected ray, and the normal line all lie in the same plane. The law of reflection states that the angle of reflection is equal to the angle of incidence.

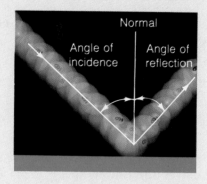

Exercises

1. A ray of light strikes a mirror at an angle that measures 53° to the normal. What is the measure of the angle of reflection? What is the measure of the angle between the incident ray and the reflected ray? 53, 106

2. A ray of light incident upon a mirror makes an angle that measures 36° with the mirror. What is the measure of the angle between the incident ray and the reflected ray? 108

Vocabulary

Chapter Summary

1. **Definition of Ray:** $\overrightarrow{PQ}$ is a ray if and only if it is the set of points $\overline{PQ}$ and all points S for which Q is between P and S. (73)
2. **Definition of Angle:** A figure is an angle if and only if it consists of two noncollinear rays with a common endpoint. (74)
3. **Angle Measure Postulate (Postulate 3-1):** For every angle there is a unique positive number between 0 and 180 called the degree measure of the angle. (77)
4. **Protractor Postulate (Postulate 3-2):** Given a ray on the edge of a half plane, for every positive number r between 0 and 180 there is exactly one ray in the half plane such that the degree measure of the angle formed by the two rays is r. (78)
5. **Definition of Congruent Angles:** Two angles are congruent if and only if they have the same measurement. (79)
6. **Theorem 3-1:** Congruence of angles is reflexive, symmetric, and transitive. (79)
7. **Definition of Adjacent Angles:** Two angles in the same plane are adjacent if and only if they have a common side and a common vertex, but no interior points in common. (79)
8. **Angle Addition Postulate (Postulate 3-3):** If R is in the interior of $\angle PQS$, then $m \angle PQR + m \angle RQS = m \angle PQS$. (79)
9. **Definition of Supplementary Angles:** Two angles are supplementary if and only if the sum of their degree measures is 180. (82)
10. **Definition of Complementary Angles:** Two angles are complementary if and only if the sum of their degree measures is 90. (82)
11. **Definition of Linear Pair:** Two angles form a linear pair if and only if they are adjacent and their noncommon sides are opposite rays. (82)
12. **Supplement Postulate (Postulate 3-4):** If two angles form a linear pair, then they are supplementary angles. (83)

13. Theorem 3-2:   If two angles are supplementary to the same angle, then they are congruent.   (83)
14. Theorem 3-3:   If two angles are supplementary to two congruent angles, then the two angles are congruent to each other.   (84)
15. Theorem 3-4:   If two angles are complementary to the same angle, then they are congruent to each other.   (85)
16. Theorem 3-5:   If two angles are complementary to two congruent angles, then the two angles are congruent to each other.   (85)
17. Definition of Right, Acute, and Obtuse Angles: A right angle is an angle whose degree measure is 90. An acute angle is an angle whose degree measure is less than 90. An obtuse angle is an angle whose degree measure is greater than 90.   (88)
18. Theorem 3-6: If two angles are right angles, then the angles are congruent.   (88)
19. Theorem 3-7:   If one angle in a linear pair is a right angle, then the other angle is also a right angle.   (88)
20. Theorem 3-8:   If two angles are congruent and supplementary, then each angle is a right angle.   (88)
21. Theorem 3-9:   If two intersecting lines form one right angle, then they form four right angles.   (89)
22. Definition of Vertical Angles: Two angles are vertical if and only if they are two nonadjacent angles formed by two intersecting lines.   (89)
23. Theorem 3-10:   If two angles are vertical, then they are congruent.   (89)
24. Definition of Perpendicular Lines: Two lines are perpendicular if and only if they intersect to form a right angle.   (93)
25. Theorem 3-11:   If two lines are perpendicular, then they form four right angles.   (94)
26. Theorem 3-12:   If a point is on a line in a given plane, then there is exactly one line in that plane perpendicular to the given line at the given point.   (94)
27. Theorem 3-13:   If two lines are perpendicular, then they form congruent adjacent angles.   (94)
28. Theorem 3-14:   If two intersecting lines form congruent adjacent angles, then they are perpendicular.   (94)
29. Definition of a Line Perpendicular to a Plane: A line is perpendicular to a plane if and only if the given line is perpendicular to every line in the plane that intersects it.   (98)
30. Definition of a Plane Perpendicular to a Line: A plane is perpendicular to a line if and only if every line in the plane that intersects the given line is perpendicular to it.   (98)
31. Theorem 3-15:   If a line is perpendicular to two intersecting lines at their point of intersection, then it is perpendicular to the plane that contains the two lines.   (98)
32. Definition of Perpendicular Planes: Two planes are perpendicular if and only if any line in one of them that is perpendicular to their line of intersection is also perpendicular to the other plane.   (99)
33. Definition of Dihedral Angle: An angle is dihedral if and only if it consists of two noncoplanar half planes with a common edge.   (99)

34. Definition of Right Dihedral Angle: A dihedral angle is a right dihedral angle if and only if its plane angles are right angles.   (100)

35. Theorem 3-16:   Two planes are perpendicular if and only if they intersect to form a right dihedral angle.   (100)

Chapter Review

3-1   **In figure, *P*, *Q*, *R*, and *S* are collinear.** ● $\overrightarrow{QP}$ and $\overrightarrow{QR}$ or $\overrightarrow{RQ}$ and $\overrightarrow{RS}$

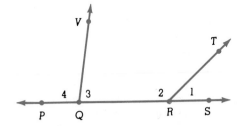

1. Name the vertex of $\angle 4$.
2. Name the sides of $\angle 4$.
3. Name a point in the interior of $\angle 3$.
4. Name a point in the exterior of $\angle 3$.
5. Name a pair of opposite rays.
6. Write another name for $\angle 2$.
7. Name a common side for $\angle 1$ and $\angle 2$.
8. Name a pair of adjacent angles.

3-2   **In the figure at the right, *m* $\angle QTS = 132$, *m* $\angle STR = 37$, and $\overrightarrow{TP}$ and $\overrightarrow{TS}$ are opposite rays.**

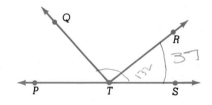

9. Find $m \angle RTQ$.
10. Find $m \angle QTP$.

Determine whether each of the following is *true* or *false*.

11. If $\angle XYZ \cong \angle JKL$, then $\angle JKL \cong \angle XYZ$.
12. If $m \angle ABC = 35$ and $\angle ABC \cong \angle RST$, then $m \angle RST = 35$.
13. If $m \angle 1 = m \angle 2$ and $m \angle 2 = m \angle 3$ and $m \angle 3 = 85$, then $m \angle 1 = 95$.

3-3   **In the figure, *m* $\angle RPS = 21$, *m* $\angle TPV = 65$, $\angle RPS \cong \angle SPT$, and $\overleftrightarrow{QV}$ and $\overleftrightarrow{WS}$ intersect at *P*. Find the degree measure for each of the following.**

14. $\angle TPS$
15. $\angle WPV$
16. $\angle QPW$
17. $\angle RPQ$

18. The degree measure of one of two complementary angles is 3 more than twice the other angle. Find the degree measure of each angle.

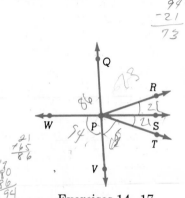

Exercises 14–17

3-4 **Prove each of the following.**

19. Given: $\angle AXB$ is a right angle.

$\angle AXD \cong \angle AXB$

Prove: $\angle AXD$ is a right angle.

20. Given: $\angle AXB$ and $\angle DXC$ are supplementary.

Prove: $\angle AXD$ and $\angle BXC$ are supplementary.

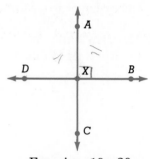

Exercises 19– 20

Use the information given in each of the following figures to find the value of x.

21.

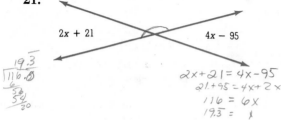

$2x + 21$ $4x - 95$

$$6\overline{)116.0} \quad \begin{array}{l} 19.3 \\ 6 \\ \overline{56} \\ 54 \\ \overline{20} \end{array}$$

$2x+21 = 4x-95$
$21+95 = 4x+2x$
$116 = 6x$
$19.3 = x$

22.

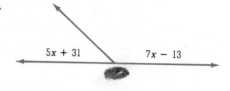

$5x + 31$ $7x - 13$

3-5 **Prove each of the following.**

23. Given: $\overline{PR} \perp \overline{RS}$

$\angle 2 \cong \angle 3$

$\angle 1 \cong \angle 4$

Prove: $\overline{PQ} \perp \overline{QS}$

24. Given: $\overline{PR} \perp \overline{RS}$

$\overline{PQ} \perp \overline{QS}$

$\angle 1 \cong \angle 4$

Prove: $\angle 6 \cong \angle 5$

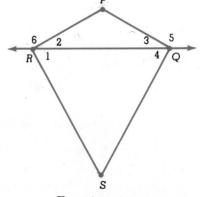

Exercises 23–24

3-6 **In the figure, $\overline{BC} \perp \overline{BE}$ and $\overline{AB} \perp \overline{BE}$. Answer each of the following.**

25. How many dihedral angles are in the figure at the right?

26. Name two dihedral angles.

27. Name a plane angle for $\angle D\text{-}\overleftrightarrow{BE}\text{-}A$.

$\angle A\text{-}\overleftrightarrow{BE}\text{-}C, \angle C\text{-}\overleftrightarrow{AF}\text{-}B, \angle A\text{-}\overleftrightarrow{CD}\text{-}B, \angle B\text{-}\overleftrightarrow{AC}\text{-}D, \angle F\text{-}\overleftrightarrow{AB}\text{-}C, \angle A\text{-}\overleftrightarrow{BC}\text{-}E, \angle F\text{-}\overleftrightarrow{ED}\text{-}B, \angle C\text{-}\overleftrightarrow{FD}\text{-}E, \angle A\text{-}\overleftrightarrow{EF}\text{-}D$

Exercises 25–27

Chapter Test

Determine whether each of the following is *true* or *false*.

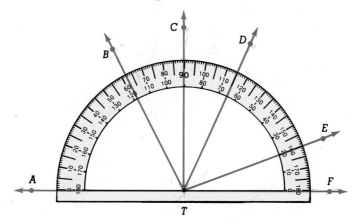

Exercises 1–14

1. $\overrightarrow{TA}$ and $\overrightarrow{TF}$ form opposite rays. T
2. $\overrightarrow{CT}$ is a side of $\angle FTC$. T
3. D is in the interior of $\angle BTC$. F
4. D is in the exterior of $\angle FTE$. T
5. $\overrightarrow{CT} \perp \overleftrightarrow{AF}$
6. $\angle BTC \cong \angle DTC$ F
7. $\angle FTD$ and $\angle DTC$ are complementary.
8. $\angle ATB$ and $\angle BTF$ are complementary.
9. $\angle ATB$ and $\angle BTF$ form a linear pair.
10. $\angle BTD$ and $\angle FTE$ are adjacent angles.
11. $m \angle ATB = m \angle DTE + m \angle FTE$
12. $m \angle BTD = m \angle CTB + m \angle DTC$
13. $\angle CTE$ is an acute angle.
14. $\angle ETC$ is an obtuse angle.

In the figure, $\mathscr{A} \perp \mathscr{B}$ and $\mathscr{B} \perp \mathscr{C}$.

15. Name a dihedral angle with edge $\overleftrightarrow{SR}$.
16. Name the faces of $\angle Y$-$\overleftrightarrow{VX}$-S.
17. Find $m \angle TVZ$.
18. Name a plane angle for $\angle P$-$\overleftrightarrow{TR}$-W.

19. If the supplement of an angle is three times the complement of an angle, what is the measure of the angle?

$180-x = 3(90-x)$
$x = 45$

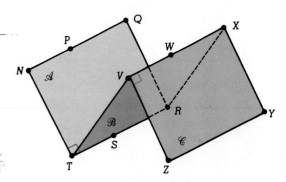

Exercises 15–18

For Exercises 20–23, see the Teacher Guide.

Prove each of the following.

20. If two angles are vertical and one angle is a right angle, then the other is also a right angle.

21. If two adjacent angles are congruent and supplementary, then their common side is perpendicular to the other two sides.

22. If two intersecting lines form two congruent adjacent angles, then they are perpendicular.

23. If the angles in a linear pair are congruent, then the common side is perpendicular to the other two sides.

Draw and label a diagram to show each of the following relationships.

1. $\overleftrightarrow{EF}$ and $\overleftrightarrow{GH}$ intersect at T.

2. Plane $\mathcal{M}$ contains $\overrightarrow{TS}$ and C.

For Exercises 1–2, see students' work.

Write each conditional statement in *if-then* form.

3. A rhombus is a quadrilateral.
If a figure is a rhombus, then it is a quadrilateral.

4. Skew lines do *not* intersect.
If two lines are skew, then they do not intersect.

Write the converse of each of the following statements in *if-then* form.

5. Every line contains at least three points.
If a figure contains at least three points, then the figure is a line.

6. Two points are on a plane only if they are in the plane. If two points are in the plane, then they are on a plane.

Write the inverse and contrapositive of each of the following statements.

7. If a figure is a square, then it is a polygon.
If a figure is not a square, it is not a polygon.
If a figure is not a polygon, it is not a square.

8. If points lie in the same plane then they are coplanar. If points do not lie in the same plane, they are not coplanar. If points are not coplanar, they do not lie in the same plane.

Change each fraction to decimal form.

9. $\frac{4}{5}$

10. $-\frac{17}{20}$

11. $\frac{19}{3}$

Change each decimal to fractional form.

12. $0.\overline{8}$

13. $0.4\overline{5}$

14. $0.0\overline{25}$

Use the number line below to find each measure.

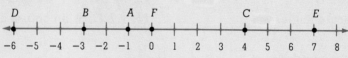

Exercises 15–20

15. FD

16. CE

17. CB

18. DF

19. AD

20. BE

21. Complete the reasons for the following proof.

> **Given:** $2x + 8 = -6$
> **Prove:** $x = -7$
> **Proof:**

STATEMENTS	REASONS
1. $2x + 8 = -6$	1. Given
2. $2x + 8 + (-8) = -6 + (-8)$	2. Addition Property of Equality
3. $2x + 0 = -14$	3. Inverse Property of Addition
4. $2x = -14$	4. Identity Property of Addition
5. $\frac{2x}{2} = -\frac{14}{2}$	5. Division Property of Equality
6. $1x = -7$	6. Substitution
7. $x = -7$	7. Identity Property of Multiplication

22. Complete the reasons for the following proof.

    Given: $\overline{AB} \cong \overline{BC}$
    Prove: $\overline{FE}$ bisects $\overline{AC}$.
    Proof:

STATEMENTS	REASONS
1. $\overline{AB} \cong \overline{BC}$	1. Given
2. $AB = BC$	2. Definition of Congruent Segments
3. B is the midpoint of $\overline{AC}$.	3.
4. $\overline{FE}$ bisects $\overline{AC}$.	4. Definition of Segment Bisector

Use the figure below for Exercises 23–28.

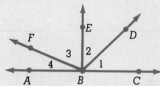

23. $\angle 2$ and $\angle$ ___ name the same angle.

24. The vertex of $\angle 3$ is ___.

25. Two names for $\angle 1$ are ___ and ___.

26. The sides of $\angle 4$ are ___ and ___.

27. Two points in the interior of $\angle FBC$ are ___ and ___.

28. Two points exterior to $\angle EBA$ are ___ and ___.

29. Complete the reasons for the following proof.

    Given: $\angle A$ is a complement of $\angle B$.
             $\angle C$ is a complement of $\angle B$.
    Prove: $\angle A \cong \angle C$
    Proof:

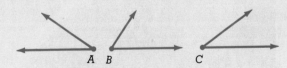

STATEMENTS	REASONS
1. $\angle A$ is a complement of $\angle B$. $\angle C$ is a complement of $\angle B$.	1. Given
2. $m \angle A + m \angle B = 90$ $m \angle C + m \angle B = 90$	2. Definition of Complementary Angles
3. $m \angle A + m \angle B = m \angle C + m \angle B$	3. Substitution
4. $m \angle A = m \angle C$	4. Subtraction Property of Equality
5. $\angle A \cong \angle C$	5. Definition of Congruent Angles

Draw a figure, state the given and the prove statement for each of the following.

30. If two lines intersect so one pair of vertical angles are supplementary, then the other pair of vertical angles are supplementary. For Exercises 30–31, see the Teacher Guide.

31. If two angles in a linear pair are congruent, then the common side of the angles is perpendicular to the other two sides.

CHAPTER 4

Congruent Triangles

The building in the photograph above is constructed using many triangles that have the same size and shape. These triangles are called congruent triangles.

4-1 Triangles

Objective: Identify the parts of a triangle; classify the triangle by its parts.

Because of their rigid form, **triangles** are used in the construction of many buildings. Notice the triangles in the photograph below.

To demonstrate the rigidity of the triangular form, have students construct triangles, squares, and other shapes with straws having a string running through them. In this way, students see that squares and other shapes are easily deformed, but triangles maintain their form.

Three noncollinear segments connected at their endpoints form a triangle. The segments are **sides** of the triangle. The endpoints are **vertices** of the triangle. An angle is formed at each vertex.

Vertices is the plural of vertex.

Triangle ABC, written $\triangle ABC$, has the following parts.

The symbol for triangle is $\triangle$.

sides	vertices	angles
$\overline{AB}$	A	$\angle BAC$ or $\angle A$
$\overline{BC}$	B	$\angle ABC$ or $\angle B$
$\overline{CA}$	C	$\angle BCA$ or $\angle C$

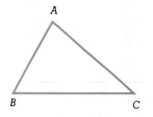

Unlike naming an angle, the order in which the vertices of a triangle are named does not matter. $\triangle ABC$ can also be named $\triangle BAC$ or $\triangle CBA$.

A triangle is a figure formed by three noncollinear segments called sides. Each endpoint of a side is an endpoint of exactly one other side.	*Definition of Triangle*

Triangles can be classified according to their angles.

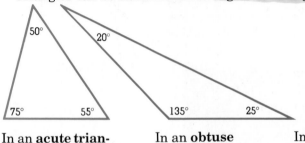

In an **acute trian-gle,** all the angles are acute.

In an **obtuse triangle,** one angle is obtuse.

In a **right trian-gle,** there is one right angle.

Point out to students that all equilateral triangles are isosceles, but not all isosceles triangles are equilateral.

When all the angles of a triangle are congruent, the triangle is **equiangular.**

Triangles can also be classified according to the number of congruent sides.

Marks on the sides of triangles are used to indicate congruent sides.

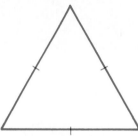

No two sides of a **scalene triangle** are congruent.

At least two sides of an **isosceles triangle** are con-gruent.

All the sides of an **equilateral triangle** are congruent.

*In an isosceles triangle, the angle formed by the congruent sides is called the **vertex angle.** The other two angles are known as **base angles.***

Notice that an equilateral triangle is also isosceles.

Show that an obtuse triangle or a right triangle may also be isosceles.

Example

1 **Suppose $\triangle PQR$ is an isosceles right triangle as shown. Solve for x and find the measure of each side.**

$\overline{PQ} \cong \overline{QR}$	*Given*
$PQ = QR$	*Definition of Congruent Segments*
$6x - 1 = 2x + 3$	*Substitution*
$4x - 1 = 3$	*Subtract 2x from both sides.*
$4x = 4$	*Add 1 to both sides.*
$x = 1$	*Divide both sides by 4.*

$$PQ = 6x - 1 \qquad QR = 2x + 3 \qquad PR = 7x + 0.07$$
$$= 6(1) - 1 \qquad = 2(1) + 3 \qquad = 7(1) + 0.07$$
$$= 5 \qquad\qquad = 5 \qquad\qquad = 7.07$$

A triangle separates a plane into three parts. The parts are the **interior,** the **exterior,** and the triangle itself.

Any point in the green part of the plane is in the interior of △*ABC*. Any point in the blue part of the plane is in the exterior of △*ABC*. Any point on the segments in black is on △*ABC*.

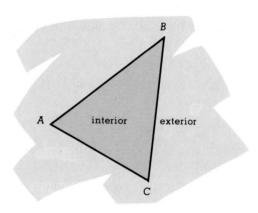

EN: 2–22 even, 2–30 even; **AV:** 2–22 even, 2–30;

Exploratory Exercises

FD: 1–22, 1–29 odd

Classify each triangle as acute, obtuse, or right.

1.

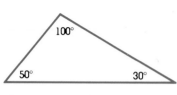

2.

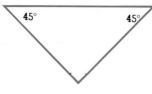

3.

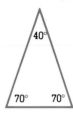

4.

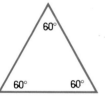

5.

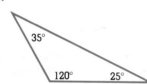

6.

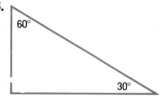

Classify each triangle as scalene, isosceles, or equilateral.

7.

8.

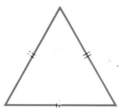

9.

10.

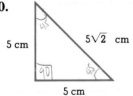

11.

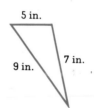

12.

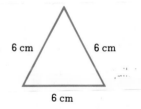

Use △DEF and △PQR to answer each of the following.

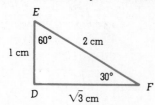

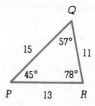

13. Name the vertices of △DEF.
15. Name the angles of △DEF.
17. Name the sides of △DEF.
19. Classify △DEF by angles.
21. Classify △DEF by sides.

14. Name the vertices of △PQR.
16. Name the angles of △PQR.
18. Name the sides of △PQR.
20. Classify △PQR by angles.
22. Classify △PQR by sides.

Written Exercises

The figure at the right contains eight triangles. For Exercises 1–12, see the Teacher Guide.

1. Name each triangle.
2. Name the angles of △QSR.
3. Name the vertices of △STR.
4. Name the vertices of △QSR.
5. Name the sides of △STR.
6. Name the sides of △QSR.
7. Name the angles of △STR.
8. Name the sides of △PRQ.

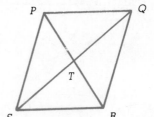

Give an *if and only if* definition for each of the following.

9. equiangular triangle
11. isosceles triangle

10. right triangle
12. equilateral triangle

For each of the following, draw a triangle that satisfies the given conditions. If no such triangle exists, write *none*. For Exercises 13–21, see students' work.

13. isosceles, right
16. scalene, acute
19. isosceles, obtuse

14. scalene, obtuse
17. scalene, right
20. equilateral, obtuse

15. isosceles, scalene
18. isosceles, acute
21. obtuse, right

Classify the following triangles as acute, right, or obtuse.

22.

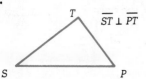

23.

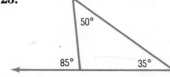

24.

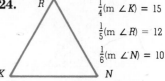

$\frac{1}{4}(m \angle K) = 15$

$\frac{1}{5}(m \angle R) = 12$

$\frac{1}{6}(m \angle N) = 10$

Classify the following triangles as scalene, isosceles, or equilateral.

25.

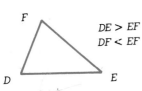

$DE > EF$
$DF < EF$

26.

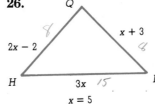

$2x - 2$
$x + 3$
$3x$
$x = 5$

27.

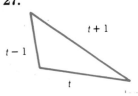

$t + 1$
$t - 1$
t

Use the given information to find the measure of each side of $\triangle PQR$.

28. $PQ = 3x - 20$
$\quad\ \ QR = x + 16$
$\quad\ \ RP = 2x - 2$

29. $PQ = x + 8$
$\quad\ \ QR = \frac{1}{3}x + 26$
$\quad\ \ RP = 2x - 19$

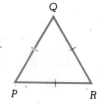

Challenge Exercises

30. Given equilateral $\triangle XYZ$, find the values of x and y.

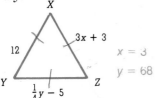

12
$3x + 3$
$\frac{1}{4}y - 5$
$x = 3$
$y = 68$

31. Give the number of triangles in the figure below.

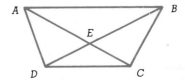

Statistics That Shape Your Life

The construction industry often projects the number of new homes that will be under construction for a given area. Such a projection is shown in the chart. When studying data like this, it is common to use the **mean** and **median.**

Hottest new home hot spots

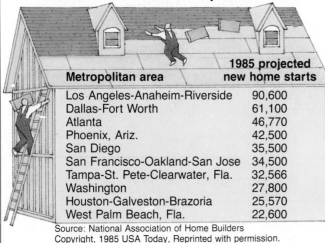

Metropolitan area	1985 projected new home starts
Los Angeles-Anaheim-Riverside	90,600
Dallas-Fort Worth	61,100
Atlanta	46,770
Phoenix, Ariz.	42,500
San Diego	35,500
San Francisco-Oakland-San Jose	34,500
Tampa-St. Pete-Clearwater, Fla.	32,566
Washington	27,800
Houston-Galveston-Brazoria	25,570
West Palm Beach, Fla.	22,600

Source: National Association of Home Builders
Copyright, 1985 USA Today, Reprinted with permission.

The mean and median are numbers that describe a set of data. The mean, or average, is the sum of all the values divided by the number of values. The median is the middle value. If there are two middle values, the median is the mean of the two values.

Exercises

41,951

1. Using the information in the chart, find the average of new home starts to the nearest whole number.

2. Find the median for the areas listed. 35,000

4-2 Angle Measures

Objective: Use the Angle Sum Theorem and other properties of angles of triangles in proofs and problem solving.

The figure at the right shows a piece of paper cut to form a triangle.

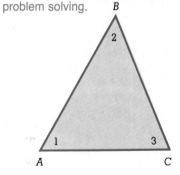

The paper is folded so that point B lies on $\overline{AC}$.

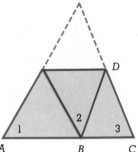

The paper is folded in two more places, so that $\angle 1$ and $\angle 3$ are positioned at point B.

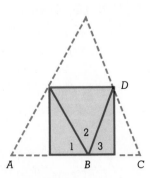

Notice that $\angle ABD$ and $\angle 3$ form a linear pair. Therefore, $m \angle ABD + m \angle 3 = 180$. Since $m \angle 1 + m \angle 2 = m \angle ABD$, by substitution it is also true that

$$m \angle 1 + m \angle 2 + m \angle 3 = 180.$$

Any triangular piece of paper can be folded in the same way as shown above. Many experiments such as this one suggest the following theorem.

Students may also confirm this by drawing arbitrary triangles and measuring the angles with a protractor.

The <u>sum of the degree measures of the angles of a triangle is 180.</u>	*Theorem 4-1* *Angle Sum Theorem*

Theorem 4-1 is proved in Chapter 6 on page 203.

Since all the angles of an equiangular triangle are congruent, they have the same measure. Thus, each angle has a degree measure of 180 ÷ 3 or 60.

If a triangle is <u>equiangular</u>, then the degree <u>measure of</u> each angle is 60.	*Theorem 4-2*

Students will prove Theorem 4-2 in Written Exercise 19.

If you know the measure of two angles of a triangle, you can find the measure of the third angle.

Have students write an equation that represents this idea.

Examples

1 **In the triangle at the right, ∠R is a right angle, and *m* ∠P = 30. Find *m* ∠ Q.**

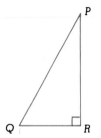

$m \angle P + m \angle Q + m \angle R = 180$	*Angle Sum Theorem*
$30 + m \angle Q + 90 = 180$	*Substitution (m ∠R = 90)*
$m \angle Q = 60$	*Subtraction Property of Equality*

2 **In the diagram at the right, *m* ∠A = 60, *m* ∠D = 30, and *m* ∠E = 85. Find *m* ∠B.**

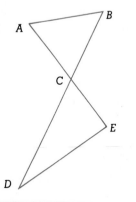

$m \angle D + m \angle E + m \angle DCE = 180$	*Angle Sum Theorem*
$30 + 85 + m \angle DCE = 180$	*Substitution*
$m \angle DCE = 65$	*Subtraction Property of Equality*
$m \angle ACB = 65$	*∠DCE and ∠ACB are vertical angles.*
$m \angle A + m \angle B + m \angle ACB = 180$	*Angle Sum Theorem*
$60 + m \angle B + 65 = 180$	*Substitution*
$m \angle B = 55$	*Subtraction Property of Equality*

The triangle in Example 1 is a right triangle. Notice that the degree measures of the other two angles total 90. The following theorem states this property for all right triangles.

Two angles are complementary if and only if the sum of their degree measures is 90.

If a triangle is a <u>right triangle</u>, then the <u>acute angles are complementary.</u>	*Theorem 4-3*

Students will prove Theorem 4-3 in Written Exercise 20.

Exploratory Exercises

Use the figure at the right to find the indicated degree measures.

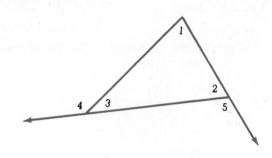

1. Find $m \angle 1$ if $m \angle 2 = 86$ and $m \angle 3 = 30$.
2. Find $m \angle 2$ if $m \angle 1 = 56$ and $m \angle 4 = 112$.
3. Find $m \angle 2$ if $m \angle 1 = 47$ and $m \angle 4 = 132$.
4. Find $m \angle 3$ if $m \angle 1 = 73$ and $m \angle 5 = 139$.
5. Find $m \angle 1$ if $m \angle 2 = 27$ and $m \angle 3 = 72$.
6. Find $m \angle 1$ if $m \angle 2 = 81$ and $m \angle 3 = 74$.
7. Find $m \angle 2$ if $m \angle 1 = 58$ and $m \angle 4 = 125$.
8. Find $m \angle 3$ if $m \angle 1 = 67$ and $m \angle 5 = 101$.

For each of the following figures, find the missing degree measures.

9.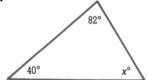

10.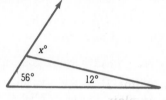

11.

12.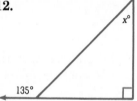

13.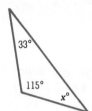

14.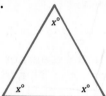

Written Exercises

Use the figure at the right to find the indicated degree measures.

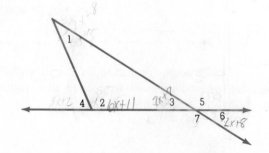

1. Find $m \angle 5$ if $m \angle 1 = 40$ and $m \angle 2 = 110$.
2. Find $m \angle 6$ if $m \angle 1 = 55$ and $m \angle 2 = 95$.
3. Find $m \angle 2$ if $m \angle 1 = x$ and $m \angle 3 = y$.
4. Find $m \angle 7$ if $m \angle 1 = x$ and $m \angle 2 = 3x$.
5. Find $m \angle 1$ if $m \angle 2 = a$ and $m \angle 6 = 35$.
6. Find $m \angle 4$ if $m \angle 1 = 2x + 8$ and
   $m \angle 3 = x + 5$.
7. Find $m \angle 3$ if $m \angle 1 = 3x$ and
   $m \angle 4 = 5x + 2$. $m \angle 3 = 2x + 2$
8. Find $m \angle 1$ if $m \angle 2 = 6x + 11$ and
   $m \angle 6 = 2x + 8$. $m \angle 1 = 161 - 8x$

In the figure, $\overline{AB} \perp \overline{BC}$, $\overline{CD} \perp \overline{BC}$, $m \angle BEC = 125$, $m \angle A = x$, and $\angle ABE \cong \angle DCE$. Find the degree measure of each of the following angles.

9. $\angle AEB$

10. $\angle EBC$

11. $\angle CED$

12. $\angle ECD$

13. $\angle ECB$

14. $\angle ABE$

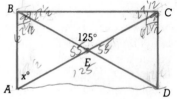
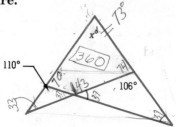

In the following exercises, find the missing degree measure.

15.

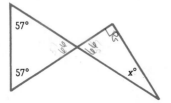

16.

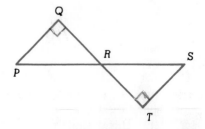

Answer each of the following. For Exercises 17–22, see the Teacher Guide.

17. Can a triangle have two right angles? Write *yes* or *no*, then explain your answer.

18. Can a triangle have two obtuse angles? Write *yes* or *no*, then explain your answer.

Complete the following proofs.

19. If a triangle is equiangular, then the degree measure of each angle is 60. (Theorem 4-2)

20. If a triangle is a right triangle, then the acute angles are complementary. (Theorem 4-3)

21. If a triangle is equiangular, then its angles are congruent to each other.

22. In the figure at the right, $\angle Q$ and $\angle T$ are right angles. Prove $m \angle P = m \angle S$.

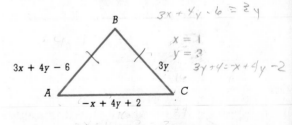

Challenge Exercises

23. Use the figure to find $m \angle 1 + m \angle 2 + m \angle 3$.

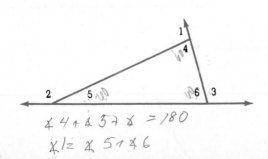

24. In $\triangle ABC$, $AB = BC$. If AC is 4 more than BC, find the values of x and y.

4-3 Congruence

Suppose a rectangular piece of paper is cut along a straight line from one corner to the opposite corner. Two triangular pieces are formed. The edges of each piece form a triangle. When one piece is placed on top of the other they can be positioned to match exactly. What must be true about the parts of the two triangles?

The corresponding parts are congruent.

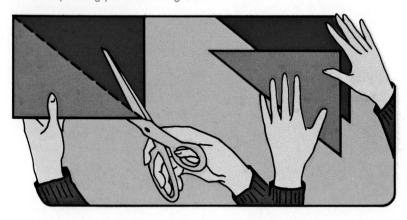

The two triangles below represent the pieces cut from the paper. Corresponding parts of the triangles can be used to describe how the pieces fit together.

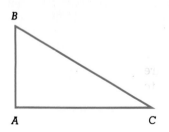 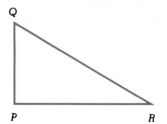

Corresponding angles describe matching the corners of the pieces of paper.	$\angle A$ corresponds to $\angle P$. $\angle B$ corresponds to $\angle Q$. $\angle C$ corresponds to $\angle R$.	It is important that students understand the meaning of corresponding parts.
Corresponding sides describe matching the edges of the pieces of paper.	$\overline{AB}$ corresponds to $\overline{PQ}$. $\overline{BC}$ corresponds to $\overline{QR}$. $\overline{CA}$ corresponds to $\overline{RP}$.	*Triangles that have the same size and shape are congruent.*

Emphasize that correspondence is not the same as congruence.

The matching parts of the pieces fit exactly. Therefore, the corresponding parts of the triangles are congruent and the two triangles are called **congruent triangles.**

Two triangles are <u>congruent</u> if and only if there is a correspondence such that their corresponding parts are congruent.

Definition of Congruent Triangles (CPCTC)

The abbreviation CPCTC means Corresponding Parts of Congruent Triangles are Congruent.

Special marks are used to show that certain parts of figures are congruent. Notice how marks are used on the triangles below.

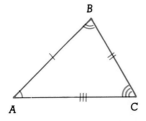
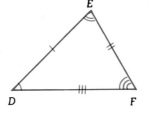

By pairing like markings on the triangles, congruent pairs of sides or angles can be identified.

corresponding angles	corresponding sides
$\angle A \cong \angle D$	$\overline{AB} \cong \overline{DE}$
$\angle B \cong \angle E$	$\overline{BC} \cong \overline{EF}$
$\angle C \cong \angle F$	$\overline{CA} \cong \overline{FD}$

The two triangles above are congruent because they have six congruent corresponding parts. To indicate the congruence, write $\triangle ABC \cong \triangle DEF$. The order of letters indicates the correspondence. The first vertices, A and D, correspond, likewise, the second vertices, B and E, and the third vertices, C and F, correspond.

If two triangles are congruent, then the corresponding parts are congruent. Often, a geometric problem involves showing that parts of a figure are congruent. One method is to show that the parts are corresponding parts of congruent triangles. Thus, it is important to recognize corresponding parts of congruent triangles.

In the above figure, $\triangle ABC \cong \triangle DEF$ but $\triangle ABC \not\cong \triangle EDF$. Emphasize the correct order of letters when naming congruent triangles.

Example

1 Suppose $\triangle PQS \cong \triangle RQS$. What angle in $\triangle PQS$ is congruent to $\angle R$ in $\triangle RQS$? Which side of $\triangle PQS$ is congruent to $\overline{QS}$ in $\triangle RQS$?

In $\triangle RQS$, R, the first vertex, will be paired with the first vertex, P, in $\triangle PQS$.

$\angle P$ is congruent to $\angle R$.
$\overline{QS}$ is congruent to $\overline{QS}$.

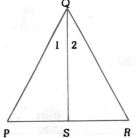

Students will prove Theorem 4-4 in Written Exercises 29–31.

Since congruence of segments and angles is reflexive, symmetric, and transitive, so is congruence of triangles.

Congruence of triangles is **reflexive, symmetric, and transitive**.	*Theorem 4-4*

EN: 2–18 even, 2–34 even; AV: 1–18, 1–32; FD: 1–18, 1–28, p. 119, 17–20;

Exploratory Exercises

ALL LEVELS: Mini Review

Suppose $\triangle PQR \cong \triangle STV$. For each of the following, name the corresponding part.

1. $\angle P$
2. $\angle Q$
3. $\overline{ST}$
4. $\angle R$
5. $\angle S$
6. $\overline{VS}$
7. $\angle T$
8. $\angle V$
9. $\overline{RP}$
10. $\overline{PQ}$
11. $\overline{QR}$
12. $\overline{TV}$

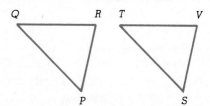

Use the drawings below to find a triangle to complete each congruence statement.

13. $\triangle ABC \cong$ ▣

14. $\triangle GIH \cong$ ▣

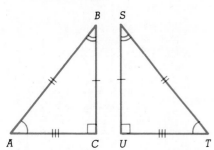
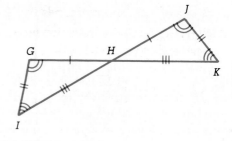

15. $\triangle WVZ \cong$ ▣

16. $\triangle RST \cong$ ▣

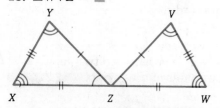
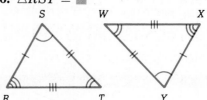

Answer each of the following.

17. Suppose $\triangle ABC \cong \triangle FGH$. List the pairs of angles and sides that are congruent.

18. List the information needed to show that $\triangle YZX \cong \triangle RPS$.

Written Exercises

Determine whether each of the following statements is *true* or *false*.

1. $\triangle ABC \cong \triangle BDC$ ▬
2. $\triangle CAB \cong \triangle CDB$ ▬
3. $\triangle CBA \cong \triangle DCB$ ▬
4. $\triangle BAC \cong \triangle BDC$ ▬
5. $\triangle ABC \cong \triangle DBC$ ▬
6. $\triangle DBC \cong \triangle BCA$ ▬

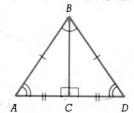

7. $\triangle GHI \cong \triangle HGF$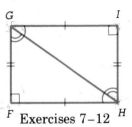

8. $\triangle GFH \cong \triangle GIH$

9. $\triangle FGH \cong \triangle IHG$

10. $\triangle FHG \cong \triangle HGI$

11. $\triangle GHF \cong \triangle HGI$

12. $\triangle GFH \cong \triangle HIG$

Exercises 7–12

13. $\triangle ZYX \cong \triangle YZA$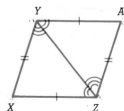

14. $\triangle YZA \cong \triangle ZYX$

15. $\triangle YZA \cong \triangle YZX$

16. $\triangle ZYX \cong \triangle ZYA$

17. $\triangle XYZ \cong \triangle AZY$

18. $\triangle ZAY \cong \triangle ZXY$

Exercises 13–18

Suppose $\triangle PQR \cong \triangle STR$. Answer each of the following.

19. Which angle in $\triangle PQR$ corresponds to $\angle T$ in $\triangle STR$?

20. Which angle in $\triangle STR$ corresponds to $\angle P$ in $\triangle PQR$?

21. Which side of $\triangle PQR$ corresponds to $\overline{RS}$ in $\triangle STR$?

22. Which side of $\triangle PQR$ corresponds to $\overline{TS}$ in $\triangle STR$?

23. Which side of $\triangle STR$ corresponds to $\overline{QR}$ in $\triangle PQR$?

24. Which side of $\triangle STR$ corresponds to $\overline{RP}$ in $\triangle PQR$?

25. Is $\triangle QPR \cong \triangle TRS$? Write *yes* or *no*.

26. Is $\triangle RQP \cong \triangle RTS$? Write *yes* or *no*.

27. Is $\triangle RST \cong \triangle RQP$? Write *yes* or *no*.

28. Is $\triangle TSR \cong \triangle PQR$? Write *yes* or *no*.

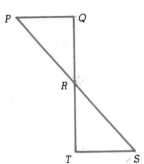

Exercises 19–28

For Exercises 29–31, see the Teacher Guide.

Prove each of the following parts of Theorem 4-4.

29. Congruence of triangles is reflexive.

30. Congruence of triangles is symmetric.

31. Congruence of triangles is transitive.

Use the information in the following exercises to find the indicated values.

32. $\triangle PIT \cong \triangle DOG$, $PI = 14$, $IT = 18$, $TP = 21$, and $DG = 2x + 7$. Find x.

33. $\triangle BLU \cong \triangle MON$, $m\angle L = 57$, $m\angle M = 64$, and $m\angle U = 5x + 4$. Find x.

34. $\triangle ABC \cong \triangle STR$, $AB = 8x$, $BC = 5x - 1$, $RS = 2x + 3$, and $ST = 4x + 4$. Find AB and RS.

mini-review

1. The coordinate of A is -20, and the coordinate of B is -4. Find AB.   16

2. The coordinate of P is -6 and $PQ = 4$. What are the two possible coordinates of the midpoint of $\overline{PQ}$?

3. Suppose $\angle ABC$ and $\angle CBD$ form a linear pair and $\angle DEF$ is a complement of $\angle ABC$. Find the degree measure of each angle if $m\angle CBD = 3(m\angle DEF)$.

4. Write the inverse of the following statement: If M is midpoint of $\overline{AB}$, then $\overline{AM} \cong \overline{MB}$.

5. Write the following statement in if-then form: Every triangle has three sides.

For Mini Review 2-5, see the Teacher Guide.

4-4 Tests for Congruence

Objective: Use the SSS, SAS, and ASA tests for congruence.

To show that two triangles are congruent, it is not necessary to show all six corresponding parts are congruent. For example, suppose straws are used to make a model of a triangle. Start with three straws, each having a certain length. Fasten the straws together at the ends. There is only one way to put the straws together to form a triangle.

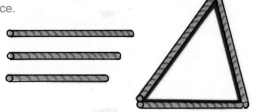

If each side of one triangle is congruent to the corresponding side of another triangle, then the triangles are congruent.	*Postulate 4-1* **SSS** *The abbreviation SSS stands for side-side-side.*

Suppose two straws are glued together to form a certain angle. There is only one length for the third straw that can be used to make a triangle. The two straws and the included angle they form completely determine the triangle.

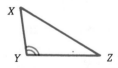

If two sides and the included angle of one triangle are congruent to the corresponding sides and included angle of another triangle, then the triangles are congruent.	*Postulate 4-2* **SAS** *The abbreviation SAS stands for side-angle-side.*

In the triangle at the right, notice that $\angle Y$ is the included angle for $\overline{XY}$ and $\overline{YZ}$.

You may want to demonstrate that SSA is not a test for congruence.

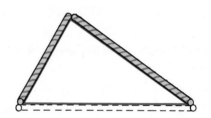

Example

1 Use the figure at the right to determine whether $\triangle AEB \cong \triangle CED$.

The marks on the figure show $\overline{AE} \cong \overline{CE}$ and $\overline{BE} \cong \overline{DE}$. It is necessary to have one more pair of congruent parts to prove the triangles are congruent by SSS or SAS. From the figure, $\angle AEB$ and $\angle CED$ are vertical angles. Since vertical angles are congruent, $\angle AEB \cong \angle CED$. Thus, $\triangle AEB \cong \triangle CED$ by SAS.

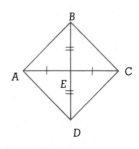

2 **Prove the following.**

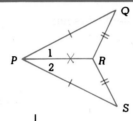

Given: $\overline{PQ} \cong \overline{PS}$
$\overline{QR} \cong \overline{SR}$

Prove: $\angle 1 \cong \angle 2$

Proof:

STATEMENTS	REASONS
1. $\overline{PQ} \cong \overline{PS}$ $\overline{QR} \cong \overline{SR}$	1. Given
2. $\overline{PR} \cong \overline{PR}$	2. Congruence of segments is reflexive (Theorem 2-2).
3. $\triangle PQR \cong \triangle PSR$	3. SSS (Postulate 4-1)
4. $\angle 1 \cong \angle 2$	4. Definition of Congruent Triangles *CPCTC*

In the triangle at the right, notice that $\overline{AB}$ is included between $\angle A$ and $\angle B$.

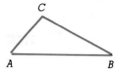

If two angles and the included side of one triangle are congruent to the corresponding angles and included side of another triangle, then the triangles are congruent.

Postulate 4-3
ASA
The abbreviation ASA stands for angle-side-angle.

3 **Prove the following.**

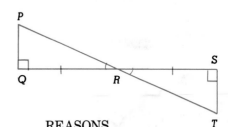

Given: $\angle Q$ and $\angle S$ are right angles.
$\overline{QR} \cong \overline{SR}$

Prove: $\angle P \cong \angle T$

Proof:

STATEMENTS	REASONS
1. $\angle Q$ and $\angle S$ are right angles.	1. Given
A 2. $\angle Q \cong \angle S$	2. If two angles are right angles, then the angles are congruent (Theorem 3-6).
S 3. $\overline{QR} \cong \overline{SR}$	3. Given
A 4. $\angle PRQ \cong \angle TRS$	4. If two angles are vertical, then they are congruent (Theorem 3-10).
5. $\triangle PRQ \cong \triangle TRS$	5. ASA (Postulate 4-3)
6. $\angle P \cong \angle T$	6. Definition of Congruent Triangles *CPCTC*

Exploratory Exercises

Determine whether the following pairs of triangles are congruent. State *yes* or *no*. If congruent, state the appropriate congruence postulate.

1.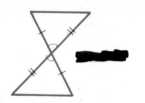

2.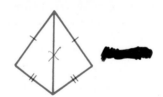

3.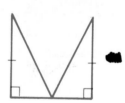

4.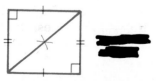

5.

6.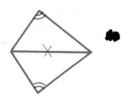

7.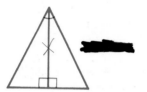

8.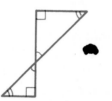

9.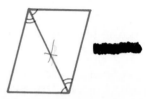

10.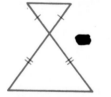

11.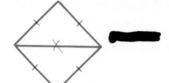

12.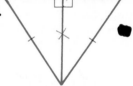

13.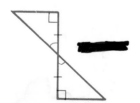

14.

15.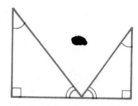

Written Exercises

Name the additional congruent, corresponding parts needed to prove the triangles congruent by the indicated postulate.

1.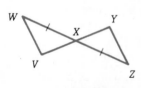

$\triangle WXV \cong \triangle ZXY$ by ASA

2.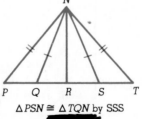

$\triangle PSN \cong \triangle TQN$ by SSS

3.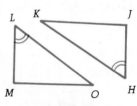

$\triangle MOL \cong \triangle JKH$ by SAS

4.

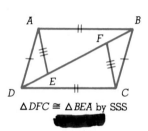

$\triangle DFC \cong \triangle BEA$ by SSS

5.

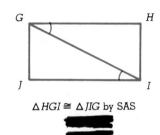

$\triangle HGI \cong \triangle JIG$ by SAS

6.

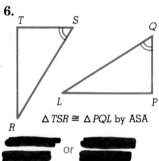

$\triangle TSR \cong \triangle PQL$ by ASA

or

Copy the following figures and mark all congruent parts and right angles. Then, complete the triangle congruence in the prove statement, and name the postulate that justifies the congruence.

7.

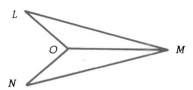

Given: $\angle LMO \cong \angle NMO$
$\angle LOM \cong \angle NOM$
Prove: $\triangle MOL \cong$ ■

8.

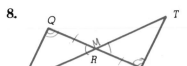

Given: R is the midpoint of $\overline{QS}$.
$\angle Q \cong \angle S$
Prove: $\triangle QRP \cong$ ■

9.

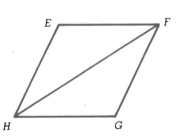

Given: $\overline{EF} \cong \overline{GH}$
$\overline{EH} \cong \overline{GF}$
Prove: $\triangle EFH \cong$ ■

10.

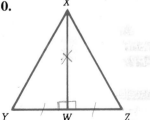

Given: $\overline{XW}$ bisects $\overline{YZ}$
$\overline{XW} \perp \overline{YZ}$
Prove: $\triangle XYW \cong$ ■

For Exercises 11–12, see the Teacher Guide.

Complete the following proofs.

11. Given: $\overline{QP} \cong \overline{ST}$
$\angle P$ and $\angle T$ are right angles.
R is the midpoint of $\overline{PT}$.
Prove: $\overline{QR} \cong \overline{SR}$

12. Given: $\angle 1 \cong \angle 2$
$\angle P$ and $\angle T$ are right angles.
$\overline{QR} \cong \overline{SR}$
Prove: $\overline{PR} \cong \overline{TR}$

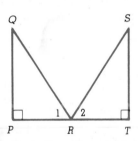

Exercises 11 and 12

For Exercises 13–16, see the Teacher Guide.

13. Given: $\angle 1 \cong \angle 6$
     $\angle 3 \cong \angle 4$
  Prove: $\overline{AD} \cong \overline{CB}$

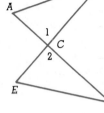

Exercises 13 and 14

14. Given: $\angle 3 \cong \angle 4$
     $\overline{DC} \cong \overline{BA}$
  Prove: $\angle 1 \cong \angle 6$

15. Given: $\overline{AC} \cong \overline{EC}$
     $\angle A \cong \angle E$
  Prove: $\overline{BC} \cong \overline{DC}$

Exercises 15 and 16

16. Given: $\overline{AC} \cong \overline{EC}$
     $\overline{BC} \cong \overline{DC}$
  Prove: $\angle B \cong \angle D$

Using the figure, fill in the blanks to make true statements. Give a reason(s) for each answer. For reasons, see the Teacher Guide.

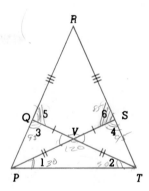

17. $\angle QVP \cong$ ■
18. $\triangle PVQ \cong$ ■ SAS
19. $\overline{PQ} \cong$ ■
20. $\angle 3 \cong$ ■
21. $\overline{QT} \cong$ ■
22. $\triangle PQT \cong$ ■
23. $\angle 2 \cong$ ■
24. $\overline{TR} \cong$ ■
25. $\overline{QR} \cong$ ■
26. $\angle 5 \cong$ ■
27. $\angle 4$ and ■ are supplementary.
28. $\angle 3$ and ■ are supplementary.
29. $\triangle QRT \cong$ ■
30. $\angle RTQ \cong$ ■
31. $\angle QVS \cong$ ■
32. $VQ =$ ■
33. $\triangle PVT$ is an ■ triangle.
34. $\triangle PRT$ is an ■ triangle.
35. If $m\angle 1 = 30$, then $m\angle PVT =$ ■.
36. If $m\angle 3 = 95$, then $m\angle 6 =$ ■.

Challenge Exercises

Use the figures and information given below to answer each problem.

Given: $\overline{AB} \cong \overline{XY}$
     $\angle A \cong \angle X$
     $\overline{AC} \cong \overline{XP}$
     $\angle ABC \cong \angle XYZ$

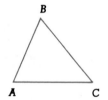

For Exercises 37–38, see the Teacher Guide.
37. Prove that $\triangle ABC \cong \triangle XYP$.
38. Prove that $\angle ABC \cong \angle XYP$.
39. How are $\angle XYP$ and $\angle XYZ$ related? (Hint: Use the results of Exercise 38.)
40. Why is the figure shown at the right misleading?

128 *Congruent Triangles*

Applications in Construction

The triangular shape is often used in the construction of bridges, roofs, and other structures that are required to support heavy loads. The triangle-based supportive framework that has such remarkable strength is known as a **truss.**

The truss is not a recent invention. In fact, the truss dates back to the Bronze Age, around 2500 B.C. Through the ages, trusses have been made from wood, iron, or steel. They have been used in constructing many homes, office buildings, lofty cathedral ceilings, and bridges. The Eiffel Tower in France is one of the best known examples of iron truss construction.

What gives the truss this strength? It consists of a triangle or a series of triangles that are in a single plane. The planes are called *chords* and the sides of the triangles are called *web* parts. A simple truss below is contrasted with an alternate type of support.

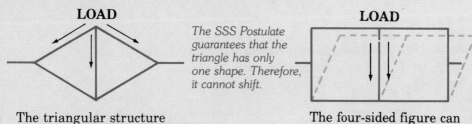

The triangular structure distributes the load throughout the entire framework.

The SSS Postulate guarantees that the triangle has only one shape. Therefore, it cannot shift.

The four-sided figure can shift, sag, or collapse.

A truss that contains a series of triangles would contain pairs of congruent triangles. One pattern of a roofing truss is shown below.

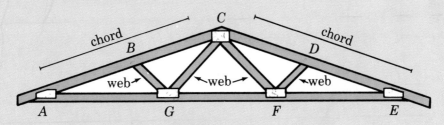

Exercises

In the figure above, the vertices of the triangles have been labeled. Name the triangle that appears to be congruent to each of the following triangles.

1. $\triangle ABG$ ■

2. $\triangle BCG$ ■

3. $\triangle AGC$ ■

4. $\triangle ACF$ ■

5. $\triangle GCF$ ■

6. $\triangle CFE$ ■

4-5 More Tests for Congruence

Objectives: Use AAS test for congruence; recognize correct tests for congruent triangles.

To show two triangles congruent, at least three congruent pairs of corresponding parts are needed. Can any three pairs of congruent corresponding parts be used? Three tests already have been postu- No lated, SSS, SAS, and ASA. Another test follows directly from these.

If two angles and a nonincluded side of one triangle are congruent to the corresponding angles and nonincluded side of another triangle, then the triangles are congruent.

Theorem 4-5
AAS

The abbreviation AAS stands for angle-angle-side.

Example

1 Prove Theorem 4-5.

Given: $\angle P \cong \angle A$
$\angle Q \cong \angle B$
$\overline{QR} \cong \overline{BC}$

Prove: $\triangle PQR \cong \triangle ABC$

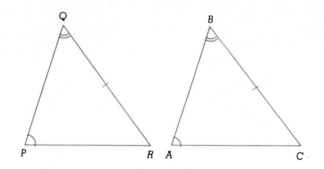

Proof:

STATEMENTS	REASONS
1. $m\angle P + m\angle Q + m\angle R$ $= 180$ $m\angle A + m\angle B + m\angle C$ $= 180$	1. Angle Sum Theorem (Theorem 4-1)
2. $m\angle P + m\angle Q + m\angle R =$ $m\angle A + m\angle B + m\angle C$	2. Substitution (Postulate 2-9)
3. $\angle P \cong \angle A$ $\angle Q \cong \angle B$	3. Given
4. $m\angle P = m\angle A$ $m\angle Q = m\angle B$	4. Definition of Congruent Angles
5. $m\angle P + m\angle Q + m\angle R =$ $m\angle P + m\angle Q + m\angle C$	5. Substitution (Postulate 2-9)
6. $m\angle R = m\angle C$	6. Subtraction Property of Equality (Postulate 2-7)
7. $\angle R \cong \angle C$	7. Definition of Congruent Angles
8. $\overline{QR} \cong \overline{BC}$	8. Given
9. $\triangle PQR \cong \triangle ABC$	9. ASA (Postulate 4-3) *Use steps 3, 7, and 8.*

Example

2 Prove the following.

Given: $\angle Q$ and $\angle S$ are right angles.
$\angle 1 \cong \angle 3$

Prove: $\triangle PQR \cong \triangle RSP$

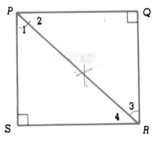

Proof:

STATEMENTS	REASONS
1. $\angle Q$ and $\angle S$ are right angles.	1. Given
2. $\angle Q \cong \angle S$	2. If two angles are right angles, then the angles are congruent (Theorem 3-6).
3. $\angle 1 \cong \angle 3$	3. Given
4. $\overline{PR} \cong \overline{PR}$	4. Congruence of segments is reflexive (Theorem 2-2).
5. $\triangle PQR \cong \triangle RSP$	5. AAS (Theorem 4-5) *Use steps 2, 3, and 4.*

To show two triangles are congruent, the SSS, SAS, ASA, and AAS tests can be applied. Is it possible to prove two triangles are congruent by SSA?

Suppose you are given measurements for two sides and a non-included angle of a triangle. The measurements of the sides are 7.3 cm and 5 cm. The angle measures 40°. Is this enough information to determine only one triangle?

No, two different triangles can be drawn using the given information. There is *not* enough information to know which is desired.

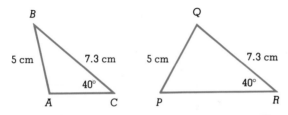

Two sides and a nonincluded angle of $\triangle ABC$ are congruent to two corresponding sides and a nonincluded angle of $\triangle PQR$. The two triangles are *not* congruent. Thus, side-side-angle or SSA is not a test for congruent triangles.

Demonstrate that the AAA is not a test for congruent triangles.

Is angle-angle-angle or AAA a test for congruent triangles? No

Exploratory Exercises

ALL LEVELS: Algebra Review

Determine whether each pair of triangles is congruent. If so, state the postulate or theorem used. If there is *not* enough information, state "not enough information."

1.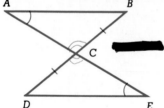

2.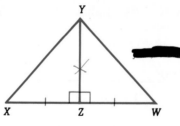

3.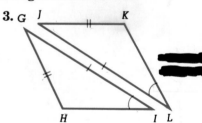

4.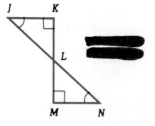

5.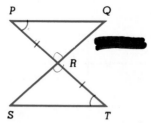

6.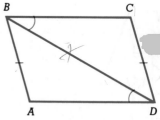

7.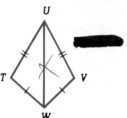

8.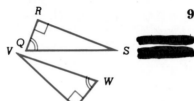

9.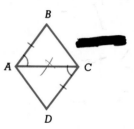

10.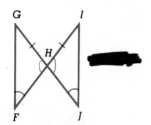

11.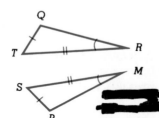

12.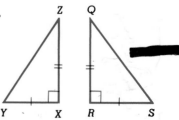

Written Exercises

Complete the following proofs.

1. Given: $\overline{BC} \cong \overline{DC}$
$\angle A \cong \angle E$
$\angle 1 \cong \angle 2$
Prove: $\overline{AC} \cong \overline{EC}$

2. Given: $\overline{BC} \cong \overline{DC}$
$\angle A \cong \angle E$
$\angle 1 \cong \angle 2$
Prove: $\overline{AB} \cong \overline{ED}$

3. Given: $\angle A \cong \angle E$
$\angle 1 \cong \angle 2$
$\overline{AC} \cong \overline{EC}$
Prove: $\angle B \cong \angle D$

4. Given: $\overline{AC} \cong \overline{EC}$
$\angle 1 \cong \angle 2$
$\overline{BC} \cong \overline{DC}$
Prove: $\angle B \cong \angle D$

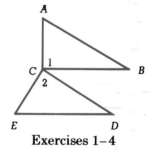

Exercises 1–4

For Exercises 1–12, see the Teacher Guide.

5. Given: $\angle A \cong \angle C$
$\overline{BD} \perp \overline{AC}$

    Prove: $\overline{AB} \cong \overline{CB}$

6. Given: $\overline{AB} \cong \overline{CB}$
$\overline{BD}$ bisects $\overline{AC}$.

    Prove: $\angle A \cong \angle C$

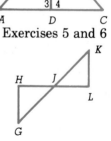

Exercises 5 and 6

7. Given: J is the midpoint of $\overline{GK}$.
$\angle H$ and $\angle L$ are right angles.

    Prove: $\overline{HG} \cong \overline{LK}$

8. Given: J is the midpoint of $\overline{HL}$.
$\angle G \cong \angle K$

    Prove: $\angle H \cong \angle L$

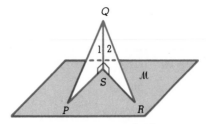

Exercises 7 and 8

9. Given: $\overline{SP}$ and $\overline{SR}$ are in $\mathcal{M}$.
$\overline{QS} \perp \mathcal{M}$
$\angle P \cong \angle R$

    Prove: $\overline{QP} \cong \overline{QR}$

10. Given: $\overline{SP}$ and $\overline{SR}$ are in $\mathcal{M}$.
$\overline{QS} \perp \mathcal{M}$
$\angle P \cong \angle R$

    Prove: $\overline{PS} \cong \overline{RS}$

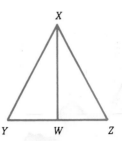

Exercises 9 and 10

11. Given: $\overline{PQ} \perp \overline{SQ}, \overline{PR} \perp \overline{RT}$
$\angle 1 \cong \angle 2, \overline{PS} \cong \overline{PT}$

    Prove: $\triangle PQR$ is isosceles.

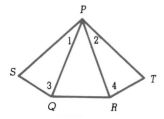

12. Given: $\overline{YX} \cong \overline{ZX}$
$\angle YXW \cong \angle ZXW$

    Prove: W is the midpoint of $\overline{YZ}$.

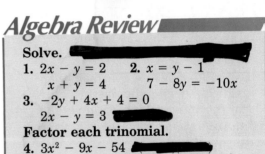

Complete the following exercises.

13. Draw two triangles that are not congruent, but for which SSA holds. Indicate all measurements. See students' work.

14. Draw two triangles that are not congruent, but for which AAA holds. Indicate all measurements. See students' work.

Algebra Review

Solve.

1. $2x - y = 2$
$x + y = 4$

2. $x = y - 1$
$7 - 8y = -10x$

3. $-2y + 4x + 4 = 0$
$2x - y = 3$

Factor each trinomial.

4. $3x^2 - 9x - 54$

5. $2q^2 - 9q - 18$

4-6 Medians, Altitudes, and Bisectors

Objective: Use medians, altitudes, and bisectors in proofs involving congruent triangles.

Every triangle has three **medians** and three **altitudes.** They are defined in the following way.

A segment is a median of a triangle if and only if its endpoints are a vertex of the triangle and the midpoint of the side opposite the vertex.	*Definition of Median of a Triangle*
A segment is an altitude of a triangle if and only if the following conditions hold. 1. Its endpoints are a vertex of a triangle and a point on the line containing the opposite side. 2. It is perpendicular to the line containing the opposite side.	*Definition of Altitude of a Triangle*

For the acute, right, and obtuse triangles, the *altitude* from vertex B is shown below.

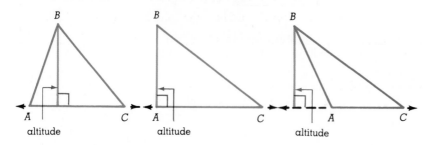

For the same acute, right, and obtuse triangles, the *median* from vertex B is shown below.

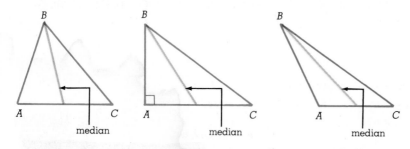

If an altitude is also a median, then it is called a **perpendicular bisector** of the opposite side. In the figure at the right, $\overline{AD}$ is the perpendicular bisector of $\overline{BC}$.

You may want to present Construction 5 on page 480 at this time.

always happens:
isosceles △

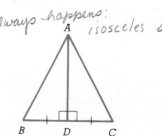

In this case, $\overline{AD}$ is a median and also an altitude.

Have students write an "if and only if" definition for ⊥ bisector.

134 *Congruent Triangles*

Example

1 **Prove the following.**

Given: $\overline{AB} \cong \overline{CB}$
$\overline{BD}$ is a median of $\triangle ABC$.

Prove: $\angle ABD \cong \angle CBD$

Proof:

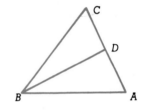

STATEMENTS	REASONS
1. $\overline{BD}$ is a median of $\triangle ABC$.	1. Given
2. D is a midpoint of $\overline{AC}$.	2. Definition of Median of a Triangle
3. $\overline{AD} \cong \overline{CD}$	3. Midpoint Theorem (Theorem 2-5)
4. $\overline{AB} \cong \overline{CB}$	4. Given
5. $\overline{BD} \cong \overline{BD}$	5. Congruence of segments is reflexive (Theorem 2-2).
6. $\triangle ABD \cong \triangle CBD$	6. SSS (Postulate 4-1) *Use steps 3, 4, and 5.*
7. $\angle ABD \cong \angle CBD$	7. Definition of Congruent Triangles *CPCTC*

In the figure at the right, $\angle PQS \cong \angle RQS$. Since $\overrightarrow{QS}$ and the sides of $\angle PQR$ form two congruent angles, $\overrightarrow{QS}$ is called the **bisector** of $\angle PQR$.

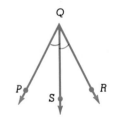

You may want to present Construction 3 on page 477 at this time.

A ray, $\overrightarrow{QS}$, is the bisector of $\angle PQR$ if and only if S is in the interior of the angle and $\angle PQS \cong \angle RQS$.	*Definition of Angle Bisector*

By using the Angle Measure Postulate and the Protractor Postulate, you can prove that an angle has *exactly one* bisector.

In the figure at the right, $\overrightarrow{CD}$ bisects $\angle ACB$. Notice that $\overline{CD}$ is contained in $\overrightarrow{CD}$ which bisects $\angle ACB$. Therefore, $\overline{CD}$ is also called an angle bisector of $\triangle ABC$.

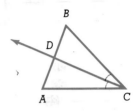

A segment is an angle bisector of a triangle if and only if it is contained in the bisector of one of the angles of the triangle and its endpoints are on the triangle.	*Definition of Angle Bisector of a Triangle*

Example

2

Prove the following.

Given: $\overline{PR}$ bisects $\angle QPS$.
$\overline{PR} \perp \overline{QS}$

Prove: $\triangle PQS$ is isosceles.

Proof:

Note that $\overline{PR}$ bisects the angle because $\overline{PR}$ is contained in $\overrightarrow{PR}$.

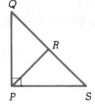

STATEMENTS	REASONS
1. $\overline{PR}$ bisects $\angle QPS$.	1. Given
2. $\angle QPR \cong \angle SPR$	2. Definition of Angle Bisector
3. $\overline{PR} \perp \overline{QS}$	3. Given
4. $\angle QRP$ and $\angle SRP$ are right angles.	4. Definition of Perpendicular Lines
5. $\angle QPR \cong \angle SRP$	5. If two angles are right angles, then the angles are congruent. (Theorem 3-6)
6. $\overline{PR} \cong \overline{PR}$	6. Congruence of segments is reflexive. (Theorem 2-2)
7. $\triangle PQR \cong \triangle PSR$	7. ASA (Postulate 4-3) *Use steps 2, 5, and 6.*
8. $\overline{QP} \cong \overline{SP}$	8. Definition of Congruent Triangles *CPCTC*
9. $\triangle PQS$ is isosceles.	9. Definition of Isosceles Triangle

EN: 2–18 even, 2–24 even; **AV:** 1–18, 1–13, 16, 18; **FD:** 1–18, 1–13, p. 133, 6, 8, 10, 11

Exploratory Exercises

In the figure at the right, $\overline{AC}$ bisects $\angle BAD$, and $\overline{CE}$ bisects $\angle ACD$. Also, $\overline{AB}$ is an altitude of $\triangle ABD$, and $\overline{CE}$ is an altitude of $\triangle ACD$. Find the degree measure for each angle.

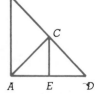

1. $\angle BAD$ ●
2. $\angle CEA$ ●
3. $\angle ECD$ ●
4. $\angle CDE$ ●
5. $\angle BAC$ ●
6. $\angle DCA$ ●
7. $\angle ACB$ ●
8. $\angle ACE$ ●
9. $\angle ECB$ ●

In the figure at the right, $\overline{PT}$ bisects $\angle QPR$, $\overline{PT}$ is an altitude of $\triangle PQR$, $\overline{TX}$ is an altitude of $\triangle PTQ$, and $\overline{TY}$ is an altitude of $\triangle TYR$. If $m \angle QPR = 54$, find the degree measure for each angle.

10. $\angle QPT$ ●
11. $\angle QXT$ ●
12. $\angle PQT$ ●
13. $\angle PTR$ ●
14. $\angle YTR$ ●
15. $\angle TRY$ ●
16. $\angle XTY$ ●
17. $\angle TPY$ ●
18. $\angle QTY$ ●

Written Exercises
For Exercises 1–8, see students' work.

Draw diagrams for Exercises 1–8 to illustrate each of the following.

1. $\overline{PS}$ is an altitude of $\triangle PQR$, and S is between Q and R.

2. $\overline{PS}$ is a median of $\triangle PQR$, and S is between Q and R.

3. $\overrightarrow{SQ}$ bisects $\angle PSR$.

4. $\overline{HL}$ is an angle bisector of $\triangle HJK$.

5. $\angle PVR$ and $\angle TVR$ form a linear pair. $\overrightarrow{VQ}$ bisects $\angle PVR$, and $\overrightarrow{VS}$ bisects $\angle TVR$.

6. $\overrightarrow{AP}$ bisects $\angle MLR$ and $\angle NLQ$.

7. $\triangle ABC$ is a right triangle with altitude $\overline{BC}$ and median $\overline{BD}$.

8. $\overline{PT}$ and $\overline{RS}$ are medians of $\triangle PQR$ and intersect at V.

9. Find x if $\overline{AD}$ is an altitude of $\triangle ABC$.

10. Find x if $\overline{PS}$ is a median of $\triangle PQR$.

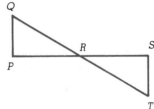

11. $\overrightarrow{YV}$ bisects $\angle XYZ$. If $m \angle XYZ = 8x - 6$ and $m \angle XYV = 2x + 7$, write an equation showing the relationship between the angles and solve for x. Then determine $m \angle XYZ$, $m \angle XYV$, and $m \angle VYZ$.

12. $\overline{LM}$ is the perpendicular bisector of $\overline{NT}$, intersecting at point O. Name a pair of congruent angles and a pair of congruent segments.
See the Teacher Guide for Exercises 11–22.

Prove each of the following.

13. Given: $\overline{AB}$ is an altitude of $\triangle ABD$.
$\overline{CD}$ is an altitude of $\triangle BCD$.
$\overline{BC} \cong \overline{AD}$, $\overline{CD} \cong \overline{AD}$
$\overline{AB} \cong \overline{CD}$

Prove: $\overline{BD}$ bisects $\angle ABC$.

14. Given: $\overline{PR}$ is an altitude of $\triangle PQR$.
R is the midpoint of $\overline{PS}$.
R is the midpoint of $\overline{QT}$.

Prove: $\overline{RS}$ is an altitude of $\triangle RST$.

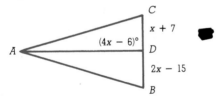

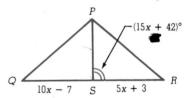

15. The median from the vertex angle of an isosceles triangle bisects the vertex angle.

16. The median from the vertex angle of an isosceles triangle is an altitude of the triangle.

17. If a median of a triangle is also an altitude, then the triangle is isosceles.

18. If a median of a triangle is also an altitude, then it is an angle bisector of the triangle.

19. If $\overrightarrow{BD}$ bisects $\angle ABC$, $\overline{DE}$ is an altitude of $\triangle ADB$, and $\overline{DF}$ is an altitude of $\triangle CDB$, then $\overline{DE} \cong \overline{DF}$.

20. Corresponding medians of congruent triangles are congruent.

21. The medians drawn to the congruent sides of an isosceles triangle are congruent.

22. If an angle and its bisector are given, then the bisector is the only bisector of the given angle.

Challenge Exercises

Draw several examples to answer each of the following questions.

23. If one median of a triangle is also an altitude, what is true about the triangle?

24. If one altitude of a triangle is also an angle bisector, what is true about the triangle?

For Exercises 23–24, see students' work. The triangles will be isosceles.

4-7 Isosceles Triangles

Objectives: Use properties of isosceles and equilateral triangles in proofs; use auxiliary segments in proofs.

Some proofs cannot be completed without using geometric figures that are not given in the theorem. These figures, usually lines or parts of lines, are called **auxiliary figures.** They are included on the diagram in color to show that they are not mentioned in the theorem. The proof of the following theorem uses an auxiliary segment.

Encourage students to draw auxiliary lines in color or as dashed lines.

If two sides of a triangle are congruent, then the angles opposite those sides are congruent.	*Theorem 4-6 Isosceles Triangle Theorem*

Example 1

Prove Theorem 4-6.

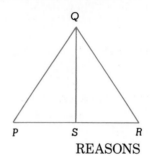

Given: $\triangle PQR$
$\overline{PQ} \cong \overline{RQ}$

Prove: $\angle P \cong \angle R$

Proof:

STATEMENTS	REASONS
1. Call S the midpoint of $\overline{PR}$, and draw $\overline{QS}$.	1. If a segment is given, then it has exactly one midpoint (Theorem 2-1), and through any two points, there is exactly one line (Postulate 1-1).
2. $\overline{PS} \cong \overline{RS}$	2. Midpoint Theorem (Theorem 2-5)
3. $\overline{PQ} \cong \overline{RQ}$	3. Given
4. $\overline{QS} \cong \overline{QS}$	4. Congruence of segments is reflexive (Theorem 2-2).
5. $\triangle PQS \cong \triangle RQS$	5. SSS (Postulate 4-1) *Use steps 2, 3, and 4.*
6. $\angle P \cong \angle R$	6. Definition of Congruent Triangles *CPCTC*

The proofs of the following theorems are based on the Isosceles Triangle Theorem.

If a triangle is equilateral, then the triangle is equiangular.	*Theorem 4-7*
If a triangle is equilateral, then each angle has a degree measure of 60.	*Theorem 4-8*

Students will prove Theorems 4-7 and 4-8 in Written Exercises 22 and 23.

It is not necessary to introduce an auxiliary figure unless it is useful for proving the given theorem. The segment in the proof of Theorem 4-6 is useful because it helps form two triangles. The proof is based on showing these two triangles are congruent.

The proof of the following theorem also uses an auxiliary segment.

Isosceles △ Theorum

If two angles of a triangle are congruent, then the sides opposite those angles are congruent.	*Theorem 4-9*

Students will prove Theorem 4-9 in Written Exercise 24.

According to Theorem 4-7 and the following theorem, a triangle is equilateral if and only if it is equiangular.

If a triangle is equiangular, then the triangle is equilateral.	*Theorem 4-10*

Examples

2 **Plan a proof for Theorem 4-9.**

Draw the bisector of $\angle PQR$ and let T be the point where the bisector intersects $\overline{PR}$. Show $\triangle PQT \cong \triangle RQT$ by AAS. Then, $\overline{PQ} \cong \overline{RQ}$ because they are corresponding parts of congruent triangles.

The diagram shows the given information and auxiliary segment.

3 **Prove Theorem 4-10.**

Given: $\triangle PQR$ is equiangular.
Prove: $\triangle PQR$ is equilateral.

Proof:

STATEMENTS	REASONS
1. $\triangle PQR$ is equiangular.	1. Given
2. $\angle P \cong \angle Q$ $\angle Q \cong \angle R$ $\angle R \cong \angle P$	2. Definition of Equiangular Triangle
3. $\overline{QR} \cong \overline{PR}$ $\overline{RP} \cong \overline{QP}$ $\overline{PQ} \cong \overline{RQ}$ *Notice that $\overline{PR}$ and $\overline{RP}$ name the same segment. Similarly, $\overline{QP}$ and $\overline{PQ}$ name the same segment.*	3. If two angles of a triangle are congruent, then the sides opposite those angles are congruent (Theorem 4-9).
4. $\triangle PQR$ is equilateral.	4. Definition of Equilateral Triangle

Exploratory Exercises

For each of the following exercises, determine whether the auxiliary figure will be helpful for the proof. State *yes* or *no*.

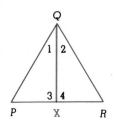

1. **Given:** $\overline{PQ} \cong \overline{QR}$
   Prove: $\angle P \cong \angle R$
   Draw $\overline{QX}$ so it bisects $\angle PQR$.

2. **Given:** $\overline{PQ} \cong \overline{QR}$
   Prove: $\angle P \cong \angle R$
   Draw $\overline{QX}$ so it bisects $\overline{PR}$.

3. **Given:** $\overline{PQ} \cong \overline{QR}$
   Prove: $\angle P \cong \angle R$
   Draw $\overline{QX}$ perpendicular to $\overline{PR}$.

4. **Given:** $\overline{PQ} \cong \overline{QR}$
   Prove: $\angle P \cong \angle R$
   Draw X, the midpoint of $\overline{PR}$.

5. **Given:** $\overline{PQ} \cong \overline{PR}$
   Prove: $\angle Q \cong \angle R$
   Draw $\overline{QX}$ so it bisects $\angle PQR$.

6. **Given:** $\angle P \cong \angle R$
   Prove: $\overline{PQ} \cong \overline{RQ}$
   Draw $\overline{QX}$ perpendicular to $\overline{PR}$.

7. **Given:** $\angle P \cong \angle R$
   Prove: $\overline{PQ} \cong \overline{RQ}$
   Draw $\overline{QX}$ so it bisects $\angle PQR$.

8. **Given:** $\angle R \cong \angle P$
   Prove: $\overline{QR} \cong \overline{QP}$
   Draw X, the midpoint of $\overline{PR}$.

9. **Given:** $\angle P \cong \angle Q$
   Prove: $\overline{PQ} \cong \overline{PR}$
   Draw median $\overline{QX}$.

For each of the following exercises find the missing degree measure.

10.

11.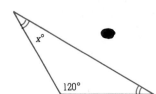

12.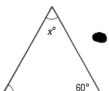

Written Exercises

Complete each of the following. See students' work for Exercises 1, 2, 4, 5, 7, and 8.

1. Draw $\triangle ABC$ so that $\overline{AD} \perp \overline{BC}$, but $\overline{BD}$ and $\overline{DC}$ are *not* congruent.

2. Draw $\triangle ABC$, so that $\overline{BD} \cong \overline{DC}$, but $\overline{AD}$ is *not* perpendicular to $\overline{BC}$.

3. Suppose $\overline{AD}$ is the perpendicular bisector of $\overline{BC}$ in $\triangle ABC$. Classify the triangle as scalene, isosceles, or equilateral.

4. Draw $\triangle ABC$ so that $\overline{AD}$ bisects $\angle BAC$, but $\overline{BD}$ and $\overline{DC}$ are *not* congruent.

5. Draw $\triangle ABC$ so that $\overline{BD} \cong \overline{DC}$, but $\overline{AD}$ does *not* bisect $\angle BAC$.

6. Suppose $\overline{AD}$ bisects both $\angle BAC$ and $\overline{BC}$ in $\triangle ABC$. Classify the triangle as scalene, isosceles, or equilateral.

7. Draw $\triangle ABC$ so that $\overline{AD}$ bisects $\angle BAC$, but $\overline{AD}$ is *not* perpendicular to $\overline{BC}$.

8. Draw $\triangle ABC$ so that $\overline{AD} \perp \overline{BC}$, but $\overline{AD}$ does *not* bisect $\angle BAC$.

9. Suppose $\overline{AD}$ bisects $\angle BAC$ and $\overline{AD} \perp \overline{BD}$ in $\triangle ABC$. Classify the triangle as scalene, isosceles, or equilateral.

Before you introduce an auxiliary figure, be sure it exists and it is *not* a special case. Determine whether you can introduce the figure in $\triangle PQR$. Write *yes* or *no*. If your answer is *no*, explain.

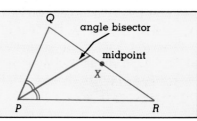

Sample   Let $\overline{PX}$ bisect $\angle P$ where X is the midpoint of $\overline{QR}$.

    No, every angle has exactly one bisector. It may *not* necessarily intersect the opposite side of the triangle at its midpoint.

For reasons to Exercises 10–15, see the Teacher Guide.

10. Let $\overline{QX}$ bisect $\angle Q$ where X is between P and R.

11. Let $\overline{RX}$ be the perpendicular bisector of $\overline{PQ}$.

12. Let $\overline{RV}$ bisect $\angle R$ and $\overline{PQ}$.

13. Let M be the midpoint of $\overline{QR}$. Draw $\overline{PM}$.

14. Let $\overline{XY}$ bisect $\overline{QP}$ and $\overline{PR}$, where X is on $\overline{QP}$ and Y is on $\overline{PR}$.

15. Let $\overline{XY}$ be perpendicular to $\overline{QP}$ and $\overline{PR}$, where X is on $\overline{QP}$ and Y is on $\overline{PR}$.

For each of the following figures find the value of x.

16.

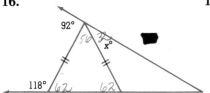

17.

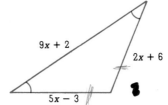

18.

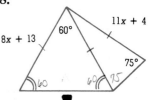

Prove each of the following exercises. For Exercises 19–24, see the Teacher Guide.

19. Given: $\overline{AB} \cong \overline{BC}$
    Prove: $\angle 3 \cong \angle 4$

20. Given: $\overline{PQ} \cong \overline{RS}$
               $\overline{PS} \cong \overline{RQ}$
    Prove: $\angle P \cong \angle R$

21. Given: $\overline{ZT} \cong \overline{ZR}$
               $\overline{TX} \cong \overline{RY}$
    Prove: $\angle 5 \cong \angle 7$

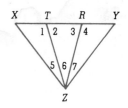

Prove each of the following theorems.

22. If a triangle is equilateral, then the triangle is equiangular. (Theorem 4-7)

23. If a triangle is equilateral, then each angle has a degree measure of 60. (Theorem 4-8)

24. If two angles of a triangle are congruent, then the sides opposite those angles are congruent. (Theorem 4-9)

4-8 Right Triangles

Objective: Recognize and use tests for congruence of right triangles in proofs.

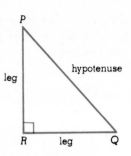

In a right triangle, the side opposite the right angle is called the **hypotenuse.** The other two sides are called the **legs.** The hypotenuse of $\triangle PQR$ is $\overline{PQ}$. The legs are $\overline{PR}$ and $\overline{RQ}$.

All right angles are congruent. Thus, any two right triangles always have one pair of angles congruent. The following theorems state ways to prove that two right triangles are congruent.

If the hypotenuse and an acute angle of one right triangle are congruent to the corresponding hypotenuse and acute angle of another right triangle, then the triangles are congruent.	*Theorem 4-11* *HA*
If the legs of one right triangle are congruent to the corresponding legs of another right triangle, then the triangles are congruent.	*Theorem 4-12* *LL*

Students will prove Theorems 4-11 and 4-12 in Written Exercises 5 and 6.
The HA and LL Theorems apply only to right triangles.

Example

1 **Prove the following.**

Given: $\angle Q$ and $\angle S$ are right angles.
$\angle 1 \cong \angle 2$
Prove: $\triangle PQR \cong \triangle RSP$

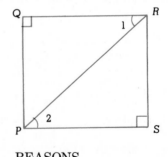

Proof:

STATEMENTS	REASONS
1. $\angle Q$ and $\angle S$ are right angles.	1. Given
2. $\triangle PQR$ and $\triangle RSP$ are right triangles.	2. Definition of Right Triangle
3. $\angle 1 \cong \angle 2$	3. Given
4. $\overline{PR} \cong \overline{PR}$	4. Congruence of segments is reflexive (Theorem 2-2).
5. $\triangle PQR \cong \triangle RSP$	5. HA (Theorem 4-11)

Suppose one leg and an acute angle of one right triangle are congruent to the corresponding leg and acute angle of another right triangle. Are the triangles congruent? There are two different cases to consider.

CASE 1: The leg is included between the acute angle and the right angle.

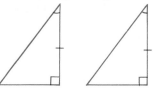

CASE 2: The leg is *not* included between the acute angle and the right angle.

In the first case, the triangles are congruent by ASA. In the second case, the triangles are congruent by AAS.

Students will prove Theorem 4-13 in Written Exercise 7.

If one leg and an acute angle of one right triangle are congruent to the corresponding leg and acute angle of another right triangle, then the triangles are congruent.	*Theorem 4-13* *LA*

Example

2 **Prove the following.**

Given: $\overline{BE} \perp \overline{AD}$
  C is the midpoint of $\overline{AD}$.
  $\angle B \cong \angle E$

Prove: $\overline{AB} \cong \overline{DE}$

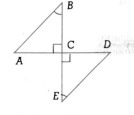

Proof:

STATEMENTS	REASONS
1. $\overline{BE} \perp \overline{AD}$	1. Given
2. $\angle BCA$ and $\angle DCE$ are right angles.	2. If two lines are perpendicular, then they form four right angles (Theorem 3-11).
3. $\triangle BCA$ and $\triangle ECD$ are right triangles.	3. Definition of Right Triangle
4. C is the midpoint of $\overline{AD}$.	4. Given
5. $\overline{AC} \cong \overline{DC}$	5. Midpoint Theorem (Theorem 2-5)
6. $\angle B \cong \angle E$	6. Given
7. $\triangle BCA \cong \triangle ECD$	7. LA (Theorem 4-13) *Use steps 3, 5, and 6.*
8. $\overline{AB} \cong \overline{DE}$	8. Definition of Congruent Triangles *CPCTC*

Viewed from the side, a ladder leaning against a building forms a right triangle. If a ladder is placed against a building so it reaches a certain window, then the foot of the ladder touches the ground at a certain spot. If any other ladder of the same length is placed in the same position, how do the triangles formed by the two ladders compare? They are congruent triangles.

If the hypotenuse and a leg of one right triangle are congruent to the corresponding sides of another right triangle, then the triangles are congruent.	*Postulate 4-4* *HL*

EN: 1–6, 2, 4, 5–7; AV: 1–6, 1–7; FD: 1–6, 1–5, p. 141, 19, 20, 22

Exploratory Exercises

Determine whether each pair of triangles is congruent. If so, state the postulate or theorem used. If there is *not* enough information, state "not enough information."

1.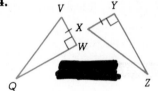

2.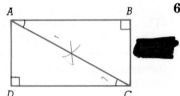

3.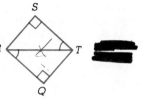

4.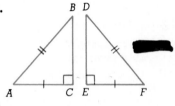

5.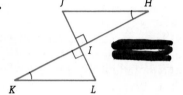

6.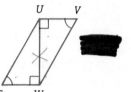

Written Exercises

For Exercises 1–7, see the Teacher Guide.

Prove each of the following exercises.

1. Given: $\angle Q$ and $\angle S$ are right angles.
$\angle 1 \cong \angle 2$
Prove: $\overline{QR} \cong \overline{SP}$

2. Given: $\angle Q$ and $\angle S$ are right angles.
$\overline{QP} \cong \overline{SR}$
Prove: $\angle 4 \cong \angle 3$

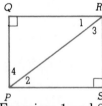
Exercises 1 and 2

3. Given: $\overline{BA} \perp \overline{AE}$
$\overline{DE} \perp \overline{AE}$
C is the midpoint of $\overline{AE}$.
$\angle ABC \cong \angle EDC$
Prove: $\angle 1 \cong \angle 2$

4. Given: $\overline{CB} \cong \overline{CD}$
$\angle 5 \cong \angle 6$
Prove: $\triangle BXC \cong \triangle DXC$

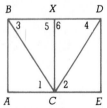
Exercises 3 and 4

Prove each of the following theorems.

5. HA (Theorem 4-11)

6. LL (Theorem 4-12)

7. LA (Theorem 4-13)

144 *Congruent Triangles*

Logic is a branch of philosophy that deals with methods of reasoning or thinking. The form of reasoning is presented as an *argument*. These arguments could be based on either **inductive** or **deductive reasoning.**

Deductive reasoning is the process of reasoning that draws conclusions from information that is accepted as true. If you accept as true "All triangles have three sides," and "This figure is a triangle," you could validly deduce "This figure has three sides."

Inductive reasoning is the process of reasoning that starts with a particular experience or a pattern of similar experiences that is then generalized. You may observe that all the apples you have eaten have been sweet. From this experience, you may then induct that all apples are sweet. Nevertheless, the next apple you eat might not be sweet. The inductive method leads to probable conclusions. Inductive reasoning is based on observation rather than true statements.

Recall that by folding the angles in $\triangle ABC$ to meet at point B, you discover that $m \angle 1 + m \angle 2 + m \angle 3 = 180$. By examining other triangles, you conclude that the sum of the degree measures of the angles of a triangle is 180. In generalizing this discovery, you have applied inductive reasoning.

Emphasize that
this is not a proof.

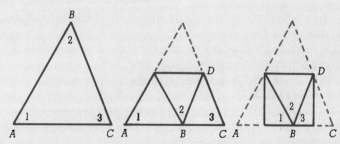

As more material is covered, you will have access to enough information to deductively *prove* that this is true.

Exercises

Identify the following arguments as applying inductive or deductive reasoning.

1. Since today is Friday, tomorrow will be Saturday.
2. Since it has snowed every New Year's Day for the past four years, it will snow on New Year's Day this year.
3. A child examines ten tulips that are each red and concludes that all tulips must be red.
4. If an isosceles triangle has at least two sides congruent, then an equilateral triangle is also isosceles.
5. Sandy earned A's on her first six geometry tests so she concludes that she will always earn A's on geometry tests.
6. If $5x = 25$, then $x = 5$.

Vocabulary

triangle (111)
sides (111)
vertices (111)
acute triangle (112)
obtuse triangle (112)
right triangle (112)
equiangular triangle (112)
scalene triangle (112)
isosceles triangle (112)
equilateral triangle (112)
congruent triangles (120)
SSS (124)
SAS (124)

ASA (125)
AAS (130)
median (134)
altitude (134)
perpendicular bisector (134)
angle bisector (135)
auxiliary figure (138)
hypotenuse (142)
legs (142)
HA (142)
LL (142)
LA (143)
HL (144)

Chapter Summary

1. **Definition of Triangle:** A triangle is a figure formed by three noncollinear segments called sides. Each endpoint of a side is an endpoint of exactly one other side. (111)
2. **Angle Sum Theorem (Theorem 4-1):** The sum of the degree measures of the angles of a triangle is 180. (116)
3. **Theorem 4-2:** If a triangle is equiangular, then the degree measure of each angle is 60. (117)
4. **Theorem 4-3:** If a triangle is a right triangle, then the acute angles are complementary. (117)
5. **Definition of Congruent Triangles:** Two triangles are congruent if and only if there is a correspondence such that their corresponding parts are congruent. (121)
6. **Theorem 4-4:** Congruence of Triangles is reflexive, symmetric, and transitive. (122)
7. **SSS (Postulate 4-1):** If each side of one triangle is congruent to the corresponding side of another triangle, then the triangles are congruent. (124)
8. **SAS (Postulate 4-2):** If two sides and the included angle of one triangle are congruent to the corresponding sides and included angle of another triangle, then the triangles are congruent. (124)
9. **ASA (Postulate 4-3):** If two angles and the included side of one triangle are congruent to the corresponding angles and included side of another triangle, then the triangles are congruent. (125)
10. **AAS (Theorem 4-5):** If two angles and a nonincluded side of one triangle are congruent to the corresponding angles and nonincluded side of another triangle, then the triangles are congruent. (130)
11. **Definition of Median of a Triangle:** A segment is a median of a triangle if and only if its endpoints are a vertex of the triangle and the midpoint of the opposite side. (134)

12. **Definition of Altitude of a Triangle:** A segment is an altitude of a triangle if and only if the following conditions hold.
    1. Its endpoints are a vertex of a triangle and a point on the line containing the opposite side.
    2. It is perpendicular to the line containing the opposite side.   (134)

13. **Definition of Angle Bisector:** A ray, $\overrightarrow{QS}$, is the bisector of $\angle PQR$ if and only if S is in the interior of the angle and $\angle PQS \cong \angle RQS$.   (135)

14. **Isosceles Triangle Theorem (Theorem 4-6):** If two sides of a triangle are congruent, then the angles opposite those sides are congruent.   (138)

15. **Theorem 4-7:** If a triangle is equilateral, then the triangle is equiangular.   (138)

16. **Theorem 4-8:** If a triangle is equilateral, then each angle has a degree measure of 60.   (138)

17. **Theorem 4-9:** If two angles of a triangle are congruent, then the sides opposite those angles are congruent.   (139)

18. **Theorem 4-10:** If a triangle is equiangular, then the triangle is equilateral.   (139)

19. **HA (Theorem 4-11):** If the hypotenuse and an acute angle of one right triangle are congruent to the corresponding hypotenuse and acute angle of another right triangle, then the triangles are congruent.   (142)

20. **LL (Theorem 4-12):** If the legs of one right triangle are congruent to the corresponding legs of another right triangle, then the triangles are congruent.   (142)

21. **LA (Theorem 4-13):** If one leg and an acute angle of one right triangle are congruent to the corresponding leg and acute angle of another right triangle, then the triangles are congruent.   (143)

22. **HL (Postulate 4-4):** If the hypotenuse and a leg of one right triangle are congruent to the corresponding hypotenuse and leg of another right triangle, then the triangles are congruent.   (144)

Chapter Review

4-1 **Use the figure at the right to answer each of the following.**

1. Name the triangle. ▬
2. Name the sides of the triangle. ▬
3. Name the angles of the triangle. ▬
4. Suppose the triangle is equilateral. Solve for x and find the measure of each side. ▬

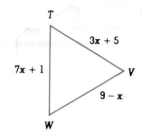

4-2 **In the figure at the right, $\overline{AB} \perp \overline{BC}$ and $\overline{BD} \perp \overline{AC}$. Also, $m \angle A = 62$. Find the degree measure for the following.**

5. $\angle ABD$ ▬
6. $\angle ABC$ ▬
7. $\angle DBC$ ▬
8. $\angle BCD$ ▬

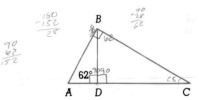

4-3 In the figure at the right, suppose $\triangle PQS \cong \triangle RQS$. Name the part of $\triangle RQS$ that is congruent to the part of $\triangle PQS$ given below.

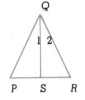

9. $\overline{PQ}$ ●

10. $\angle P$ ●

11. $\overline{QS}$ ●

12. $\angle 1$ ●

13. $\overline{SP}$ ●

14. $\angle PSQ$ ━

For proofs, see the Teacher Guide.

4-4 Use the figures at the right to complete each exercise.

15. Suppose $\overline{BA} \perp \overline{AD}$, $\overline{CD} \perp \overline{AD}$, and $\overline{BA} \cong \overline{CD}$. If $BD = 4x + 7$, and $CA = 13x - 11$, find x. ●

16. **Given:** E is the midpoint of $\overline{AC}$.
    $\angle 1 \cong \angle 2$
    Prove: $\angle 3 \cong \angle 4$

4-5 17. **Given:** $\overline{PR} \perp \overline{QS}$
    $\angle Q \cong \angle S$
    Prove: R is the midpoint of $\overline{QS}$.

18. In isosceles $\triangle PQS$, $\overline{PR} \perp \overline{SQ}$ and $\angle S \cong \angle Q$. If $m \angle S = 2x + 10$, and $m \angle 1 = 3x - 5$, find x. ●

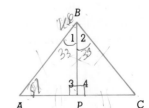

4-6 19. **Given:** $\overline{BC} \cong \overline{BA}$
    $\overline{BP}$ is a median of $\triangle ABC$.
    Prove: $\overline{BP}$ is an altitude of $\triangle ABC$.

20. $\overline{BP}$ is the angle bisector of $\angle ABC$ and $\overline{BP}$ is an altitude of $\triangle ABC$. If $m \angle 1 = 33$, find the degree measures of the three angles of $\triangle ABC$.

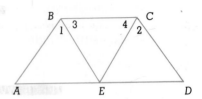

4-7 Complete a proof for each exercise.

21. **Given:** $\angle A \cong \angle D$
    $\overline{AB} \cong \overline{DC}$
    E is the midpoint of $\overline{AD}$.
    Prove: $\angle 3 \cong \angle 4$.

22. **Given:** $\angle A$ and $\angle C$ are right angles.
    $\angle 2 \cong \angle 4$
    Prove: $\overline{AB} \cong \overline{DC}$

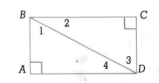

Chapter Test

In △EDF, ∠E is a right angle. Complete the following exercises.

1. Name the hypotenuse of △EDF. ●

2. Name a leg of △EDF. ▬▬

Suppose △ATC has the measurements shown in the figure at the right. Find the following measures if △PZK ≅ △TCA.

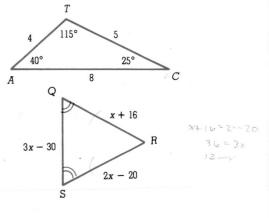

3. m ∠K ●
4. KZ ●

Complete the following exercise.

5. Use the information given in △QRS at the right to find the value of x. ●

Define the following terms.

6. median   For Exercises 6–8, see the Teacher Guide.
7. obtuse triangle
8. equilateral triangle.

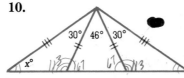

$x + 16 = 2x - 20$
$36 = 3x$
$12 = x$

In the following figures, find the missing degree measures.

9.
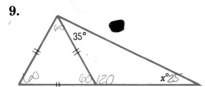

10.
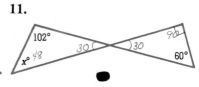

11.

In △AHW, m ∠A = 65, m ∠AHW = 80, and m ∠AWH = 35. If $\overline{WP}$ is an angle bisector and $\overline{HQ}$ is an altitude, find the following degree measures.

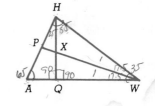

12. m ∠PWA ▬▬
13. m ∠AQH ●
14. m ∠AHQ ▬

For the triangles at the right, name the congruence necessary to prove the triangles congruent by the given postulate.

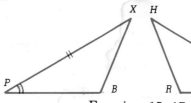

15. ASA ▬▬▬
16. SAS ▬▬▬
17. AAS ▬▬▬

Exercises 15–17

18. **Given:** $\overline{AB} ≅ \overline{CB}$, $\overline{AD} ≅ \overline{CD}$
    Prove: ∠A ≅ ∠C
    See the Teacher Guide.

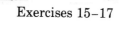

SSS
∠A ≅ ∠C   CPCTC

CHAPTER 5

Triangle Inequalities

Many structures use triangular shapes. Triangles can be used to compare distances or to determine the shortest path from one point to another.

5-1 Exterior Angles

Objectives: Write inequalities relating the interior and exterior angles of triangles; use inequality and exterior angle theorems in proofs.

In the figure below, $\angle 1$ is an **exterior angle** of $\triangle PQR$.

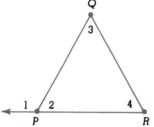

An angle is an exterior angle of a triangle if and only if it forms a linear pair with one of the angles of the triangle.	*Definition of Exterior Angle of a Triangle*

Notice that $\angle 1$ and $\angle 2$ are adjacent angles and form a linear pair. The other angles of the triangle are not adjacent to $\angle 1$. These two angles, $\angle 3$ and $\angle 4$, are called **remote interior angles** with respect to $\angle 1$.

An exterior angle is not vertical to an angle of a triangle.

There are two exterior angles at each vertex. In the figure below $\angle 1$ and $\angle 5$ are the exterior angles at vertex P. There are a total of six exterior angles for a given triangle.

Exterior Angle	Remote Interior Angles
$\angle 1$	$\angle 3$ and $\angle 4$
$\angle 5$	$\angle 3$ and $\angle 4$
$\angle 6$	$\angle 2$ and $\angle 4$
$\angle 7$	$\angle 2$ and $\angle 4$
$\angle 8$	$\angle 2$ and $\angle 3$
$\angle 9$	$\angle 2$ and $\angle 3$

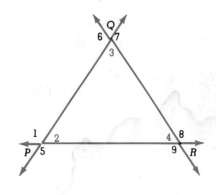

By Postulate 3-4, the angles in a linear pair are supplementary. Thus, the degree measure of an exterior angle of a triangle is related to the degree measures of the remote interior angles.

$$m \angle 1 + m \angle 2 = 180$$
$$m \angle 2 + m \angle 3 + m \angle 4 = 180$$
$$m \angle 1 + m \angle 2 = m \angle 2 + m \angle 3 + m \angle 4$$
$$m \angle 1 = m \angle 3 + m \angle 4$$

The angles in a linear pair are supplementary.
Angle Sum Theorem
Substitution
Subtraction Property of Equality

If an angle is an exterior angle of a triangle, then its measure is equal to the sum of the measures of the two remote interior angles.	*Theorem 5-1* *Exterior Angle* *Theorem*

Students will prove Theorem 5-1 in Written Exercise 19.

Example

1   Use the information from the figure to find the measures x, y, and z.

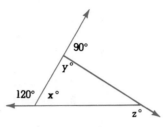

$$120 + x = 180 \qquad 90 + y = 180 \qquad z = x + y$$
$$x = 60 \qquad\qquad y = 90 \qquad\qquad = 60 + 90$$
$$= 150$$

This lesson provides the opportunity to review concepts of inequalities.

The following theorem is a direct result of the inequality properties. It is useful in proofs involving inequalities.

The Inequality Theorem could be used as a definition for inequality.

For any numbers a and b, $a > b$ if and only if there is a positive number c such that $a = b + c$.	*Theorem 5-2* *Inequality Theorem*

Example

2   Write an inequality that relates only x and y if $y + 10 = x + 19$.

$$y + 10 = x + 19$$
$$y + 10 - 10 = x + 19 - 10$$
$$y = x + 9$$

Therefore, $y > x$.

The Inequality Theorem leads to the following theorem concerning triangles and the measures of their angles.

If an angle is an exterior angle of a triangle, then its measure is greater than the measure of either remote interior angle.	*Theorem 5-3*

This theorem also can be proved indirectly. See Chapter 6.

Example

3 Prove Theorem 5-3.

Given: $\angle 4$ is an exterior angle of $\triangle RST$.
Prove: $m \angle 4 > m \angle 1$
$m \angle 4 > m \angle 2$

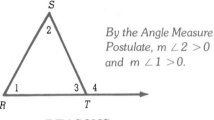

By the Angle Measure Postulate, $m \angle 2 > 0$ and $m \angle 1 > 0$.

Proof:

STATEMENTS	REASONS
1. $\angle 4$ is an exterior angle of $\triangle RST$.	1. Given
2. $m \angle 4 = m \angle 1 + m \angle 2$	2. Exterior Angle Theorem (Theorem 5-1)
3. $m \angle 4 > m \angle 1$ $m \angle 4 > m \angle 2$	3. Inequality Theorem (Theorem 5-2)

Show students how the statements in Step 3 follow from the Inequality Theorem.

EN: 3, 6, 9, . . . 24, 2–24 even, 19; **AV:** 2–24 even, 1–23 odd; **FD:** 1–24, 1–23 odd

Exploratory Exercises

For each of the following equations, write an inequality that relates only x and y.

1. $x = 45 + y$
2. $x - y = 25$
3. $180 - x = 53 - y$
4. $75 - y = 180 - x$
5. $x + 30 = y$
6. $60 + 45 + x = 180 + y$
7. $46 + x + 89 = 91 + y$
8. $y + 85 = x$

For each of the following equations, write an inequality that relates only $m \angle 1$ and $m \angle 2$.

9. $m \angle 1 = 180 + m \angle 2$
10. $m \angle 1 = 46 + m \angle 2$
11. $55 + m \angle 1 = m \angle 2$
12. $25 + 30 + m \angle 1 = m \angle 2$ $m \angle 1 < m \angle 2$
13. $180 - m \angle 1 = 55 + 70 - m \angle 2$
14. $180 + m \angle 1 - 91 = m \angle 2 - 46$
15. $m \angle 1 = m \angle 2 + m \angle 3 + m \angle 4$
16. $m \angle 1 + m \angle 3 = m \angle 2 - m \angle 4$

14. $m \angle 1 < m \angle 2$ 16. $m \angle 2 > m \angle 1$

For each of the following figures, find the missing measure.

17.

18.

19.

20.
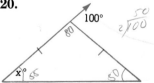

21.
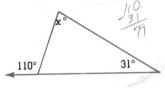

22.
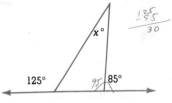

23.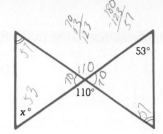

24.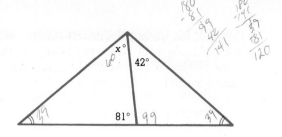

Written Exercises

Use the information given in the figure to find each measure.

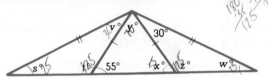

1. x
2. y
3. z
4. w
5. t
6. s
7. v
8. r

Use the information given in the figure to find each measure.

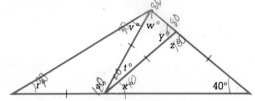

9. x
10. z
11. y
12. w
13. t
14. v

Prove the following. For Exercises 15–19, see the Teacher Guide.

15. **Given:** $\angle 1 \cong \angle 2$
    Prove: $\triangle PQR$ is isosceles.

16. **Given:** $m \angle 1 > m \angle 3$
    Prove: $m \angle 1 > m \angle 2$

17. **Given:** P, Q, and N are collinear.
    Prove: $m \angle 1 > m \angle 3$

18. **Given:** $\overline{NM} \cong \overline{MO}$
    N, O, and K are collinear.
    N, M, and L are collinear.
    Prove: $m \angle 1 > m \angle 2$

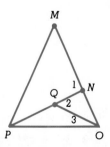

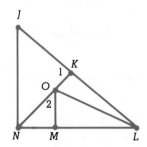

19. Prove if an angle is an exterior angle of a triangle, then its measure is equal to the sum of the measures of the two remote interior angles. (Theorem 5-1)

20. Use the information given in the figure to find $m \angle 1$, $m \angle 2$, and $m \angle 3$.

$$m \angle 1 =$$
$$m \angle 2 =$$
$$m \angle 3 =$$

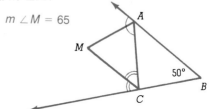

21. Use the information given in the figure to find the value of x and y.

$$x =$$
$$y =$$

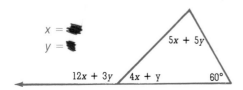

22. Use the information given in the figure to find $m \angle M$.

$$m \angle M = 65$$

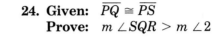

Prove each of the following. For Exercises 23–24, see the Teacher Guide.

23. Given: $b = x + c$
Prove: $y > x$

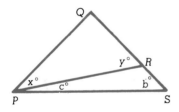

24. Given: $\overline{PQ} \cong \overline{PS}$
Prove: $m \angle SQR > m \angle 2$

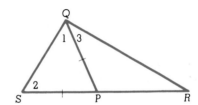

⊞ *Using Calculators* _____ **Powers**

Some calculators have keys that can be used to find the powers of a number. The key, $\boxed{y^x}$ is read "y to the x power." The following example shows how you can use this key to find 1.35^4.

Example Evaluate 1.35^4.

Enter: 1.35 $\boxed{y^x}$ 4 $\boxed{=}$ $\qquad y = 1.35, \; x = 4$

Display: 1.35 $\qquad$ 4 $\quad$ 3.32150625

Exercises
Evaluate each expression.

1. 2^3 8

2. 3^2 9

3. $(4.1)^6$ 4750.1042

4. $(5.7)^4$ 1055.6001

5. $(2.2)^{1/4}$ 1.2178833

6. $(0.45)^{1/7}$ 0.89219324

7. $7^4 + 3^{1/2}$ 2402.732

8. $4 + 5^{1/2} + 3^3$ 33.236068

9. $8^{2/3} + 2^{3/2}$ 6.8284271

5-2 Using Diagrams

Objectives: Recognize information which can and cannot be assumed from a diagram; use diagrams effectively in writing proofs.

Diagrams help state given information. They may be used to show any of the following.

Existence

When points, lines, rays, angles, triangles, and so on appear on a figure, you may *assume* they exist.

These assumptions shorten the number of steps in a proof.

Relative Position

When points appear on a line or part of a line, you may *assume* they are collinear. Also, you may *assume* betweenness with respect to points on a line, and location with respect to half-planes, interiors, and exteriors. Adjacent angles and linear pairs are shown in figures, too.

Intersection

When lines, rays, or segments appear to intersect, you may *assume* that they do intersect.

Note that a strictly logical proof does not depend on a diagram. Such proofs use postulates, definitions, and previously proven theorems.

Diagrams are marked to give further information about congruence and measure. Such information normally is written in the given statements, if the diagram is with a proof.

DO *NOT* ASSUME *ANY* OF THE FOLLOWING UNLESS A FIGURE IS MARKED.

congruence
equality of measure
inequality of measure
bisectors or midpoints
perpendiculars or right angles
specific measures

The properties listed must be given or proven.

Example

1 **Which of the following statements can be assumed from the appearance of the figure?**

1. V is between Q and T.
2. $\overline{PR}$ bisects $\angle QPS$.
3. $\overline{PT} \cong \overline{TS}$
4. $\overline{PR}$ bisects $\overline{QS}$.
5. $\overline{QR} \cong \overline{RS}$
6. $\overline{QT} \perp \overline{PS}$
7. $\angle QRV$ is a right angle.
8. $\angle QTP$ and $\angle QTS$ form a linear pair.

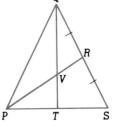

The statements **1, 4, 5,** and **8** can be assumed.

Often, a geometric proof shows that parts of a figure are congruent. One method of proving parts congruent is to show they are corresponding parts of congruent triangles. Thus, the problem becomes one of locating two triangles that contain the parts and then proving that the triangles are congruent. For example, consider the following.

Given: $\overline{RP} \cong \overline{RT}$
$\phantom{\textbf{Given:}}\ \overline{RQ} \cong \overline{RS}$
Prove: $\overline{PS} \cong \overline{TQ}$

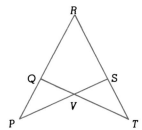

Altogether there are four triangles in the figure. To see the overlapping triangles in the diagram, it is helpful to outline the separate triangles in different colors.

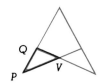

These concepts can be reinforced with the use of paper cutouts and chalkboard diagrams.

Another way to see the triangles is to draw them separately. Keep in mind the given statements and the assumptions that can be made from the original diagram.

When redrawing triangles make sure they are labeled correctly and in the same position.

Two overlapping triangles, $\triangle PSR$ and $\triangle TQR$, contain the corresponding parts $\overline{PS}$ and $\overline{TQ}$.

To complete the proof, show that $\triangle PSR \cong \triangle TQR$ by using SAS. Then, conclude $\overline{PS} \cong \overline{TQ}$ since they are corresponding parts of congruent triangles.

CPCTC

2 **Name two triangles that can be used to prove the following.**

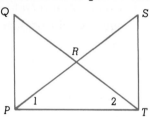

Given: $\overline{QP} \perp \overline{PT}$
$\overline{ST} \perp \overline{PT}$
$\angle Q \cong \angle S$
Prove: $\overline{PR} \cong \overline{TR}$

One way of completing the proof is to first show $\angle 1$ and $\angle 2$ are corresponding parts of congruent triangles and then use the converse of the Isosceles Triangle Theorem.

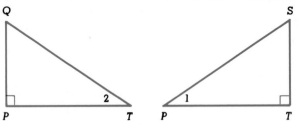

$\triangle TQP$ and $\triangle PST$ are right triangles that are congruent by LA. $\triangle TQP$ contains $\angle 2$ and $\triangle PST$ contains $\angle 1$.

3 **Name two triangles that can be used to prove the following.**

Given: $\overline{PQ} \cong \overline{SQ}$
Prove: $m \angle 2 > m \angle 1$

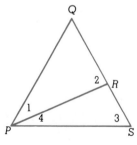

$\triangle PQS$ is a triangle that can be used to prove $m \angle 3 = m \angle 1 + m \angle 4$ since $\overline{PQ} \cong \overline{SQ}$.

$\triangle PRS$ is the triangle that can be used to prove $m \angle 2 = m \angle 4 + m \angle 3$ by using an exterior angle and remote interior angles.

You may want to have students complete this proof in class.

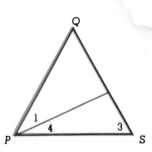

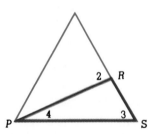

Exploratory Exercises

Determine whether each of the following may be assumed from a diagram.

1. adjacent angles yes
2. existence of a point yes
3. congruent segments no
4. perpendicular lines no
5. equality of distance measure no
6. intersection of rays yes
7. existence of a ray yes
8. perpendicular rays no
9. existence of a triangle yes
10. collinearity of segments yes
11. linear pair yes
12. vertical angles yes
13. intersection of lines yes
14. perpendicular segments no
15. right angles no

Using the figure, determine whether each of the following statements can be assumed.

16. $\angle PST$ and $\angle RST$ form a linear pair.
17. $\overline{QR} \perp \overline{PV}$
18. $RV + VQ = RQ$
19. T is between P and V.
20. $\angle SPT$ and $\angle VQT$ are congruent.
21. $\overline{PS} \cong \overline{QV}$
22. $\overline{PT} \cong \overline{QT}$
23. $PV = TV + PT$
24. $\angle QVT$ is a right angle.
25. $\angle PTS$ is adjacent to $\angle STV$.
26. $\overline{PV}$ bisects $\overline{QS}$.
27. T is the midpoint of $\overline{PV}$.

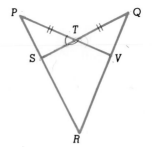

Written Exercises

Determine whether each of the following can be assumed from a diagram. If the answer is sometimes, draw diagrams to show when it can be assumed and when it cannot be assumed.   For diagrams, see students' work.

1. angle bisectors
2. existence of a line
3. betweenness of points
4. equality of angle measures
5. intersection of a line and a ray
6. inequality of distance measures
7. collinearity of points
8. congruent triangles
9. congruent angles
10. existence of segments
11. bisector of segments
12. existence of an angle

Using the figure, answer each of the following.

13. Which angles can be assumed to be congruent?
14. Can we assume $m \angle 7 + m \angle 6 = 180$?
15. Which sides can be assumed to be congruent?
16. Can we assume A, E, and D are collinear?
17. Can we assume $m \angle 2 = m \angle 4$?
18. Can we assume B, C, and D exist?
19. Can we assume F is in the interior of $\triangle BEC$?
20. Can we assume F is in the interior of $\triangle ABD$?

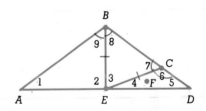

Name all the triangles contained in each of the following figures.

21.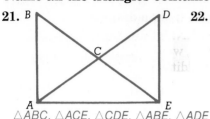
△ABC, △ACE, △CDE, △ABE, △ADE

22.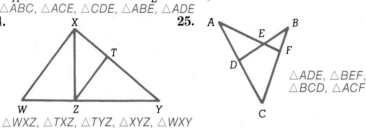
△RST, △PQS

23.
△MNQ,
△MPQ,
△MNP

24.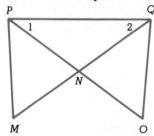
△WXZ, △TXZ, △TYZ, △XYZ, △WXY

25. A
△ADE, △BEF,
△BCD, △ACF

26.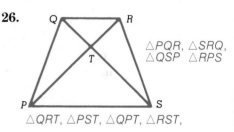
△PQR, △SRQ,
△QSP △RPS
△QRT, △PST, △QPT, △RST,

Prove each of the following. For Exercises 27–28, see the Teacher Guide.

27. Given: $\overline{PM} \cong \overline{QO}$
$\angle MPQ \cong \angle OQP$
Prove: $\overline{PN} \cong \overline{QN}$

28. Given: $\overline{XW} \perp \overline{WZ}$, $\overline{YZ} \perp \overline{WZ}$
$\overline{XW} \cong \overline{YZ}$
Prove: $\overline{XP} \cong \overline{YP}$

For each of the following exercises, answer
A if the measure in Column A is greater;
B if the measure in Column B is greater;
C if the two measures are equal;
D if the relationship cannot be determined from the information given.

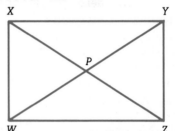

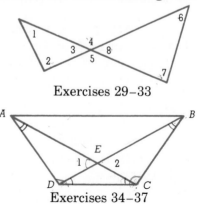

	Column A	Column B
29.	$m \angle 1$	$m \angle 5$
30.	$m \angle 8$	$m \angle 3$
31.	$m \angle 6$	$m \angle 7$
32.	$m \angle 7$	$m \angle 4$
33.	$m \angle 1 + m \angle 2$	$m \angle 5$
34.	$m \angle ADC$	$m \angle BCD$
35.	AC	DB
36.	$m \angle 1$	$m \angle ECD$
37.	AC	AB

Exercises 29–33

Exercises 34–37

160   *Triangle Inequalities*

The first electronic computer was called **ENIAC** (Electronic Numerical Integrator And Calculator). It went into operation in 1946. ENIAC weighed about 30 tons and occupied about 1500 square feet of floor space, which is about the size of a tennis court. ENIAC could perform 5000 additions or 300 multiplications per second.

In less than 50 years, a new breed of "supercomputer" has been developed. The fastest one in operation today is the $17.6 million Cray-2. It is capable of a top speed of 1.2 billion FLOPS (arithmetic operations per second), which is 50,000 times faster than a personal computer.

The computer is housed in a C-shaped cabinet about 50 in. across and 48 in. high. By densely packing 240,000 computer chips in this arrangement, the time it takes electric currents to travel from one part of the machine to another is greatly reduced. However, this speed creates a problem. The heat generated by the electric currents traveling through the circuits could melt the machine. To dissipate the heat, the circuits are submerged in 200 gallons of liquid fluorocarbon coolant. The Cray-2 is nicknamed "Bubbles" because of the sound made by its liquid cooling system.

Who needs this speed? Aircraft manufacturers can simulate airflow around an entire aircraft. Automobile designers can simulate crash tests for 150 models in the time it used to take to build and test one model. Meteorologists can make more accurate weather predictions. Oil companies can improve their chances of finding oil. Intelligence agencies need a supercomputer to categorize surveillance data from satellites.

As fast as the Cray-2 is, researchers are demanding still faster computers. The Cray-2 will be surpassed soon by the Cray-3. This supercomputer should be able to complete 10 billion calculations per second.

5-3 Sides and Angles

Objectives: Recognize relationships between sides and angles of triangles and use these relationships in proofs; use theorems regarding the distance between a point and line in proofs.

If two sides of a triangle are *not* congruent, then the angles opposite those sides are *not* congruent. The following diagram suggests how the sides and angles are related.

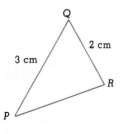

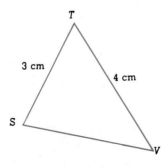

$$PQ > RQ$$
$$m \angle QRP > m \angle QPR$$

$$ST < VT$$
$$m \angle TVS < m \angle TSV$$

The angle with the greater measure is opposite the side with the greater measure.

If the measures of two sides of a triangle are unequal, then the measures of the angles opposite those sides are unequal in the same order.	✗ **Theorem 5-4**

Students will prove Theorem 5-4 in Written Exercise 3.

Example

1 **Plan a proof for Theorem 5-4.**

Given: $\triangle PQR$
$PQ > RQ$
Prove: $m \angle 2 > m \angle 1$

Students may need help identifying the triangles used and finding the corresponding parts.

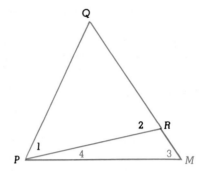

Extend $\overline{QR}$ to M so that $\overline{QM} \cong \overline{QP}$. The new triangle formed, $\triangle PQM$, is isosceles. Thus, the base angles are congruent. Using this information, you must show that $m \angle 1 + m \angle 4 = m \angle 3$.

Also, $m \angle 2 = m \angle 3 + m \angle 4$, since $\angle 2$ is an exterior angle of $\triangle PRM$. From substitution, conclude that $m \angle 2 = m \angle 1 + m \angle 4 + m \angle 4$. As a result, $m \angle 2 > m \angle 1$ by the Inequality Theorem. *By Postulate 3-1, $m \angle 4 + m \angle 4 > 0$.*

Suppose two angles of a triangle are not congruent. For example, in the figure at the right, $m \angle P > m \angle R$. The sides opposite these angles can be related in exactly one of the following ways.

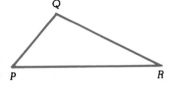

$QR = QP$	$QR < QP$	$QR > QP$
If the two sides have equal measures, they are congruent. The triangle is isosceles and the two angles must be congruent, which is impossible.	If two sides have unequal measures, then the measures of the angles opposite those sides are unequal in the same order. Thus, $m \angle P < m \angle R$, which is impossible.	The measures of the two sides must be related in this way, since the other two ways are impossible.

$m \angle P > m \angle R$
$QR \; ? \; QP$

The side with the greater measure is opposite the angle with the greater measure.

The reasoning leading to Theorem 5-5 is indirect. Students will learn to write formal indirect proofs in Chapter 6.

If the measures of two angles of a triangle are unequal, then the measures of the sides opposite those angles are unequal in the same order.	*reverse of 5-4* **Theorem 5-5**

Example

2 Illustrate Theorem 5-5 by drawing $25° - 60° - 95°$ and $30° - 30° - 120°$ triangles.
Prove that if a segment is the perpendicular segment from a point to a line, then it is the shortest segment.

Given: $\overline{PQ} \perp t$
$\overline{PR}$ is any other segment from P to t.
Prove: $PR > PQ$

Proof:

STATEMENTS	REASONS
1. $\overline{PQ} \perp t$	1. Given
2. $\angle 1 \cong \angle 2$	2. If two lines are perpendicular, then they form congruent adjacent angles. (Theorem 3-13)
3. $m \angle 1 = m \angle 2$	3. Definition of Congruent Angles
4. $m \angle 1 > m \angle 3$	4. If an angle is an exterior angle of a triangle, then its measure is greater than the measure of either remote interior angle. (Theorem 5-3)
5. $m \angle 2 > m \angle 3$	5. Substitution (Postulate 2-9)
6. $PR > PQ$	6. If the measures of two angles of a triangle are unequal, then the measures of the sides opposite those angles are unequal in the same order. (Theorem 5-5)

The proof in Example 2 leads to the following theorems.
A physical model, such as a plumb line, is helpful in illustrating these theorems.

A segment is the shortest segment from a point to a line if and only if it is the segment perpendicular to the line.	*Theorem 5-6*
A segment is the shortest segment from a point to a plane if and only if it is the segment perpendicular to the plane.	*Theorem 5-7*

Students will prove Theorem 5-7 in Written Exercise 4.

EN: 2–8 even, 2, 3, 4, 8, 9; **AV:** 1–8, 1–3, 5, 7; **FD:** 1–8, 1–3, 5, p. 160, 29–33

Exploratory Exercises   **ALL LEVELS:** Algebra Review

For each of the following triangles, list the angles in order from the angle with the least measure to the angle with the greatest measure.

1. ∠B, ∠A, ∠C

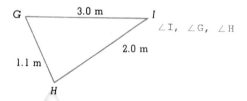

2. ∠F, ∠E, ∠D

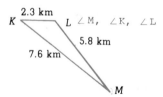

3. ∠I, ∠G, ∠H

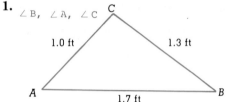

4. ∠M, ∠K, ∠L

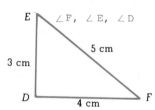

For each of the following triangles, list the sides in order from the side with the least measure to the side with the greatest measure.

5. $\overline{ML}$, $\overline{LN}$, $\overline{MN}$

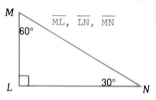

6. $\overline{PR}$, $\overline{RQ}$, $\overline{PQ}$

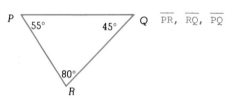

7. $\overline{ST}$, $\overline{TV}$, $\overline{SV}$

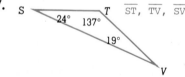

8. $\overline{WX}$, $\overline{XY}$, $\overline{WY}$

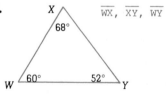

164   *Triangle Inequalities*

Written Exercises

1. Find the shortest segment in the figure at the right. The figure is not drawn to scale. QC

2. Find the longest segment in △ABC if m ∠A = 7x + 6, m ∠B = 8x − 10, and m ∠C = 7x + 8. AB

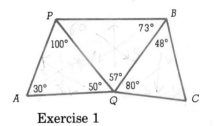

Exercise 1

Prove each of the following. For Exercises 3–8, see the Teacher Guide.

3. If the measures of two sides of a triangle are unequal, then the measures of the angles opposite those sides are unequal in the same order. (Theorem 5-4)

4. A segment is the shortest segment from a point to a plane if and only if it is the segment perpendicular to the plane. (Theorem 5-7)

5. **Given:** △ABC
   ∠A is a right angle.
   Prove: BC > BA

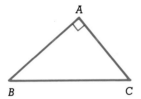

6. **Given:** △PQR, QR > QP
   $\overline{PR} \cong \overline{PQ}$
   Prove: m ∠P > m ∠Q

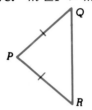

7. **Given:** TE > AE
   m ∠P > m ∠PAE
   Prove: TE > PE

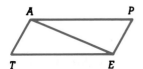

8. **Given:** $\overline{AC} \cong \overline{AE} \cong \overline{KE}$
   Prove: m ∠1 > m ∠2

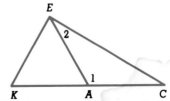

Challenge Exercise

9. Given quadrilateral PQRS with sides $\overline{PS}$ and $\overline{QR}$ extended to intersect at T, find the value of $\dfrac{x° + y°}{w° + z°}$. 1

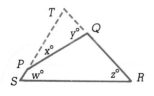

Different forms of geometry can be used to solve the problem of making a flat map of the curved surface of the earth. One such geometry is called **projective geometry.**

To understand the idea of projection, imagine that a glass globe is painted with the outlines of the continents. If a light is placed in the center of the globe, the lines can be projected onto a flat surface such as a piece of paper. The shape of the shadows depends on where the paper is positioned.

The drawings below show how the earth's surface can be projected onto a cylinder, a cone, and a plane.

One way the earth can be drawn is by using a cylinder. Imagine placing a cylinder around the earth. Points are projected from the sphere to the cylinder. In this projection, also called a Mercator projection, the points near the equator are placed on the map with little change in their position. Points near the poles can have a great deal of distortion. The Mercator projection is used in nautical charts.

In a conic projection, a cone of paper is placed over a section of the globe. This type of map has less distortion than a cylindrical projection because there is more earth surface closely aligned with its map. A conic projection is often used in maps showing the earth as viewed from the North Pole.

The third type of projection occurs when the surface of the globe is projected onto a plane that touches the globe at a single point. There are many different types of plane projections depending on the location of the light source. There is great distortion in this projection. However, it is important for determining long-distance airplane flights because a straight line in this map represents the great-circle route, or the shortest flying distance between two points.

Exercises

1. Which type of map would most accurately project the points of the North Pole? conic

2. Research other ways that maps are drawn. Compare the other mappings to the projections named above. See student's work.

5-4 The Triangle Inequality

Objective: Recognize and use the Triangle Inequality Theorem.

If you were planning to drive from Orlando, Florida, to West Palm Beach, Florida, you probably would not go by way of Daytona Beach. Intuitively, you know that the shortest distance between two points is along a straight line. The following theorem applies this principle to triangles.

Emphasize that the Triangle Inequality Theorem concerns only a single triangle.

3rd side: less than sum; greater than difference

| The sum of the measures of any two sides of a triangle is greater than the measure of the third side. | *Theorem 5-8* *Triangle Inequality* |

The Triangle Inequality must hold for all combinations of measures.

According to the Triangle Inequality Theorem, certain sets of measures cannot be used to form a triangle.

Example

1 **Determine whether it is possible to draw a triangle with sides of 2 units, 3 units, and 6 units.**

Additional examples include 6, 3, 3; 7, 8, 9; and 4, 5, 10.

$2 + 6 > 3$ $3 + 6 > 2$ $2 + 3 > 6$
True? *Yes*   True? *Yes*   True? *No*

The sum of the measures of any two sides must be greater than the measure of the third side. Ask students to describe what happens if the sum of the measures is equal to the measure of the third side.

No, it is *not* possible to draw a triangle with the given sides.

The proof of the Triangle Inequality Theorem uses an auxiliary segment.

Example

2 **Prove the Triangle Inequality Theorem.**

Given: $\triangle PQR$
Prove: $PQ + PR > RQ$

Draw diagrams showing $\angle QPR$ as a right angle, and $\angle QPR$ as an acute angle.

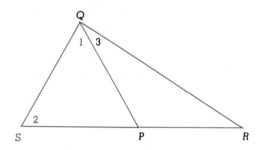

Proof:

STATEMENTS	REASONS
1. Draw $\overline{PS}$ so that P is between S and R and $PQ = PS$.	1. Ruler Postulate (Postulate 2-2)
2. $PS + PR = RS$	2. Definition of Betweenness
3. $\overline{PQ} \cong \overline{PS}$	3. Definition of Congruent Segments
4. $\angle 1 \cong \angle 2$	4. Isosceles Triangle Theorem (Theorem 4-6)
5. $m \angle 1 = m \angle 2$	5. Definition of Congruent Angles
6. $m \angle SQR = m \angle 1 + m \angle 3$	6. Angle Addition Postulate (Postulate 3-3)
7. $m \angle SQR = m \angle 2 + m \angle 3$	7. Substitution (Postulate 2-9)
8. $m \angle SQR > m \angle 2$	8. Inequality Theorem (Theorem 5-2)
9. $RS > RQ$	9. If the measure of two angles of a triangle are unequal, then the measures of the sides opposite those angles are unequal in the same order. (Theorem 5-5)
10. $PS + PR > RQ$	10. Substitution (Postulate 2-9)
11. $PQ + PR > RQ$	11. Substitution (Postulate 2-9)

If you know the measure of two sides of a triangle, it is possible to determine the greatest and least possible measure of the third side of the triangle. Consider the following example.

Example

3 The measures of two sides of a triangle are 6 and 10. Find the greatest and least possible measure of the third side.

Let x = the measure of the third side.

By the Triangle Inequality Theorem, each of these statements must be true.

$$x + 6 > 10 \qquad x + 10 > 6 \qquad 10 + 6 > x$$
$$x > 4 \qquad\qquad \cancel{x > -4} \qquad\qquad 16 > x$$

Disregard the second inequality because the measure of x must be positive. Therefore, the measure of the third side of the triangle must be greater than 4 but less than 16.

EN: 2–20 even, 2–10 even, 14, 16; **AV:** 1–19 odd, 1–8, 10, 11; **FD:** 1–20, 1–8, p. 165, 6, 7

Exploratory Exercises   ALL LEVELS: Mini Review

For each of the following, determine whether it is possible to draw a triangle with sides of the given measures. Write *yes* or *no.*

1. 1, 2, 3 no
2. 11, 12, 17 yes
3. 2.5, 6, 6.5 yes

4. 9, 40, 41 yes
5. 16, 12, 17 yes
6. 4.7, 9, 4.1 no

7. 2.2, 12, 14.3 no
8. 20, 48, 52 yes
9. 14, 15, 30 no

10. 2.3, 12, 12.2 yes
11. 215, 204, 7 no
12. 100, 100, 5 yes

Use the Triangle Inequality to complete the following table.

	first side measure	second side measure	third side measure must be	
			difference greater than	*sum* less than
13.	3	7	4	10
14.	6	10	4	16
15.	12	15	3	27
16.	1.19	2.34	1.15	3.53
17.	5.2	8.3	3.1	13.5
18.	13	19	6	32
19.	0.2	1.0	0.8	1.2
20.	1.7	1.8	0.1	3.5

Written Exercises

Two sides of a triangle are 14 centimeters and 15 centimeters in length. Determine whether each of the following can be the length of the third side.

1. 5 centimeters ~~yes~~   **2.** 17 centimeters ~~yes~~   **3.** 9 centimeters ~~yes~~

4. 16 centimeters ~~yes~~   **5.** 29 centimeters ~~no~~   **6.** 34 centimeters ~~no~~

Prove each of the following. For Exercises 7–14, see the Teacher Guide.

7. Given: $\angle ABC \cong \angle ACB$
    Prove: $AD + AB > CD$

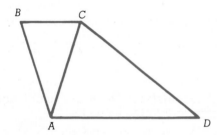

8. Given: $\triangle PTS \cong \triangle QRS$
    Prove: $PR > QR$

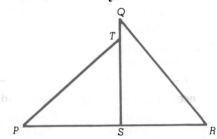

9. Given: $\overline{ED}$ bisects $\overline{AC}$.
         $\overline{ED} \perp \overline{AC}$
    Prove: $BC > BA$

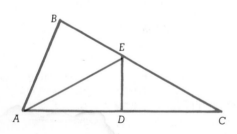

10. Given: $MN = MQ$
     Prove: $OP + ON > PQ$

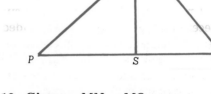
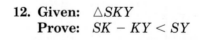

11. Given: $\triangle GRC$
          $\overline{RA}$ is an altitude.
      Prove: $RC > RA$

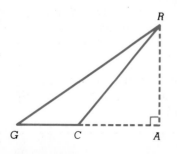

12. Given: $\triangle SKY$
      Prove: $SK - KY < SY$

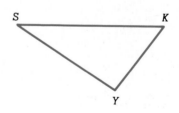

13. Given: $\triangle ABC$
  $\overline{AD}$, $\overline{BE}$, and $\overline{CF}$ are altitudes.
  Prove: $AB + BC + AC >$
  $AD + BE + CF$

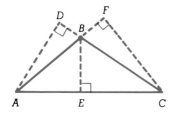

14. Given: $\triangle DAB$ and $\triangle DAC$
  Prove: $DA + AB + BC + CD >$
  $DB + CA$

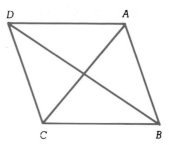

Solve each problem.

15. A metal rod that is 9 inches long is cut into pieces of integral length to be welded together to form a triangle. Of the possible solutions, what is the measure of the shortest piece? Is the triangle isosceles, scalene, or equilateral? 1, isosceles

16. If the sides of a triangle have measures of $3x + 2$, $8x - 10$, and $5x + 8$, find all possible values for x.

mini-review

1-6 **1.** How many planes can contain two intersecting lines? ~~exactly one~~

3-3 **2.** If $m \angle A = 2x$, $m \angle B = 3x + 15$, and angles A and B are complementary, find the value of x. 🖊

2-1 **3.** Change $0.0\overline{4}$ to a fraction in simplest form. 🖊

3-4 **4.** In $\triangle RPQ$, $\angle Q$ is a right angle and $m \angle R = 32$. Find $m \angle P$. 🖊

4-4 **5.** Name the triangle congruence tests for any pair of triangles.

Statistics That Shape Your Life

The population in a statistical study is all of the items or individuals in the group being considered. It rarely happens that 100% of a population is accessible as a source of data. Therefore, a random sample of the population must be selected. It is expected that a random sample will give results representative of the entire population.

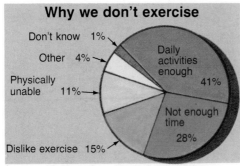

Why we don't exercise

Don't know 1%
Other 4%
Physically unable 11%
Dislike exercise 15%
Daily activities enough 41%
Not enough time 28%

Source: AP, Media General poll of 1,402 adults
Copyright, 1985 USA Today. Reprinted with permission.

The graph at the left shows the results of a survey in which 1402 adults were asked their reasons for not exercising.

Exercises

1. For a population of 100,000 adults, about how many would not exercise because they did not have enough time? 28,000

2. Survey the members of your class. Are the results similar to the results of the sample? Answers will vary.

Ruth Warren owns interior design shops in four cities and is planning to build a distribution center to serve all four shops. To lower freight costs, she wishes to locate the distribution center so that the total distance from the center to each of the shops will be the shortest distance possible.

This problem can be solved using the Triangle Inequality. The figure below shows a quadrilateral whose vertices, A, B, C, and D, represent the four cities. The following plan of a proof should convince you that the distribution center should be located at the intersection of the diagonals of the quadrilateral.

Given: Quadrilateral $ABCD$
$\overline{AC}$ and $\overline{BD}$ intersect at X.
X' is any other point in the interior of quadrilateral $ABCD$.

Prove: $AX + BX + CX + DX < AX' + BX' + CX' + DX'$

Plan of Proof:

By the definition of Between, $DB = DX + XB$ and $AC = AX + XC$.

Using the Triangle Inequality for $\triangle DBX'$, $DB < DX' + X'B$. Also, in $\triangle AX'C$, $AC < AX' + X'C$.

Using Substitution, $DX + XB < DX' + X'B$. Also, $AX + XC < AX' + X'C$.

From these steps, you can conclude the following.

$$AX + BX + CX + DX < AX' + BX' + CX' + DX'$$

Exercise For the proof, see the Teacher Guide.
The Duquesne Coal Company is planning to locate a coal terminal along the Allegheny River to receive coal from two of its mines. The total distance from the terminal to each of the mines should be minimized.

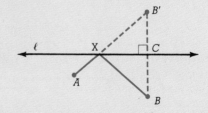

In the figure at the right, A and B represent the mines and ℓ represents the river. $\overline{BB'}$ was drawn perpendicular to ℓ and $BC = B'C$. Point X, the location of the terminal, is the intersection of $\overline{AB'}$ and ℓ. Prove that $AX + BX$ is the shortest possible distance.

5-5 The Hinge Theorem

Objective: Recognize and use the Hinge Theorem and its converse.

Drafting artists sometimes use compasses to compare lengths. If the angle of the compass is changed, the distance between the compass points changes.

The greater the angle of the compass, the greater the distance between its points. The smaller the angle of the compass, the shorter the distance between its points.

If two sides of one triangle are congruent to two sides of another triangle and the measures of the included angles are unequal, then the measures of the third sides are unequal in the same order.	*Theorem 5-9* *Hinge Theorem*

Emphasize that the Hinge Theorem concerns two separate triangles.

In the following diagram, notice that $AB < CD$. If the compass is not changed after matching the points to A and B, then it will not match the points C and D. How do you change the angle of the compass so its points match C and D? The converse of the Hinge Theorem describes this situation.

A plan for a proof of the Hinge Theorem is in the Challenge Exercises on page 177.

If two sides of one triangle are congruent to two sides of another triangle and the measures of the third sides are unequal, then the measures of the angles included between the pairs of congruent sides are unequal in the same order.	*Theorem 5-10* *Converse of the* *Hinge Theorem*

The reasoning behind the converse of the Hinge Theorem is presented in Written Exercises 13–14.

Examples

1

Given: $\overline{AB} \cong \overline{CB}$
$m \angle 1 < m \angle 2$
Prove: $AD < CD$

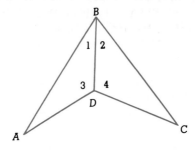

Proof:

STATEMENTS	REASONS
1. $\overline{AB} \cong \overline{CB}$	1. Given
2. $\overline{BD} \cong \overline{BD}$	2. Congruence of segments is reflexive. (Theorem 2-2)
3. $m \angle 1 < m \angle 2$	3. Given
4. $AD < CD$	4. The Hinge Theorem (Theorem 5-9)

2

In the figure below, $\triangle QTS$ has $\angle 1 \cong \angle 2$, $\overline{PQ} \cong \overline{SR}$, and $PT < QR$. Write an inequality to show how the measures of $\angle PQT$ and $\angle QSR$ are related.

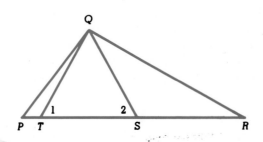

$\angle 1 \cong \angle 2$	*Given*
$\overline{QT} \cong \overline{QS}$	*Converse of Isosceles Triangle Theorem* (Theorem 4-9)
$\overline{PQ} \cong \overline{SR}$	*Given*
$PT < QR$	*Given*

By the statements above, it can be seen that $\triangle PQT$ and $\triangle QSR$ satisfy the hypothesis of the Converse of the Hinge Theorem; that is, two sides of one triangle are congruent to two sides of another triangle, and the measures of the third side are unequal. Therefore, the measures of the angles included between the pairs of congruent sides are unequal in the same order. Since $PT < QR$, $m \angle PQT < m \angle QSR$.

Exploratory Exercises

Name the theorem that best describes each situation.

1. When a door opens, the measure of the distance between the edge of the door and the frame increases. Theorem 5-9

2. A pendulum swings in a triangular frame. The distances of the weight from the endpoints of the frame depend on the angles formed at the vertex of the frame. Theorem 5-9

3. To mark off a segment shorter than a given segment, match the points of a compass with the endpoints, then decrease the angle of the compass. Theorem 5-10

4. To mark off a segment longer than a given segment, match the points of a compass with the endpoints, then increase the angle of the compass. Theorem 5-10

5. If two noncongruent triangles have two sides of one congruent to two sides of the other, then the triangle with the included angle with the lesser measure has the shorter third side. Theorem 5-9

6. If two noncongruent triangles have two sides of one congruent to two sides of the other, then the triangle with the shorter third side has the included angle with the lesser measure. Theorem 5-10

Written Exercises

In △*ABC* shown at the right, *M* is the midpoint of $\overline{AB}$. If $m\angle BMC = 8x - 100$ and $m\angle AMC = 5x + 20$, determine which measure is greater.

1. *BC* or *AC*

2. $m\angle B$ or $m\angle A$

3. $m\angle 1$ or $m\angle 2$

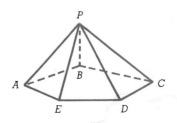

In the figure at the right, all segments are congruent except $\overline{PB}$. Name the angle of least measure given the following conditions.

4. $PB > AP$ ∠ABP, ∠APB, ∠CBP, or ∠CPB

5. $PB < PE$ ∠PAB or ∠PCB

Prove each of the following. 14, see the Teacher Guide.

6. **Given:** $\overline{PQ} \cong \overline{SQ}$

   Prove: $PR > SR$

7. **Given:** $\overline{PQ} \cong \overline{RS}$
   $QR < PS$

   Prove: $m\angle 3 < m\angle 1$

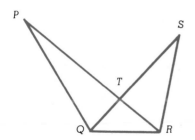

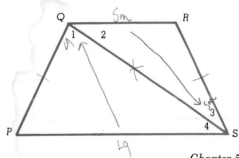

8. **Given:** D is the midpoint of $\overline{AC}$.
   $AB > CB$
   Prove: $m \angle 1 > m \angle 2$

9. **Given:** $\overline{BD}$ bisects $\overline{AC}$.
   $AB > CB$
   Prove: $m \angle 1 > m \angle 3$

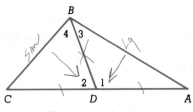

Exercises 8–9

10. **Given:** $\overline{PR} \cong \overline{PQ}$
    $SQ > SR$
    Prove: $m \angle 1 < m \angle 2$

11. **Given:** $\triangle TER$
    $\overline{TR} \cong \overline{EU}$
    Prove: $TE > RU$

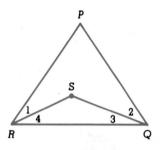

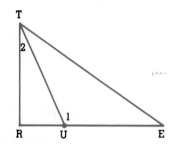

12. **Given:** $\overline{ER} \cong \overline{EC}$
    $\overline{GE} \cong \overline{AE}$
    $RA > RG$
    $m \angle CEA > m \angle REA$
    Prove: $m \angle CEA > m \angle GER$

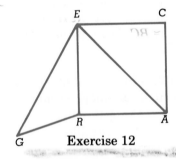

Exercise 12

Use the diagram and the given statements below for each of the following exercises.

Given: $\overline{PQ} \cong \overline{AB}$
$\overline{PR} \cong \overline{AC}$
$QR > BC$

Exercises 13–14 provide reasoning behind the converse of the Hinge Theorem.

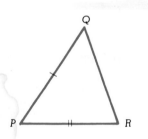

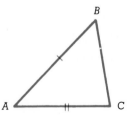

13. It is impossible for $\angle P$ and $\angle A$ to have the same measure. Show that assuming $m \angle P = m \angle A$, implies $QR = BC$, which contradicts $QR > BC$.

14. It is impossible for $m \angle P$ to be less than $m \angle A$. Show that assuming $m \angle P < m \angle A$, implies $QR < BC$, which contradicts $QR > BC$.

The following is a plan for a proof of the Hinge Theorem.

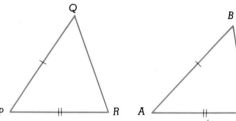

Given: $\triangle PQR$ and $\triangle ABC$
$\overline{PQ} \cong \overline{AB}$
$\overline{PR} \cong \overline{AC}$
$m \angle P > m \angle A$

Prove: $QR > BC$

Plan for proof: On $\triangle PQR$ draw $\overrightarrow{PS}$ so that $\angle SPR \cong \angle BAC$ and $\overline{PS} \cong \overline{AB}$.

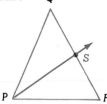

Case 1: S lies on $\overline{QR}$.
By SAS, show that $\triangle SPR \cong \triangle BAC$. Conclude $\overline{SR} \cong \overline{BC}$. Therefore, $QR = QS + SR$, since S is between Q and R. Thus $QR > SR$ and, by substitution, $QR > BC$.

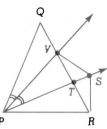

Case 2: S does *not* lie on $\overline{QR}$.
Let $\overrightarrow{PS}$ intersect $\overline{QR}$ at T and draw $\overrightarrow{PV}$ so that $\angle QPT$ is bisected and V lies on $\overline{QR}$. By SAS, show that $\triangle QPV \cong \triangle SPV$ and conclude $\overline{QV} \cong \overline{VS}$. The Triangle Inequality implies $VR + VS > SR$. Thus, by substitution, $VR + QV > SR$, or $QR > SR$. Next, use SAS to show $\triangle SPR \cong \triangle BAC$ and conclude $\overline{SR} \cong \overline{BC}$. Thus, using substitution, $QR > BC$.

For Exercises 15–16, see the Teacher Guide.

15. Write a proof for **Case 1** of the Hinge Theorem. The first statement should be the following.
    On $\triangle PQR$, draw $\overrightarrow{PS}$ so that $\angle SPR \cong \angle BAC$, $\overline{PS} \cong \overline{AB}$, and S lies on $\overline{QR}$.

16. Write a proof for **Case 2** of the Hinge Theorem. The first statement should be the following.
    On $\triangle PQR$, draw $\overrightarrow{PS}$ so that $\angle SPR \cong \angle BAC$ and $\overline{PS} \cong \overline{AB}$.
    Let T be the intersection of $\overrightarrow{PS}$ and $\overline{QR}$.

Excursions in Geometry _____ **Triangles**

How many triangles can you find in the figure below? 44 triangles

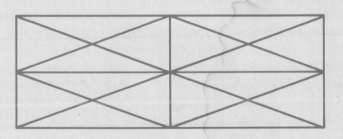

Vocabulary

exterior angle   (151)
remote interior angles   (151)

Triangle Inequality   (167)
Hinge Theorem   (173)

Chapter Summary

1. **Exterior Angle Theorem (Theorem 5-1):** If an angle is an exterior angle of a triangle, then its measure is equal to the sum of the measures of the two remote interior angles.   (152)

2. **Inequality Theorem (Theorem 5-2):** For any numbers a and b, $a > b$ if and only if there is a positive number c such that $a = b + c$.   (152)

3. **Theorem 5-3:** If an angle is an exterior angle of a triangle, then its measure is greater than the measure of either remote interior angle.   (152)

4. Diagrams may be used to show the existence of figures, the relative position of figures, or intersections.   (156)

5. To see overlapping triangles in a diagram, it is helpful to outline each triangle in a color or to draw each triangle separately in the same position.   (157)

6. **Theorem 5-4:** If the measures of two sides of a triangle are unequal, then the measure of the angles opposite those sides are unequal in the same order.   (162)

7. **Theorem 5-5:** If the measures of two angles of a triangle are unequal, then the measures of the sides opposite those angles are unequal in the same order.   (163)

8. **Theorem 5-6:** A segment is the shortest segment from a point to a line if and only if it is the segment perpendicular to the line.   (164)

9. **Theorem 5-7:** A segment is the shortest segment from a point to a plane if and only if it is the segment perpendicular to the plane.   (164)

10. **Triangle Inequality Theorem (Theorem 5-8):** The sum of the measures of any two sides of a triangle is greater than the measure of the third side.   (167)

11. **Hinge Theorem (Theorem 5-9):** If two sides of one triangle are congruent to two sides of another triangle and the measures of the included angles are unequal, then the measures of the third sides are unequal in the same order.   (173)

12. **Converse of the Hinge Theorem (Theorem 5-10):** If two sides of one triangle are congruent to two sides of another triangle and the measures of the third sides are unequal, then the measures of the angles included between the pairs of congruent sides are unequal in the same order.   (173)

Chapter Review

5-1 Write an inequality that relates only *PQ* and *PR*.

1. $PQ + QR = PR$ ▬▬▬
2. $PR - PQ = QR$ ▬▬▬
3. $4 + PQ - PR = 10$ ▬▬▬
4. $PQ - PR = 25$ ▬▬▬

Use the information given in the figure to find each measure.

5. x ▬▬
6. y ▬
7. z ▬
8. v ▬
9. w ▬
10. r ▬
11. s ▬
12. t ▬

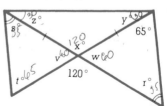

5-2 Determine if the following statements can be assumed from the appearance of the figure. Write *yes* or *no*.

13. *E* is between *A* and *D*. ▬▬
14. $\overline{BD}$ bisects $\overline{EC}$. ▬▬
15. $\overline{BF} \cong \overline{CF}$ ▬▬
16. $\overline{EA} \cong \overline{DA}$ ▬▬
17. $\overline{EA} \cong \overline{ED}$ ▬▬
18. $\angle BED$ is a right angle. ▬▬

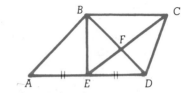

Name all the triangles in each of the following figures.

19.

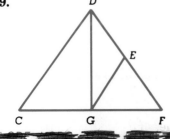

20.

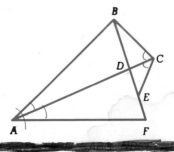

5-3 For each of the following triangles, list the sides from least to greatest measure and list the angles from least to greatest measure.

21.

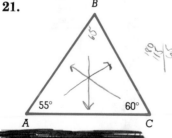

22.

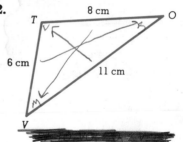

Prove each of the following. For Exercises 23–24, see the Teacher Guide.

23. Given: $\overline{AK} \cong \overline{AC}$
Prove: $m \angle 1 > m \angle 2$

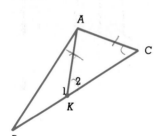

24. Given: $\triangle APE$ is equilateral.
Prove: $PQ > QA$

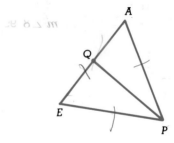

5-4   Two sides of a triangle measure 23 feet and 7 feet. Determine whether each of the following can be a measurement for the third side.

25. 45 feet ~~no~~   **26.** 29 feet ~~yes~~   **27.** 9 feet ~~no~~
28. 37 feet ~~no~~   **29.** 27 feet ~~yes~~   **30.** 24 feet ~~yes~~

30 – 16

Use the Triangle Inequality Theorem to complete each of the following exercises.

2 – 16

31. If a triangle has two sides measuring 7 units and 9 units, then the measure of the third side is longer than ___ units and shorter than ___ units.

32. If a triangle has two sides measuring 5 units and 11 units, then the measure of the third side is longer than ___ units and shorter than ___ units.

16 – 6

Prove the following. For Exercises 33–35, see the Teacher Guide.

33. Given: $\triangle XYZ$
Prove: $XY - YZ < XZ$

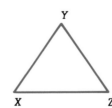

5-5   Prove each of the following.

34. Given: $\overline{AB} \cong \overline{CB}$
$m \angle ABE > m \angle CBE$
Prove: $AE > CE$

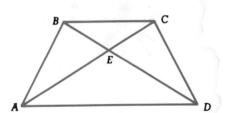

35. Given: $AD > BC$
Prove: $m \angle ABD > m \angle BAC$

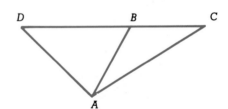

In the figure at the right, $\overline{PQ} \cong \overline{PV}$, $\overline{PR} \cong \overline{PT}$, $m \angle 9 = 60$, and $m \angle 4 = 20$. Find each measure.

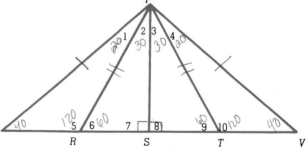

1. $m \angle 7$ 90
2. $m \angle 8$ 90
3. $m \angle 3$ 30
4. $m \angle 6$ 60
5. $m \angle 2$ 30
6. $m \angle 5$ 120
7. $m \angle 10$ 120
8. $m \angle V$ 40
9. $m \angle Q$ 40
10. $m \angle 1$ 20

12. Theorem 3-7 or Theorem 3-9; Definition of Right Angle

Name the postulates or theorems that justify each of the following statements.

11. The midpoint of $\overline{AC}$ is D. Definition of Midpoint
12. $m \angle 5 = 90$
13. $\overline{BD} \cong \overline{BD}$ Theorem 2-2
14. $\triangle ABD \cong \triangle CBD$ Definition of Right $\triangle$; LL or SAS
15. $AB = CB$ CPCTC; Definition of Congruent Segments
16. $\angle 1 \cong \angle 2$ CPCTC

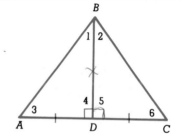

Using the figure at the right, determine which measure is greater.

17. $m \angle 5$ or $m \angle 4$ $m \angle 5$
18. $m \angle WRS$ or $m \angle 2$ $m \angle WRS$
19. PT or PV PV

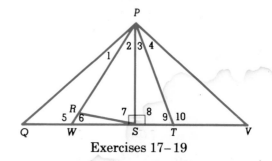

Exercises 17–19

For Exercise 20, see the Teacher's Guide.

20. **Given:** $\overline{NO} \cong \overline{QP}$
     $PN > OQ$
     Prove: $MP > MO$

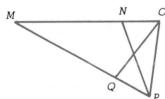

21. In a scalene triangle, the measure of the side opposite the greatest angle is 7. If all sides have integral lengths, how many unique triangles are possible? What are the dimensions of each triangle with these characteristics? 6 triangles,
7, 2, 6; 7, 3, 5; 7, 3, 6; 7, 4, 5; 7, 4, 6; 7, 5, 6

The following questions each consist of two quantities, one in Column A and one in Column B. Compare the two quantities and write your answer as follows:

Write A if the quantity in Column A is greater.
Write B if the quantity in Column B is greater.
Write C if the two quantities are equal.
Write D if there is not enough information.

All variables represent real numbers. A symbol appearing in both columns represents the same quantity in Column A as it does in Column B.

In some questions, information concerning one or both of the quantities to be compared is centered above the two columns. Geometric figures may *not* be drawn to scale.

Examples

Column A	Column B

1. $10x$ $100x$

The answer is **D** because the value of x is not known.

---

2. AB 17

By the Triangle Inequality, AB must be less than the sum of the other two sides of the triangle. Therefore, AB is less than 17 and the answer is **B**.

A > B
B > A
C = D not enough

Column A		Column B

1. $2 \times 5 \times 7$ 60

2. $(36)^2$ 6^4

$0 < x < y$

3. $3x$ y

$x \in$ real numbers

4. x x^2

5. $m \angle 2$ $m \angle 1$

Column A	Column B

$$x > 3$$

6. ▨ $\sqrt{x^2 - 9}$ $x + 3$

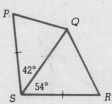

7. ▨ QR PQ

8. ▨ $\sqrt{80}$ 9

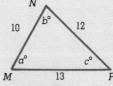

9. ▨ a c

10. ▨ ST $m \angle T < m \angle R < m \angle S$ SR

$$x^2 + 15x + 56 = 0$$
$$(x + 8)(x + 7) = 0$$
$$x = \{-8, -7\}$$

11. ▨ x -3

12. ▨   The largest prime factor of 858 143   The largest prime factor of 2310

$$3x + 4y = -2$$
$$-4x + 2y = -12$$

13. ▨ x y

$$-1 < p + q < 0$$

14. ▨ p 0

15. ▨   The sum of the integers from 1 to 20 210

CHAPTER 6

Parallels

Many real-life phenomena may be described using parallel lines. Light rays are parallel. Buildings are constructed with parallel steel girders. Notice the parallel lines suggested in this photograph.

6-1 **Parallels and Transversals** angles formed by pairs of lines and a transversal.

The sides of a road never meet. An optical illusion makes it appear as though they intersect.

In a plane, lines that never meet are called **parallel lines.**

Two lines are parallel if and only if they lie in the same plane and do not intersect.	*Definition of Parallel Lines*

The symbol, ∥, means **is parallel to.** In the figure below, the two lines are parallel.

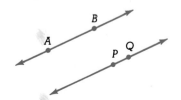

$$\overleftrightarrow{AB} \parallel \overleftrightarrow{PQ} \qquad \textit{symbols}$$
$$\overleftrightarrow{AB} \textit{ is parallel to } \overleftrightarrow{PQ}. \qquad \textit{words}$$

You may want to present Construction 7 on page 481 at this time.

The same term, parallel, and the same notation, ∥, are used for lines, segments, rays, and planes.

Parts of lines are parallel to each other if the lines containing them are parallel. For example, a ray can be parallel to a segment. In the figure above, $\overrightarrow{AB} \parallel \overrightarrow{PQ}$. *What other combinations are possible?*

Some lines do not intersect and yet are not parallel. They are called **skew lines.**

Some combinations include
$\overrightarrow{AB} \parallel \overrightarrow{PQ}, \overrightarrow{AB} \parallel \overrightarrow{PQ}, \overline{AB} \parallel \overleftrightarrow{PQ},$
$\overleftrightarrow{AB} \parallel \overline{PQ}, \overleftrightarrow{AB} \parallel \overrightarrow{PQ}, \overline{AB} \parallel \overleftrightarrow{PQ}.$

Two lines are skew if and only if they do not intersect and are not in the same plane.	*Definition of Skew Lines*

Thus, there are three different ways that two lines can be positioned in space. Lines can be intersecting, parallel, or skew.

Using a corner of a room and the intersection of a wall and the ceiling, illustrate skew lines.

1 In the figure below, name the lines that appear to be parallel to $\overleftrightarrow{EH}$. Then, name the lines that appear to be skew to $\overrightarrow{EH}$.

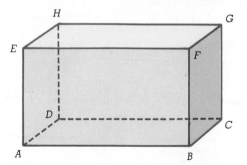

The lines that appear to be parallel to $\overleftrightarrow{EH}$ are $\overrightarrow{AD}$, $\overleftrightarrow{BC}$, and $\overleftrightarrow{GF}$.

The lines that appear to be skew to $\overleftrightarrow{EH}$ are $\overleftrightarrow{GC}$, $\overleftrightarrow{BF}$, $\overleftrightarrow{AB}$, and $\overleftrightarrow{DC}$.

Can you name additional pairs of parallel and skew lines?

In a plane, a line is a **transversal** if and only if it intersects two other lines in two different points.	*Definition of Transversal*

Note that the two lines cut by a transversal must be coplanar.

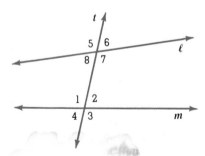

The transversal, *t*, *intersects*, or *cuts*, lines ℓ and *m*.

Eight angles are formed by the intersection of a transversal and two lines. Different names are used for various sets of these angles.

Interior Angles	$\angle 1$, $\angle 2$, $\angle 7$, $\angle 8$
Alternate Interior Angles	$\angle 1$ and $\angle 7$, $\angle 2$ and $\angle 8$
Exterior Angles	$\angle 3$, $\angle 4$, $\angle 5$, $\angle 6$
Alternate Exterior Angles	$\angle 6$ and $\angle 4$, $\angle 5$ and $\angle 3$
Corresponding Angles	$\angle 1$ and $\angle 5$, $\angle 2$ and $\angle 6$, $\angle 3$ and $\angle 7$, $\angle 4$ and $\angle 8$
Consecutive Interior Angles	$\angle 7$ and $\angle 2$, $\angle 1$ and $\angle 8$

Emphasize the lines cut by a transversal do not have to be parallel.

The following theorems state how some of the pairs of angles are related.

If two lines are cut by a transversal and one pair of alternate interior angles are congruent, then the other pair of alternate interior angles also are congruent.	*Theorem 6-1*
If two lines are cut by a transversal and one pair of corresponding angles are congruent, then all pairs of corresponding angles are congruent.	*Theorem 6-2*

Students will prove Theorem 6-2 in Written Exercise 33.

Example

2 **Prove Theorem 6-1.**

Given: $\angle 4 \cong \angle 6$
Prove: $\angle 3 \cong \angle 5$

Note that linear pairs are assumed from the diagram.

Proof:

STATEMENTS	REASONS
1. $\angle 4$ and $\angle 3$ form a linear pair. $\angle 5$ and $\angle 6$ form a linear pair.	1. Definition of Linear Pair
2. $\angle 4$ and $\angle 3$ are supplementary. $\angle 5$ and $\angle 6$ are supplementary.	2. Supplement Postulate (Postulate 3-4)
3. $\angle 4 \cong \angle 6$	3. Given
4. $\angle 3 \cong \angle 5$	4. If two angles are supplementary to two congruent angles, then the two angles are congruent to each other. (Theorem 3-3)

EN: 2–28 even, 12–32 even, 33–36; **AV:** 1–27 odd, 2–34 even; **FD:** 1–28, 1–32

Exploratory Exercises

Describe each of the following as intersecting, parallel, or skew lines.

1. rungs on a ladder parallel
2. railroad crossing sign intersecting
3. airline flight paths skew, parallel, or intersecting
4. rows of corn parallel
5. airport runways parallel or intersecting
6. electric power lines parallel or skew
7. lines on writing paper parallel
8. guitar strings parallel
9. spokes on a wheel intersecting
10. artist's T-square intersecting
11. slats on blinds parallel
12. bowling alleys parallel
13. skis on a skier parallel, skew, or intersecting
14. columns on the front of a building parallel

Determine whether each of the following statements is *true* or *false*.

15. Two lines are parallel if they do not intersect. false

16. A line that intersects two skew lines is a transversal. false

17. If a line intersects two parallel lines, then it is a transversal. true

18. Skew lines are parallel. false

19. Alternate interior angles are on the same side of a transversal. false

20. It is possible for two parallel lines both to be parallel to a third line. true

21. Alternate exterior angles are on opposite sides of a transversal. true

22. A transversal can be perpendicular to two lines. true

Using the diagram at the right, name the transversal that forms the given angle pairs.

23. ∠4 and ∠11 *p*

24. ∠2 and ∠7 *q*

25. ∠3 and ∠8 *p*

26. ∠10 and ∠14 *m*

27. ∠5 and ∠9 *p*

28. ∠12 and ∠13 *m*

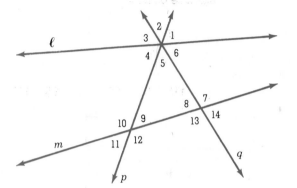

Written Exercises

Using the diagram at the right, name the relationship between the following angle pairs, given *m* ∥ *ℓ* and *n* ∥ *p*.

1. ∠1 and ∠5 alternate exterior

2. ∠12 and ∠6 alternate exterior

3. ∠14 and ∠10 alternate interior

4. ∠1 and ∠9 corresponding

5. ∠6 and ∠8 corresponding

6. ∠7 and ∠10 consecutive interior

7. ∠1 and ∠15 alternate exterior

8. ∠11 and ∠10 consecutive interior

9. ∠3 and ∠7 alternate interior

10. ∠5 and ∠13 corresponding

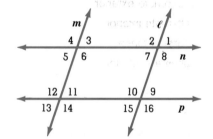

Using the figure at the right, complete the following exercises.

11. Name the pair of lines for which ∠2 and ∠4 are alternate interior angles. $\overleftrightarrow{WX}$ and $\overleftrightarrow{ZY}$

12. Name the pair of lines for which ∠1 and ∠3 are alternate interior angles. $\overleftrightarrow{WZ}$ and $\overleftrightarrow{XY}$

13. Name the transversals of $\overleftrightarrow{WZ}$ and $\overleftrightarrow{XY}$. $\overleftrightarrow{XZ}$, $\overleftrightarrow{WY}$

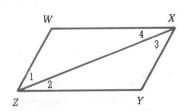

Using the figure at the right, name the relationship between the given pairs of angles.

14. $\angle 1$ and $\angle 2$ ▮▮▮▮▮
15. $\angle 11$ and $\angle 8$ ▮▮▮▮▮
16. $\angle 11$ and $\angle 4$ ▮▮▮▮▮
17. $\angle 11$ and $\angle 5$ ▮▮▮▮▮
18. $\angle 7$ and $\angle 4$ ▮▮▮▮▮
19. $\angle 7$ and $\angle 12$ ▮▮▮▮▮
20. $\angle 6$ and $\angle 3$ ▮▮▮▮▮
21. $\angle 3$ and $\angle 5$ ▮▮▮▮▮

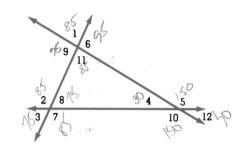

22. Use the figure above. Copy and complete the following table.

angle	1	2	3	4	5	6	7	8	9	10	11	12
degree measure of angle	85	115	65	30	150	95	115	65	95	150	85	30

Using the figure at the right, identify the given angle pairs as alternate interior, alternate exterior, consecutive interior, corresponding, or none of these.

23. $\angle 9$ and $\angle 11$ ▮▮▮▮▮
24. $\angle 1$ and $\angle 5$ ▮▮▮▮▮
25. $\angle 10$ and $\angle 13$ ▮▮▮▮▮
26. $\angle 8$ and $\angle 9$ ▮▮▮▮▮
27. $\angle 7$ and $\angle 15$ ▮▮▮▮▮
28. $\angle 3$ and $\angle 5$ ▮▮▮▮▮
29. $\angle 12$ and $\angle 16$ ▮▮▮▮▮
30. $\angle 10$ and $\angle 8$ ▮▮▮▮▮
31. $\angle 10$ and $\angle 6$ ▮▮▮▮▮
32. $\angle 11$ and $\angle 5$ ▮▮▮▮▮

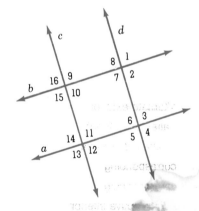

Prove each of the following exercises. For Exercises 33–37, see the Teacher Guide.

33. If two lines are cut by a transversal and one pair of corresponding angles are congruent, then all pairs of corresponding angles are congruent. (Theorem 6-2)

34. If two lines are cut by a transversal and one pair of consecutive interior angles is supplementary, then the other pair of consecutive interior angles is supplementary.

Challenge Exercises

Determine whether each statement is *true* or *false*. Then, explain.

35. Parallelism of lines is reflexive.

36. Parallelism of lines is symmetric.

37. Parallelism of lines is transitive.

6-2 Indirect Proof

Objectives: Write the assumption used in an indirect proof; write an indirect proof.

Until now, proofs that have been covered have always been direct proofs. It is not always possible to construct a proof using this type of reasoning. Therefore, an alternate type of reasoning can be used.

This kind of reasoning is called **indirect reasoning.** It is based on a contradiction. A conditional statement where p is the hypothesis and q is the conclusion is true if the statement "p and *not* q" is false. You must assume "p and *not* q" to be true and check to see if a contradiction is found.

Suppose you wish to prove the following.

If a triangle is equiangular, then it is not a right triangle.

To prove this statement by indirect reasoning, we assume that a triangle is equiangular and it is a right triangle. Is this possible? If a triangle is a right triangle, it has a right angle. Because the sum of the measures of all three angles in a triangle is 180, this means that the sum of the measures of the other two angles must be 90. Can all three angles be equal in measure by the definition of an equiangular triangle if one angle is a right angle? No, there is a contradiction!

Frequently, indirect proofs are written in paragraph form.

Students may need several examples of indirect proofs in order to develop greater understanding of this concept.

In order to use this type of indirect reasoning, you must first be able to state the assumption from the "if-then" statement. Consider the following example.   Note the assumption is not an if-then statement.

Example

1 State the assumption necessary to use indirect reasoning from the following "if-then" statement.

If two sides of a triangle are congruent, then the angles opposite those sides are congruent.

The assumption can be stated as follows.

Two sides of a triangle are congruent and the angles opposite those sides are *not* congruent.

Following is an example of indirect reasoning in geometry.

Example

2 Write an argument using indirect reasoning to prove the following statement.

If a triangle is a right triangle, then it has no more than one right angle.

The assumption can be stated as follows.

A triangle is a right triangle and it has more than one right angle.

If two of the angles of the triangle are right angles, then the third angle must measure 0, because the sum of the degree measures of all three angles is 180. Thus, a contradiction is found since the degree measure of an angle must be greater than 0. Therefore, if a triangle is a right triangle, then it has no more than one right angle.

If a triangle is a right triangle, then it has no more than one right angle.	*Theorem 6-3*

The method of indirect reasoning demonstrated in Example 2 can be summarized in the following steps. These steps will be used to write indirect proofs.

1. **Make the assumption *p* and *not q*.** 2. **Show that the assumption leads to a contradiction.** 3. **State that "*p* and *not q*" is false.** 4. **Conclude that the statement to be proven is true.**	*How to Write an* *Indirect Proof*

These steps can be applied to indirect proofs in algebra.

Example

3 **Prove if $x \neq 4$, then $2x + 3 \neq 11$.**

Given: $x \neq 4$
Prove: $2x + 3 \neq 11$

Proof:

Step 1: Assume: $x \neq 4$ and $2x + 3 = 11$.

Step 2: If $2x + 3 = 11$, then $2x = 8$ by applying the Subtraction and Inverse Properties. Then, $x = 4$ because of the Division and Inverse Properties. It is impossible for $x = 4$ and $x \neq 4$ at the same time. Therefore, a contradiction has been reached.

Step 3: The original assumption, $x \neq 4$ and $2x + 3 = 11$, is false.

Step 4: Thus, if $x \neq 4$, then $2x + 3 \neq 11$ is true.

The pairs of angles formed by a transversal and two parallel lines have many relationships that can be proven. The following theorem can be proven using indirect reasoning.

In a plane, if two lines are cut by a transversal so that a pair of alternate interior angles are congruent, then the two lines are parallel.	*Theorem 6-4*

Example

4 **Prove Theorem 6-4.**

> **Given:** $\angle 1 \cong \angle 2$
> **Prove:** $\ell \parallel m$

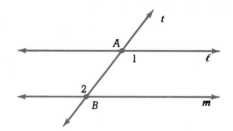

Proof:

Step 1: Assume: $\angle 1 \cong \angle 2$ and ℓ and m are *not* parallel.

Step 2: Then, ℓ and m intersect, at point P. Now, $\angle 2$ is in the exterior of $\triangle BAP$. Thus, $m\angle 2 > m\angle 1$ because the measure of an exterior angle of a triangle is greater than the measure of either remote interior angle. But, $\angle 1 \cong \angle 2$ implies that $m\angle 1 = m\angle 2$. The Comparison Property has been contradicted. The measures of two angles cannot be both equal and unequal at the same time.

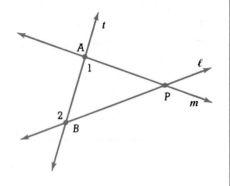

Step 3: The original assumption, $\angle 1 \cong \angle 2$ and ℓ and m are *not* parallel is false.

Step 4: Thus, $\ell \parallel m$.

EN: 3, 8, 12, 2–6 even, 7, 8–12 even; **AV:** 2–12 even, 2–6 even, 7–11; **FD:** 1–12, 1–8, p. 189, 33

Exploratory Exercises

For each of the following exercises, state the assumption you would use to start an indirect proof. For Exercises 1–12, see the Teacher Guide.

1. If the leaves of a plant are in groups of three, then the plant is poison ivy.

2. If a mushroom is red, then it is poisonous.

3. If the radio does *not* play well, then it is defective.

4. If the lamp will *not* turn on, then the light bulb is defective.

5. If two lines intersect, then they intersect in at least one point.

6. If a line *not* in a plane intersects the plane, then they intersect in no more than one point.

7. A right triangle has no more than two acute angles.

8. A triangle has at most one obtuse angle.

9. In a plane, if two lines are parallel to the same line, then they are parallel to each other.

10. If two lines *not* in the same plane do *not* intersect, then they are skew lines.

11. If the measures of two angles of a triangle are unequal, then the measures of the sides opposite those angles are unequal in the same order.

12. If two sides of one triangle are congruent to two sides of another triangle, but the lengths of the third sides are unequal, then the measures of the angles included between the pairs of congruent sides are unequal in the same order.

Written Exercises

For Exercises 1–12, see the Teacher Guide.

Write the assumption that would be used to start an indirect proof.

1. If two lines in the same plane are cut by a transversal so a pair of alternate exterior angles are congruent, then the two lines are parallel.

2. If two lines in the same plane are cut by a transversal so a pair of consecutive interior angles are supplementary, then the two lines are parallel.

3. If a plane and a line *not* in the plane intersect, then they intersect in no more than one point.

4. Given a line and a point *not* on the line, then there is no more than one plane that contains them.

5. If a transversal intersects two parallel lines, then both pairs of alternate interior angles formed are congruent.

6. If two lines intersect, then no more than one plane contains them.

7. Copy and complete the following indirect proof. Fill in the blanks where indicated.

Theorem: If a triangle is a right triangle, then it has no more than two acute angles.

Note that the triangle shown illustrates the assumption for the indirect proof.

Given: △ABC is a right triangle with right angle C.

Prove: △ABC has no more than two acute angles.

Assumption for indirect proof: _____

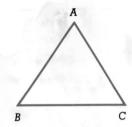

Triangle ABC has three acute angles. ∠A, ∠B, and ∠C. Why? __(a)__ The degree measure of angle C is less than 90. Why? __(b)__ But, triangle ABC is a right triangle with right angle C. Why? __(c)__ Therefore, the degree measure of angle C is 90. Why? __(d)__ But, the degree measure of angle C cannot be equal to 90 and less than 90 at the same time. Why? __(e)__ Thus, triangle ABC has no more than two acute angles. Why? __(f)__

8. Copy and complete the following indirect proof. Fill in the blanks where indicated.

Theorem: If two lines intersect, then they intersect in no more than one point.

Given: Lines ℓ and m intersect.

Prove: Lines ℓ and m intersect in no more than one point.

Assumption for indirect proof: _____

   Lines ℓ and m have two points in their intersection, P and Q. Why? __(a)__ Both lines ℓ and m contain P and Q. Why? __(b)__ But, through any two points, there is exactly one line. Why? __(c)__ Thus, lines ℓ and m intersect in no more than one point. Why? __(d)__

Write an indirect proof for each of the following exercises.

9. Given: $x \neq 5$

   Prove: $\frac{x}{5} + 1 \neq 2$

10. Given: $x \neq 0$

   Prove: $x + x + 8 \neq x + 8$

11. A triangle has at most one obtuse angle.

12. If a line *not* in a plane intersects the plane, then they intersect in no more than one point.

Statistics That Shape Your Life

How electric rates vary		
Utility	Residential rate (cents per kilowatt-hour)	Typical bill for June-August*
Cleveland Electric Illuminating	8.5	$127.50
Commonwealth Edison (Chicago)	9.5	$142.50
Consolidated Edison (New York)	16.7	$250.50
Florida Power & Light (Miami)	8.5	$127.50
Northern States Power (Minneapolis)	5.2	$78.00
Public Service Co. Colorado (Denver)	7.0	$105.00
Puget Sound Power & Light (Seattle)	4.7	$70.50
Southern California Edison (Los Angeles)	7.7	$115.50

*based on 1,500 kilowatt/hours
Source: National Association of Regulatory Utility Commissioners
Copyright 1985, USA Today. Reprinted with permission

   The cost of living is affected by many things. For example, rising incomes, increased spending, and abundance of credit make the cost of living increase. The cost of living varies in cities across the United States. It is interesting to see how location affects the cost of different services. The table at the left compares electric rates and average bills for several cities in the United States.

Exercises

1. Which utility has the highest rates? ~~████████████~~

2. What would your utility bill be if you used 1500 kilowatt hours in Denver? ~~████~~

3. What is the average utility rate for the companies listed? ~~████████~~

6-3 Testing for Parallel Lines

Objectives: Recognize and use tests for parallel lines.

Making a quilt takes much time and skill. Not only must the pieces of fabric be cut properly, but in order to carry out a design, they must be sewn together as indicated by the pattern. In the quilt to the right, notice how the pieces must be placed at the same angle in order to develop the parallel designs. This situation suggests the following theorem for parallel lines.

In a plane, if two lines are cut by a transversal so that a pair of corresponding angles are congruent, then the two lines are parallel.	*Theorem 6-5*

Example

1 **Prove Theorem 6-5.**

Given: $\angle 1 \cong \angle 2$

Prove: $\ell \parallel m$

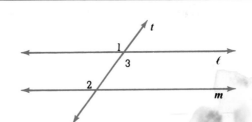

Proof:

STATEMENTS	REASONS
1. $\angle 1 \cong \angle 2$	1. Given
2. $\angle 3 \cong \angle 1$	2. If two angles are vertical, then they are congruent. (Theorem 3-10)
3. $\angle 3 \cong \angle 2$	3. Congruence of angles is reflexive, symmetric, and transitive. (Theorem 3-1)
4. $\ell \parallel m$	4. In a plane, if two lines are cut by a transversal so that a pair of alternate interior angles are congruent, then the two lines are parallel. (Theorem 6-4)

Using Theorems 6-4 and 6-5, the following theorems can be proven.

In a plane, if two lines are cut by a transversal so that a pair of consecutive interior angles are supplementary, then the lines are parallel.	*Theorem 6-6*
In a plane, if two lines are cut by a transversal so that a pair of alternate exterior angles are congruent, then the lines are parallel.	*Theorem 6-7*
In a plane, if two lines are perpendicular to the same line, then the two lines are parallel.	*Theorem 6-8*

Students will prove Theorems 6-6 and 6-7 in Written Exercises 19 and 20.

These theorems are tests for parallel lines. Example **2** shows how these tests are used to prove lines parallel.

Example

2 **Prove the following.**

Given: $\overline{BD}$ and $\overline{EA}$ bisect each other.

Prove: $\overline{AB} \parallel \overline{ED}$

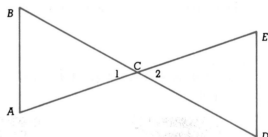

Proof:

STATEMENTS	REASONS
1. $\overline{BD}$ and $\overline{EA}$ bisect each other.	1. Given
2. $\overline{BC} \cong \overline{DC}$ $\overline{AC} \cong \overline{EC}$	2. Bisector Theorem (Theorem 2-6)
3. $\angle 1 \cong \angle 2$	3. If two angles are vertical, then they are congruent. (Theorem 3-10)
4. $\triangle BCA \cong \triangle DCE$	4. SAS (Postulate 4-2)
5. $\angle A \cong \angle E$	5. Definition of Congruent Triangles *CPCTC*
6. $\overline{AB} \parallel \overline{ED}$	6. In a plane, if two lines are cut by a transversal so that a pair of alternate interior angles are congruent, then the two lines are parallel. (Theorem 6-4)

Example

3   **Prove Theorem 6-8.**

Given: $\ell \perp t$
$m \perp t$

Prove: $\ell \parallel m$

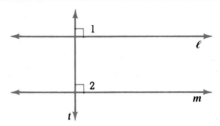

Proof:

STATEMENTS	REASONS
1. $\ell \perp t$ $m \perp t$	1. Given
2. $\angle 1$ is a right angle. $\angle 2$ is a right angle.	2. If two lines are perpendicular, then they form four right angles. (Theorem 3-11)
3. $\angle 1 \cong \angle 2$	3. If two angles are right angles, then the angles are congruent. (Theorem 3-6)
4. $\ell \parallel m$	4. In a plane, if two lines are cut by a transversal so that a pair of corresponding angles are congruent, then the two lines are parallel. (Theorem 6-5)

EN: 1–9 odd, 3, 6, 9, . . . 18, 19–21; **AV:** 1–9, 1–17, 19, 20; **FD:** 1–9, 1–15, p. 194, 10, 11

Exploratory Exercises

For each of the following exercises, determine which postulates or theorems you would use to prove $\ell \parallel m$. Answers may vary. Typical answers are given.

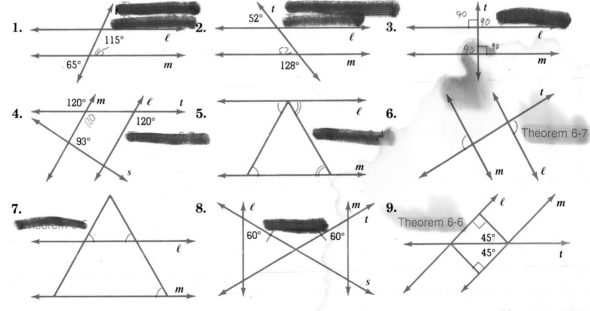

Written Exercises

For each of the following exercises, find x so that $\ell \parallel m$.

1.
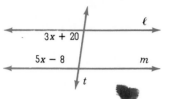
$3x + 20$
$5x - 8$

2.
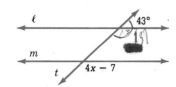
$43°$
$4x - 7$

3.
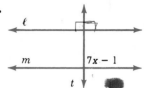
$7x - 1$

4.
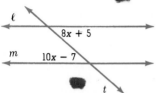
$8x + 5$
$10x - 7$

5.
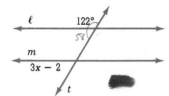
$122°$
58
$3x - 2$

6.
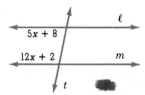
$5x + 8$
$12x + 2$

7. Use the information in the figure at the right to determine which lines are parallel. Then state the theorem that justifies your conclusion.

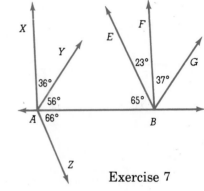

Exercise 7

Use the figure at the right and the given information to determine which lines, if any, are parallel.

8. $\angle 3 \cong \angle P$
9. $\angle 4$ and $\angle 5$ supplementary
10. $\angle Q \cong \angle 7$
11. $\angle 8 \cong \angle 7$ none
12. $\angle 5$ and $\angle X$ supplementary
13. $\angle Z \cong \angle 4$ $\overleftrightarrow{WZ} \parallel \overleftrightarrow{QP}$
14. $\angle 1 \cong \angle P$ $\overleftrightarrow{ZY} \parallel \overleftrightarrow{PS}$

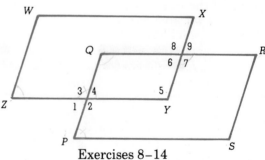

Exercises 8–14

Prove each of the following exercises.

15. Given: $\angle R$ and $\angle S$ are supplementary.
$\angle Q \cong \angle S$
Prove: $\overline{QP} \parallel \overline{RS}$

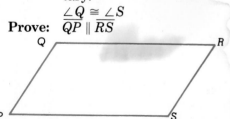

16. Given: $\overline{AD} \cong \overline{CB}$
$\overline{DC} \cong \overline{BA}$
Prove: $\overline{DC} \parallel \overline{AB}$

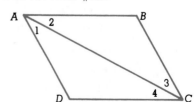

For Exercises 15–21, see the Teacher Guide.

17. Given: $\overline{MP} \cong \overline{MQ}$
$\quad\quad\quad \angle 1 \cong \angle N$
Prove: $\overline{PQ} \parallel \overline{LN}$

18. Given: $\angle F$ and $\angle 2$ are complementary.
$\quad\quad\quad\quad \angle C$ and $\angle 1$ are complementary.
Prove: $\overline{AF} \parallel \overline{CD}$

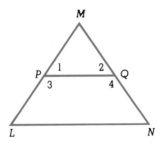

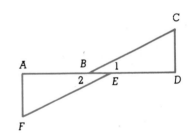

Prove each of the following exercises.

19. In a plane, if two lines are cut by a transversal so that a pair of consecutive interior angles are supplementary, then the lines are parallel. (Theorem 6-6)

20. In a plane, if two lines are cut by a transversal so that a pair of alternate exterior angles are congruent, then the lines are parallel. (Theorem 6-7)

21. If two lines are cut by a transversal so a pair of corresponding angles are congruent, then the bisectors of those angles are parallel.

Excursions in Geometry _____ **Eratosthenes**

Eratosthenes, an astronomer who lived in Greece in the 3rd century B.C., is credited with providing the first accurate measure of the earth's circumference. To do this, Eratosthenes assumed the earth to be round and the sun's rays to be parallel.

At noon on the day of the summer solstice, the sun is directly over the city of Syene. Therefore, a vertical pole would cast no shadow. At the same time, in Alexandria, which is north of Syene, a vertical pole casts a shadow at an angle of $7\frac{1}{5}°$.

Eratosthenes used geometry to determine that the measure of the angle formed by the pole equals the measure of the angle at the earth's center formed by imaginary lines from the two cities.

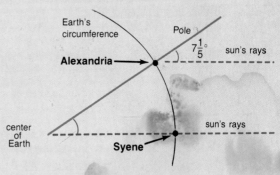

Eratosthenes calculated the earth's circumference by measuring the distance from Syene to Alexandria, and multiplying it by the number of times the angle at the earth's center is contained in 360°. Surprisingly, his calculation for the earth's circumference was only 158 miles less than the currently accepted value.

Exercise

Using Eratosthenes' method and 500 miles as the distance between Alexandria and Syene, calculate the circumference of the earth. 25,000 miles

Applications in Physics

A smooth surface that reflects most of the light striking it is a mirror. Most mirrors are pieces of glass that have been coated with a reflecting material such as silver or aluminum.

The figure at the right represents a parabolic concave mirror. A concave mirror reflects light from its inner curved surface. This mirror has a vertex represented by point A. The line shown passing through point A and containing point F is the principal axis.

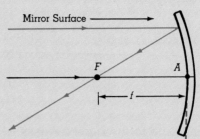

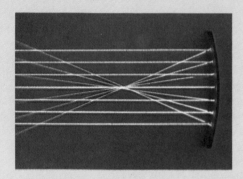

When parallel rays of light strike the mirror parallel to the principal axis and reflect, they meet at a focal point, F. The distance from F to A is called the focal length, f.

Two important rules concerning concave mirrors are as follows.
1. Any light ray parallel to the principal axis of a mirror is reflected through the focal point.
2. Any ray that passes through the focal point is reflected parallel to the principal axis.

It is possible to determine the location of an image reflected in the concave mirror by applying the following equation.

$$\text{distance from image to vertex } A = \frac{(\text{distance of object to } A)(\text{focal length})}{\text{distance of object to } A - \text{focal length}}$$

Example An object is 30 cm from a concave mirror. If the focal length of the mirror is 10 cm, what is the location of the image?

$$d_i = \frac{(d_0)(f)}{d_0 - f}$$

$$= \frac{(30)(10)}{30 - 10}$$

$$= \frac{300}{20}$$

$$= 15 \text{ cm} \quad \text{The location of the image is 15 cm from point } A.$$

Exercise

An object is 15 cm from a parabolic concave mirror having a 10 cm focal length. Locate the image. 30 cm

6-4 The Parallel Postulate

Objectives: Use properties of parallel lines to find measures of angles; use the Parallel Postulate and related theorems in proofs.

Around 300 B.C., Euclid developed a system for geometry similar to what is used today. He wrote five postulates. His first four postulates were very basic and simple. In contrast, the fifth postulate was more complex.

Many mathematicians throughout history thought Euclid's fifth postulate could be proven. They tried to prove it, without success.

The Parallel Postulate is one version of Euclid's fifth postulate.

This statement is called Playfair's Axiom after John Playfair's statement published in 1795.

If there is a line and a point *not* on the line, then there is exactly one line through the point that is parallel to the given line.	*Postulate 6-1* *Parallel Postulate*

Notice that "exactly one" is used in the Parallel Postulate. Thus, the Parallel Postulate assumes two cases.

Other geometries have been developed based on the two cases stated. One geometry states that no line can be drawn parallel while another geometry states that more than one line can be drawn parallel.

One such example can be found on page 210.

First, it states that at least one line can be drawn through a given point parallel to a given line.

Second, it states that no more than one line can be drawn parallel to a given line.

In using the Parallel Postulate to prove statements about parallel lines, it is helpful to use indirect proofs.

If two parallel lines are cut by a transversal, then each pair of corresponding angles are congruent.	*Theorem 6-9*
If two parallel lines are cut by a transversal, then each pair of alternate interior angles are congruent.	*Theorem 6-10*
If two parallel lines are cut by a transversal, then each pair of consecutive interior angles are supplementary.	*Theorem 6-11*
If two parallel lines are cut by a transversal, then each pair of alternate exterior angles are congruent.	*Theorem 6-12*

Students will prove Theorems 6-10, 6-11, and 6-12 in Written Exercises 33, 34, and 35.

1 Prove Theorem 6-9.

Given: $\ell \parallel m$

Prove: $\angle 1 \cong \angle 2$
$\angle 3 \cong \angle 4$
$\angle 5 \cong \angle 6$
$\angle 7 \cong \angle 8$

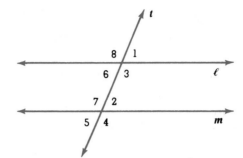

Proof:

Suppose $\angle 1$ is *not* congruent to $\angle 2$.

Draw $\overrightarrow{QP}$ so that $m \angle RQP = m \angle 2$. The Protractor Postulate justifies such a construction and guarantees that $\overleftrightarrow{QP}$ and ℓ are different lines. By the definition of congruent angles, $\angle RQP \cong \angle 2$. Thus, since they are corresponding angles, $\overleftrightarrow{QP} \parallel m$. But, $\ell \parallel m$. Since $\overleftrightarrow{QP}$ and ℓ are different lines, and both go through Q, the Parallel Postulate is contradicted.

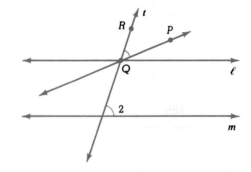

The original assumption is false.

Thus, $\angle 1 \cong \angle 2$.

If one pair of corresponding angles is congruent, then all pairs of corresponding angles are congruent. Since $\angle 1 \cong \angle 2$, all other pairs are congruent. Thus, $\angle 3 \cong \angle 4$, $\angle 5 \cong \angle 6$, and $\angle 7 \cong \angle 8$.

Can you identify the four steps of an indirect proof in the example above?

Many theorems of Euclidean geometry depend on the Parallel Postulate. These theorems will be used as reasons in many proofs.

The sum of the degree measures of the angles of a triangle was accepted to be 180 without proof in Chapter 4. Using the Parallel Postulate, we can now prove it.

Example

2

Prove that the sum of the degree measures of the angles of a triangle is 180.

This is the Angle Sum Theorem,
Theorem 4-1, p. 116.

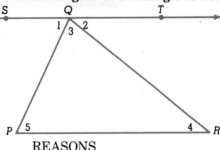

Given: $\triangle PQR$

Prove: $m \angle 5 + m \angle 4 + m \angle 3 = 180$

Proof:

STATEMENTS	REASONS
1. Draw $\overleftrightarrow{ST}$ through Q and parallel to $\overline{PR}$.	1. Parallel Postulate (Postulate 6-1)
2. $m \angle 1 + m \angle PQT = 180$	2. If two angles form a linear pair, then they are supplementary. (Postulate 3-4); Definition of Supplementary
3. $m \angle 2 + m \angle 3 = m \angle PQT$	3. Angle Addition Postulate (Postulate 3-3)
4. $m \angle 1 + m \angle 2 + m \angle 3 = 180$	4. Substitution (Postulate 2-9)
5. $\angle 2 \cong \angle 4$ $\angle 1 \cong \angle 5$	5. If two parallel lines are cut by a transversal, then each pair of alternate interior angles are congruent. (Theorem 6-10)
6. $m \angle 2 = m \angle 4$ $m \angle 1 = m \angle 5$	6. Definition of Congruent Angles
7. $m \angle 5 + m \angle 4 + m \angle 3 = 180$	7. Substitution (Postulate 2-9)

EN: 7–12, 2–32 even, 34–36; **AV:** 1–4, 7–13, 2–18 even, 19–32, 34, 37; **FD:** 1–13, 1–32, p. 199, 17, 18;

Exploratory Exercises

ALL LEVELS: Algebra Review

In the figure at the right, $t \parallel s$ and $\ell \parallel m$. Complete each exercise.

1. Name four pairs of congruent alternate interior angles and the transversals that form them.

2. Name four pairs of congruent corresponding angles and the transversals that form them.

3. Name four pairs of supplementary consecutive interior angles and the transversals that form them.

4. Name four pairs of congruent exterior angles and the transversals that form them.

For Exercises 1–4, see the Teacher Guide.

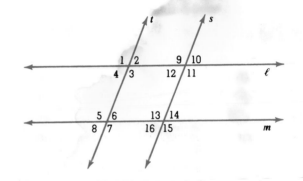

In the figure at the right, $\overline{ST} \parallel \overline{PR}$.

5. Name four pairs of congruent alternate interior angles.

6. Name four pairs of supplementary consecutive interior angles.

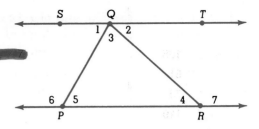

Find the measure of each of the following angles if $\ell \parallel m$ and $m \angle 2 = 62$.

7. $m \angle 1$

8. $m \angle 3$

9. $m \angle 4$

10. $m \angle 5$

11. $m \angle 6$ 62

12. $m \angle 7$

13. $m \angle 8$

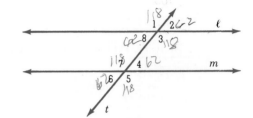

Written Exercises

Each of the following might be a statement in a formal proof. For each statement, name a postulate or theorem that justifies the statement.

1. Draw $\overleftrightarrow{QT}$ so that $\overline{QT} \parallel \overline{PR}$. Parallel Postulate (6-1)

2. Draw $\overline{SV}$ so that $\overline{PR} \parallel \overline{SV}$. Parallel Postulate (6-1)

3. Draw $\overline{SV}$ so that $\angle QSV \cong \angle SPR$. Protractor Postulate (3-2)

4. Call W the midpoint of $\overline{PR}$. Theorem 2-1

5. On $\overline{RQ}$, call A the point such that $\overline{RA} \cong \overline{AQ}$. Theorem 2-1, Theorem 2-5

6. Draw $\overline{RM}$ such that $\overline{RM} \parallel \overline{PQ}$. Parallel Postulate (6-1)

7. On $\overline{RQ}$, call C the point such that $\overline{SC}$ bisects $\overline{RQ}$. Bisector Theorem (2-6)

8. On $\overline{PR}$, call D the point such that $\overline{SD} \parallel \overline{RQ}$. Parallel Postulate (6-1)

9. Draw $\overline{RS}$. Postulate 1-1

10. Draw $\overline{PF}$ so that $\angle SPF \cong \angle SQR$. Protractor Postulate (3-2)

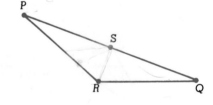

In the diagram at the right, $\overline{QR} \parallel \overline{TV}$. Find the degree measure for each angle.

11. $m \angle 1$ 33

12. $m \angle 4$

13. $m \angle 2$ 57

14. $m \angle 6$

15. $m \angle 3$ 123

16. $m \angle 5$

17. $m \angle 7$ 90

18. $m \angle Q$

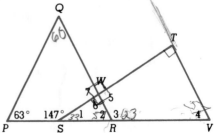

If $\ell \parallel m$, $p \parallel r$, $m \angle 10 = 75$, and $m \angle 12 = 119$, find the measure of each of the indicated angles.

19. $m \angle 1$ ~~105~~
20. $m \angle 2$ ~~75~~
21. $m \angle 3$ ~~61~~
22. $m \angle 4$ ~~119~~
23. $m \angle 5$ ~~75~~
24. $m \angle 6$ ~~106~~
25. $m \angle 7$ ~~119~~
26. $m \angle 8$ ~~61~~
27. $m \angle 9$ ~~105~~
28. $m \angle 15$ ~~44~~
29. $m \angle 13$ ~~105~~
30. $m \angle 14$ ~~75~~

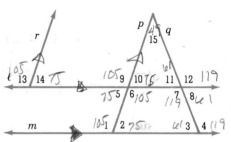
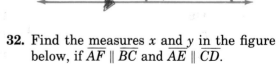
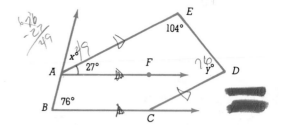

31. In the figure below, $\ell \parallel m$. Find $m \angle 1$. (Hint: Draw a line through X parallel to ℓ and m.)

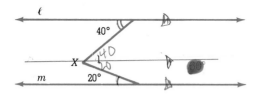

32. Find the measures x and y in the figure below, if $\overline{AF} \parallel \overline{BC}$ and $\overline{AE} \parallel \overline{CD}$.

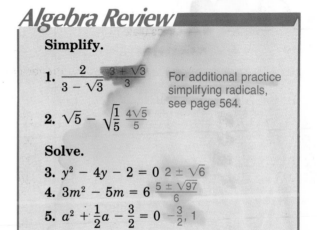

For Exercises 33–37, see the Teacher Guide.

Prove each of the following theorems by indirect proof, contradicting the Parallel Postulate.

33. If two parallel lines are cut by a transversal, then each pair of alternate interior angles are congruent. (Theorem 6-10)

34. If two parallel lines are cut by a transversal, then each pair of consecutive interior angles are supplementary. (Theorem 6-11)

35. If two parallel lines are cut by a transversal, then each pair of alternate exterior angles are congruent. (Theorem 6-12)

Prove the following exercises.

36. If $\ell \parallel m$ and $m \parallel n$, then $\ell \parallel n$.

37. Given: $\overline{PQ} \parallel \overline{ST}$

    R is the midpoint of $\overline{PT}$.

    Prove: $\triangle PQR \cong \triangle TSR$

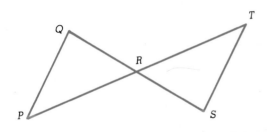

Algebra Review

Simplify.

1. $\dfrac{2}{3 - \sqrt{3}}$ $\dfrac{3 + \sqrt{3}}{3}$

   For additional practice simplifying radicals, see page 564.

2. $\sqrt{5} - \sqrt{\dfrac{1}{5}}$ $\dfrac{4\sqrt{5}}{5}$

Solve.

3. $y^2 - 4y - 2 = 0$ $2 \pm \sqrt{6}$

4. $3m^2 - 5m = 6$ $\dfrac{5 \pm \sqrt{97}}{6}$

5. $a^2 + \dfrac{1}{2}a - \dfrac{3}{2} = 0$ $-\dfrac{3}{2}, 1$

6-5 Using Parallels

Natural beauty, as displayed by rows of citrus trees, can be viewed as parallel lines. The road, serving as a transversal, meets each row of trees at an angle.

If the road is perpendicular to one of the rows, what angle will it form with the other rows? 90°

In a plane, if a line is perpendicular to one of two parallel lines, then it is perpendicular to the other.	*Theorem 6-13*

Example

1 **Prove Theorem 6-13.**

Given: $t \perp m$
$\ell \parallel m$
Prove: $t \perp \ell$

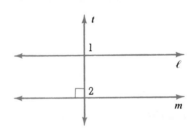

Proof:

STATEMENTS	REASONS
1. $t \perp m$	1. Given
2. $\angle 2$ is a right angle.	2. If two lines are perpendicular, then they form four right angles. (Theorem 3-11)
3. $m \angle 2 = 90$	3. Definition of Right Angle
4. $\ell \parallel m$	4. Given
5. $\angle 1 \cong \angle 2$	5. If two parallel lines are cut by a transversal, then each pair of corresponding angles are congruent. (Theorem 6-9)
6. $m \angle 1 = m \angle 2$	6. Definition of Congruent Angles
7. $m \angle 1 = 90$	7. Substitution (Postulate 2-9)
8. $\angle 1$ is a right angle.	8. Definition of Right Angle
9. $t \perp \ell$	9. Definition of Perpendicular Lines

Many geometric figures have parallel segments. By using the properties of parallel lines, you can discover properties of the figures themselves.

Examples

2 **In the figure at the right, opposite sides are parallel. How are the measures of the opposite sides related?**

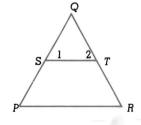

Draw $\overline{BD}$.
Since $\overline{BC} \parallel \overline{AD}$, show that $\angle 2 \cong \angle 4$. Similarly, since $\overline{AB} \parallel \overline{CD}$, you can show that $\angle 1 \cong \angle 3$. Finally, $\overline{BD} \cong \overline{DB}$. Thus, the two triangles formed are congruent. That is, $\triangle ABD \cong \triangle CDB$.

The opposite sides of the figure are corresponding parts of congruent triangles and are congruent. Since congruent segments have the same measures, you can conclude that $AB = CD$ and $DA = BC$.

3 **Complete the following proof.**

Given: $\overline{QS} \cong \overline{QT}$
$\overline{ST} \parallel \overline{PR}$

Prove: $\angle P \cong \angle R$

Proof:

STATEMENTS	REASONS
1. $\overline{QS} \cong \overline{QT}$	1. Given
2. $\angle 1 \cong \angle 2$	2. Isosceles Triangle Theorem (Theorem 4-6)
3. $\overline{ST} \parallel \overline{PR}$	3. Given
4. $\angle P \cong \angle 1$ $\angle 2 \cong \angle R$	4. If two parallel lines are cut by a transversal, then each pair of corresponding angles are congruent. (Theorem 6-9)
5. $\angle P \cong \angle R$	5. Congruence of angles is reflexive, symmetric, and transitive. (Theorem 3-1)

Exploratory Exercises

In the diagram, $m \parallel n$. For each of the following, state *yes* or *no*.

1. $\angle 5 \cong \angle 5$
2. $\angle 3 \cong \angle 8$
3. $\angle 3 \cong \angle 4$
4. $\angle 2 \cong \angle 6$
5. $\angle 4 \cong \angle 8$
6. $m \angle 5 + m \angle 6 = m \angle 7$
7. $m \angle 3 + m \angle 6 = m \angle 12$
8. $\angle 4$ and $\angle 12$ are alternate interior angles.

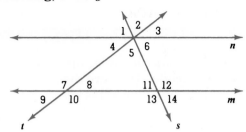

In the diagram, $\ell \parallel m$ and $r \parallel s$. For each of the following, state *yes* or *no*.

9. $\angle 3 \cong \angle 5$
10. $\angle 1 \cong \angle 4$
11. $\angle 7 \cong \angle 8$
12. $\angle 6 \cong \angle 9$
13. $m \angle 3 + m \angle 4 + m \angle 7 = 180$
14. $m \angle 1 + m \angle 2 + m \angle 7 = 180$
15. $\angle 5$ and $\angle 2$ are corresponding angles.
16. $\angle 4$ and $\angle 7$ are supplementary angles.

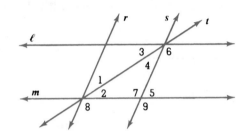

Written Exercises

Prove each of the following exercises. For Exercises 1–8, see the Teacher Guide.

1. **Given:** $\overline{AB} \parallel \overline{CD}$
$\overline{BC} \perp \overline{CD}$, $\overline{AB} \perp \overline{AD}$
Prove: $\overline{BC} \parallel \overline{AD}$

2. **Given:** $\overline{QS} \parallel \overline{PT}$
$\angle T$ is a right angle.
Prove: $\triangle RQS$ is a right triangle.

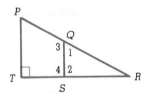

3. **Given:** $\overline{BA} \parallel \overline{ED}$
$\overline{AE}$ bisects $\overline{BD}$ at C.
Prove: $\overline{EC} \cong \overline{AC}$

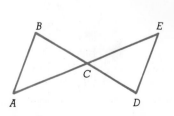

4. **Given:** $\overline{QS} \parallel \overline{PT}$
$\triangle QRS$ is equilateral.
R is the midpoint of $\overline{PT}$.
Prove: $\angle P \cong \angle T$

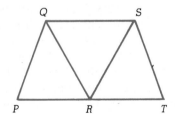

5. Given: $\overline{AB} \parallel \overline{CE}$
$\overline{BD} \cong \overline{AD}$

Prove: $\angle BDC \cong \angle ADE$

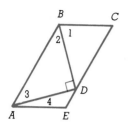

6. Given: $\angle 3$ is supplementary to $\angle 1$.
$\angle 1 \cong \angle 4$

Prove: $\overleftrightarrow{PQ} \parallel \overleftrightarrow{RS}$

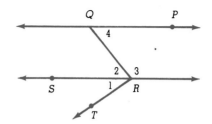

7. Given: $\triangle ABE$ is isosceles with base $\overline{BE}$.
$\angle 4 \cong \angle 2$

Prove: $\overline{CD} \parallel \overline{BE}$

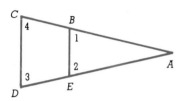

8. Given: $\overrightarrow{ZW}$ bisects $\angle XZV$
$\overline{XY} \parallel \overline{ZW}$

Prove: $\overline{XZ} \cong \overline{YZ}$

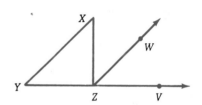

Application Exercises

Drafting artists normally have two different triangles. For each of the following, name the degree measure of the angles the parallel lines form with the straightedge.

9. Triangle: 45, 135; T-square: 75, 105

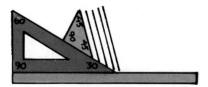

10. Triangle: 90, 90; T-square: 120, 60

Complete the following exercise.

11. In a house, seldom are walls completely vertical. To avoid slanted strips of wallpaper, a true vertical line is drawn by the use of a plumb bob, a string with an attached weight. The plumb line is used to align the first strip of wallpaper. Explain how the properties of parallel lines are applied in order to ensure the other strips of wallpaper will be truly vertical. See the Teacher Guide.

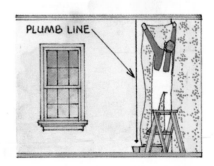

PLUMB LINE

One of the basic postulates of Euclidean geometry, the geometry that you are studying in this text, is the Parallel Postulate. This postulate is as follows: If there is a line and a point not on the line, then there is exactly one line through the point and parallel to the given line.

In the nineteenth century, consistent mathematical theories that contradicted Euclid's Parallel Postulate were discovered. One theory was called hyperbolic or Lobachevskian geometry. In Lobachevskian geometry, the Parallel Postulate is as follows: If there is a line and a point not on the line, then there are at least two lines through the point parallel to the given line.

Euclidean Parallel Postulate

Lobachevskian Parallel Postulate

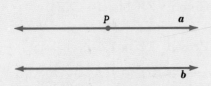

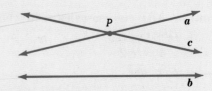

There is exactly one line *a* that contains point *P* and is parallel to line *b*.

There are at least two lines, line *a* and line *c*, that contain point *P* and are parallel to line *b*.

The figure above that illustrates the Lobachevskian Parallel Postulate looks impossible. It appears that when lines *a* and *c* are extended they will intersect line *b*. Try to imagine that space is infinite and that lines *a* and *b* extend forever. The lines could get closer and closer to each other but never intersect. Thus, in hyperbolic geometry, parallel lines never meet but the distance between them becomes less as they are further extended.

An important theorem of Euclidean geometry states: If a figure is a triangle, then the sum of the degree measures of the angles is 180. In hyperbolic geometry, the sum of the degree measures of the angles of a triangle is less than 180. As a triangle increases in area, the sum of the measures of its angles decreases. Thus, in hyperbolic geometry only triangles equal in area have the same sum of angle measures.

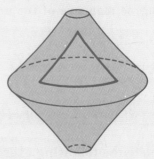

Exercises For Exercises 1–3, see the Teacher Guide.

Find a reference for hyperbolic geometry. Then, answer the questions.

1. Find at least one other theorem of hyperbolic geometry that contradicts a theorem of Euclidean geometry.

2. Use a model for hyperbolic geometry and draw a quadrilateral. How does it differ from a quadrilateral in Euclidean geometry?

3. Write a brief biographical sketch of the life of either Nicholas Lobachevsky, Janos Bolyais, or Karl Friedrich Gauss.

6-6 Distance

Objective: Recognize and use distance relationships between lines and between points and lines.

Given a line and a point *not* on the line, it is possible to draw another line through the point, perpendicular to the given line. In fact, there is only one such line.

Given a line and a point *not* on the line, there is exactly one line through the point that is perpendicular to the given line.	*Theorem 6-14*

The proof of Theorem 6-14 is examined in the Written Exercises.

Because there is only one perpendicular segment between a point and a line, it can be used to define the distance from a point to a line.

The distance between a point and a line is the length of the segment perpendicular to the line from the point. The measure of the distance between a line and a point on the line is zero.	*Definition of the Distance Between a Point and a Line*

Can you talk about the distance between two lines? If the two lines are parallel, the answer is yes.

In a plane, two lines are parallel if and only if they are everywhere equidistant.	*Theorem 6-15*

When weavers stretch yarn on a frame, they adjust the distance between strips of yarn both at the top and at the bottom of the frame. Then they know the strips of yarn are the same distance apart from top to bottom.

Equidistant means at the same distance.

Knowing two lines are parallel, we can define the distance by using any point of one line and the other line.

Remember, this distance is relative to perpendicular.

The distance between two parallel lines is the distance between one of the lines and any point on the other line.	***Definition of the Distance Between Parallel Lines***

Example

1 **Prove Theorem 6-15.**

Given: $\ell \parallel m$
Prove: $AC = DB$

A flow proof can be used to help students visualize the sequence of ideas.

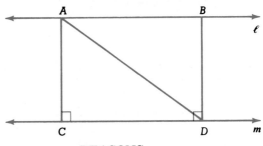

Proof:

STATEMENTS	REASONS
1. A and B lie on ℓ.	1. A line contains at least two points. (Postulate 1-3)
2. $\overline{AC} \perp m$ $\overline{BD} \perp m$	2. Given a line and a point *not* on a line, there is exactly one line through the point that is perpendicular to the given line. (Theorem 6-14)
3. $\ell \parallel m$	3. Given
4. $\overline{BD} \perp \ell$	4. In a plane, if a line is perpendicular to one of two parallel lines, then it is perpendicular to the other. (Theorem 6-13)
5. $\angle ACD$ is a right angle. $\angle DBA$ is a right angle.	5. Definition of Perpendicular Lines
6. Draw $\overline{AD}$.	6. Through any two points, there is exactly one line. (Postulate 1-1)
7. $\triangle ACD$ is a right triangle. $\triangle DBA$ is a right triangle.	7. Definition of Right Triangle
8. $\angle CDA \cong \angle BAD$	8. If two parallel lines are cut by a transversal, then each pair of alternate interior angles are congruent. (Theorem 6-10)
9. $\overline{AD} \cong \overline{AD}$	9. Congruence of segments is reflexive. (Theorem 2-2)
10. $\triangle ACD \cong \triangle DBA$	10. HA (Theorem 4-11)
11. $\overline{AC} \cong \overline{DB}$	11. Definition of Congruent Triangles *CPCTC*
12. $AC = DB$	12. Definition of Congruent Segments

Exploratory Exercises

ALL LEVELS: Mini Review

Use the theorem to answer each of the following. For Exercises 1–8, see the Teacher Guide.

> **Given a line and a point *not* on the line there is exactly one line through the point that is perpendicular to the given line.**

1. State the hypothesis of the theorem.

2. Draw and label a diagram to illustrate the hypothesis of the theorem.

3. State the given for a proof of the theorem.

4. State the conclusion of the theorem.

5. State the prove statement for a proof of the theorem.

6. The conclusion of the theorem contains the word exactly. Thus, the conclusion actually has two parts. State the two parts.

> **In a plane, two lines are parallel if and only if they are everywhere equidistant.**

7. Rewrite this theorem as two if-then statements.

8. Draw and label a diagram to illustrate both parts of this theorem.

Written Exercises

Use a protractor and the theorems from this chapter to determine whether the lines shown in color are parallel. Write *yes* or *no*. Explain your answer.

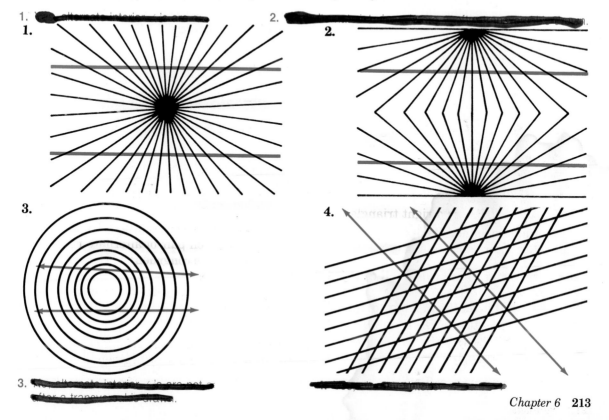

1.

2.

3.

4.

Use the following proof of Theorem 6-14 to answer the questions.

Theorem: Given a line and a point *not* on the line, there is exactly one line through the point that is perpendicular to the given line.

Given: ℓ and P *not* on ℓ

Prove: There is exactly one line through P that is perpendicular to ℓ.

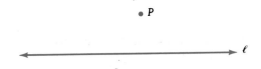

Proof:

Part 1: Prove there is at least one perpendicular.

Through P draw m so that $m \parallel \ell$. Then, through P draw $\overleftrightarrow{PQ}$ so that $\overleftrightarrow{PQ} \perp m$. Therefore, $\overleftrightarrow{PQ} \perp \ell$.

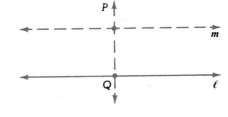

Part 2: Prove there is no more than one perpendicular.

Suppose there is more than one perpendicular. Call $\overleftrightarrow{PQ}$ and $\overleftrightarrow{PR}$ two different lines through P and perpendicular to ℓ.
Then, $\angle 1$ and $\angle 2$ are right angles. Thus, $\triangle PQR$ has two right angles.

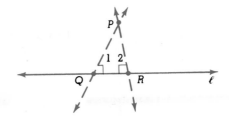

This is a contradiction, since Theorem 6-3 states that a right triangle has no more than one right angle. Therefore, there is no more than one line through P perpendicular to ℓ.

5. Determine whether **Part 1** is proven by direct or indirect reasoning.

6. State the postulate or theorem that justifies the **Part 1** statement, through P draw m so that $m \parallel \ell$.

7. State the postulate or theorem that justifies the **Part 1** statement, through P draw $\overleftrightarrow{PQ}$ so that $\overleftrightarrow{PQ} \perp m$.

8. State the postulate or theorem that justifies the **Part 1** statement, $\overleftrightarrow{PQ} \perp \ell$.

9. Determine whether **Part 2** is proven by direct or indirect reasoning.

10. State the assumption made in **Part 2** of the proof.

Use the theorem to answer each of the following.

If a point is on the bisector of an angle, then it is equidistant from the sides of the angle. For Exercises 11–18, see the Teacher Guide.

11. State the given for a proof of this theorem.

12. Draw and label a diagram to illustrate the hypothesis of the theorem.

13. Plan a proof of the theorem.

14. Write a formal proof for the theorem.

15. State the converse of the theorem.

16. Plan a proof for the converse of the theorem. Assume the point and the angle are coplanar.

17. Write a formal proof for the converse of the theorem.

18. Write an *if and only if* definition for the bisector of an angle, using "equidistant."

In the figure at the right, $\overline{PS} \perp \overline{SQ}$, $\overline{PQ} \perp \overline{QR}$, and $\overline{QR} \perp \overline{SR}$. Name the segment whose length represents the distance between the following points and lines.

19. P to $\overleftrightarrow{SQ}$

20. R to $\overleftrightarrow{PQ}$

21. S to $\overleftrightarrow{QR}$

22. Q to $\overleftrightarrow{SR}$

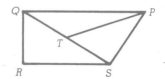

Application Exercises

23. What is the shortest route from Polyclinic Hospital to Central Avenue? Support your conclusion.

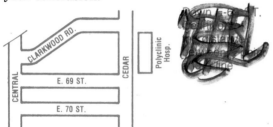

24. Roseanne is putting chair railing on her living room walls. In order for the chair railing to be parallel to the baseboards, she is measuring and marking 36 inches up from the baseboard at various intervals around the room. If she installs the chair railing at these markings, which theorem guarantees the chair railing will be parallel to the baseboard?

Challenge Exercises

Two planes, or a plane and a line, are parallel if and only if they do not intersect. Answer each question.

For Exercises 25–28, see the Teacher Guide.

25. If two lines lie in parallel planes, are the lines parallel? Write *yes* or *no*. Explain.

26. If a line is perpendicular to one of two parallel planes, is it perpendicular to the other? Write *yes* or *no*. Explain.

27. Explain how you would find the distance between two parallel planes.

28. Are parallel planes everywhere equidistant? Write *yes* or *no*. Explain.

mini-review

3-4 **1.** Find x if $\angle A$ and $\angle B$ are vertical angles, $m \angle A = 5x - 6$, and $m \angle B = 3x + 20$.

2-6 **2.** Apply the Comparison Property by writing three statements for any two numbers, x and y.

3-3 **3.** Show that the difference between the supplement and the complement of any angle is 90.

4-8 **4.** In $\triangle PQR$, $\overline{QS} \perp \overline{PR}$ and $\angle P \cong \angle R$. Name the postulate or theorem that supports the conclusion $\triangle PQS \cong \triangle RQS$.

2-5 **5.** True or false: If $\overline{PQ}$ is bisected at M, then $PM = 2MQ$.

Vocabulary

parallel lines (185)
skew lines (185)
transversal (186)
interior angles (186)
alternate interior angles (186)
exterior angles (186)

alternate exterior angles (186)
corresponding angles (186)
consecutive interior angles (186)
indirect reasoning (190)
equidistant (211)

Chapter Summary

1. There are three different ways that two lines can be positioned in space. They can be intersecting, parallel, or skew. (185)

2. Theorem 6-1: If two lines are cut by a transversal and one pair of alternate interior angles are congruent, then the other pair of alternate interior angles also are congruent. (187)

3. Theorem 6-2: If two lines are cut by a transversal and one pair of corresponding angles are congruent, then all pairs of corresponding angles are congruent. (187)

4. Theorem 6-3: If a triangle is a right triangle, then it has no more than one right angle. (191)

5. How to Write an Indirect Proof: (191)

   1. Make the assumption "*p* and *not q*."
   2. Show that the assumption leads to a contradiction.
   3. State that "*p* and *not q*" is false.
   4. Conclude that the statement to be proven is true.

6. Theorem 6-4: In a plane, if two lines are cut by a transversal so that a pair of alternate interior angles are congruent, then the two lines are parallel. (192)

7. Theorem 6-5: In a plane, if two lines are cut by a transversal so that a pair of corresponding angles are congruent, then the two lines are parallel. (195)

8. Theorem 6-6: In a plane, if two lines are cut by a transversal so that a pair of consecutive interior angles are supplementary, then the lines are parallel. (196)

9. Theorem 6-7: In a plane, if two lines are cut by a transversal so that a pair of alternate exterior angles are congruent, then the lines are parallel. (196)

10. Theorem 6-8: In a plane, if two lines are perpendicular to the same line, then the two lines are parallel. (196)

11. Parallel Postulate (Postulate 6-1): If there is a line and a point *not* on the line, then there is exactly one line through the point that is parallel to the given line. (201)

12. Theorem 6-9: If two parallel lines are cut by a transversal, then each pair of corresponding angles are congruent. (201)

13. Theorem 6-10: If two parallel lines are cut by a transversal, then each pair of alternate interior angles are congruent. (201)

14. Theorem 6-11: If two parallel lines are cut by a transversal, then each pair of consecutive interior angles are supplementary. (201)

15. Theorem 6-12: If two parallel lines are cut by a transversal, then each pair of alternate exterior angles are congruent. (201)

16. Theorem 6-13: In a plane, if a line is perpendicular to one of two parallel lines, then it is perpendicular to the other. (206)

17. Theorem 6-14: Given a line and a point *not* on the line, there is exactly one line through the point that is perpendicular to the given line. (211)

18. Definition of the Distance Between a Point and a Line: The distance between a point and a line is the length of the segment perpendicular to the line from the point. The measure of the distance between a line and a point on the line is zero. (211)

19. Theorem 6-15: In a plane, two lines are parallel if and only if they are everywhere equidistant. (211)

20. Definition of the Distance Between Parallel Lines: The distance between two parallel lines is the distance between one of the lines and any point on the other line. (212)

Chapter Review

6-1 **Using the diagram at the right, find an example for each of the following exercises.**

1. Two parallel lines
2. Two parallel rays
3. Two skew lines
4. Two noncoplanar lines
5. Two parallel lines and a transversal
6. Two coplanar lines that intersect

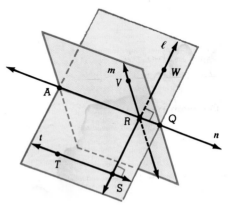

For Exercises 7–10, see the Teacher Guide.

6-2 **Prove each of the following exercises by indirect proof.**

7. A triangle has no more than one right angle.

8. If a plane and a line *not* in the plane intersect, then they intersect in no more than one point.

6-3   Use the figure to prove each of the following exercises.

   9. Given: *T* is the midpoint of $\overline{QS}$
      and $\overline{PR}$.
   Prove: $\overline{QP} \parallel \overline{RS}$

   10. Given: $\triangle QPT \cong \triangle SRT$
   Prove: $\overline{QR} \parallel \overline{PS}$

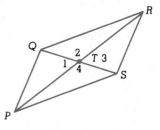

6-4   **11.** Complete the missing reasons for the following proof.

   Given: $\triangle PQR$
   Prove: $m \angle 5 + m \angle 4 + m \angle 3 = 180$

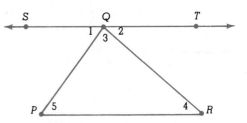

   Proof:

STATEMENTS	REASONS
1. Draw $\overleftrightarrow{ST}$ through Q and parallel to $\overleftrightarrow{PR}$.	1. ~~illegible~~
2. $m \angle 1 + m \angle PQT = 180$	2. The angles in a linear pair are supplementary. (Postulate 3-4)
3. $m \angle 2 + m \angle 3 = m \angle PQT$	3. ~~illegible~~
4. $m \angle 1 + m \angle 2 + m \angle 3$ $= 180$	4. ~~illegible~~
5. $\angle 2 \cong \angle 4$ $\angle 1 \cong \angle 5$	5. ~~illegible~~
6. $m \angle 2 = m \angle 4$ $m \angle 1 = m \angle 5$	6. ~~illegible~~
7. $m \angle 5 + m \angle 4 + m \angle 3$ $= 180$	7. Substitution (Postulate 2-9)

For Exercises 12–14, see the Teacher Guide.

6-5   Use the figure to prove the following exercise.

   12. Given: $\overline{DE} \parallel \overline{AC}$
      E is the midpoint of $\overline{BC}$.
      $\overline{EF} \cong \overline{BE}$
   Prove: D is the midpoint of $\overline{AB}$.

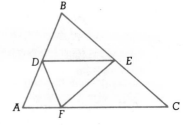

6-6   Prove each of the following exercises.

   13. In a plane, if two lines are everywhere equidistant, then the lines are parallel.

   14. If two lines are parallel, then they are everywhere equidistant.

Chapter Test

In the figure below, $n \parallel m$. Determine whether each of the following statements is *true* or *false*.

1. $\angle 6$ and $\angle 11$ are alternate interior angles. ~~true~~
2. $\angle 4$ and $\angle 7$ are supplementary angles. ~~~~
3. $\angle 6$ and $\angle 4$ are vertical angles. ~~~~
4. $\angle 5$ and $\angle 8$ are consecutive interior angles. ~~~~
5. $\angle 4$ and $\angle 9$ are corresponding angles. ~~~~
6. $\angle 10$ and $\angle 13$ are supplementary angles. ~~~~
7. $\angle 1$ and $\angle 6$ are vertical angles. ~~~~
8. $\angle 14$ and $\angle 7$ are alternate exterior angles. ~~~~
9. $\angle 6 \cong \angle 7$ ~~~~
10. $\angle 14 \cong \angle 3$ ~~~~
11. $\angle 1 \cong \angle 5$ ~~~~
12. $\angle 9 \cong \angle 8$ ~~~~
13. $m \angle 11 + m \angle 12 = 180$ ~~~~
14. $m \angle 2 + m \angle 3 = 180$ ~~~~
15. $m \angle 5 + m \angle 6 + m \angle 8 = 180$ ~~~~
16. $m \angle 8 + m \angle 5 + m \angle 11 = 180$ ~~~~
17. $m \angle 2 + m \angle 3 = m \angle 12$ ~~~~
18. $m \angle 5 + m \angle 6 = m \angle 7$ ~~~~

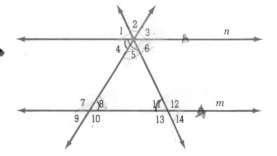

Using the figure at the right, find the measure of each of the following angles given $\overline{BC} \parallel \overline{FE}$.

19. $m \angle 1$ ~~~~   20. $m \angle E$ ~~~~
21. $m \angle 2$ ~~~~   22. $m \angle 3$ ~~~~
23. $m \angle 5$ ~~~~   24. $m \angle B$ ~~~~
25. $m \angle 4$ ~~~~   26. $m \angle 6$ ~~~~

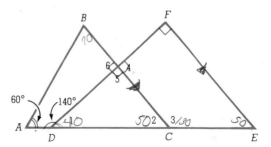

27. State the assumption and draw the appropriate figure to prove the following statement by indirect proof: If $\angle 1 \cong \angle 2$, then $m \parallel n$.

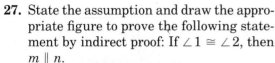

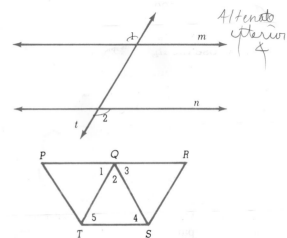

Alternate exterior ∠

Prove the following exercise using the figure at the right. See the Teacher Guide.

28. **Given:** $\triangle SQT$ is equilateral.
    $\overrightarrow{QS}$ bisects $\angle TQR$.
    Prove: $\overline{PR} \parallel \overline{TS}$

Complete each of the following statements.

1. Points have ~~zero~~ dimensions.

2. A line contains at least ~~two~~ point(s).

3. The inverse of a conditional statement is formed by ~~negating~~ both the hypothesis and the conclusion.

4. A number associated with a point on a number line is called the ~~coordinate~~ of the point.

5. To find the measure of the distance between two points on a number line, find the ~~absolute~~ value of the difference of their coordinates.

6. If a segment is given, then it has exactly ~~one~~ midpoint(s).

7. Two angles are _____ if and only if the sum of their degree measures is 180. ~~supplementary~~

8. A ~~right~~ angle is an angle whose degree measure is 90.

9. Two angles are ~~vertical~~ if and only if they are two nonadjacent angles formed by two intersecting lines.

10. An angle is ~~dihedral~~ if and only if it consists of two noncoplanar half planes with a common edge.

For Exercises 11–12, see the Teacher Guide.

Prove each of the following exercises.

11. **Given:** $\overline{DB} \perp \overline{AC}$
    B is the midpoint of $\overline{AC}$.
    Prove: $\overline{AD} \cong \overline{CD}$

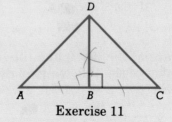

Exercise 11

12. **Given:** T is the midpoint of $\overline{SW}$.
    $\overline{SW} \perp \overline{RS}, \overline{SW} \perp \overline{WV}$
    Prove: $\triangle RST \cong \triangle VWT$

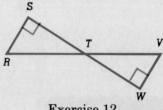

Exercise 12

Use the information given in the figure to find each of the following angle measures.

13. $m \angle 1$

14. $m \angle 5$

15. $m \angle 6$

16. $m \angle 4$

17. $m \angle 8$

18. $m \angle 7$

19. $m \angle 2$

20. $m \angle 3$

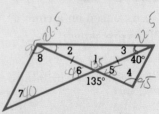

Exercises 13–20

Two sides of a triangle have measures 14 and 21 respectively. Determine whether each of the following lengths can be a measure for the third side.

21. 5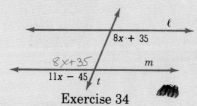

22. 18

23. 36

24. 31

25. 8

26. 20

For Exercises 27–33, see the Teacher Guide.

Using the diagram at the right, find an example for each of the following exercises.

27. Two parallel lines
28. Two parallel rays
29. Two skew lines
30. Two noncoplanar lines
31. Two parallel lines and a transversal

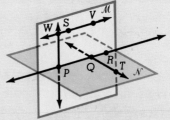

Exercises 27–31

Provide the given, prove, and figure for the following statements. Then, write the assumption that would be used to start an indirect proof.

32. If two angles are supplementary to two congruent angles, then the two angles are congruent to each other.

33. The acute angles of a right triangle are complementary.

34. In the figure below, $\ell \parallel m$. Find the value of x.

$8x + 35$

$8x + 35$

$11x - 45$

ℓ

m

t

Exercise 34

Prove the following exercise. See the Teacher Guide.

35. **Given:** $\triangle BGD \cong \triangle GDF$

    Prove: $\angle GCF$ and $\angle DFC$ are supplementary.

Exercise 35

Complete each of the following statements. 38. transversal

36. Reasoning based on a contradiction is called ~~indirect~~ reasoning.
37. Two lines are skew if and only if they do not intersect and ~~are noncoplanar~~.
38. In a plane, a line is a _____ if and only if it intersects two other lines in two different points.
39. Alternate interior angles are ~~congruent~~ if they are formed by two parallel lines and a transversal.
40. The Parallel Postulate states "if there is a line and a point *not* on the line, then there is ~~exactly~~ ~~one~~ line through the point that is parallel to the given line."

Polygons

The honeycomb shape of a beehive is a common example of a six-sided figure found in nature. But this six-sided figure also occurs in the molecular structure of organic compounds. Benzene is an extremely important organic compound. Benzene rings can join to form thousands of different compounds such as dyes, paints, perfumes, plastics, and adhesives that are used daily.

7-1 Classifying Polygons

Objectives: Recognize polygons; name polygons by sides and by angles; classify polygons as convex, concave, regular, or not regular.

The molecular structure represented at the right is benzene, C_6H_6. The benzene molecule or ring consists of six carbon atoms arranged in a flat, six-sided shape with a hydrogen atom attached to each carbon atom. The symbol for benzene is . The figure represents the shape in which the atoms are bonded together.

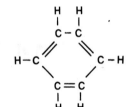

In geometry, a **polygon** can be formed by connecting a series of points. Each of the following shapes is a polygon.

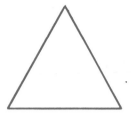 

The term polygon is derived from a Greek word meaning "many-angled."

A figure is a polygon if and only if it meets each of the following conditions.
1. It is formed by three or more coplanar segments called sides.
2. Sides that have a common endpoint are noncollinear.
3. Each side intersects exactly two other sides, but only at their endpoints.

Definition of Polygon

If a figure fails to meet one or more of the above conditions, then it is *not* a polygon. For example, the figure at the right is *not* a polygon. It fails to meet condition 2 because $\overline{AB}$ and $\overline{BD}$ have a common endpoint and are collinear. The figure also fails to meet condition 3 because $\overline{AB}$ intersects $\overline{BC}$, $\overline{BE}$, and $\overline{BD}$.

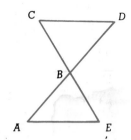

The endpoints of the sides of a polygon are the **vertices**. The vertices of the polygon at the right are A, B, C, D, E, and F. When referring to a polygon, the vertices are listed in consecutive order. For example, the polygon at the right can be referred to as *polygon ABCDEF*.

The sides of polygon $ABCDEF$ are $\overline{AB}$, $\overline{BC}$, $\overline{CD}$, $\overline{DE}$, $\overline{EF}$, and $\overline{FA}$. Two consecutive sides are $\overline{DE}$ and $\overline{EF}$.

Name two consecutive angles.

Polygons may be classified by the number of sides. The chart at the right gives some common names for polygons. In general, a polygon with n sides is called an **n-gon.** Thus, an octagon can also be called an 8-gon. A polygon with 13 sides is called a 13-gon.

Number of Sides	Polygon
3	triangle
4	quadrilateral
5	pentagon
6	hexagon
7	heptagon
8	octagon
9	nonagon
10	decagon
12	dodecagon

Have students draw diagonals in a concave polygon and note that some diagonals will lie in the exterior.

Polygons may also be classified as **convex** or **concave.** A polygon is convex if and only if any line containing a side of the polygon does *not* contain a point in the interior of the polygon. A polygon is concave if and only if it is *not* a convex polygon.

Another word for concave is nonconvex.

The line containing $\overline{QT}$ contains interior points of quadrilateral QRST.

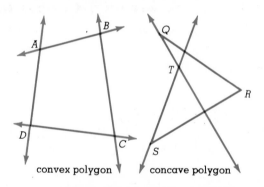

convex polygon   concave polygon

A polygon is regular if and only if it is a convex polygon with all sides congruent and all angles congruent.

Definition of Regular Polygon

For a convex polygon to be a regular polygon, it must be *both* equilateral *and* equiangular. A polygon meeting one of these conditions but *not* the other is not a regular polygon.

Note that concave polygons cannot be regular by the second condition.

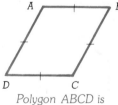

Polygon ABCD is equilateral but not equiangular. It is not regular.

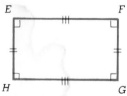

Polygon EFGH is equiangular but not equilateral. It is not regular.

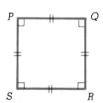

Polygon PQRS is equiangular and equilateral. It is regular.

1 Classify the following polygons by the number of sides, as convex or concave, and as regular or *not* regular.

Remind students that all regular polygons are convex.

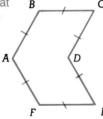

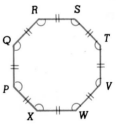

Polygon *ABCDEF* has 6 sides. It is a hexagon.

If $\overline{CD}$ is extended through *D*, it passes through the interior of the hexagon. Thus, the polygon is concave.

Since it is concave, it is *not* regular even though all its sides are congruent.

Polygon *PQRSTVWX* has 8 sides. It is an octagon.

No side of the octagon can be extended to pass through the interior. Thus, the polygon is convex.

Since all sides are congruent and all angles are congruent, it is regular.

EN: 1–9, 2–28 even; **AV:** 1–9, 1–28; **FD:** 1–9, 1–24

Exploratory Exercises

Determine whether each of the following figures is a polygon.

1.

2.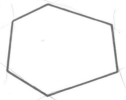

3.

4.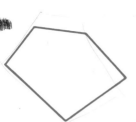

5.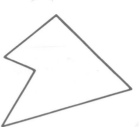

6.

7.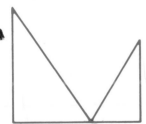

8.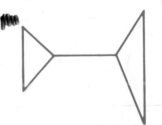

9.

Written Exercises

Classify each of the following polygons by the given number of sides.

1. 3  2. 8 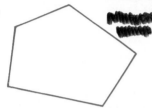 3. 10 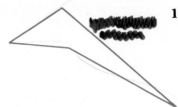 4. 4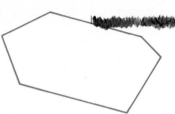

5. 24 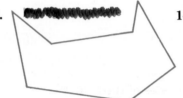 6. 6 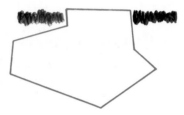 7. n 8. x

Classify each of the following polygons by the number of sides. Then classify each polygon as *convex* or *concave*.

9.   10.   11.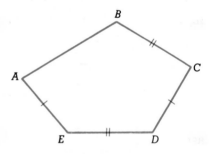

12. 13. 14.

For Exercises 15–28, see the Teacher Guide.

Use polygon *ABCDE* to complete each exercise.

15. Name the vertices of the polygon.
16. Name the angles of the polygon.
17. Name the sides of the polygon.
18. Classify the polygon by the number of sides.
19. Classify the polygon as convex or concave.
20. Classify the polygon as regular or not regular.
21. Name a pair of consecutive angles of the polygon.
22. Name a pair of consecutive sides of the polygon.

Exercises 15 – 22

Give an if and only if definition for each of the following exercises.

23. a pair of consecutive angles of a polygon   24. a pair of consecutive sides of a polygon

Classify each figure as *regular* or *not regular*. Then explain your answer.

25. 26. 27. 28.

7-2 Angles of Polygons

Objectives: Find the sum of the degree measures of a polygon; find the degree measure of one angle of a regular polygon; find the degree measure of each interior and exterior angle of a regular polygon; use problem-solving procedures.

Recall that the sum of the degree measures of the angles of a triangle is 180. Is there a fixed sum for the degree measures of the angles of a convex quadrilateral or convex pentagon? Consider the following argument.

A segment joining two nonconsecutive vertices of a convex polygon is called a **diagonal** of the polygon. In each of the following polygons, all possible diagonals from one vertex are shown.

quadrilateral   pentagon   hexagon

Notice that in each case, the polygon is separated into triangles. The sum of the measures of the angles of each polygon can be found by adding the measures of the angles of the triangles.

Polygon	Number of Sides	Number of Triangles	Sum of Degree Measures of Angles
triangle	3	1	$(1 \cdot 180)$ or 180
quadrilateral	4	2	$(2 \cdot 180)$ or 360
pentagon	5	3	$(3 \cdot 180)$ or 540
hexagon	6	4	$(4 \cdot 180)$ or 720
heptagon	7	5	$(5 \cdot 180)$ or 900
octagon	8	6	$(6 \cdot 180)$ or 1080
nonagon	9	7	$(7 \cdot 180)$ or 1260
decagon	10	8	$(8 \cdot 180)$ or 1440
.	.	.	.
.	.	.	.
.	.	.	.
n-gon	n	$n - 2$	$(n - 2)180$

These and many other examples suggest the following theorem.
This theorem can be proved by induction.

If a convex polygon has n sides, and S is the sum of the degree measures of its angles, then $S = (n - 2)180$.	*Theorem 7-1*

Remind students that $n \geq 3$.

1 **Find the sum of the degree measures of the angles of a hexagon.**

$$S = (n - 2)180$$
$$= (6 - 2)180 \quad \textit{A hexagon has 6 sides.}$$
$$= 4 \cdot 180$$
$$= 720$$

Recall that an **exterior angle** of a triangle forms a linear pair with one of the interior angles of the triangle. In the figure at the right, $\angle 4$ is an exterior angle of $\triangle ABC$.

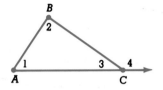

Similarly, in the hexagon at the right, the sides are extended to form one exterior angle at each vertex. At each vertex, the interior angle of the hexagon and the exterior angle form a linear pair. Altogether, there are six linear pairs. Using this relationship it is possible to determine the sum of the degree measures of the exterior angles.

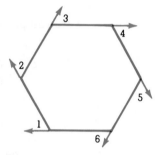

sum of measures of exterior angles	=	sum of measures of linear pairs	−	sum of measures of interior angles
	=	$6 \cdot 180$	−	$(6 - 2)180$
	=	1080	−	720
	=	360		

The sum of the degree measures of the exterior angles of a hexagon is 360. What sum would you find for an *n*-gon?

sum of measures of exterior angles	=	sum of measures of linear pairs	−	sum of measures of interior angles
	=	$n \cdot 180$	−	$(n - 2)180$
	=	$n \cdot 180$	−	$n \cdot 180 + 360$
	=	360		

This relationship is summarized in the following theorem.

> **If a polygon is convex, then the sum of the degree measures of the exterior angles, one at each vertex, is 360.** *Theorem 7-2*

Many complex geometric problems can be solved by using equations. A four-step plan for problem solving is presented below.

<table>
<tr><td>

1. **Explore the problem.**
2. **Plan the solution.**
3. **Solve the problem.**
4. **Examine the solution.**

</td><td>

Problem-Solving Plan

</td></tr>
</table>

Example

2 **The degree measure of one interior angle of a regular polygon is 140. Find the number of sides.**

Explore Explore the problem carefully and define a variable.

Let n = the number of sides.
$(n - 2) \cdot 180$ = the sum of the degree measures of the interior angles.

Plan A polygon has the same number of angles as it has sides. Since a regular polygon is equiangular, each of its interior angles has the same degree measure. Therefore, the following equation can be used to find the number of sides.

$$\text{degree measure of one interior angle} = \frac{\text{sum of degree measures of interior angles}}{\text{number of angles}}$$

Solve

$$140 = \frac{(n - 2)180}{n}$$

$140n = (n - 2)180$	*Multiply by n.*
$140n = 180n - 360$	*Distributive Property*
$-40n = -360$	*Subtract 180n from both sides.*
$n = 9$	*Divide by −40.*

Examine

$$140 = \frac{(n - 2)180}{n} \qquad \textit{Check your solution.}$$

$$140 \overset{?}{=} \frac{(9 - 2)180}{9}$$

$$140 \overset{?}{=} \frac{1260}{9}$$

$$140 = 140 \qquad \textit{The solution checks.}$$

Therefore, the polygon has 9 sides.

Exploratory Exercises
ALL LEVELS: Algebra Review

For each of the following convex polygons, find the number of diagonals that can be drawn from one vertex. Then, find the number of triangles formed by these diagonals.

1. triangle
2. quadrilateral
3. pentagon
4. hexagon
5. heptagon
6. octagon
7. nonagon
8. decagon
9. 15-gon
10. n-gon

11. Give an if and only if definition for an exterior angle of a convex polygon.
See the Teacher Guide.

Written Exercises

Find the sum of the degree measures of the angles of a convex polygon for each number of sides given.

1. 17
2. 20
3. 12
4. 13
5. 59
6. 15
7. x
8. t

For each of the following, the degree measure of one angle of a regular polygon is given. Find the number of sides.

9. 150
10. 160
11. 120
12. 60
13. 165
14. 156
15. 144
16. 179

For each of the following, the number of sides of a regular polygon is given. Find the degree measure of each interior angle and each exterior angle.

17. 4
18. 5
19. 8
20. 10
21. 7
22. 20
23. d
24. x

Solve each problem.

25. The sum of the degree measures of the angles of a convex polygon is 3240. Find the number of sides.

26. The sum of the degree measures of the angles of a convex polygon is 1260. Find the number of sides.

27. The degree measure of one exterior angle of a regular polygon is 30. Find the number of sides.

28. The degree measure of one exterior angle of a regular polygon is 45. Find the number of sides.

29. Explain why the sum of the degree measures of the angles of a convex polygon cannot be less than 180.

30. Two angles of a convex hexagon are congruent. Each of the other angles has a degree measure twice that of each of the first two angles. Find the degree measure of each angle.

31. Two angles of a convex quadrilateral are congruent. Each of the other two angles has a degree measure three times that of each of the first two angles. Find the degree measure of each angle.

32. Explain why the sum of the degree measures of the angles of a convex polygon cannot be 2070.
But the number of sides of a polygon must be a natural number.

Complete the following chart for each convex polygon and then use the results to answer Exercises 39–42.

	Polygon	Number of vertices	Number of diagonals from each vertex	Total number of diagonals
33.	quadrilateral			
34.	pentagon			
35.	hexagon			
36.	heptagon			
37.	octagon			
38.	nonagon			

39. Find the total number of diagonals in a convex decagon.

40. Find the total number of diagonals in a convex 15-gon.

41. Write an expression for the number of diagonals from each vertex in a convex n-gon.

42. Write an expression for the total number of diagonals in a convex n-gon.

Each of the following figures was formed by extending the sides of a regular polygon. Find the degree measure of the angles formed at each labeled vertex.

43.

44.

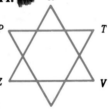

45.

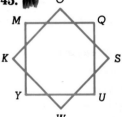

Write an algebraic proof for each of the following exercises. See the Teacher Guide.

46. The sum of the degree measures of a regular pentagon is 540.

47. The sum of the degree measures of the exterior angles, one at each vertex, of a convex quadrilateral is 360.

48. The sum of the degree measures of the exterior angles, one at each vertex, of a convex n-gon is 360.

49. The sum of the degree measures of the exterior angles, two at each vertex, of a convex n-gon is 720.

Challenge Exercises

50. Find the number of sides of a polygon if the sum of the degree measures of all interior angles except one is 2550.

51. What is the maximum number of sides of a convex polygon if exactly four of the interior angles are obtuse?

Algebra Review

Solve.

1. $\frac{x}{5} + 2 = 7$
2. $\frac{d - 10}{6} = 14$
3. $\frac{4 + d}{10} = 16$
4. $\frac{3d + 2}{6} = 14$
5. $8(x - 2) = 16$

Additional practice in solving equations can be found on page 559 of the Diagnostic Skills Review.

Chapter 7   231

A **tessellation,** or tiling, is a complete covering of the plane by polygons without gaps or overlapping. You have probably seen many examples of tessellations in floor coverings, wallpaper patterns, and fabric designs.

A tessellation is a *regular* tessellation if it is formed by congruent regular polygons. Only three regular polygons form regular tessellations.

  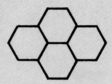

Notice that the degree measure of an interior angle of a regular hexagon, square, and triangle is 120, 90, and 60, respectively. Each of these measures is a factor of 360.

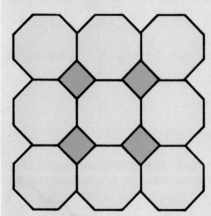

More interesting tessellations occur when there is a combination of two or more regular polygons. Some of these tessellations are called *semiregular* tessellations. The tessellation shown at the left uses a square and a regular octagon. This would be named 4-8-8 for the number of sides of each polygon that meet at the vertex point. There are only eight semiregular tessellations.

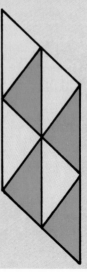

Exercises See the Teacher Guide.

1. Name the eight semiregular tessellations.

2. Polygons that are not regular also tessellate. The figure at the right shows a tessellation of obtuse triangles. Explain why any triangle will tessellate a plane.

3. Explain why any quadrilateral will tessellate a plane.

4. Design your own tessellation. See students' work.

7-3 Parallelograms

Objective: Recognize and use properties of parallelograms.

When a carpenter builds a stair rail, it is important that the spindles are parallel. It is also important that the top railing is parallel to the base of the stairs. The quadrilateral formed is called a **parallelogram.**

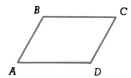

The figure is called *parallelogram ABCD* and written □*ABCD*.

A quadrilateral is a parallelogram if and only if both pairs of opposite sides are parallel.	*Definition of Parallelogram*

The following theorem states an important characteristic of all parallelograms.

If a quadrilateral is a parallelogram, then a diagonal separates it into two congruent triangles.	*Theorem 7-3*

Example

1 **Prove Theorem 7-3.**

Given: □*ABCD* with diagonal $\overline{BD}$

Prove: $\triangle ABD \cong \triangle CDB$

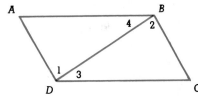

Proof:

STATEMENTS	REASONS
1. □*ABCD* with diagonal $\overline{BD}$	1. Given
2. $\overline{AB} \parallel \overline{DC}$ $\overline{AD} \parallel \overline{BC}$	2. Definition of Parallelogram
3. $\angle 1 \cong \angle 2$ $\angle 3 \cong \angle 4$	3. If two parallel lines are cut by a transversal, then each pair of alternate interior angles is congruent. (Theorem 6-10)
4. $\overline{BD} \cong \overline{BD}$	4. Congruence of line segments is reflexive. (Theorem 2-2)
5. $\triangle ABD \cong \triangle CDB$	5. ASA (Postulate 4-3)

In the parallelogram at the right, $\angle R$ and $\angle T$ are **opposite angles.** Name another pair of opposite angles. $\angle Q$ and $\angle S$

One pair of **opposite sides** is $\overline{RS}$ and $\overline{QT}$. Name another pair of opposite sides. RQ and ST

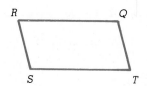

Students will prove Theorems 7-4 and 7-5 in Written Exercises 15–16.

If a quadrilateral is a parallelogram, then its opposite angles are congruent.	*Theorem 7-4*
If a quadrilateral is a parallelogram, then its opposite sides are congruent.	*Theorem 7-5*

The diagonals of a parallelogram intersect and four triangles are formed. Notice that $\triangle ABE$ and $\triangle CDE$ appear to be congruent. Also, $\triangle AED$ and $\triangle CEB$ appear to be congruent. The proof of the following theorem is based on these pairs of triangles.

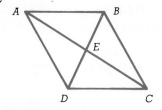

If a quadrilateral is a parallelogram, then its diagonals bisect each other.	*Theorem 7-6*

Example

2 **Prove Theorem 7-6.**

Given: $\square EFGH$ with diagonals $\overline{EG}$ and $\overline{FH}$
Prove: $\overline{ED} \cong \overline{GD}$
$\overline{DH} \cong \overline{DF}$

Proof:

STATEMENTS	REASONS
1. $\square EFGH$ with diagonals $\overline{EG}$ and $\overline{FH}$	1. Given
2. $\overline{FG} \cong \overline{HE}$	2. If a quadrilateral is a parallelogram, then its opposite sides are congruent. (Theorem 7-5)
3. $\overline{FG} \parallel \overline{EH}$	3. Definition of Parallelogram
4. $\angle 1 \cong \angle 3$ $\angle 2 \cong \angle 4$	4. If two parallel lines are cut by a transversal, then each pair of alternate interior angles is congruent. (Theorem 6-10)
5. $\triangle EDH \cong \triangle GDF$	5. ASA (Postulate 4-3)
6. $\overline{ED} \cong \overline{GD}$ $\overline{DH} \cong \overline{DF}$	6. Definition of Congruent Triangles *CPCTC*

Exploratory Exercises

Determine whether each of the following statements must be true about the parallelogram at the right. State *yes* or *no*.

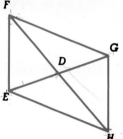

1. $\overline{FE} \parallel \overline{GH}$

2. $\angle FGH \cong \angle FEH$

3. $\angle FDE \cong \angle GDH$

4. $\overline{EH} \parallel \overline{FG}$

5. $\overline{GH} \cong \overline{FE}$

6. $\overline{FD} \cong \overline{DG}$

7. $\overline{FD} \cong \overline{DE}$

8. $\overline{FD} \cong \overline{HD}$

9. D is the midpoint of $\overline{EG}$.

10. D is the midpoint of $\overline{FH}$.

11. $\triangle FDE \cong \triangle HDG$

12. $\triangle FHE \cong \triangle GHE$

Complete each statement about the parallelogram at the right. Then name the theorem or definition that justifies your answer.

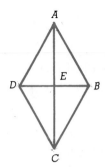

13. $\overline{AB} \parallel$ _____

14. $\overline{DA} \cong$ _____

15. $\triangle ADC \cong$ _____

16. $\angle CDA \cong$ _____

17. $\overline{DE} \cong$ _____

18. $\angle BAC \cong$ _____

Written Exercises

For each of the following exercises, use the parallelogram at the right and the given information to find the value of x.

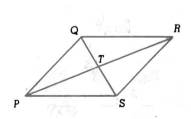

1. $QR = 16$
   $PS = x$

2. $PT = 7$
   $PR = x$

3. $QS = 2.4$
   $TQ = x$

4. $RS = 3.9$
   $PQ = x$

5. $RQ = 4x + 9$
   $PS = 7x - 6$

6. $QP = 2x + 5$
   $SR = 3x$

7. $TR = 3x - 10$
   $PR = 28$

8. $QS = 2x + 7$
   $TS = 5x - 8$

For each of the following exercises, use the parallelogram at the right and the given information to find the value of x.

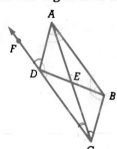

9. $m \angle AEB = 2x$
   $m \angle AED = x$

10. $m \angle BDC = x$
    $m \angle ADB = x + 40$
    $m \angle ABC = 110$

11. $m \angle BAE = x$
    $m \angle EAD = x + 20$
    $m \angle BAD = 70$

12. $m \angle BCE = 45$
    $m \angle ECD = 25$
    $m \angle ADF = x$

13. In $\square ABCD$, $AB = 2x + 5$, $CD = y + 1$, $AD = y + 5$, and $BC = 3x - 4$. Find the lengths of the sides.

14. In $\square ABCD$, $m \angle C = x + 75$ and $m \angle D = 3x - 199$. Find the degree measures of the angles.

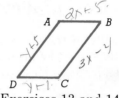
Exercises 13 and 14

For Exercises 15–21, see the Teacher Guide.
Complete a proof for each exercise.

15. If a quadrilateral is a parallelogram, then its opposite angles are congruent. (Theorem 7-4)

16. If a quadrilateral is a parallelogram, then its opposite sides are congruent. (Theorem 7-5)

Exercise 17

17. Given: $\square HIJK$
   Prove: $\angle HKJ$ is supplementary to $\angle IJK$.
   Hint: Extend $\overline{KJ}$.

18. Given: $\square ABCD$
   $\overline{DE} \perp \overline{AC}$
   $\overline{BF} \perp \overline{AC}$
   Prove: $\overline{DE} \parallel \overline{BF}$

19. Given: $\square ABCD$
   $\overline{DE} \perp \overline{AC}$
   $\overline{BF} \perp \overline{AC}$
   Prove: $\overline{DE} \cong \overline{BF}$

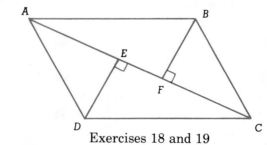
Exercises 18 and 19

Challenge Exercises

20. Given: $\square PQST$
   $\overline{RP}$ bisects $\angle QPT$.
   $\overline{VS}$ bisects $\angle QST$.
   Prove: $\overline{RP} \parallel \overline{VS}$

21. Given: $\square PQST$
   $\overline{RP}$ bisects $\angle QPT$.
   $\overline{VS}$ bisects $\angle QST$.
   Prove: $\overline{RP} \cong \overline{VS}$

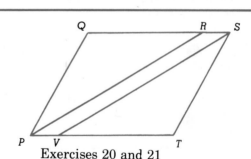
Exercises 20 and 21

7-4 Tests for Parallelograms

Rita Lopez designed the stained glass piece shown at the right. She needed to be sure that the pattern used for cutting the pieces of glass was in the shape of a parallelogram.

There are several tests to determine if a polygon is a parallelogram. Rita most likely used the following test.

If both pairs of opposite sides of a quadrilateral are congruent, then the quadrilateral is a parallelogram.	*Theorem 7-7*

Example

1 **Prove Theorem 7-7.**

Given: $\overline{AB} \cong \overline{CD}$
$\overline{AD} \cong \overline{CB}$

Prove: Quadrilateral $ABCD$ is a parallelogram.

Show that opposite sides are parallel.

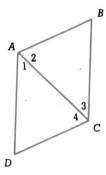

Proof:

STATEMENTS	REASONS
1. $\overline{AB} \cong \overline{CD}$ $\quad \overline{AD} \cong \overline{CB}$	1. Given
2. $\overline{AC} \cong \overline{AC}$	2. Congruence of line segments is reflexive. (Theorem 2-2)
3. $\triangle ABC \cong \triangle CDA$	3. SSS (Postulate 4-1)
4. $\angle 2 \cong \angle 4$ $\quad \angle 1 \cong \angle 3$	4. Definition of Congruent Triangles *CPCTC*
5. $\overline{AB} \parallel \overline{DC}$ $\quad \overline{AD} \parallel \overline{BC}$	5. In a plane, if two lines are cut by a transversal so that a pair of alternate interior angles are congruent, then the lines are parallel. (Theorem 6-4)
6. Quadrilateral $ABCD$ is a parallelogram.	6. Definition of Parallelogram

The proofs of Theorem 7-7 and Theorem 7-8 are very similar. They both use the triangles formed by the diagonals and sides of a given quadrilateral.

Students will prove Theorem 7-8 in Written Exercise 7.

If two sides of a quadrilateral are parallel and congruent, then the quadrilateral is a parallelogram.	*Theorem 7-8*

The following theorem is the converse of Theorem 7-6.

If the diagonals of a quadrilateral bisect each other, then the quadrilateral is a parallelogram.	*Theorem 7-9*

Example

2 **Prove Theorem 7-9.**

> **Given:** $\overline{BD}$ bisects $\overline{AC}$.
> $\overline{AC}$ bisects $\overline{BD}$.
>
> **Prove:** Quadrilateral $ABCD$ is a parallelogram.

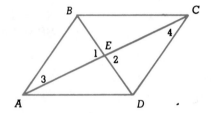

Proof:

STATEMENTS	REASONS
1. $\overline{BD}$ bisects $\overline{AC}$. $\overline{AC}$ bisects $\overline{BD}$.	1. Given
2. $\overline{AE} \cong \overline{CE}$ $\overline{BE} \cong \overline{DE}$	2. Bisector Theorem (Theorem 2-6)
3. $\angle 1 \cong \angle 2$	3. If two angles are vertical, then they are congruent. (Theorem 3-10)
4. $\triangle BEA \cong \triangle DEC$	4. SAS (Postulate 4-2)
5. $\angle 3 \cong \angle 4$ $\overline{AB} \cong \overline{CD}$	5. Definition of Congruent Triangles *CPCTC*
6. $\overline{AB} \parallel \overline{CD}$	6. In a plane, if two lines are cut by a transversal so that a pair of alternate interior angles are congruent, then the lines are parallel. (Theorem 6-4)
7. Quadrilateral $ABCD$ is a parallelogram.	7. If two sides of a quadrilateral are parallel and congruent, then the quadrilateral is a parallelogram. (Theorem 7-8)

Exploratory Exercises

Determine whether each of the following tests could be used to prove that a quadrilateral is a parallelogram. State *yes* or *no*.

1. Pairs of opposite sides are parallel.
2. Pairs of opposite sides are congruent.
3. The quadrilateral is regular.
4. Pairs of consecutive sides are congruent.
5. Pairs of consecutive angles are congruent.
6. Pairs of opposite angles are congruent.

For explanations of Exercises 7–16, see the Teacher Guide.

For each of the following given set of conditions, determine whether the quadrilateral must be a parallelogram. State *yes* or *no*. Then explain.

7. $\overline{RQ} \cong \overline{SP}$
   $\angle 2 \cong \angle 6$

8. $\angle 2 \cong \angle 3$
   $\overline{QR} \cong \overline{PS}$

9. $QT = 5$
   $RT = 9$
   $PT = 5$
   $ST = 5$

10. $m \angle 1 = 60$
    $m \angle 2 = 70$
    $m \angle 5 = 60$
    $m \angle 6 = 70$

11. $m \angle PQR = 71$
    $m \angle QPS = 109$
    $\angle PQR \cong \angle RSP$

12. $QR = 8$
    $PQ = 8$
    $RS = 4$
    $SP = 4$

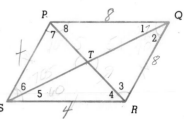

Exercises 7–12

13. E is the midpoint of $\overline{BD}$.
    E is the midpoint of $\overline{AC}$.

14. $\overline{AB} \cong \overline{BC}$
    $\overline{CD} \cong \overline{AD}$

15. $\triangle ABC \cong \triangle CDA$

16. $\triangle ABE \cong \triangle CDE$

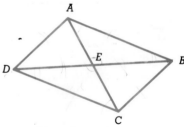

Exercises 13–16

Written Exercises

The figure at the right is a parallelogram. Use this figure and the information given to complete each exercise.

1. $AB = 6$, $BC = 9$, and $m \angle ABC = 80$. Find CD.
2. $m \angle ABC = 115$. Find $m \angle DAB$.
3. $AC = 5x - 12$ and $AT = 14$. Find x.
4. $BC = 4x + 7$ and $AD = 8x - 5$. Find x.
5. $m \angle C = 3x + 14$ and $m \angle D = x + 10$. Find $m \angle D$.
6. $BT = 3x + 1$ and $BD = 4x + 8$. Find x.

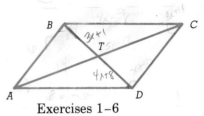

Exercises 1–6

For Exercises 7–8, see the Teacher Guide.

Complete a proof for each of the following exercises.

7. If two sides of a quadrilateral are parallel and congruent, then the quadrilateral is a parallelogram. (Theorem 7-8)

8. If both pairs of opposite angles of a quadrilateral are congruent, then the quadrilateral is a parallelogram.

Complete a proof for each of the following exercises. See the Teacher Guide.

9. If one pair of opposite angles of a quadrilateral is congruent and one pair of opposite sides is parallel, then the quadrilateral is a parallelogram.

10. If quadrilateral $EFGH$ has $\angle FGH \cong \angle HEF$ and $\overline{FG} \cong \overline{GH} \cong \overline{HE}$, then the quadrilateral is a parallelogram.

11. **Given:** $\overline{AE} \cong \overline{CE}$
    $\angle ECD \cong \angle EAB$
    Prove: Quadrilateral $ABCD$ is a parallelogram.

12. **Given:** $\overline{BA} \parallel \overline{CD}$
    $\angle DBC \cong \angle ADB$
    Prove: Quadrilateral $ABCD$ is a parallelogram.

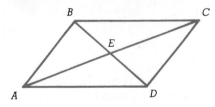

Exercises 11 and 12

13. **Given:** $\triangle PQR \cong \triangle STV$
    $\overline{PR} \parallel \overline{VS}$
    Prove: Quadrilateral $PRSV$ is a parallelogram.

14. **Given:** $\square PQST$
    $\overline{QR} \cong \overline{TV}$
    Prove: Quadrilateral $PRSV$ is a parallelogram.

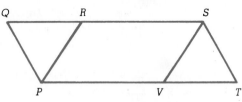

Exercises 13 and 14

15. **Given:** $\overline{AF} \cong \overline{CF}$
    $\overline{BE} \cong \overline{GD}$
    F is the midpoint of $\overline{EG}$.
    Prove: Quadrilateral $ABCD$ is a parallelogram.

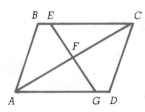

Exercise 15

16. **Given:** $\overline{FB} \perp \overline{AC}$
    $\overline{FD} \perp \overline{CE}$
    $\overline{FB} \perp \overline{FD}$
    Prove: Quadrilateral $FBCD$ is a parallelogram.

17. **Given:** $\angle ABF \cong \angle EDF$
    $\overline{FD} \parallel \overline{AC}$
    Prove: Quadrilateral $FBCD$ is a parallelogram.

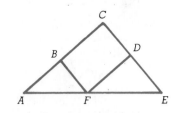

Exercises 16 and 17

18. **Given:** $\square ACEF$
    $\angle G \cong \angle F$
    $\overline{BG} \parallel \overline{CD}$
    Prove: Quadrilateral $BCDG$ is a parallelogram.

19. **Given:** $\square BCDG$
    $\angle E \cong \angle A$
    $\overline{CE} \parallel \overline{AF}$
    Prove: Quadrilateral $ACEF$ is a parallelogram.

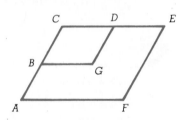

Exercises 18 and 19

7-5 Special Parallelograms

Bob Medved is building a deck in the shape of a rectangle. He needs to be sure that the support posts are set at the vertices of a rectangle.

There are several tests to determine if a parallelogram is a **rectangle**. Bob most likely measures to be sure that opposite sides are congruent. He then measures to be sure that the diagonals are congruent.

Students will prove that these conditions guarantee a rectangle in Written Exercise 36.

A quadrilateral is a rectangle if and only if it is a parallelogram with four right angles.	*Definition of Rectangle*

Since a rectangle is a parallelogram, it has all of the properties of a parallelogram. In addition, the diagonals of a rectangle are congruent.

If a quadrilateral is a rectangle, then its diagonals are congruent.	*Theorem 7-10*

Example

1 **Prove Theorem 7-10.**

Given: Rectangle $ABCD$ with diagonals $\overline{AC}$ and $\overline{BD}$

Prove: $\overline{AC} \cong \overline{BD}$

It may be helpful to redraw the figure, separating the overlapping triangles.

Proof:

STATEMENTS	REASONS
1. Rectangle $ABCD$ with diagonals $\overline{AC}$ and $\overline{BD}$	1. Given
2. $\overline{AB} \cong \overline{CD}$	2. If a quadrilateral is a parallelogram, then its opposite sides are congruent. (Theorem 7-5)
3. $\angle BAD$ and $\angle CDA$ are right angles.	3. Definition of Rectangle
4. $\angle BAD \cong \angle CDA$	4. If two angles are right angles, then the angles are congruent. (Theorem 3-6)
5. $\overline{AD} \cong \overline{AD}$	5. Congruence of line segments is reflexive. (Theorem 2-2)

6. $\triangle BAD$ and $\triangle CDA$ are right triangles.	6. Definition of Right Triangle
7. $\triangle BAD \cong \triangle CDA$	7. LL (Theorem 4-12)
8. $\overline{BD} \cong \overline{CA}$	8. Definition of Congruent Triangles *CPCTC*

A quadrilateral is a rhombus if and only if it is a parallelogram with all four sides congruent.	*Definition of Rhombus*

The plural forms of rhombus are "rhombuses" and "rhombi."

The diagonals of a **rhombus** not only bisect each other, but also bisect opposite angles of the rhombus. This property can be proven by showing pairs of triangles congruent.

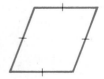

If a quadrilateral is a rhombus, then each diagonal bisects a pair of opposite angles.	*Theorem 7-11*

Example

2 **Prove Theorem 7-11.**

Given: Rhombus $QRST$ with diagonals $\overline{RT}$ and $\overline{QS}$

Prove: $\overline{QS}$ bisects $\angle RQT$ and $\angle RST$.
$\overline{RT}$ bisects $\angle QRS$ and $\angle STQ$.

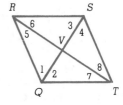

Proof:

STATEMENTS	REASONS
1. Rhombus $QRST$ with diagonals $\overline{RT}$ and $\overline{QS}$	1. Given
2. $\overline{QR} \cong \overline{QT}$, $\overline{SR} \cong \overline{ST}$ $\overline{QR} \cong \overline{SR}$, $\overline{QT} \cong \overline{ST}$	2. Definition of Rhombus
3. $\overline{QS} \cong \overline{QS}$, $\overline{RT} \cong \overline{RT}$	3. Congruence of line segments is reflexive. (Theorem 2-2)
4. $\triangle QRS \cong \triangle QTS$ $\triangle TQR \cong \triangle TSR$	4. SSS (Postulate 4-1)
5. $\angle 1 \cong \angle 2$, $\angle 3 \cong \angle 4$ $\angle 5 \cong \angle 6$, $\angle 7 \cong \angle 8$	5. Definition of Congruent Triangles *CPCTC*
6. $\overline{QS}$ bisects $\angle RQT$ and $\angle RST$. $\overline{RT}$ bisects $\angle QRS$ and $\angle STQ$.	6. Definition of Angle Bisector of a Triangle

Another property of the diagonals of a rhombus is that they intersect to form four right angles.

Students will prove Theorem 7-12 in Written Exercise 34.

If a quadrilateral·is a rhombus, then its diagonals are perpendicular.	*Theorem 7-12*

A rhombus may or may not be a rectangle. Also, a rectangle may or may not be a rhombus. A quadrilateral that is both a rectangle and a rhombus is called a **square**.

A quadrilateral is a square if and only if it is a rectangle and all four sides are congruent.	*Definition of Square*

EN: 2–8 even, 3, 6, 9, . . . 27, 30, 31, 34–38 even; **AV:** 1–8, 1–14, 16–28 even, 29–35 odd;
FD: 1–8, 1–14, 15–29 odd; p. 240, 11, 13, 15;
ALL LEVELS: Mini Review

Exploratory Exercises

Name which quadrilaterals have each of the following properties.

1. All angles are right angles.

2. The opposite sides are parallel.

3. The opposite sides are congruent.

4. The opposite angles are congruent.

5. All sides are congruent.

6. It is equiangular.

7. It is equilateral.

8. It is equiangular and equilateral.

For Exercises 1–8, see the Teacher Guide.

Written Exercises

Copy and complete the following table by indicating whether the quadrilaterals have the indicated properties. Write *yes* or *no*.

	Property	Parallelogram	Rectangle	Rhombus	Square
1.	The diagonals bisect each other.				
2.	The diagonals are congruent.				
3.	Each diagonal bisects a pair of opposite angles.				
4.	The diagonals form two pairs of congruent triangles.				
5.	The diagonals form four congruent triangles.				
6.	The diagonals are perpendicular.				

Determine whether each of the following statements is *always* true, *never* true, or *sometimes* true.

7. A square is a rhombus.

8. A parallelogram is a rectangle.

9. A rectangle is *not* a quadrilateral.

10. The diagonals of a rhombus are perpendicular.

11. A rhombus is a square.

12. The diagonals of a quadrilateral bisect each other.

13. The diagonals of a rectangle are congruent.

14. A square is *not* regular.

Use the rhombus and the given information to solve each problem.

15. $ST = 10\frac{7}{8}$
Find TV.

16. $ST = 12.3$
Find TV.

17. $SP = 52.1$
Find SV.

18. $SP = 22\frac{5}{8}$
Find SV.

19. $PT = 6\frac{3}{4}$
Find RT.

20. $PT = 7.6$
Find RT.

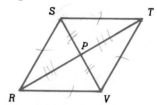

Exercises 15–20

Use the rhombus and the given information to solve each problem.

21. $m\angle EBC = 112.6$
Find $m\angle EBD$.

22. $m\angle BCD = 75.0$
Find $m\angle BCE$.

23. $m\angle BDC = 25.9$
Find $m\angle EDC$.

24. $m\angle CDE = 123.4$
Find $m\angle DBC$.

25. Find $m\angle BFE$.

26. Find $m\angle DFC$.

27. $m\angle BEC = 2x + 10$
$m\angle CED = 5x - 20$
Find x.

28. $m\angle CBD = 2x + 24$
$m\angle EBD = x^2$
Find x.

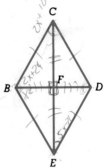

Exercises 21–28

For Exercises 29–36, see the Teacher Guide.

Prove each of the following exercises.

29. If a quadrilateral is a square, then its diagonals bisect each other.

30. If a quadrilateral is a square, then its diagonals are perpendicular.

31. If a parallelogram has one right angle, then it is a rectangle.

32. If the diagonals of a parallelogram are perpendicular, then it is a rhombus.

33. If a parallelogram has two consecutive sides that are congruent, then it is a rhombus.

34. If a quadrilateral is a rhombus, then its diagonals are perpendicular. (Theorem 7-12)

35. If a diagonal bisects two opposite angles of a parallelogram, then it is a rhombus.

36. If the diagonals of a parallelogram are congruent, then it is a rectangle.

For Exercises 37–38, see the Teacher Guide.

Challenge Exercises

37. Given: *PRTW* is a square.
       Q is the midpoint of $\overline{PR}$.
       S is the midpoint of $\overline{RT}$.
       V is the midpoint of $\overline{TW}$.
       X is the midpoint of $\overline{PW}$.
 Prove: $\overline{QV} \perp \overline{SX}$

4-8
4-4
4-4

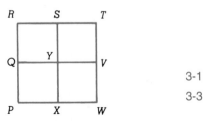

38. Given: $\square ABCD$ is a rhombus.
       $\overline{AF} \cong \overline{BG}$
       $\overline{BG} \cong \overline{CH}$
       $\overline{CH} \cong \overline{DE}$
       $\overline{DE} \cong \overline{AF}$
 Prove: Quadrilateral *EFGH* is a
       parallelogram.

mini-review

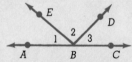

Determine whether each test represents a test for congruent triangles.

1. HA �(scribbled)   **2.** SSA ▪(scribbled)   **3.** SAS ▪(scribbled)

Use the figure to answer each question.

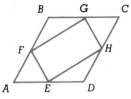

3-1   **4.** Name a pair of opposite rays. (scribbled)

3-3   **5.** If $m \angle 3 = 45$, find $m \angle ABD$. (scribbled)

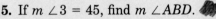

Exercise 38

Statistics That Shape Your Life

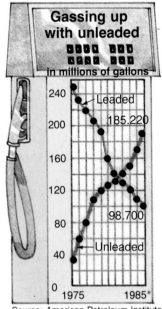

Gassing up with unleaded
in millions of gallons

Source: American Petroleum Institute;
Energy Information Administration
Copyright 1985, USA Today
Reprinted with Permission   *projection

Beginning in 1975, all new cars were required to run on unleaded gas. The graph at the left shows the average daily consumption of unleaded and leaded gas since 1975.

When analyzing the data, it is important to recognize the units represented on the graph. In this case, the average daily consumption of gasoline is given in *millions of gallons*.

Exercises   Leaded has decreased; unleaded has increased.
1. Describe the trends in the average daily consumption of leaded and unleaded gas since 1975.

2. In what year was the gas consumption of leaded and unleaded gas approximately equal? 1981

3. Has total gas consumption increased or decreased since 1975? decreased

Applications in Chemistry Crystals

Kathy Seall is a chemist for the B. T. Duvall Power Company. As a chemist, she studies the properties of various crystals. Crystals are among the most beautiful materials found in nature, and they are also among the most useful industrial materials. For example, crystals can be used to change sunshine into electric current.

The photograph at the right shows galena with fluorite crystals. In their original state, crystals are solids with flat surfaces. The flat surfaces, called faces, have different geometric shapes, depending on the type of crystal.

A crystal, like any substance, is composed of atoms. What distinguishes a crystal from other substances is that the atoms of a crystal are arranged in a single, repeating pattern called a lattice. The simplest repeating unit in this arrangement is called a unit cell. Unit cells are often illustrated with a three-dimensional drawing.

Not all patterns can repeat themselves in a way suitable to forming crystals. To be repeatable, a pattern has to contain parts that mirror one another. There are only 32 possible crystal patterns.

Crystal patterns are three-dimensional "tessellations."

Exercises

Each diagram represents a unit cell of the given crystal. Name the number of faces, the shape of the faces, and identify any congruent faces.

1. borax — 6 — rectangles; opposite faces

2. calcite — 12 — triangles; all faces

3. quartz — 18 — rectangles and triangles; all triangles

4. gypsum — 10 — rectangles and quadrilaterals; opposite faces

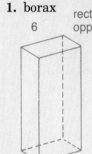

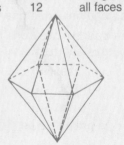

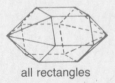
all rectangles

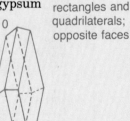

7-6 Trapezoids

Objectives: Recognize trapezoids; recognize and use properties of trapezoids in proofs and other problems.

The design of the College Park Pyramids in Indianapolis is based on a quadrilateral called a **trapezoid.**

A quadrilateral is a trapezoid if and only if it has exactly one pair of parallel sides.	*Definition of Trapezoid*

The parallel sides of a trapezoid are called **bases.** The nonparallel sides of a trapezoid are called **legs.** If the legs are congruent, then the trapezoid is called an **isosceles trapezoid.** One pair of **base angles** is ∠B and ∠C. Another pair of base angles is ∠A and ∠D.

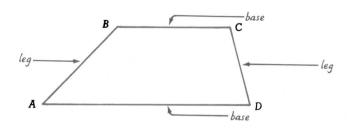

It is helpful to illustrate various examples of trapezoids in which the parallel sides are not always horizontal.

Isosceles trapezoids have special properties.

If a trapezoid is isosceles, then each pair of base angles is congruent.	*Theorem 7-13*

In the following example, one pair of base angles is proven to be congruent.

Example

1

Prove the following.

Given: $\overline{PS} \parallel \overline{QR}$
$\overline{PQ} \cong \overline{SR}$

Prove: $\angle P \cong \angle S$

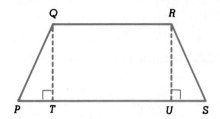

Proof:

STATEMENTS	REASONS
1. Draw $\overline{QT}$ perpendicular to $\overline{PS}$. Draw $\overline{RU}$ perpendicular to $\overline{PS}$.	1. Given a line and a point not on the line, there is exactly one line through the point and perpendicular to the given line. (Theorem 6-14)
2. $\overline{PS} \parallel \overline{QR}$ $\overline{PQ} \cong \overline{SR}$	2. Given
3. $\overline{QT} \cong \overline{RU}$	3. In a plane, two lines are parallel if and only if they are everywhere equidistant. (Theorem 6-15)
4. $\angle QTP$ and $\angle RUS$ are right angles.	4. If two lines are perpendicular, then they form four right angles. (Theorem 3-11)
5. $\triangle QTP$ and $\triangle RUS$ are right triangles.	5. Definition of Right Triangle
6. $\triangle QTP \cong \triangle RUS$	6. HL (Postulate 4-4)
7. $\angle P \cong \angle S$	7. Definition of Congruent Triangles *CPCTC*

Theorem 7-13 can be used to prove Theorem 7-14.

If a trapezoid is isosceles, then its diagonals are congruent.	*Theorem 7-14*

Students will prove Theorem 7-14 in Written Exercise 22.

In trapezoid $ACDF$ at the right, B is the midpoint of $\overline{AC}$ and E is the midpoint of $\overline{DF}$. Segment BE is called the **median** of the trapezoid.

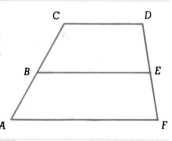

A line segment is the median of a trapezoid if and only if its endpoints are the midpoints of the legs of the trapezoid.	*Definition of Median*

The median of a trapezoid has the following property.

If a quadrilateral is a trapezoid, then the median is parallel to the bases, and its measure is one-half the sum of the measures of the bases.	*Theorem 7-15*

In general, if the measure of the short base of a trapezoid is represented by a, the measure of the long base is represented by b, and the measure of the median is represented by x, then the following is true.

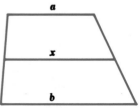

measure of median $= \frac{1}{2}$(measure of short base + measure of long base)

$$x = \frac{1}{2}(a + b)$$

Example

2 **The bases of a trapezoid have lengths of 22 inches and 14 inches. Find the length of the median.**

$x = \frac{1}{2}(a + b)$

$\quad = \frac{1}{2}(14 + 22)$

$\quad = \frac{1}{2}(36)$

$\quad = 18 \qquad$ The median is 18 inches long.

EN: 2–12 even, 13, 3, 6, 9, . . . 18, 19, 20–30 even, 31 **AV:** 1–13, 2–28 even; **FD:** 1–13, 1–18, p. 244, 30, 33, 35

Exploratory Exercises

Determine whether it is possible for a trapezoid to have the following conditions. State yes or no. If yes, draw the trapezoid. See students' work.

1. a leg longer than either base
2. two congruent sides, but not be isosceles
3. three congruent sides
4. congruent bases
5. congruent diagonals
6. bisecting diagonals
7. one pair of opposite angles congruent
8. two pairs of opposite sides parallel
9. two right angles
10. two obtuse angles
11. three obtuse angles
12. four acute angles

13. The opposite angles of an isosceles trapezoid are supplementary. Explain why this is true.
    See the Teacher Guide.

Written Exercises

The figure at the right is an isosceles trapezoid with bases $\overline{AD}$ and $\overline{BC}$. Use this figure and the information given to find the indicated measures.

1. $BD = 8.2$. Find AC. ▓
2. $AB = 14.6$. Find DC. ▓
3. $BD = 2y + 3$ and $AC = 4y - 5$. Find BD and AC. ▓
4. $DC = y^2$ and $BA = 7y + 8$. Find DC and BA. ▓
5. $m \angle CBA = 80$. Find $m \angle BAD$. ▓
6. $m \angle CDA = 100$. Find $m \angle DAB$. ▓

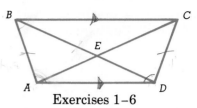

Exercises 1–6

The figure at the right is an isosceles trapezoid with bases $\overline{QR}$ and $\overline{PS}$. Use this figure and the information given to find the indicated measures.

7. $QR = 6$ and $PS = 18$. Find TV. ▓
8. $PS = 32.1$ and $TV = 23.2$. Find QR. ▓
9. $QR + PS = 5y + 2$ and $TV = y + 7$. Find y. ▓
10. $QR = x - 3$, $PS = 2x + 4$, and $TV = 3x - 10$.
    Find QR, PS, and TV. ▓
11. $m \angle QTV = 65$. Find $m \angle RVT$. ▓
12. $m \angle TPS = x$. Find $m \angle VTP$ in terms of x. ▓

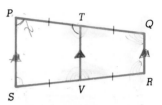

Exercises 7–12

The figure at the right is a trapezoid with bases $\overline{RS}$ and $\overline{TW}$. Use this figure and the information given to find the indicated measures.

13. $m \angle SRX = 35$. Find $m \angle RWT$. ▓
14. $m \angle RSW = 135$. Find $m \angle TWS$. ▓
15. $\angle RTW$ is a right angle. Find $m \angle SRT$. ▓
16. $m \angle XTW = 23$ and $m \angle SXW = 87$. Find $m \angle XWT$. ▓
17. $RS = 23\frac{1}{4}$ and $TW = 18\frac{1}{4}$. Find the measure of
    the median of trapezoid $RSWT$. ▓
18. $RS = x$, $TW = 3x + 10$, and the measure of
    the median is $3x - 5$. Find x. ▓

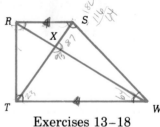

Exercises 13–18

Solve.

19. A land developer purchased a parcel of land in the
    shape of a trapezoid. The land will be divided
    into three lots as shown in the figure at the right.
    If d and e are medians, and $c = 85$, find a, b, d, and e.
    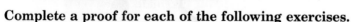

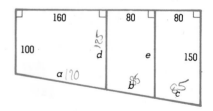

Complete a proof for each of the following exercises.

20. If a trapezoid is isosceles, then its opposite angles are
    supplementary.
21. If the base angles of a trapezoid are congruent, then
    the trapezoid is isosceles.
    For Exercises 20–30, see the Teacher Guide.

250 *Polygons*

22. If a trapezoid is isosceles, then its diagonals are congruent. (Theorem 7-14)

23. Given: $\overline{LM} \parallel \overline{RN}$
$\overline{LR} \cong \overline{MN}$
$\overline{RP} \perp \overline{LM}, \overline{NQ} \perp \overline{LM}$
Prove: $\triangle LRP \cong \triangle MNQ$

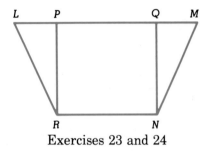

24. Given: $\overline{LM} \parallel \overline{RN}$
$\overline{LR} \cong \overline{MN}$
$\overline{RP} \perp \overline{LM}, \overline{NQ} \perp \overline{LM}$
Prove: $\angle RLP \cong \angle NMQ$

Exercises 23 and 24

Use the following information in Exercises 25–28.
Given: $\overline{RT} \parallel \overline{PW}$
$\overline{TX} \parallel \overline{RP}$
Q is the midpoint of $\overline{PR}$.
V is the midpoint of $\overline{SW}$.

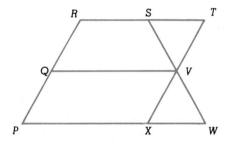

25. Prove: V is the midpoint of $\overline{TX}$.
26. Prove: $\triangle SVT \cong \triangle WVX$
27. Prove: Quadrilateral $QRTV$ is a parallelogram.
28. Prove: $\overline{QV} \parallel \overline{PW}$

Exercises 25–28

29. Given: Trapezoid $RSPT$ is isosceles.
Prove: $\triangle RSQ$ is isosceles.

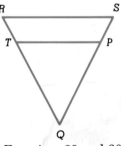

30. Given: $\triangle SQR$ is isosceles.
$\triangle PQT$ is isosceles.
$\overline{TP} \parallel \overline{RS}$
Prove: Quadrilateral $RSPT$ is an isosceles trapezoid.

Exercises 29 and 30

Challenge Exercise

31. The figure at the right is a trapezoid with bases $\overline{SR}$ and $\overline{PQ}$. $PS = QS$, $m \angle SRQ = 120$, and $m \angle RQS = 20$. Find the measure of $\angle PSQ$. **100**

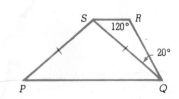

Problem Solving

An effective problem-solving strategy is to look for a pattern. When using this strategy, it is important to organize information about the problem. Study the following example.

Example **How many diagonals can be drawn for a polygon with *n* sides, where *n* is less than or equal to 12?**

Try several cases. That is, draw several polygons and see how many diagonals you can draw for each polygon. Use a table to record the number of sides and the number of diagonals for each polygon. Then study the pattern formed by the numbers in the table.

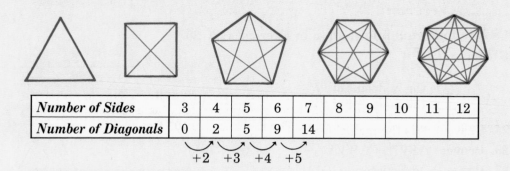

Number of Sides	3	4	5	6	7	8	9	10	11	12
Number of Diagonals	0	2	5	9	14					

+2 +3 +4 +5

Check to see that the rest of the numbers that belong in the table above are 20, 27, 35, 44, and 54. Do you see why?

Exercises

Solve each problem.

1. There were 10 people at a party. Each person shook hands with each of the other people exactly once. How many handshakes occurred? 45

2. How many squares are shown at the right? (Hint: There are more than 16.) 30

3. How many rectangles are shown below? 15

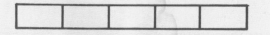

4. How many triangles are shown at the right? 27

5. Imagine 25 lockers, all closed, and 25 people. Suppose the first person opens every locker. Then the second person closes every second locker. Next the third person changes the state of every third locker. (If it's open, she closes it. If it's closed, she opens it.) Suppose this procedure is continued until the 25th person changes the state of the 25th locker. Which lockers will be open at the end of the procedure? 1, 4, 9, 16, 25

7-7 Application: Perimeter

Objectives: Find the perimeter of a polygon; apply the concept of perimeter to real-world situations.

Julie Newton is a carpenter. The floor plan below shows a room she will panel on her next job.

You can assume the corners of the room in this floor plan are right angles.

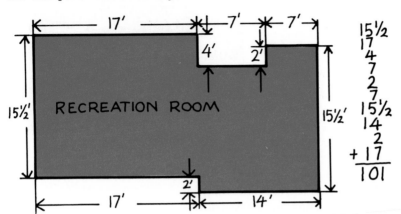

To determine the amount of molding she needs for ceiling trim, Ms. Newton first finds the **perimeter** of the room. She adds the measures for each side of the room. The perimeter is 101 feet.

The perimeter of a polygon is the total length of its sides.

The sum of the measures of the sides of a polygon is the measure of the perimeter of the polygon.	***Definition of Perimeter***

Each pair of opposite sides of a rectangle is congruent. Thus, only two measurements, the length and the width, are needed to find the perimeter of a rectangle.

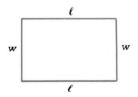

Let ℓ be the measure of the length.
Let w be the measure of the width.
Let P be the measure of the perimeter.

$$P = \ell + w + \ell + w \qquad \text{\textit{Definition of Perimeter}}$$
$$= \ell + \ell + w + w \qquad \text{\textit{Commutative Property of Addition}}$$
$$= 2\ell + 2w \qquad \text{\textit{Substitution}}$$
$$= 2(\ell + w) \qquad \text{\textit{Distributive Property}}$$

If a rectangle has a perimeter of P units, a length of ℓ units, and a width of w units, then $P = 2(\ell + w)$.	***Theorem 7-16*** ***Perimeter of Rectangle***

Example

1 Find the amount of crown molding needed around the ceiling of a rectangular room measuring 12.4 meters by 4.7 meters.

$$P = 2(\ell + w)$$
$$= 2(12.4 + 4.7)$$
$$= 2(17.1)$$
$$= 34.2$$

The amount of crown molding needed is 34.2 meters.

Recall that all sides of a regular polygon are congruent. Therefore, to find the perimeter of a regular polygon the only information you need is the measure of one side and the number of sides of the polygon.

Example

2 Find the perimeter of a regular polygon with 5 sides.

Let s stand for the measure of a side.
Let P stand for the measure of the perimeter.

$$P = s + s + s + s + s \qquad \textit{Definition of Perimeter}$$
$$= 5s \qquad \textit{Substitution}$$

It can be helpful to show other examples similar to Example 2 before presenting Theorem 7-17.

This, and many other examples, suggest the following theorem.

If a regular n-gon has a perimeter of P units and a side measures s units, then $P = ns$.	**Theorem 7-17** *Perimeter of Regular Polygon*

The formal proof of this theorem uses mathematical induction.

Example

3 The perimeter of a regular octagon is 32 feet. Find the length of each side.

$$P = ns$$
$$32 = 8s \qquad \textit{Substitute 32 for P and 8 for n.}$$
$$4 = s \qquad \textit{Solve for s.}$$

The length of each side is 4 feet.

You can also apply the geometric concept of perimeter to algebraic problems involving polygons.

Example

4 In a certain isosceles triangle the third side is 3 inches shorter than either of the congruent sides. If the perimeter is 69 inches, find the lengths of the sides.

Explore Let s = length of each congruent side.
$s - 3$ = length of the third side.

Plan The perimeter of a triangle is the sum of the lengths of its sides.

$$\underset{Side}{First} + \underset{Side}{Second} + \underset{Side}{Third} = \underset{the\ Triangle}{Perimeter\ of}$$

Solve
$$s + s + (s - 3) = 69$$
$$3s - 3 = 69$$
$$3s = 72$$
$$s = 24$$

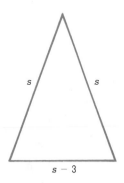

Therefore, the length of each congruent side is 24 inches. The length of the third side is $24 - 3$ or 21 inches.

Examine The perimeter of the triangle is $24 + 24 + 21$ or 69 inches.

EN: 2–8 even, 10–38 even; AV: 1–8, 2–32 even; FD: 1–8, 1–31 odd, pp. 250–251, 20–24 even

Exploratory Exercises

Find the perimeter for each of the following floor plans. Assume all angles that appear to be right angles are right angles.

1.

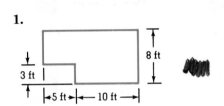

2.

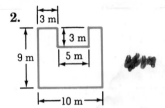

3.

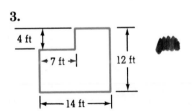

4.

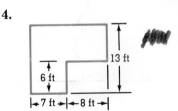

5.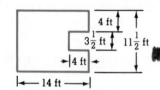

6.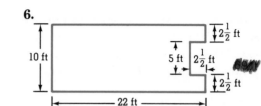

7.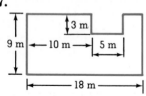

8.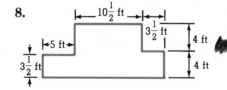

Written Exercises

The length and width of rectangles are given below. Find the perimeter.

1. 3.4 m, 1.6 m

2. 3.2 m, 1.4 m

3. $3\frac{1}{8}$ in., $1\frac{1}{4}$ in.

4. $17\frac{1}{2}$ ft, $16\frac{2}{3}$ ft

5. 43.8 mi, 38 mi

6. 34.5 mm, 27.9 mm

7. 25.7 cm, 2.1 cm

8. $22\frac{1}{2}$ yd, 15 yd

9. $5\frac{1}{4}$ in., $4\frac{3}{4}$ in.

The perimeter and width of a rectangle are given below. Find the length.

10. 141.4 km, 33.4 km

11. 21.6 mi, 6.9 mi

12. 19.4 cm, 9.3 cm

13. 12 in., $3\frac{1}{2}$ in.

14. $18\frac{1}{4}$ ft, $7\frac{3}{4}$ ft

15. $10\frac{2}{3}$ yd, $3\frac{1}{4}$ yd

For each of the following regular polygons, the length of a side is given. Find the perimeter for each.

16. decagon, 15.4 cm

17. hexagon, 12 ft

18. pentagon, $4\frac{1}{4}$ in.

19. square, 24.9 mm

20. octagon, 32.3 mi

21. nonagon, $3\frac{1}{3}$ yd

For each of the following regular polygons, the perimeter is given. Find the length of a side for each.

22. square, 15.40 mm

23. pentagon, 12.0 m

24. hexagon, 69 yd

25. heptagon, 21.7 cm

26. octagon, $55\frac{1}{2}$ ft

27. nonagon, 6.3 km

Answer each question.

28. How many inches of lead molding are needed to put around 24 hexagons and 15 rhombuses of stained glass with sides measuring $1\frac{1}{2}$ inches?

29. How many feet of chain link fencing are needed for an L-shaped yard measuring 35 feet by 20 feet by 32 feet by 20 feet by 67 feet by 40 feet?

30. How many yards of lace trim should be purchased to make borders for two rectangular tablecloths each with width 4 feet and length 6 feet?

31. How many centimeters of metal edging are needed for a rectangular table measuring 2.5 meters by 5 meters?

Use an equation to solve each problem.

32. The length of a rectangle is 4 feet more than twice the width. The perimeter is 116 feet. Find the dimensions of the rectangle.

33. A certain triangle has two congruent sides. The third side is 17 cm shorter than either of the equal sides. If the perimeter is 91 cm, what is the length of the third side?

34. The second side of a triangle is twice the length of the first. The third side is 3 cm less than the second side. If the perimeter is 37 cm, find the lengths of the sides.

35. The three sides of a triangle have measures that are consecutive odd numbers. What are the lengths of the sides if the perimeter is 87 m?

Find the perimeter for each of the following figures. Assume all angles that appear to be right angles are right angles.

36.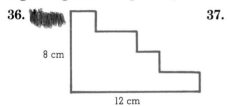

8 cm

12 cm

37.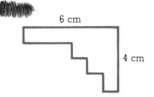

6 cm

4 cm

38.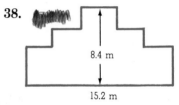

8.4 m

15.2 m

Excursions in Geometry ———————————— Closed Curves

The figure below can be traced so that, starting at one point, every other point is touched exactly once before reaching the starting point again. This figure is a **simple closed curve.**

Simple closed curves separate a plane into the inside, the outside, and the curve itself. One way to test whether a point is inside or outside is to first draw a segment from the given point to another point outside the curve. Then, count the number of times the segment crosses the curve. If the number is odd, the point is inside. If the number is even, the point is outside.

Exercises

Determine whether the point given is inside or outside the curve.

1. A ~~inside~~
2. B ~~inside~~
3. C ~~inside~~
4. D ~~inside~~
5. E ~~inside~~
6. F ~~outside~~

7-8 Polyhedrons

A crystal is a solid that is composed of atoms arranged in an orderly pattern. Certain metals and rocks, as well as snowflakes, salt, and sugar, are made up of crystals.

Well-developed crystals have a distinct, regular shape as a result of their geometrically ordered arrangement of atoms. These crystals have smooth, flat surfaces that intersect to form sharp edges. A magnification of a salt crystal is pictured at the right. Notice that it resembles a cube.

In geometry, **solids** are boundaries that enclose a part of space. Solids with flat surfaces that form polygons are called **polyhedrons** or **polyhedra.**

The flat surfaces formed by polygons and their interiors are called **faces.** Pairs of faces intersect at line segments called **edges.** Three or more edges intersect at a point called a **vertex.**

The following table lists the 4 faces, 6 edges, and 4 vertices for the polyhedron at the right.

Spheres, cones, and cylinders are not polyhedrons because they have curved surfaces.

The faces of a convex polyhedron are convex polygons.

Three dimensional models are most useful for discussion purposes.

Faces	Edges		Vertices
△ABC	$\overline{AB}$	$\overline{DC}$	A
△BCD	$\overline{BD}$	$\overline{AC}$	B
△ACD	$\overline{AD}$	$\overline{BC}$	C
△ABD			D

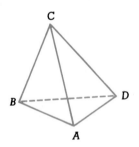

Example

1 **Name the faces, edges, and vertices of the polyhedron at the right.**

The 7 faces are quadrilaterals *AEJF, DEJI, CDIH, BCHG, ABGF,* and pentagons *ABCDE* and *FGHIJ.*

The 15 edges are $\overline{AB}$, $\overline{BC}$, $\overline{CD}$, $\overline{DE}$, $\overline{EA}$, $\overline{FG}$, $\overline{GH}$, $\overline{HI}$, $\overline{IJ}$, $\overline{JF}$, $\overline{FA}$, $\overline{GB}$, $\overline{HC}$, $\overline{ID}$, and $\overline{JE}$.

The 10 vertices are *A, B, C, D, E, F, G, H, I,* and *J.*

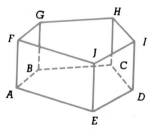

Each face of the polyhedron at the right forms a regular polygon. All the polygons formed are congruent to each other. Therefore, each edge has the same measure. Polyhedrons with such properties are called **regular polyhedrons.**

A polyhedron must have *at least* three polygons intersecting at each vertex. Also, the total degree measures of the angles formed at each vertex must be *less than* 360.

Two polygons do not form a polyhedron.

If the sum of the angle degree measures at a vertex is 360, the figure is flat.

There are only five types of regular polyhedrons. These polyhedrons often are called **Platonic solids.** Each is named according to the number of faces.

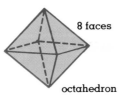

4 faces

tetrahedron

8 faces

octahedron

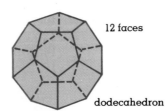

20 faces

icosahedron

Students can make models or mobiles of solids using straws and/or construction paper. Nets are found on pages 10–14 in the Teacher Resource Book.

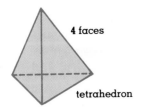

6 faces

hexahedron

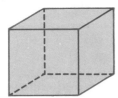

12 faces

dodecahedron

The different regular polyhedrons are determined by the regular polygons that form the faces.

regular polyhedron	regular polygon	degree measure of one angle	number of angles at vertex	total degree measure of angles at vertex
tetrahedron	triangle	60	3	180
octahedron	triangle	60	4	240
icosahedron	triangle	60	5	300
hexahedron	square	90	3	270
dodecahedron	pentagon	108	3	324

Note that totals in the last column must be less than 360, otherwise the figure is flat.

Exploratory Exercises

Name the faces, edges, and vertices for each of the following polyhedra.

For Exercises 1–3, see the Teacher Guide.

1.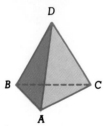

2.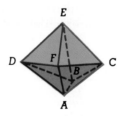

3.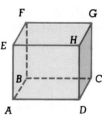

4. The sum of the degree measures of the angles formed at one vertex of a convex polyhedron must be less than what number? ▓▓▓

5–7. Find the number of polygons intersecting at vertex *D* for each polyhedron in Exercises 1–3. ▓▓▓▓▓▓▓▓

8–10. Find the sum of the degree measures at vertex *D* for each regular polyhedron in Exercises 1–3. ▓▓▓▓▓▓▓

Written Exercises

For each of the following polyhedra, name the type of polygons that form the faces.

1. tetrahedron ▓▓▓

2. hexahedron ▓▓▓

3. octahedron ▓▓▓

4. dodecahedron ▓▓▓

5–8. Find the degree measure of one angle for a face of each polyhedron in Exercises 1–4.
5. ▓ **6.** ▓ **7.** ▓ **8.** ▓

Given below are a possible number of polygons intersecting at one vertex of a polyhedron. Find the sum of the degree measures of the angles formed at that vertex.

9. 4 equilateral triangles ▓▓

10. 6 equilateral triangles ▓▓

11. 3 squares ▓▓

12. 4 squares ▓▓

13. 5 squares ▓▓

14. 3 regular pentagons ▓▓

15. 3 regular hexagons ▓▓

16. 2 regular octagons ▓▓

For each of the following polyhedra, give the number of faces, vertices, and edges.

17. tetrahedron ▓▓▓

18. hexahedron ▓▓▓

19. octahedron ▓▓▓

Excursions in Geometry _____ Euler's Formula

The Swiss mathematician Leonhard Euler discovered that the number of faces, vertices, and edges of a regular polyhedron are related by the following formula.

$$\left(\begin{array}{c}\text{number of}\\\text{vertices}\end{array}\right) - \left(\begin{array}{c}\text{number of}\\\text{edges}\end{array}\right) + \left(\begin{array}{c}\text{number of}\\\text{faces}\end{array}\right) = 2$$

$$V - E + F = 2$$

Exercise

Verify Euler's formula by substituting the values from Written Exercises 17–19.

See the Teacher Guide.

Vocabulary

Chapter Summary

1. **Definition of Polygon:** A figure is a polygon if and only if it meets each of the following conditions.
    1. It is formed by three or more coplanar segments called sides.
    2. Sides that have a common endpoint are noncollinear.
    3. Each side intersects exactly two of the other sides, but only at their endpoints. (223)

2. **Theorem 7-1:** If a convex polygon has n sides and S is the sum of the degree measures of its angles, then $S = (n - 2)180$. (227)

3. **Theorem 7-2:** If a polygon is convex, then the sum of the degree measures of the exterior angles, one at each vertex, is 360. (228)

4. **Four-step plan for problem solving:**
    1. Explore the problem.
    2. Plan the solution.
    3. Solve the problem.
    4. Examine the solution. (229)

5. **Definition of Parallelogram:** A quadrilateral is a parallelogram if and only if both pairs of opposite sides are parallel. (233)

6. **Theorem 7-3:** If a quadrilateral is a parallelogram, then a diagonal separates it into two congruent triangles. (233)

7. Theorem 7-4: If a quadrilateral is a parallelogram, then its opposite angles are congruent. (234)

8. Theorem 7-5: If a quadrilateral is a parallelogram, then its opposite sides are congruent. (234)

9. Theorem 7-6: If a quadrilateral is a parallelogram, then its diagonals bisect each other. (234)

10. Theorem 7-7: If both pairs of opposite sides of a quadrilateral are congruent, then the quadrilateral is a parallelogram. (237)

11. Theorem 7-8: If two sides of a quadrilateral are parallel and congruent, then the quadrilateral is a parallelogram. (238)

12. Theorem 7-9: If the diagonals of a quadrilateral bisect each other, then the quadrilateral is a parallelogram. (238)

13. Definition of Rectangle: A quadrilateral is a rectangle if and only if it is a parallelogram with four right angles. (241)

14. Theorem 7-10: If a quadrilateral is a rectangle, then its diagonals are congruent. (241)

15. Definition of Rhombus: A quadrilateral is a rhombus if and only if it is a parallelogram with all four sides congruent. (242)

16. Theorem 7-11: If a quadrilateral is a rhombus, then each diagonal bisects a pair of opposite angles. (242)

17. Theorem 7-12: If a quadrilateral is a rhombus, then its diagonals are perpendicular. (243)

18. Definition of Square: A quadrilateral is a square if and only if it is a rectangle and all four sides are congruent. (243)

19. Definition of Trapezoid: A quadrilateral is a trapezoid if and only if it has exactly one pair of parallel sides. (247)

20. Theorem 7-13: If a trapezoid is isosceles, then each pair of base angles is congruent. (247)

21. Theorem 7-14: If a trapezoid is isosceles, then its diagonals are congruent. (248)

22. Theorem 7-15: If a quadrilateral is a trapezoid, then the median is parallel to the bases, and its measure is one-half the sum of the measures of the bases. (249)

23. Definition of Perimeter: The sum of the measures of the sides of a polygon is the measure of the perimeter of the polygon. (253)

24. Perimeter of a Rectangle (Theorem 7-16): If a rectangle has a perimeter of P units, a length of ℓ units, and a width of w units, then $P = 2(\ell + w)$. (253)

25. Perimeter of a Regular Polygon (Theorem 7-17): If a regular n-gon has a perimeter of P units and a side measures s units, then $P = ns$. (254)

26. Polyhedrons are geometric solids with flat surfaces that form polygons. (258)

27. Regular polyhedrons have faces that are regular polygons. All the polygons formed are congruent to each other. Each edge has the same measure. There are only five regular polyhedrons. (259)

Chapter Review

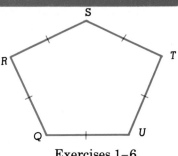

7-1 Use the polygon to complete each exercise.

    1. Name the vertices. *Q, R, S, T, U*

    2. Name the sides. $\overline{QR}, \overline{RS}, \overline{ST}, \overline{TU}, \overline{UQ}$

    3. Name the angles. $\angle Q, \angle R, \angle S, \angle T, \angle U$

    4. Classify the polygon by the number of sides. pentagon

    5. Classify the polygon as *convex* or *concave.* convex

    6. Classify the polygon as *regular* or *not regular.* not regular

Exercises 1–6

7-2 For each of the following convex polygons, find the sum of the degree measures of the interior angles.

    7. hexagon 720   **8.** pentagon 540   **9.** 12-gon 1800

    10–12. Suppose each polygon in Exercises **7–9** is a regular polygon. Find the degree measure of one angle. **10.** 120   **11.** 108   **12.** 150

    13. Find the degree measure of one exterior angle of a regular nonagon. 40

7-3 Use the parallelogram to complete each exercise.

    14. If *BE* = 45, find *BD*. 90

    15. If *CD* = 7.2, find *BA*. 7.2

    16. If $m \angle 1 = 2a + 5$ and $m \angle 2 = 3a - 7$, find *a*. 12

    17. If $m \angle BCD = 6x + 3$ and $m \angle DAB = 3x + 12$, find *x*. 3

    18. If $m \angle ABC = 4y + 9$ and $m \angle BCD = 3y + 24$, find *y*. 21

    19. If *AC* = 16.4, find *EC*. 8.2

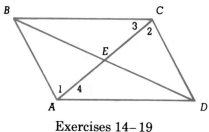

Exercises 14–19

7-4 Prove each of the following exercises.

    20. Given: $\angle 1$ and $\angle 2$ are supplementary.
                   $\angle 2 \cong \angle 3$
        Prove: Quadrilateral *PQRS* is a parallelogram.

For Exercises 20–21, see the Teacher Guide.

    21. Given: $\square ABCD$
                   $\overline{AE} \cong \overline{CF}$
        Prove: Quadrilateral *EBFD* is a parallelogram.

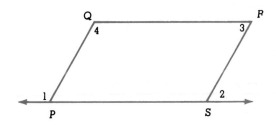

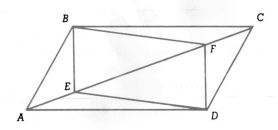

7-5   Determine whether each of the following statements must be true. Write *yes* or *no*.

22. The diagonals of a rhombus bisect each other. yes

23. The diagonals of a rectangle bisect the opposite angles. no

24. All sides of parallelograms are congruent. no

25. Every square is a rhombus. yes

Use the rhombus to complete each exercise.

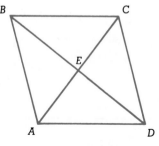

Exercises 26–28

26. Suppose $AE = 6$, find AC. 12

27. Suppose $m \angle ABE = 23\frac{3}{4}$, find $m \angle ABC$. $47\frac{1}{2}$

28. Find $m \angle CED$. 90

For Exercises 29–30, see the Teacher Guide.

7-6   **Prove each of the following exercises.**

29. **Given:** $\overline{BC} \parallel \overline{AD}$, $\overline{AB} \nparallel \overline{CD}$
    $AB \cong \overline{DC}$
    Prove: $\triangle AED$ is isosceles.

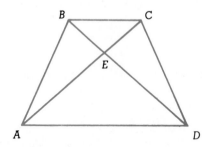

30. **Given:** $\overline{RS} \parallel \overline{PV}$
    $\overline{QT}$ is a median of trapezoid $PRSV$.
    Prove: W is the midpoint of $\overline{RV}$.

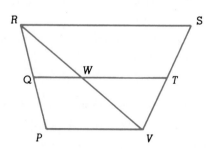

7-7   **Find the perimeter for each of the following polygons.**

31. rectangle with length 4.2 m and width 3.8 m 16 m

32. regular octagon with each side measuring $4\frac{1}{4}$ ft 34 ft

33. How many centimeters of lead are needed to put around 25 hexagons of stained glass each with sides measuring 5.7 centimeters? 855 cm

7-8   34. Find the sum of the degree measures of the angles formed at each vertex of an icosahedron. 300

Chapter Test

Solve each of the following.

1. Find the number of diagonals that can be drawn for a decagon.

2. Find the sum of the degree measures of the angles of a 15-gon.

3. Find the degree measure of one exterior angle of a regular pentagon.

4. Find the degree measure of one angle of a regular octagon.

Use ▱ QRST for each of the following.

5. If $m \angle RST = 45$, find $m \angle QRS$.

6. If $m \angle QRS = 6x + 4$, find $m \angle QTS$.

7. If $RT = 18$, find PR.

8. If $QP = 12$, find SQ.

9. If $m \angle QTS = 4x - 2$ and $m \angle TSR = 5x - 7$, find x.

10. If $RP = 8x - 3$ and $PT = 6x + 5$, find x.

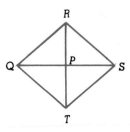

Exercises 5–10

Determine whether each statement is *true* or *false*.

11. The diagonals of a parallelogram are perpendicular.

12. The diagonals of a rectangle bisect each other.

13. The diagonals of a trapezoid bisect each other.

14. The base angles of a trapezoid are congruent.

15. The diagonals of a square bisect each other.

16. The diagonals of a rectangle bisect the angles of the rectangle.

17. If all the sides of a quadrilateral are congruent, then it is regular.

18. The diagonals of a rhombus bisect the angles of the rhombus.

19. Every square is a rectangle.

20. Every rhombus is a parallelogram.

Prove each of the following. For Exercises 21–22, see the Teacher Guide.

21. **Given:** ▱ $ABCD$, $\overline{AC} \cong \overline{BD}$
    Prove: ▱ $ABCD$ is a rectangle.

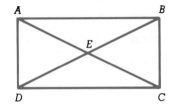

22. **Given:** ▱ $LMNP$, $\overline{MP} \perp \overline{LN}$
    Prove: ▱ $LMNP$ is a rhombus.

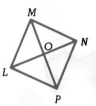

Solve each problem.

23. Suppose the bases of a trapezoid measure 6.8 mm and 15.7 mm. Find the measure of the median.

24. Suppose a rectangle measures $2\frac{1}{2}$ inches by $1\frac{3}{4}$ inches. Find its perimeter.

CHAPTER 8

Similarity

Artists and cartoonists often design their sketches larger than the ones that will finally appear in books, magazines, or newspapers. Many of the line drawings in this book were reduced in size from the artist's original figures. The illustrations you see are similar to the original figures.

8-1 Ratios and Proportions

Objectives: Write ratios for problems; write and solve proportions for problems.

Team records often are compared using ratios. For example, the league standings shown below indicate that the National League Baseball team from St. Louis won 66 of the 109 games it has played to date. The ratio of games won to games played is $\frac{66}{109}$ or about 0.606.

NATIONAL LEAGUE STANDINGS			
EAST	W	L	Pct.
New York	67	42	.615
St. Louis	66	43	.606
Montreal	62	49	.559
Chicago	55	54	.505
Philadelphia	51	59	.464
Pittsburgh	33	75	.306

A **ratio** is a comparison of two numbers. The ratio of a to b can be expressed as $\frac{a}{b}$ where b is *not* zero.

What is the ratio of games won to games lost for St. Louis?

Example

1 The pitch of a roof is the ratio of the rise to the run. If a roof has a rise measuring 3.5 m and a run measuring 2.1 m, what is the pitch?

$$\text{pitch} = \frac{\text{rise}}{\text{run}}$$
$$= \frac{3.5}{2.1}$$
$$= \frac{5}{3}$$
$$\approx 1.667$$

The pitch to 1 decimal place is 1.7.

A **proportion** shows that two ratios are equivalent. For example, another roof having a rise measuring 4.0 m and a run measuring 2.4 m has a pitch of 1.667. This roof has the same pitch as the roof in Example 1. The ratios of rise to run are the same.

$$\frac{4.0}{2.4} = \frac{3.5}{2.1}$$

An equation that shows two equivalent ratios is a proportion.

Every proportion has two **cross products.** In the proportion $\frac{4.0}{2.4} = \frac{3.5}{2.1}$, the cross products are 4.0 times 2.1 and 2.4 times 3.5. The cross products of a proportion are equal.

$$\frac{4.0}{2.4} \diagup\!\!\!\!\diagdown \frac{3.5}{2.1}$$
$$4.0 \times 2.1 = 2.4 \times 3.5$$
$$8.4 = 8.4$$

2.4 and 3.5 are called the **means.**
4.0 and 2.1 are called the **extremes.**

For any numbers a and c, and any nonzero numbers b and d, $\frac{a}{b} = \frac{c}{d}$ if and only if $ad = bc$.	**Theorem 8-1** *Equality of Cross Products*

The two parts of this theorem will be proven in Example 3 and Written Exercise 42.

Examples

2 A racing car uses alcohol for fuel. The alcohol weighs 4.8 pounds per gallon and is burned with a fuel to air ratio of 1 to 15. Use a proportion to find how many pounds of air are used in burning 1 gallon of alcohol.

Let x = the amount of air used in pounds.

$$\frac{4.8}{x} = \frac{1}{15}$$ Each ratio compares fuel to air.
$$x = 4.8 \times 15$$
$$= 72$$

The car will use 72 pounds of air in burning 1 gallon of alcohol.

3 Prove that for any numbers a and c, and any nonzero numbers b and d, if $\frac{a}{b} = \frac{c}{d}$, then $ad = bc$.

Given: $\frac{a}{b} = \frac{c}{d}$, b and d are nonzero.

Prove: $ad = bc$

Proof:

STATEMENTS	REASONS
1. $\frac{a}{b} = \frac{c}{d}$, b and d are nonzero	1. Given
2. $bd\left(\frac{a}{b}\right) = bd\left(\frac{c}{d}\right)$	2. Multiplication Property of Equality (Postulate 2-8)
3. $ad\left(\frac{b}{b}\right) = bc\left(\frac{d}{d}\right)$	3. Commutative Property for Multiplication (Postulate 2-10) and Associative Property for Multiplication (Postulate 2-11)
4. $ad = bc$	4. Substitution (Postulate 2-9) and Identity Property for Multiplication (Postulate 2-12)

Exploratory Exercises   **ALL LEVELS:** Algebra Review

Use the standings listed in the chart at the right to find the ratios for each of the following exercises. Then, express each ratio as a decimal rounded to three decimal places. For Exercises 1–8, see the Teacher Guide.

1. games won to games lost for Milwaukee

2. games won to games lost for Chicago

3. games won to games played for New York

4. games won to games played for Texas

5. longest winning streak in the West division to the longest winning streak in the East division

6. longest losing streak in the West division to the longest losing streak in the East division

7. games won to games lost in the last ten games for New York

8. games lost to games won in the last ten games for Seattle

AMERICAN LEAGUE STANDINGS						
EAST	**W**	**L**	**Pct.**	**GB**	**Last 10 Games**	**Streak**
Toronto	70	42	.625	—	6-4	Lost 1
New York	63	47	.573	6	8-2	Won 7
Detroit	58	52	.527	11	4-6	Lost 2
Boston	56	54	.509	13	4-6	Lost 4
Baltimore	55	54	.505	13½	4-6	Lost 1
Milwaukee	50	58	.463	18	6-4	Won 1
Cleveland	37	73	.336	32	5-5	Won 2
WEST	**W**	**L**	**Pct.**	**GB**	**Last 10 Games**	**Streak**
California	63	47	.573	—	6-4	Lost 1
Kansas City	60	49	.550	2½	6-4	Won 1
Oakland	59	52	.532	4½	6-4	Lost 3
Chicago	54	54	.500	8	4-6	Lost 1
Seattle	51	59	.464	12	4-6	Won 2
Minnesota	50	59	.459	12½	4-6	Won 2
Texas	42	68	.382	21	3-7	Won 1

Gears on bicycles are called sprockets. To find bicycle gear ratios, you must first find the ratio of the number of rear sprocket teeth to the number of front sprocket teeth. Find the ratio for each of the following to two decimal places.

9. 12 rear sprocket teeth
24 front sprocket teeth

10. 15 rear sprocket teeth
55 front sprocket teeth

11. 13 rear sprocket teeth
52 front sprocket teeth

12. 20 rear sprocket teeth
30 front sprocket teeth

13. 26 rear sprocket teeth
46 front sprocket teeth

14. 24 rear sprocket teeth
54 front sprocket teeth

Written Exercises

Referring to pentagon *PQRST*, find the following ratios. Express answers as fractions in simplest form.

1. *PT* to *PQ*

2. *QR* to *ST*

3. *RQ* to *RS*

4. $\dfrac{PQ}{ST}$

5. $\dfrac{PT + QP}{RS + QR}$

6. $\dfrac{PQ + PT}{ST + SR}$

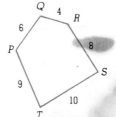

$\overline{AD}$ **is a median of $\triangle ABC$ shown at the right. Complete the following exercises.**

7. Find the ratio of *BD* to *DC*.

8. Find the ratio of *DC* to *BC*.

9. $\triangle ABD$ is an equilateral triangle.
Find the ratio of $m \angle ABD$ to $m \angle ADC$.

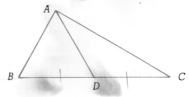

Solve each of the following proportions using cross products.

10. $\dfrac{11}{24} = \dfrac{x}{24}$

11. $\dfrac{5}{8} = \dfrac{20}{x}$

12. $\dfrac{t}{18} = \dfrac{5}{6}$

13. $\dfrac{14}{b} = \dfrac{7}{8}$

14. $\dfrac{1.2}{1.6} = \dfrac{k}{4}$

15. $\dfrac{7}{12} = \dfrac{9.8}{m}$

16. $\dfrac{b}{3.24} = \dfrac{1}{8}$

17. $\dfrac{7.29}{a} = \dfrac{27}{9}$

18. $\dfrac{n-3}{12} = \dfrac{5}{4}$

19. $\dfrac{2}{5} = \dfrac{3}{x-3}$

20. $\dfrac{16+x}{4+x} = \dfrac{x}{4}$

21. $\dfrac{1}{3} = \dfrac{t}{8-t}$

22. $\dfrac{x}{30-x} = \dfrac{2}{3}$

23. $\dfrac{5+x}{8+x} = \dfrac{3}{4}$

24. $\dfrac{3-n}{n+1} = \dfrac{2}{1}$

25. $\dfrac{n+3}{10} = \dfrac{3n-2}{8}$

26. $\dfrac{t-1}{t+1} = \dfrac{5}{8}$

27. $\dfrac{p}{p-1} = 1\dfrac{2}{3}$

28. $\dfrac{3-2y}{3y+7} = \dfrac{2}{5}$

29. $\dfrac{x}{5} = \dfrac{x+5}{14}$

Proportions can be used to change a fraction to a percent. For example, to change $\dfrac{5}{6}$ to a percent, you solve the proportion $\dfrac{5}{6} = \dfrac{n}{100}$. For each of the following use a proportion to change the fraction to a percent.

30. $\dfrac{5}{8}$

31. $\dfrac{1}{12}$

32. $\dfrac{1}{3}$

33. $\dfrac{3}{16}$

34. $\dfrac{3}{8}$

35. $\dfrac{7}{8}$

36. $\dfrac{5}{12}$

37. $\dfrac{3}{4}$

38. $\dfrac{4}{5}$

39. $\dfrac{3}{5}$

40. $\dfrac{1}{10}$

41. $\dfrac{6}{10}$

42. Prove that for any numbers a and c, and any nonzero numbers b and d, if $ad = bc$, then $\dfrac{a}{b} = \dfrac{c}{d}$. See the Teacher Guide.

Application Exercises

Use proportions to solve each of the following.

43. Ann Towns plays basketball for a university team. Last season she attempted 156 field goals and made 117. What percent of the field goals attempted did she make?

44. The sales tax on $140 is $8.40. What is the rate of sales tax? (Hint: Find a percent.)

45. A designated hitter made 8 hits in 9 games. If he continues hitting at that rate, how many hits will he make in 108 games?

46. A recipe for preparing material to dye calls for 4 parts alum to 1 part washing soda. How much washing soda should be used for 150 grams of alum?

47. Bob Stapleton earns 2% of sales on all truck bodies he sells. Last month he earned $974. What were his sales?

48. Henri Rici paid $5000 for a car. After one year, its value had decreased by $1500. By what percent had the car depreciated in value? 30%

Algebra Review

Simplify. Assume no denominator is equal to zero.

1. $\dfrac{y^2 - 9}{y^2 + 6y + 9} \quad \dfrac{y-3}{y+3}$

2. $\dfrac{x^2 - x - 20}{x^2 + 7x + 12} \quad \dfrac{x-5}{x+3}$

Simplify.

3. $\sqrt{81}$ 9

4. $\sqrt{8}$ $2\sqrt{2}$

5. $\sqrt{150}$ $5\sqrt{6}$

Applications in Publishing   Reductions and Enlargements

Tami Parker is on the yearbook staff at Brunswick High School. One of her tasks is to determine the sizes of the different parts of copy on a page. Proportions are used to determine the adjusted size of reductions or enlargements of photographs.

Tami must reduce the photograph of the co-captains of the football team to fill a space two inches wide on the sports page. To determine the length of the reduced photograph, Tami must calculate the percent the photograph must be reduced.

The percent of reduction is found as follows.

$$\begin{array}{l} \text{new width} \\ \text{original width} \end{array} \quad \frac{2.0}{4.75} = \frac{n}{100} \quad \begin{array}{c} \textit{percent means parts} \\ \textit{per hundred} \end{array}$$

$$4.75\, n = 200.0$$
$$n = 42.11$$

The percent of reduction of the original photograph to the nearest tenth is 42.1%.

A percent greater than 100% is called an enlargement.

Exercises

Using the following dimensions, find the percent reduction or enlargement of the original photograph to the nearest tenth.

	Original Width	Original Length	Final Width
1.	5 in.	9 in.	4 in.
3.	14 in.	20 in.	12 in.

	Original Width	Original Length	Final Length
2.	$4\frac{1}{2}$ in.	6 in.	4 in.
4.	$6\frac{1}{4}$ in.	7 in.	$12\frac{1}{2}$ in.

5. State the numbers of the exercises that represent enlargements. 4

1. ⬛⬛ 2. ⬛⬛⬛ 3. ⬛⬛⬛ 4. ⬛⬛⬛

8-2 Properties of Proportions

Objectives: Name properties of proportions; prove properties of proportions; apply properties of proportions to geometric figures.

Proportions have many interesting properties. The properties can be derived using cross products and the properties of equality. The following chart summarizes these properties.

For any numbers a, b, c, and d, the following properties hold whenever all denominators are nonzero.	
	Emphasize that the denominators must be nonzero.
If $\frac{a}{b} = \frac{c}{d}$, then $\frac{a}{c} = \frac{b}{d}$ or $\frac{d}{b} = \frac{c}{a}$.	*Theorem 8-2*
If $\frac{a}{b} = \frac{c}{d}$, then $\frac{b}{a} = \frac{d}{c}$.	*Theorem 8-3*
$\frac{a}{b} = \frac{c}{d}$ if and only if $\frac{a+b}{b} = \frac{c+d}{d}$.	*Theorem 8-4* *Addition Property of Proportions*
$\frac{a}{b} = \frac{c}{d}$ if and only if $\frac{a-b}{b} = \frac{c-d}{d}$.	*Theorem 8-5* *Subtraction Property of Proportions*
$\frac{a}{b} = \frac{c}{d}$ if and only if $\frac{a}{b} = \frac{a+c}{b+d}$ or $\frac{c}{d} = \frac{a+c}{b+d}$.	*Theorem 8-6* *Summation Property of Proportions*

Students will prove Theorems 8-2, 8-3, 8-5, and 8-6 in Written Exercises 17–22.

Example

1 Prove that for any numbers a, b, c, and d, if $\frac{a}{b} = \frac{c}{d}$, then $\frac{a+b}{b} = \frac{c+d}{d}$, whenever all denominators are nonzero. This is one part of the proof for the biconditional statement in Theorem 8-4.

Given: $\frac{a}{b} = \frac{c}{d}$

Prove: $\frac{a+b}{b} = \frac{c+d}{d}$

Proof:

STATEMENTS	REASONS
1. $\frac{a}{b} = \frac{c}{d}$	1. Given
2. $ad = bc$	2. Equality of Cross Products (Theorem 8-1)
3. $ad + bd = bc + bd$	3. Addition Property of Equality (Postulate 2-7)
4. $(a + b)d = b(c + d)$	4. Distributive Property (Postulate 2-14)
5. $\frac{a+b}{b} = \frac{c+d}{d}$	5. Equality of Cross Products (Theorem 8-1)

The pictures above show special rectangles, called **golden rectangles.** The golden rectangle has a pleasing shape. Because of this, it can be found in ancient as well as modern art and architecture. Golden rectangles also have interesting mathematical properties. See the Teacher Guide for a discussion of these properties.

The two rectangles below are golden rectangles.

Draw other similar polygons to help reinforce proportional parts.

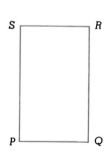

The measures of the width and length of each golden rectangle are in the ratio 1 to 1.618. *This ratio is called the **golden ratio.***

$$\frac{AB}{BC} = \frac{AB}{DA} = \frac{CD}{CB} = \frac{CD}{DA} \approx \frac{1}{1.618}$$

$$\frac{PQ}{QR} = \frac{PQ}{PS} = \frac{RS}{RQ} = \frac{RS}{SP} \approx \frac{1}{1.618}$$

The symbol $\approx$ means "approximately equal to."

Using properties of proportions, you can show that there is a correspondence between the rectangles so that the measures of their corresponding sides are **proportional.**

$$\frac{AB}{PQ} = \frac{BC}{QR} = \frac{CD}{RS} = \frac{DA}{SP}$$

Example

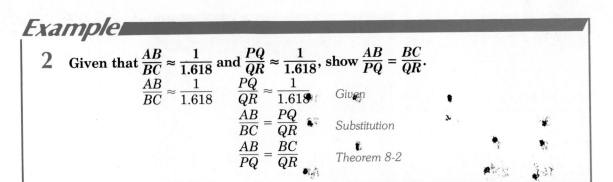

2 Given that $\dfrac{AB}{BC} \approx \dfrac{1}{1.618}$ and $\dfrac{PQ}{QR} \approx \dfrac{1}{1.618}$, show $\dfrac{AB}{PQ} = \dfrac{BC}{QR}$.

$\dfrac{AB}{BC} \approx \dfrac{1}{1.618} \qquad \dfrac{PQ}{QR} \approx \dfrac{1}{1.618}$	*Given*
$\dfrac{AB}{BC} = \dfrac{PQ}{QR}$	*Substitution*
$\dfrac{AB}{PQ} = \dfrac{BC}{QR}$	*Theorem 8-2*

EN: 2–14 even, 2–28 even; **AV:** 1–14, 1–16, 17–27 odd; **FD:** 1–14, 1–18, p. 270, 43–45

Exploratory Exercises

Name the property shown in each of the following.

1. If $\dfrac{3}{1} = \dfrac{6}{2}$, then $\dfrac{3-1}{1} = \dfrac{6-2}{2}$. Theorem 8-5

2. If $\dfrac{3}{1} = \dfrac{6}{2}$, then $\dfrac{2}{1} = \dfrac{4}{2}$. Theorem 8-5

3. If $\dfrac{3}{1} = \dfrac{6}{2}$, then $\dfrac{4}{1} = \dfrac{8}{2}$. Theorem 8-4

4. If $\dfrac{3+1}{1} = \dfrac{6+2}{2}$, then $\dfrac{3}{1} = \dfrac{6}{2}$. Theorem 8-4

5. If $\dfrac{6}{8} = \dfrac{7}{x}$, then $\dfrac{8}{6} = \dfrac{x}{7}$. Theorem 8-3

6. If $\dfrac{2}{10} = \dfrac{1}{y}$, then $\dfrac{y}{10} = \dfrac{1}{2}$. Theorem 8-2

7. If $\dfrac{3}{4} = \dfrac{3+y}{8}$, then $\dfrac{3}{4} = \dfrac{y}{4}$. Theorem 8-6

8. If $\dfrac{2}{3} = \dfrac{x}{6}$, then $\dfrac{2}{3} = \dfrac{x+2}{9}$. Theorem 8-6

9. If $\dfrac{12}{b} = \dfrac{11}{a}$, then $\dfrac{a}{b} = \dfrac{11}{12}$. Theorem 8-2

10. If $\dfrac{x}{27} = \dfrac{y}{13}$, then $\dfrac{x}{y} = \dfrac{27}{13}$. Theorem 8-2

11. If $\dfrac{25}{14} = \dfrac{7}{AB}$, then $\dfrac{14}{25} = \dfrac{AB}{7}$. Theorem 8-3

12. If $\dfrac{25}{14} = \dfrac{7}{AB}$, then $\dfrac{AB}{14} = \dfrac{7}{25}$. Theorem 8-2

13. If $\dfrac{PQ}{QR} = \dfrac{PQ}{SP}$, then $\dfrac{QR}{SP} = \dfrac{PQ}{PQ}$. Theorem 8-2, Postulate 2-5

14. If $\dfrac{CD}{BC} = \dfrac{RS}{QR}$, then $\dfrac{CD}{RS} = \dfrac{BC}{QR}$. Theorem 8-2

Written Exercises

Suppose the measures of corresponding sides of the polygons at the right are proportional. For each of the following, find the indicated measures.

1. If $AB = 5$, $AD = 2$, and $PQ = 3$, find PS.

2. If $RS = 4.5$, $CD = 6.3$, and $BC = 7.0$, find QR.

3. If $CD = 43.6$, $DA = 21.8$, and $SR = 33.0$, find SP.

4. If $QR = x + 3$, $PQ = 4$, $BC = x + 5$, and $AB = 5$, find BC and RQ.

5. If $DA = x + 2$, $AB = x - 3$, $PS = 5$, and $PQ = 3$, find AB and DA.

6. If $BC = 7$, $RS = 2x + 1$, $QR = 4$, and $CD = 3x + 3$, find CD and RS.

7. If $RS = 3$, $QR = 3x$, $CD = x + 2$, and $BC = x^2 + 4$, find QR, CD, and BC.

8. If $AB = x$, $QR = x + 3$, $PQ = 3$, and $BC = x + 12$, find AB, QR, and BC.

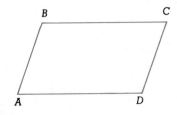

In the figure at the right, $\dfrac{RS}{SP} = \dfrac{RT}{TQ}$. Using proportions, complete the following table.

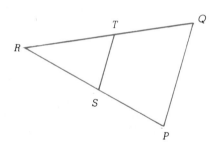

	RS	SP	RP	RT	TQ	RQ
9.	2	3	⬤	4	⬤	⬤
10.	⬤	45	⬤	32	40	⬤
11.	⬤	⬤	3	16	⬤	24
12.	⬤	⬤	36	36	48	⬤

Applying the properties of proportions, complete the following statements.

13. If $\dfrac{CD}{MN} = \dfrac{KJ}{GH}$, then $\dfrac{GH}{MN} = \dfrac{\blacksquare}{\blacksquare}$ ⬤

14. If $\dfrac{AB + BC}{BC} = \dfrac{PQ + QR}{QR}$, then $\dfrac{AB}{BC} = \dfrac{\blacksquare}{\blacksquare}$ ⬤

15. If $\dfrac{ST}{TR} = \dfrac{PQ}{QR}$, then $\dfrac{TR}{ST} = \dfrac{\blacksquare}{\blacksquare}$ ⬤

16. If $EF \cdot UV = OL \cdot RS$, then $\dfrac{EF}{OL} = \dfrac{\blacksquare}{\blacksquare}$ ⬤

For Exercises 17–22, see the Teacher Guide.

Prove each of the following exercises whenever all denominators are nonzero.

17. For any numbers a, b, c, and d,
if $\dfrac{a}{b} = \dfrac{c}{d}$, then $\dfrac{a}{c} = \dfrac{b}{d}$.

18. For any numbers a, b, c, and d,
if $\dfrac{a}{b} = \dfrac{c}{d}$, then $\dfrac{b}{a} = \dfrac{d}{c}$.

19. For any numbers a, b, c, and d,
if $\dfrac{a}{b} = \dfrac{c}{d}$, then $\dfrac{a - b}{b} = \dfrac{c - d}{d}$.

20. For any numbers a, b, c, and d,
if $\dfrac{a - b}{b} = \dfrac{c - d}{d}$, then $\dfrac{a}{b} = \dfrac{c}{d}$.

21. For any numbers a, b, c, and d,
if $\dfrac{a}{b} = \dfrac{a + c}{b + d}$, then $\dfrac{a}{b} = \dfrac{c}{d}$.

22. For any numbers a, b, c, and d,
if $\dfrac{a}{b} = \dfrac{c}{d}$, then $\dfrac{c}{d} = \dfrac{a + c}{b + d}$.

Application Exercises

Use a proportion to solve each of the following problems. Express answers as decimals rounded to the nearest tenth.

23. John Frank is a potter making a rectangular clay plaque 25 inches by 36 inches. The plaque shrinks uniformly in the oven to a 30 inches length. What is the width after the plaque shrinks? 20.8 in.

24. Cindy Lawyer has a 55 cm by 60 cm oil painting. She wants to paint a copy that will fit a 40 cm width. What will be the corresponding length? ⬤ cm

25. A map is scaled so that 1 cm represents 15 km. How far apart are two towns if they are 7.9 cm apart on the map? ⬤ km

26. A 75-foot tree casts a 40-foot shadow. How tall is a tree that casts a 10-foot shadow at the same time of day? 18.8 ft

27. The scale on a map is 1 cm to 57 km. Fargo and Bismarck are 4.7 cm apart on the map. What is the actual distance between these cities? ⬤ km

28. The scale on a map is 2 cm to 5 km. Dove Creek and Kent are 15.75 km apart. How far apart are they on the map? 6.3 cm

8-3 Similar Polygons

Objectives: Identify similar polygons; use properties of similar polygons to solve problems.

Enlargements of an original photograph are shown below. All the copies have the same shape but differ in size.

Ask students to name objects that have the same shape but different sizes.

In geometry, figures that have the same shape, but may differ in size are called **similar figures.**

Corresponding parts of polygons are used to tell if they are similar. For example, the parallelograms $ABCD$ and $PQRS$ are similar.

The word "may" suggests that similar figures can be the same size or congruent.

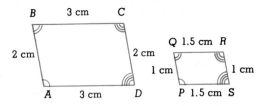

The corresponding angles of parallelograms $ABCD$ and $PQRS$ are congruent. The measures of their corresponding sides have the same ratio, so they are proportional.

$$\angle A \cong \angle P$$
$$\angle B \cong \angle Q$$
$$\angle C \cong \angle R$$
$$\angle D \cong \angle S$$

$$\frac{AB}{PQ} = \frac{BC}{QR} = \frac{CD}{RS} = \frac{DA}{SP} = \frac{2}{1}$$

Relate the pairing of proportional parts of similar triangles to the corresponding parts of congruent triangles.

The symbol ~ means *similar* or *is similar to*. We write, $\square ABCD \sim \square PQRS$, and we say *parallelogram ABCD is similar to parallelogram PQRS*. The order of letters indicates the vertices that correspond.

Two polygons are similar if and only if there is a correspondence such that their corresponding angles are congruent and the measures of their corresponding sides are proportional.

Definition of Similar Polygons

For two polygons to be similar, there are two conditions to be proven. If *only one* of the conditions is proven, then the polygons will *not* be similar.

The corresponding angles for these two figures are congruent. The measures of the corresponding sides are *not* proportional.

The measures of corresponding sides are proportional for these two figures. The corresponding angles are *not* congruent.

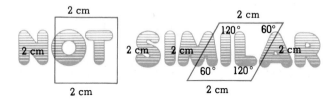

Example

1 **Determine whether all squares are similar.**

All squares have four right angles, and all right angles are congruent. Thus, any correspondence between squares will have corresponding angles congruent.

All four sides of a square are congruent. Thus, the measures of each set of corresponding sides form equal ratios. That is, the measures of the corresponding sides are proportional.

Therefore, all squares are similar.

$$\frac{s}{x} = \frac{s}{x} = \frac{s}{x} = \frac{s}{x}$$

If s = x, are the squares similar? Yes. They would also be congruent.

Ask if all rectangles are similar. See Written Exercise 3.

If the measures of some parts of two similar figures are known, then it may be possible to find the measures of other parts.

Example

2 **Suppose quadrilaterals *ABCD* and *PQRS* are similar. Find the value of *x*.**

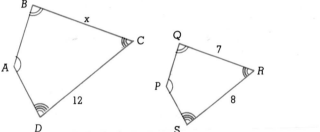

$$\frac{BC}{QR} = \frac{DC}{SR}$$

$$\frac{x}{7} = \frac{12}{8}$$

$$8x = 84$$

$$x = 10.5$$

Example

3 Contractors refer to blueprints when constructing a house. The blueprint and constructed house are similar. The blueprint shown at the right is in the scale of 1 inch on the figure equals an actual length of 16 feet. Using the properties of similar figures, determine the dimensions of the kitchen.

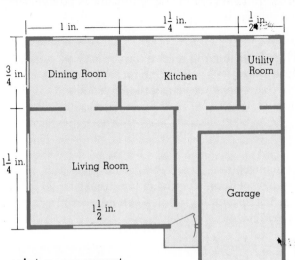

$$\frac{\text{blueprint measurement}}{\text{actual measurement}} = \frac{\text{kitchen blueprint measurement}}{\text{actual kitchen measurement}}$$

length of kitchen

$$\frac{1}{16} = \frac{1.25}{\ell} \qquad 1\frac{1}{4} = 1.25$$
$$\ell = 20$$

width of kitchen

$$\frac{1}{16} = \frac{0.75}{w} \qquad \frac{3}{4} = 0.75$$
$$w = 12$$

The kitchen is 12 feet wide and 20 feet long.

EN: 4–8, 2–24 even; **AV:** 1–8, 1–18, 19–23 odd; **FD:** 1–8, 1–20, p. 275, 24–28

Exploratory Exercises   **ALL LEVELS:** Mini Review

For each of the following exercises, list the information needed to show that the figures in each pair are similar. For Exercises 1–4, see the Teacher Guide.

1. $\triangle ABC \sim \triangle DEF$

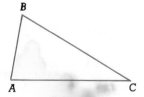

2. polygon $PQRS \sim$ polygon $ABCD$

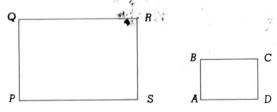

3. polygon $RSTVWX \sim$ polygon $LMNOPQ$

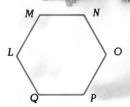

4. polygon $ABCD \sim$ polygon $NMLP$

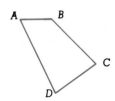

Determine whether the figures in each of the following pairs are similar. Give a reason for each answer. For reasons to Exercises 5–8, see the Teacher Guide.

5. ~~yes~~

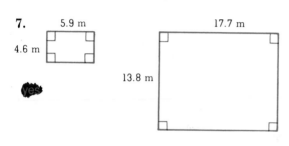

6. ~~no~~

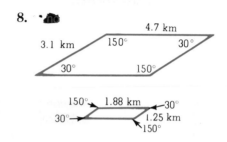

7.

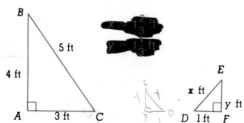

~~yes~~

8. ~~no~~

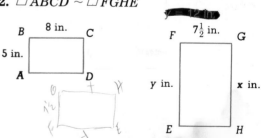

Written Exercises

For reasons to Exercises 1–10, see the Teacher Guide.

Determine whether each statement is *true* or *false*. Then explain your answer.

1. All equilateral triangles are similar. ~~true~~
2. All isosceles triangles are similar. ~~false~~
3. All rectangles are similar. ~~false~~
4. All regular hexagons are similar. ~~true~~
5. All rhombuses are similar. ~~false~~
6. Congruent triangles are similar. ~~true~~
7. All trapezoids are similar. ~~false~~
8. All parallelograms are similar. ~~false~~
9. Similar quadrilaterals are congruent. ~~false~~
10. Congruent quadrilaterals are similar. ~~true~~

For each of the following, find the values of *x* and *y*.

11. $\triangle ABC \sim \triangle FED$

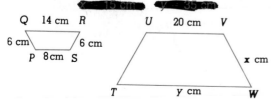

12. $\square ABCD \sim \square FGHE$

~~x = 12 in.~~
~~12 in.~~

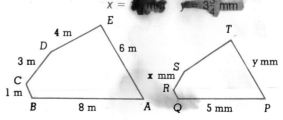

13. trapezoid $PQRS \sim$ trapezoid $VWTU$

~~x = 15 cm~~ ~~y = 35 cm~~

14. pentagon $ABCDE \sim$ pentagon $PQRST$

$x =$ ~~4 mm~~ $y = 3\frac{3}{4}$ mm

Complete the following exercises.

15. In the figure below, the two triangles are similar. If $\overline{ST} \parallel \overline{VW}$, state the similarity for the triangles. Write three equal ratios to show corresponding sides are proportional.

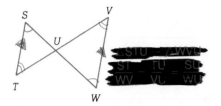

16. In the figure below, quadrilateral $EFGH$ ~ quadrilateral $PQRS$. If the perimeter of $EFGH$ is 36 cm, find the values of x, y, and z.

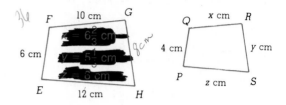

17. If $\triangle ABC \sim \triangle DEF$, find x and y.

18. If $\triangle TXW \sim \triangle TUV$, find XV.

Prove each of the following statements. For Exercises 19–22, see the Teacher Guide.

19. Similarity of triangles is reflexive.
21. Similarity of triangles is transitive.

20. Similarity of triangles is symmetric.
22. If two triangles are congruent, then the triangles are similar.

Application Exercises——————

Answer each of the following exercises.

23. The poster shown below has a width of 14 inches and a height of 21 inches. The manufacturer plans to issue an enlarged poster with an 18 inch width. Find the new height. 27 inches

24. Joan Shaull designs automobiles using scale drawings. Suppose one length on a model is 1.2 cm and corresponds to 3 cm on the drawing. Find the length on the model that corresponds to 2 cm on the drawing. 0.8 cm.

8-4 Similar Triangles

Objectives: Recognize the conditions for similar triangles; use the tests for similar triangles in proofs and other problem-solving situations.

To show that two triangles are similar, it is *not* necessary to prove all the conditions of the definition of similar polygons. The following postulate tells you that the shape of a triangle is completely determined by the measures of its angles.

If two angles of one triangle are congruent to two corresponding angles of another triangle, then the triangles are similar.

Postulate 8-1
AA Similarity

Example

1 **Prove the following.** It may be helpful to redraw these triangles separately to help students visualize the proportional parts.

Given: $\overline{ST} \parallel \overline{PR}$
$QS = 3$
$SP = 1$
$TR = 1.2$

Prove: $QT = 3.6$

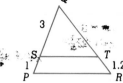

Proof:

STATEMENTS	REASONS
1. $\overline{ST} \parallel \overline{PR}$	1. Given
2. $\angle QST \cong \angle QPR$ $\angle QTS \cong \angle QRP$	2. If two parallel lines are cut by a transversal, then each pair of corresponding angles are congruent. (Theorem 6-9)
3. $\triangle SQT \sim \triangle PQR$	3. AA Similarity (Postulate 8-1)
4. $\dfrac{QT}{QR} = \dfrac{QS}{QP}$	4. Definition of Similar Polygons
5. $QS = 3$ $SP = 1$ $TR = 1.2$	5. Given
6. $QP = QS + SP$ $\quad = 3 + 1$ $\quad = 4$ $QR = QT + TR$ $\quad = QT + 1.2$	6. Definition of Between and Substitution (Postulate 2-9)
7. $\dfrac{QT}{QT + 1.2} = \dfrac{3}{4}$	7. Substitution (Postulate 2-9)
8. $4QT = 3(QT + 1.2)$ $\quad = 3QT + 3.6$	8. Equality of Cross Products (Theorem 8-1) and Distributive Property (Postulate 2-14)
9. $QT = 3.6$	9. Subtraction Property of Equality (Postulate 2-7)

To check triangles for similarity, it is only necessary to test angle measures. Could similarity of triangles be checked by testing the measures of corresponding sides for proportionality? yes

Point out how this theorem differs from SSS congruence.

If there is a correspondence between the two triangles so that the measures of their corresponding sides are proportional, then the two triangles are similar.	*Theorem 8-7* *SSS Similarity*

Emphasize that these conditions must be true for all three pairs of sides.

Example

2   **Prove Theorem 8-7.**

  Given: $\dfrac{PQ}{AB} = \dfrac{QR}{BC} = \dfrac{RP}{CA}$

  Prove: $\triangle BAC \sim \triangle QPR$

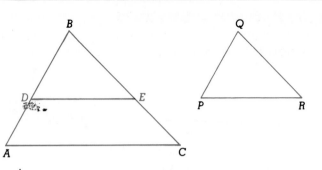

Proof:

STATEMENTS	REASONS
1. $\dfrac{PQ}{AB} = \dfrac{QR}{BC} = \dfrac{RP}{CA}$	1. Given
2. Locate D on $\overline{AB}$ so that $\overline{DB} \cong \overline{PQ}$.	2. Ruler Postulate (Postulate 2-2) and Definition of Congruent Segments
3. Draw $\overline{DE}$ so that $\overline{DE} \parallel \overline{AC}$.	3. Parallel Postulate (Postulate 6-1)
4. $\angle BDE \cong \angle A$ $\angle BED \cong \angle C$	4. If two parallel lines are cut by a transversal, then each pair of corresponding angles are congruent. (Theorem 6-9)
5. $\triangle BDE \sim \triangle BAC$	5. AA Similarity (Postulate 8-1)
6. $\dfrac{DB}{AB} = \dfrac{BE}{BC} = \dfrac{ED}{CA}$	6. Definition of Similar Polygons
7. $DB = PQ$	7. Definition of Congruent Segments
8. $\dfrac{DB}{AB} = \dfrac{QR}{BC} = \dfrac{RP}{CA}$	8. Substitution (Postulate 2-9) *Steps 1 and 7*
9. $\dfrac{QR}{BC} = \dfrac{BE}{BC}$ $\dfrac{RP}{CA} = \dfrac{ED}{CA}$	9. Substitution (Postulate 2-9) *Steps 6 and 8*
10. $QR = BE,\ RP = ED$	10. Multiplication Property of Equality (Postulate 2-8)
11. $\overline{QR} \cong \overline{BE},\ \overline{RP} \cong \overline{ED}$	11. Definition of Congruent Segments
12. $\triangle BDE \cong \triangle QPR$	12. SSS (Postulate 4-1)

13. $\angle B \cong \angle Q$, $\angle BDE \cong \angle P$	13. Definition of Congruent Triangles
14. $\angle A \cong \angle P$	14. Transitive Property of Congruence (Postulate 3-1) *Steps 4 and 13*
15. $\triangle BAC \sim \triangle QPR$	15. AA Similarity (Postulate 8-1)

| If the measures of two sides of a triangle are proportional to the measures of two corresponding sides of another triangle, and the included angles are congruent, then the triangles are similar. | *Theorem 8-8* *SAS Similarity* |

EN: 2–6 even; 1–7, 11, 12; **AV:** 1–6, 1–6, 8, 10, 12; **FD:** 1–6, 1–6, 8, p. 280, 23–24

Exploratory Exercises

Use each figure and the information given to determine whether each pair of triangles are similar. Give a reason for each answer. See the Teacher Guide.

1. yes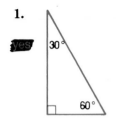

2. yes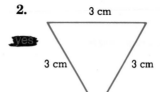

3. no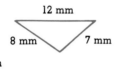

4. yes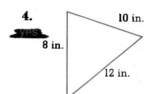

5. yes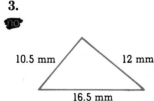

6. no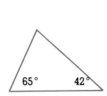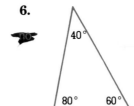

Written Exercises

For each of the following exercises, use the figure at the right and the given information to find the value of x.

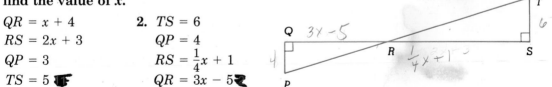

1. $QR = x + 4$
$RS = 2x + 3$
$QP = 3$
$TS = 5$

2. $TS = 6$
$QP = 4$
$RS = \frac{1}{4}x + 1$
$QR = 3x - 5$

Determine if the following pairs of triangles are similar. If similar, find the missing measures.

3.

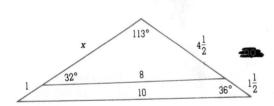

4.

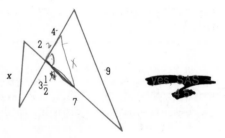

In the figure at the right, $\triangle HKJ \sim \triangle HLM$. Complete the following exercises.

5. State the relationship between $\overline{KJ}$ and $\overline{LM}$. Give a reason for your answer.
   See the Teacher Guide.

6. If $HK = 3$, $KL = x + 2$, $KJ = 4$, and $LM = 2x + 4$, write a proportion to solve for x. Then, find KL, HL, and LM.

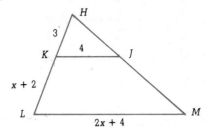

Prove each of the following exercises. For Exercises 7–12, see the Teacher Guide.

7. If the measures of two sides of a triangle are proportional to the measures of two corresponding sides of another triangle, and the included angles are congruent, the triangles are similar. (Theorem 8-8)

8. If the measures of the sides adjacent to the right angles of two right triangles are proportional, the triangles are similar.

9. **Given:** $\angle D$ is a right angle.
   $\overline{BE} \perp \overline{AC}$
   Prove: $\triangle ADC \sim \triangle ABE$

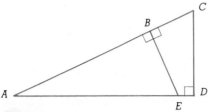

10. **Given:** $\overline{QS} \parallel \overline{PT}$
    Prove: $\triangle QRS \sim \triangle TRP$

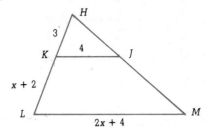

11. **Given:** $\angle Q$ is a right angle.
    $\square WSTV$ is a square.
    Prove: $\triangle PWS \sim \triangle TVR$

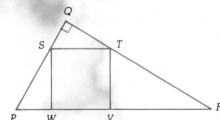

12. **Given:** $\overline{PR} \cong \overline{TR}$
    $\overline{VQ} \perp \overline{PR}$
    $\overline{VS} \perp \overline{RT}$
    Prove: $\dfrac{PQ}{TS} = \dfrac{VQ}{VS}$

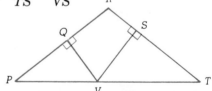

8-5 Proportional Parts

Objective: Recognize and use the relationships between parallels and proportional parts of triangles in problem-solving.

Proportional parts of a triangle can be used to prove that lines are parallel.

> If a line intersects two sides of a triangle, and separates the sides into segments of proportional lengths, then the line is parallel to the third side.
>
> *Theorem 8-9*

You may want to present Constructions 12 and 13 on page 486 at this time.

Example

1 **Prove Theorem 8-9.**

Given: $\dfrac{BA}{CB} = \dfrac{DE}{CD}$

Prove: $\overleftrightarrow{BD} \parallel \overline{AE}$

These triangles can be redrawn separately to help show the proportional parts.

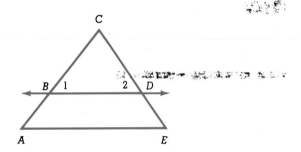

Proof:

STATEMENTS	REASONS
1. $\dfrac{BA}{CB} = \dfrac{DE}{CD}$	1. Given
2. B is between C and A. D is between C and E.	2. Given
3. $CA = CB + BA$ $CE = CD + DE$	3. Definition of Between
4. $BA = CA - CB$ $DE = CE - CD$	4. Subtraction Property of Equality (Postulate 2-7)
5. $\dfrac{CA - CB}{CB} = \dfrac{CE - CD}{CD}$	5. Substitution (Postulate 2-9) *Steps 1 and 4*
6. $\dfrac{CA}{CB} = \dfrac{CE}{CD}$	6. Subtraction Property of Proportions (Theorem 8-5)
7. $\angle C \cong \angle C$	7. Congruence of angles is reflexive. (Theorem 3-1)
8. $\triangle CBD \sim \triangle CAE$	8. SAS Similarity (Theorem 8-8) *Steps 6 and 7*
9. $\angle 1 \cong \angle 4$	9. Definition of Similar Polygons
10. $\overleftrightarrow{BD} \parallel \overline{AE}$	10. In a plane, if two lines are cut by a transversal so that a pair of corresponding angles are congruent, then the two lines are parallel. (Theorem 6-5)

Geometric concepts can be demonstrated by physical representation. Consider each horizontal support in the stained glass window as the base of a triangle with part of the window as sides. Each support is parallel to the others. The following theorem tells you that because the supports are parallel, the triangles formed are similar.

If a line is parallel to one side of a triangle and intersects the other two sides, then it separates the sides into segments of proportional lengths.	*Theorem 8-10*

Example

2 **Prove Theorem 8-10.**

Given: $\overline{BD} \parallel \overline{AE}$

Prove: $\dfrac{BA}{CB} = \dfrac{DE}{CD}$

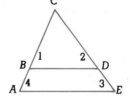

Proof:

STATEMENTS	REASONS
1. $\overline{BD} \parallel \overline{AE}$	1. Given
2. $\angle 1 \cong \angle 4$ $\angle 2 \cong \angle 3$	2. If two parallel lines are cut by a transversal, then each pair of corresponding angles are congruent. (Theorem 6-9)
3. $\triangle ACE \sim \triangle BCD$	3. AA Similarity (Postulate 8-1)
4. $\dfrac{CA}{CB} = \dfrac{CE}{CD}$	4. Definition of Similar Polygons
5. B is between A and C. D is between C and E.	5. Given
6. $CA = BA + CB$ $CE = DE + CD$	6. Definition of Between
7. $\dfrac{BA + CB}{CB} = \dfrac{DE + CD}{CD}$	7. Substitution (Postulate 2-9) *Steps 4 and 6*
8. $\dfrac{BA}{CB} = \dfrac{DE}{CD}$	8. Addition Property of Proportions (Theorem 8-4)

The proof of the following theorem is based on Theorems 8-9 and 8-10.

Students will complete a proof of this theorem in Written Exercise 10.

> **If a segment has as its endpoints the midpoints of two sides of a triangle, then it is parallel to the third side and its length is one-half the length of the third side.**

Theorem 8-11

In the triangle below, suppose that B is the midpoint of $\overline{AC}$ and D is the midpoint of $\overline{CE}$.

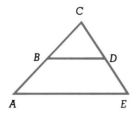

By Theorem 8-11, $\overline{BD} \parallel \overline{AE}$ and $BD = \frac{1}{2}AE$.

This relationship can also be expressed $2BD = AE$.

Three or more parallel lines separate transversals into proportional parts as stated below.

> **If three parallel lines intersect two transversals, then they divide the transversals proportionally.**

Theorem 8-12

> **If three parallel lines cut off congruent segments on one transversal, then they cut off congruent segments on any transversal.**

Theorem 8-13

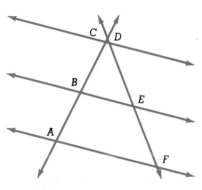

In the figure at the left, $\overleftrightarrow{CD} \parallel \overleftrightarrow{BE} \parallel \overleftrightarrow{AF}$. The transversals $\overleftrightarrow{AC}$ and $\overleftrightarrow{FD}$ have been separated into proportional segments. Sample proportions are listed below.

$$\frac{CB}{BA} = \frac{DE}{EF}; \frac{CA}{DF} = \frac{BA}{EF}; \frac{AC}{BC} = \frac{FD}{ED}$$

You may want students to name other proportions in class discussion.

Exploratory Exercises

In the figure, $\overline{BD} \parallel \overline{AE}$. Determine whether each statement is *true* or *false*.

1. $\dfrac{BC}{ED} = \dfrac{AB}{CD}$ false

2. $\dfrac{AB}{BC} = \dfrac{DE}{CD}$

3. $\dfrac{CB}{CD} = \dfrac{CA}{CE}$ true

4. $\dfrac{BA}{DE} = \dfrac{CA}{CE}$ true

5. $\dfrac{AC}{EC} = \dfrac{DC}{BC}$ false

6. $\dfrac{CB}{BA} \ne \dfrac{DE}{DC}$ false

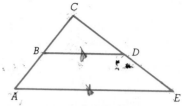

In the figure below, $\overleftrightarrow{YA} \parallel \overleftrightarrow{OE} \parallel \overleftrightarrow{BR}$. Complete each of the following statements.

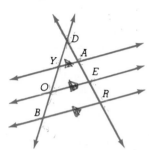

7. $\dfrac{YO}{OB} = \dfrac{AE}{\blacksquare}$

8. $\dfrac{YB}{OB} = \dfrac{\blacksquare}{ER}$

9. $\dfrac{\blacksquare}{AE} = \dfrac{YB}{YO}$

10. $\dfrac{DY}{YO} = \dfrac{DA}{\blacksquare}$

11. $\dfrac{DR}{\blacksquare} = \dfrac{DB}{YB}$

12. $\dfrac{\blacksquare}{AE} = \dfrac{DO}{YO}$

13. $\dfrac{AE}{DR} = \dfrac{\blacksquare}{DB}$

14. $\dfrac{ER}{\blacksquare} = \dfrac{OB}{DO}$

In $\triangle XYZ$ at the right, L and M are midpoints of $\overline{XZ}$ and $\overline{XY}$. Using the given information, complete the following exercises.

15. Find LM if $ZY = 12$.

16. If $LZ = 8$, find XL.

17. If $XY = 18$, find MY.

18. Find YZ if $LM = 2.6$.

19. Find $m \angle Z$ if $m \angle X = 39$ and $m \angle XML = 27$.

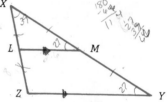

Written Exercises

For each of the following exercises, determine whether $\overline{QT} \parallel \overline{RS}$. Write *yes* or *no*.

1. $PR = 30$
   $PQ = 9$
   $PT = 12$
   $PS = 18$

2. $QR = 22$
   $TS = 9$
   $RP = 65$
   $SP = 27$

3. $RP = 13.5$
   $RQ = 7.2$
   $TP = 4.2$
   $SP = 9.0$

4. $PQ = 34.88$
   $RQ = 18.32$
   $PS = 33.25$
   $TS = 11.45$ yes

For the figure below, determine the value for x that would make $\overline{PQ} \parallel \overline{DF}$.

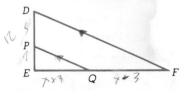

5. $EQ = 3$
   $PD = 12$
   $QF = 8$
   $PE = x + 2$

6. $DE = 12$
   $PE = 7$
   $EQ = x + 3$
   $QF = x - 3$

288 *Similarity*

For each of the following exercises, use the figure at the right and the given information to find the value of *x*.

7. $\overline{BD} \parallel \overline{AE}$
   $AB = 6$
   $DE = 8$
   $DC = 4$
   $BC = x$ ▬▬

8. $\overline{AC} \parallel \overline{DF}$
   $DC = 7$
   $DE = 5$
   $FA = 8$
   $FE = x$ ▬▬

9. $\overline{DF} \parallel \overline{CA}$
   $AF = 3.42$
   $FE = 3.35$
   $DE = 6.7$
   $CD = x$ ▬▬

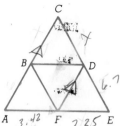

10. **Complete the proof of Theorem 8-11.**

   Given: Q is the midpoint of $\overline{RP}$.
   S is the midpoint of $\overline{RT}$.
   Prove: $\overline{QS} \parallel \overline{PT}$
   $QS = \frac{1}{2}PT$

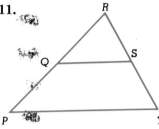

Proof:

STATEMENTS	REASONS
1. Q is the midpoint of $\overline{RP}$. S is the midpoint of $\overline{RT}$.	1. Given
2. $QR = PQ$, $SR = TS$	2. Definition of Midpoint
3. $RP = PQ + QR$, $TR = TS + SR$	3. ~~Definition of Between~~
4. $RP = QR + QR$, $TR = SR + SR$	4. Substitution (Postulate 2-9)
5. $RP = 2QR$, $TR = 2SR$	5. ~~Postulate 2-14, Postulate 2-9~~
6. $\frac{RP}{QR} = 2$, $\frac{TR}{SR} = 2$	6. Division Property of Equality (Postulate 2-8)
7. $\frac{RP}{QR} = \frac{TR}{SR}$	7. Substitution (Postulate 2-9)
8. $\angle R \cong \angle R$	8. ~~Theorem 8-1~~
9. $\triangle RPT \sim \triangle RQS$	9. ~~SAS Similarity~~
10. $\angle RPT \cong \angle RQS$	10. ~~Definition of Similar Polygons~~
11. $\overline{QS} \parallel \overline{PT}$	11. ~~Theorem 6-5~~
12. $\frac{RP}{QR} = \frac{PT}{QS}$	12. ~~Definition of Similar Polygons~~
13. $\frac{PT}{QS} = 2$	13. Substitution (Postulate 2-9)
14. $QS = \frac{1}{2}PT$	14. Multiplication Property of Equality (Postulate 2-8), Symmetric Property of Equality (Postulate 2-5), and Division Property of Equality (Postulate 2-8).

8-6 Parts of Similar Polygons

Objective: Recognize and use the proportional relationships of corresponding perimeters, altitudes, angle bisectors, and medians of similar triangles.

When two triangles are similar, the measures of their corresponding sides are proportional. What about their corresponding altitudes, medians, and so on? Are the measures of these proportional to the measures of the corresponding sides of the triangles? yes

By using the Summation Property of Proportions, you can show that the measures of corresponding perimeters are proportional to the measures of corresponding sides of similar triangles.

Review this property of proportions.

In the figure at the right, suppose $\triangle ABC \sim \triangle PQR$.

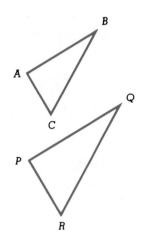

$$\frac{AB}{PQ} = \frac{BC}{QR} = \frac{CA}{RP} \qquad \textit{Definition of Similar Triangles}$$

$$\frac{AB}{PQ} = \frac{AB + BC}{PQ + QR} \qquad \textit{Summation Property of Proportions}$$

$$\frac{AB + BC}{PQ + QR} = \frac{CA}{RP} \qquad \textit{Substitution}$$

$$\frac{AB + BC + CA}{PQ + QR + RP} = \frac{CA}{RP} \qquad \textit{Summation Property of Proportions}$$

This procedure can be repeated as many times as necessary to prove that corresponding perimeters are proportional to corresponding sides for any set of similar polygons.

If two triangles are similar, then the measures of corresponding perimeters are proportional to the measures of corresponding sides.	*Theorem 8-14*

Example

1 In the figure at the right, suppose $\triangle ABD \sim \triangle ADC$. If the perimeter of $\triangle ABD$ measures 37, the perimeter of $\triangle ADC$ measures 71, and $AD = 16$, find AB.

$$\frac{AB}{AD} = \frac{AB + BD + DA}{AD + DC + CA}$$

$$\frac{AB}{16} = \frac{37}{71}$$

$$71 \cdot AB = 37 \cdot 16$$

$$AB = \frac{37 \cdot 16}{71}$$

$$\approx 8.3$$

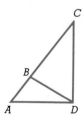

In the figure below, suppose $\triangle ABC \sim \triangle PQR$. Then $\angle A \cong \angle P$ because they are corresponding angles. Since $\overline{BD}$ is an altitude of $\triangle ABC$, it forms a right angle, $\angle BDA$. Similarly, $\angle QSP$ is a right angle. By AA Similarity, $\triangle ABD \sim \triangle PQS$. Thus, $\dfrac{BD}{QS} = \dfrac{BA}{QP}$.

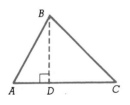

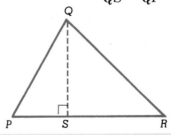

Help students find the corresponding parts.

Students may need to review the properties of altitudes, angle bisectors, and medians.

If two triangles are similar, then the measures of corresponding altitudes are proportional to the measures of corresponding sides.	*Theorem 8-15*

Students will prove this theorem in Written Exercise 14.

In the figure below, suppose $\triangle RST \sim \triangle EFG$. Then $\angle SRT \cong \angle FEG$ because they are corresponding angles. $\overrightarrow{RV}$ bisects $\angle SRT$ and $\overrightarrow{EH}$ bisects $\angle FEG$. Then $\angle SRV \cong \angle FEH$. Using AA Similarity, $\triangle RSV \sim \triangle EFH$. Thus, $\dfrac{RV}{EH} = \dfrac{RS}{EF}$.

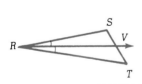

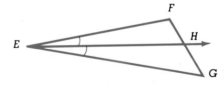

If two triangles are similar, then the measures of corresponding angle bisectors of the triangles are proportional to the measures of corresponding sides.	*Theorem 8-16*

Students will plan a proof for this theorem in Written Exercise 15.

Example

2 State five different proportions for $\triangle KLM$ and $\triangle WXY$ if $\triangle KLM \sim \triangle WXY$.

The proportions include the following.

$$\frac{AM}{BY} = \frac{LM}{XY}, \frac{AM}{BY} = \frac{KM}{WY}$$

$$\frac{AM}{BY} = \frac{KL}{WX}, \frac{AL}{LM} = \frac{BX}{XY}$$

$$\frac{KA + AM + MK}{WB + BY + YW} = \frac{KA}{WB}$$

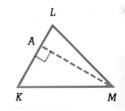

> If two triangles are similar, then the measures of corresponding medians are proportional to the measures of corresponding sides.

Theorem 8-17

Example

3 Plan a proof for Theorem 8-17.

Students will complete this proof in Written Exercise 16.

Given: $\triangle ABC \sim \triangle PQR$
$\overline{BD}$ is a median of $\triangle ABC$.
$\overline{QS}$ is a median of $\triangle PQR$.

Prove: $\dfrac{BD}{QS} = \dfrac{BA}{QP}$

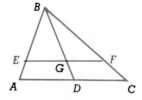

Proof:

Draw $\overline{EF}$ so that $\overline{BE} \cong \overline{QP}$ and $\angle BEF \cong \angle QPR$.

Since $\triangle ABC \sim \triangle PQR$, conclude that $\angle QPR \cong \angle BAC$. Thus, by transitivity of angle congruence, $\angle BEF \cong \angle BAC$. Since $\angle ABD$ is congruent to itself, AA Similarity implies that $\triangle BEG \sim \triangle BAD$.

Since $\overline{BD}$ is a median of $\triangle ABC$ and $\overline{QS}$ is a median of $\triangle PQR$, then D is the midpoint of $\overline{AC}$ and S is the midpoint of $\overline{PR}$.

Using proportions and substitution, show that $\overline{EG} \cong \overline{PS}$. Then, $\triangle BEG \cong \triangle QPS$ by SAS. Substitute in proportions to show that $\dfrac{BD}{QS} = \dfrac{BA}{QP}$.

EN: 2–12 even, 5–8, 12, 14, 16; AV: 1–12, 1, 3–9, 12, 14; FD: 1–12, 1–10, p. 289, 9, 10

Exploratory Exercises

In the figure, $\triangle EFG \sim \triangle QRS$. $\overline{GH}$ bisects $\angle EGF$ and $\overline{ST}$ bisects $\angle QSR$. Determine whether each of the following statements is *true* or *false*.

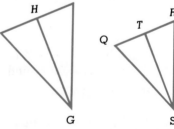

1. $\dfrac{HG}{TS} = \dfrac{EF}{QR}$ true

2. $\dfrac{TS}{HG} = \dfrac{RQ}{FG}$ false

3. $\dfrac{TS}{HG} = \dfrac{SQ}{GE}$ true

4. $\dfrac{FG}{RS} = \dfrac{HG}{TS}$ true

5. $\dfrac{FE}{RQ} = \dfrac{TS}{HG}$ false

6. $\dfrac{ST}{QS} = \dfrac{GH}{EG}$ true

In the figure at the right, $\triangle ABC \sim \triangle PQR$. Also, $\overline{BD}$ is an altitude of $\triangle ABC$, and $\overline{QS}$ is an altitude of $\triangle PQR$. Determine whether each of the following statements is *true* or *false*.

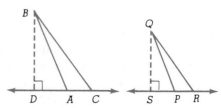

7. $\dfrac{BD}{QS} = \dfrac{AB}{PQ}$ true

8. $\dfrac{AD}{PS} = \dfrac{QR}{BC}$ false

9. $\dfrac{QP}{AB} = \dfrac{BD}{QS}$ false

10. $\dfrac{QR}{BC} = \dfrac{QS}{BD}$ true

11. $\dfrac{BD}{QS} = \dfrac{AC}{PR}$ true

12. $\dfrac{AB}{BD} = \dfrac{PQ}{QS}$ true

Written Exercises

For Exercises 1–2, see the Teacher Guide.

In the figure, $\triangle TVX \sim \triangle LMO$.

1. Suppose $\overline{WT}$ bisects $\angle VTX$, and $\overline{NL}$ bisects $\angle MLO$. State eight different proportions that follow from this information.

2. Suppose $\overline{TW}$ is a median of $\triangle TVX$, and $\overline{LN}$ is a median of $\triangle LMO$. State eight different proportions that follow from this information.

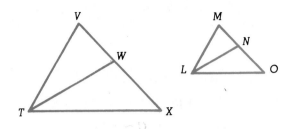

In the figure, $\triangle WXY \sim \triangle JKL$, $\overline{XZ}$ is a median for $\triangle WYZ$, and $\overline{KM}$ is a median for $\triangle JKL$. Use the given information to find each of the following lengths.

3. $KM = 3$; $XZ = 4$
   $KL = 6$; $XY = \blacksquare$

4. $XZ = \blacksquare$; $KM = 4$
   $WY = 10$; $JL = 8$

Complete the following exercises.

5. In the figure, $\triangle ABC \sim \triangle DEF$. $\overline{AX}$ and $\overline{DY}$ are altitudes. Using the lengths given, find DY.

6. The measures of the sides of right triangles PQR and TUV are given. If $\triangle PQR \sim \triangle TUV$ and $\overline{PS}$ and $\overline{TW}$ are corresponding angle bisectors, find TW.

7. In the figure, $\overline{GM}$ and $\overline{JN}$ are medians and $\triangle GHI \sim \triangle JKL$. Using the measures given, find the value of x.

8. In the figure, $\triangle STU \sim \triangle WZY$. If the perimeter of $\triangle STU$ is 30, find the value of x.

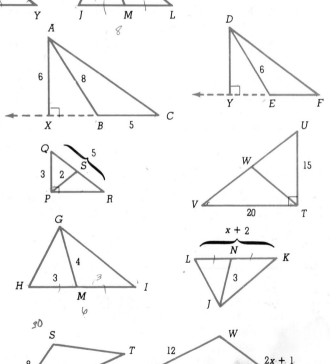

9. Two quadrilaterals are similar. The perimeter of the smaller quadrilateral is 24 units and the perimeter of the larger quadrilateral is 36 units. The measures of the sides of the smaller quadrilateral are 4, 6, 6, and 8. Find the measure of the longest side of the larger quadrilateral.

Solve each problem. When necessary, express answers to the nearest hundredth.

10. Suppose $\triangle PQR \sim \triangle ABC$. If $PR = 1.8$, $AC = 1.2$, and the measure of the perimeter of $\triangle ABC$ is 3.4, find the measure of the perimeter of $\triangle PQR$. 🔳

11. Suppose $\triangle LMN \sim \triangle XYZ$. If the perimeter of $\triangle LMN$ measures 7.6, $LM = 3.0$, $MN = 2.8$, and $XY = 2.7$, find XZ. 🔳

12. The perimeters of two equilateral triangles measure 18.0 and 41.4. Suppose an altitude of the first triangle measures 5.2. Find the measure of the altitude of the second triangle. ▬

13. The perimeters of two similar triangles measure 51.3 and 27.0. Suppose an angle bisector of the first triangle measures 17.1. Find the measure of the corresponding angle bisector in the second triangle. ▮

Complete the following exercises. For Exercises 14–16, see the Teacher Guide.

14. Plan a proof for Theorem 8-15: If two triangles are similar, then the measures of corresponding altitudes are proportional to the measures of corresponding sides. Then, prove the theorem.

15. Plan a proof for Theorem 8-16: If two triangles are similar, then the measures of corresponding angle bisectors of the triangles are proportional to the measures of corresponding sides.

16. Prove Theorem 8-17: If two triangles are similar, then the measures of corresponding medians are proportional to the measures of corresponding sides.

Statistics That Shape Your Life

Recall that the mean and median are measures of central tendency. They are statistics that describe a certain important characteristic of a set of data. However, they do not indicate anything about how the data varies. For example, the mean of 35, 40, and 45 is 40, and the mean of 10, 40, and 70 is also 40. The variability is much greater in the second case than in the first, but this is not indicated by the mean.

The variability in a set of data is called **dispersion.** The simplest measure of dispersion is called the **range.** The range is the difference between the least and greatest values in a set of data. In the two examples above, the range of 35, 40, and 45 is 45 − 35, or 10. The range of 10, 40, and 70 is 70 − 10, or 60.

Exercises

The partial chart at the right lists projected state spending in billions of dollars. Use the information in the chart to answer each of the following.

1. Find the range of the set of data. $27.42 billion

2. Find the range if the value for California was excluded. $5.82 billion

3. Do you think that the measure of dispersion from Exercise 1 or Exercise 2 is more representative of the data in the chart? Exercise 2

State	Expected '86 spending (in billions)
Ala.	$2.73
Alaska	$3.09
Ariz.	$2.34
Ark.	$1.67
Calif.	$28.36
Colo.	$1.90
Conn.	$4.01
Del.	$0.94
Fla.	$6.76
Ga.	$4.84

Copyright, 1985 USA Today.
Reprinted with permission.

Problem Solving

Tia plans to drive on a trip of 600 miles. Her time, in hours, for the trip will be determined by her average rate in miles per hour. The following table shows the time (t) for various rates (r).

r	30	40	45	50	60
t	20	15	$13\frac{1}{3}$	12	10

The formula $d = rt$ is used to find values for t.

Notice that as the rate *increases*, the time to make the trip *decreases*. As the rate *decreases*, the time *increases*. You can say that the rate varies inversely as the time.

In general, an **inverse variation** is described by an equation of the form $xy = k$, where k is not zero.   *y varies inversely as x.*

Consider again the table of rates and times for Tia's trip. There are many ways to form true mathematical statements from the data.

$$30 \cdot 20 = 40 \cdot 15 \qquad \frac{50}{60} = \frac{10}{12}$$

Two general forms for these mathematical statements can be derived from the equation $xy = k$.

First, let (x_1, y_1) be a solution of an inverse variation, $xy = k$. Let (x_2, y_2) be a second solution. This means that $x_1y_1 = k$ and $x_2y_2 = k$. Therefore,

$$x_1y_1 = x_2y_2 \qquad \textit{This is called the product rule for inverse variation.}$$

Second, this equation can also be written as a proportion by dividing each side by x_2y_1.

$$\frac{x_1}{x_2} = \frac{y_2}{y_1}$$

Example   If y varies inversely as x and $y = 3$ when $x = 12$, find x when $y = 4$.   *Let $x_1 = 12$, $y_1 = 3$, and $y_2 = 4$. Solve for x_2.*

$$\begin{aligned} x_1y_1 &= x_2y_2 \\ (12)(3) &= (x_2)(4) \\ 36 &= 4(x_2) \\ 9 &= x_2 \end{aligned}$$

Exercises

Solve each problem. Express answers to the nearest tenth. For Exercises 1 and 2, assume that y varies inversely as x.

1. If $x = 2.7$ when $y = 8.1$, find y when $x = 3.6$. 6.1

2. If $y = -8$ when $x = 2$, find x when $y = 7$. −2.3

3. Boyle's law states that the volume of gas (V) varies inversely with applied pressure (P). This is shown in the formula $P_1V_1 = P_2V_2$. If pressure acting on 60 m^3 of a gas is raised from 1 atmosphere to 2 atmospheres, what new volume would the gas occupy? 30 m^3

8-7 Application: Using Similarity

Objective: Use properties of similarity in problem-solving situations.

Properties of similar triangles can be used to solve problems such as the following.

> Jeane Johnston measured the height of an oak tree by placing a mirror a short distance from the tree, on a level surface, and facing up. She stood where she could see the top of the tree in the mirror. The mirror was 6 feet from the tree. Jeane was $\frac{1}{2}$ foot from the mirror and her eyes were 5 feet from the ground. A beam of light forms the same angle with a mirror as its reflection. Find the height of the tree.

Apply the four-step problem-solving plan presented in Chapter 7.

Explore
The problem asks for the height of the tree. Let x = the measure of the height.

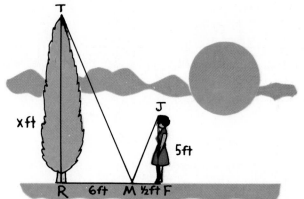

Make a drawing.

Notice the two triangles in the drawing. The angles of reflection, $\angle TMR$ and $\angle JMF$, are congruent.

Plan
Assume that Jeane and the tree are both perpendicular to the ground. Also, $\angle TMR \cong \angle JMF$ since they represent the angles formed by a beam of light and its reflection. Thus, $\triangle TMR \sim \triangle JMF$ by AA Similarity and the measures of corresponding sides are proportional.

$$\frac{TR}{JF} = \frac{RM}{FM}$$

Solve
$$\frac{x}{5} = \frac{6}{\frac{1}{2}}$$

$$\frac{1}{2}x = 30$$

$$x = 2 \cdot 30 \text{ or } 60$$

Examine
$$\frac{60}{5} \overset{?}{=} \frac{6}{\frac{1}{2}}$$ *Equality of Cross Products Theorem 8-1*

$$30 = 30$$

Thus, the tree is 60 feet tall.

The problem-solving plan previously studied can be adjusted for proportions.

1. Explore the problem:	Define the variable. Make a drawing.	*Problem-Solving Procedure for Proportions*
2. Plan the solution:	Write a proportion.	
3. Solve the problem:	Solve the proportion.	
4. Examine the solution:	Check the solution. Answer the problem.	

Example

1 **A triangle is made from a 12-inch length of metal. The piece of metal tapers from 8 inches wide to a point. Find the width of the tapered metal for a length of 15 inches.**

Point out how helpful it is to draw a diagram to analyze a problem.

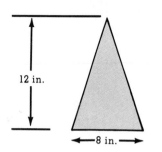

 Let x = the width of the metal.

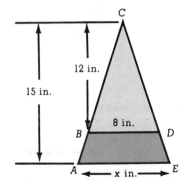

Plan Assume $\overline{BD} \parallel \overline{AE}$. Thus, $\triangle BCD \sim \triangle ACE$. By Theorem 8-15, the measures of corresponding altitudes of similar triangles are proportional to the measures of corresponding sides.

$$\frac{AE}{BD} = \frac{\text{altitude of } \triangle ACE}{\text{altitude of } \triangle BCD}$$

Solve
$$\frac{x}{8} = \frac{15}{12}$$
$$12x = 120$$
$$x = 10$$

Examine $\frac{10}{8} = \frac{15}{12}$ or $120 = 120$ *Equality of Cross Products*

The width of the tapered metal is 10 inches.

Example

2

A hypsometer shown at the right can be used to measure the height of a tree. Look through the straw to the top of the tree. Note where the free-hanging string crosses the scale. Suppose Al Henke used the readings shown. His eye was 167 cm from the ground, and he was 15 m, or 1500 cm, from the tree. Find the height of the tree.

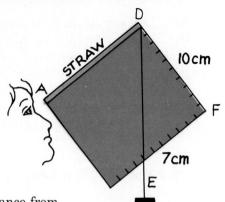

Explore

Let x = the measure of the distance from eye level to the tip of the tree.

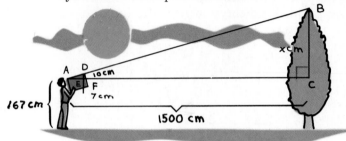

Plan

First, assume that $\angle DFE$ and $\angle BCA$ are right angles. $\overline{DE} \parallel \overline{BC}$, and $\overline{AD} \parallel \overline{EF}$.

$\angle FED \cong \angle ADE$	*They are alternate interior angles of $\overline{AD}$ and $\overline{EF}$.*
$\angle ADE \cong \angle ABC$	*They are corresponding angles of $\overline{DE}$ and $\overline{BC}$.*
$\angle FED \cong \angle ABC$	*Angle congruence is transitive.*
$\angle DFE \cong \angle BCA$	*All right angles are congruent.*
$\triangle DEF \sim \triangle ABC$	*AA Similarity*

The measures of corresponding sides of similar triangles are proportional. Emphasize this correspondence relationship between the scales of the hypsometer and the triangle's sides.

$$\frac{BC}{EF} = \frac{AC}{DF} \qquad \frac{vertical}{horizontal\ scale} = \frac{horizontal}{vertical\ scale}$$

Solve

$$\frac{x}{7} = \frac{1500}{10}$$
$$10x = 10{,}500$$
$$x = 1050$$

Examine

$$\frac{1050}{7} = \frac{1500}{10} \text{ or } 10{,}500 = 10{,}500 \quad \textit{Equality of Cross Products}$$

The tree is 1050 + 167 or 1217 cm tall.

3 **Ann Lawson made a camera from a box. Suppose the film is 1.8 cm from the lens and the person being photographed is 360 cm from the camera. Find the height of the image on the film if the height of the person is 260 cm.**

Let h = the height of the image on the film.

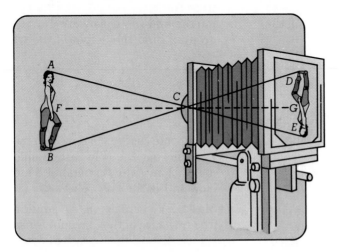

The dashed lines are the altitudes of $\triangle ABC$ and $\triangle EDC$.

Assume that $\overline{AB} \parallel \overline{DE}$.

$\angle ACB \cong \angle ECD$ *They are vertical angles of $\overline{AE}$ and $\overline{BD}$.*
$\angle BAC \cong \angle DEC$ *They are alternate interior angles of*
$\angle ABC \cong \angle EDC$ *parallel segments, $\overline{AB}$ and $\overline{DE}$.*
$\triangle ABC \sim \triangle EDC$ *AA Similarity*

The measures of the corresponding altitudes of similar triangles are proportional to the measures of corresponding sides.

$\dfrac{AB}{FC} = \dfrac{ED}{GC}$ Help students recognize these proportions.

$\dfrac{260}{360} = \dfrac{x}{1.8}$

$360x = 468$

$x = 1.3$

The height of the image on the film is 1.3 cm.   *Examine the solution.*

Exploratory Exercises

Answer each of the following exercises. When necessary, express answers to the nearest tenth.

1. A triangle is made from an 8 cm length of metal. The piece of metal tapers from 4 cm wide to a point. Find the width of the tapered metal for a length of 9 cm. 4.5 cm

2. A triangle is made from a 5 cm length of metal. The piece of metal tapers from 3 cm wide to a point. Find the width of the tapered metal for a length of 6 cm. 3.6 cm

3. Elena Rogelio used a hypsometer to measure the height of a chestnut tree. She had a reading of 10 cm on the vertical scale and 5.5 cm on the horizontal scale. She was 20 m from the tree. Elena's eyes are 1.5 m from the ground. Find the height of the tree in meters. 11 + 1.5 = 12.5 m

Have students relate Exercise 3 to Example 2.

4. Lamar Presley measured the height of a pecan tree by sighting the top of the tree in a mirror that was a short distance from the tree and facing up. The mirror was 6.0 m from the tree. Lamar was 0.9 m from the mirror and his eyes were 1.8 m from the ground. Find the height of the tree. 12 m

Written Exercises

Using proportions, solve the following exercises.

1. A tower casts a shadow 64 feet long. A 6-foot tall pole near the tower casts a shadow 8 feet long. How tall is the tower?

2. A flag pole casts a shadow 3 meters long. A woman near the pole casts a shadow 0.75 meters long. The woman is 1.5 meters tall. How tall is the flag pole?

3. Use similar triangles to find the length of the lake.

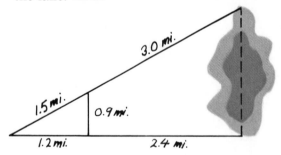

4. Most T.V. screens have similar shapes. The measure of the diagonal is used to give screen size. Suppose the dimensions of a 9-inch screen are $5\frac{1}{2}$ inches by $7\frac{1}{2}$ inches. Find the dimensions of an 18-inch screen.

5. Suppose a person is 300 cm from a camera lens, and the film is 1.3 cm from the lens. If the person is 180 cm tall, how tall is his image on the film?

6. Suppose film is 1.3 cm from a camera lens and can have an image no more than 4.5 cm tall. If the person in front of the lens is 180 cm tall, how far from the lens can he be for a full length picture?

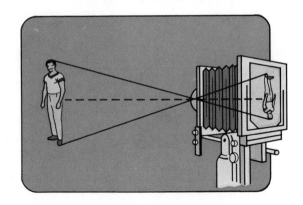

ratio   (267)   golden rectangle   (273)
proportion   (267)   similar figures   (276)
cross products   (268)

Chapter Summary ■■■■■■■■■■■■■

1. A ratio is a comparison of two numbers by division. The ratio of a to b is $\dfrac{a}{b}$ where b is not zero.   (267)

2. An equation of the form $\dfrac{a}{b} = \dfrac{c}{d}$, which states that two ratios are equal, is called a proportion.   (267)

3. Equality of Cross Products (Theorem 8-1):   For any numbers a and c, and any nonzero numbers b and d, $\dfrac{a}{b} = \dfrac{c}{d}$ if and only if $ad = bc$.   (268)

4. Properties of Proportion: (272)

For any numbers a, b, c, and d, the following properties hold whenever all denominators are nonzero.	
Theorem 8-2	If $\dfrac{a}{b} = \dfrac{c}{d}$, then $\dfrac{a}{c} = \dfrac{b}{d}$ or $\dfrac{d}{b} = \dfrac{c}{a}$.
Theorem 8-3	If $\dfrac{a}{b} = \dfrac{c}{d}$, then $\dfrac{b}{a} = \dfrac{d}{c}$.
Theorem 8-4: Addition Property of Proportions	$\dfrac{a}{b} = \dfrac{c}{d}$ if and only if $\dfrac{a + b}{b} = \dfrac{c + d}{d}$.
Theorem 8-5: Subtraction Property of Proportions	$\dfrac{a}{b} = \dfrac{c}{d}$ if and only if $\dfrac{a - b}{b} = \dfrac{c - d}{d}$.
Theorem 8-6: Summation Property of Proportions	$\dfrac{a}{b} = \dfrac{c}{d}$ if and only if $\dfrac{a}{b} = \dfrac{a + c}{b + d}$ or $\dfrac{c}{d} = \dfrac{a + c}{b + d}$.

5. **Definition of Similar Polygons:** Two polygons are similar if and only if there is a correspondence such that their corresponding angles are congruent and the measures of their corresponding sides are proportional. (276)

6. **AA Similarity (Postulate 8-1):** If two angles of one triangle are congruent to two corresponding angles of another triangle, then the triangles are similar. (281)

7. **SSS Similarity (Theorem 8-7):** If there is a correspondence between two triangles so that the measures of their corresponding sides are proportional, then the two triangles are similar. (282)

8. **SAS Similarity (Theorem 8-8):** If the measures of two sides of a triangle are proportional to the measures of two corresponding sides of another triangle, and the included angles are congruent, then the triangles are similar. (283)

9. **Theorem 8-9:** If a line intersects two sides of a triangle and separates the sides into segments of proportional lengths, then the line is parallel to the third side. (285)

10. **Theorem 8-10:** If a line is parallel to one side of a triangle and intersects the other two sides, then it separates the sides into segments of proportional lengths. (286)

11. **Theorem 8-11:** If a segment has as its endpoints the midpoints of two sides of a triangle, then it is parallel to the third side and its length is one-half the length of the third side. (287)

12. **Theorem 8-12:** If three parallel lines intersect two transversals, then they divide the transversals proportionally. (287)

13. **Theorem 8-13:** If three parallel lines cut off congruent segments on one transversal, they cut off congruent segments on any transversal. (287)

14. **Theorem 8-14:** If two triangles are similar, then the measures of corresponding perimeters are proportional to the measures of corresponding sides. (290)

15. **Theorem 8-15:** If two triangles are similar, then the measures of corresponding altitudes are proportional to the measures of corresponding sides. (291)

16. **Theorem 8-16:** If two triangles are similar, then the measures of corresponding angle bisectors of the triangles are proportional to the measures of corresponding sides. (291)

17. **Theorem 8-17:** If two triangles are similar, then the measures of corresponding medians are proportional to the measures of corresponding sides. (292)

18. **Problem-Solving Procedure for Proportions:** (297)

    1. **Explore the problem:**   Define the variable.
                                Make a drawing.
    2. **Plan the solution:**   Write a proportion.
    3. **Solve the problem:**   Solve the proportion.
    4. **Examine the solution:**   Check the solution.
                                Answer the problem.

Chapter Review

8-1 **Write the cross products for each of the following proportions and solve.**

1. $\dfrac{5}{x} = \dfrac{2}{3}$ 2. $\dfrac{x}{9} = \dfrac{7}{15}$ 3. $\dfrac{1}{x} = \dfrac{5}{x+5}$ 4. $\dfrac{n+4}{3} = \dfrac{5n-3}{8}$

For Exercises 1–4, see the Teacher Guide.

Solve each of the following exercises.

5. Two gears have a ratio of 5 to 4. If the larger gear has 60 teeth, find the number of teeth in the other gear. 48 teeth

6. A certain metal is composed of 85% copper and 15% zinc. How many pounds of copper are there in 25 pounds of the metal? $21\frac{1}{4}$ pounds

8-2 **Determine whether each of the following statements is *true* or *false*.**

7. If $\dfrac{a}{b} = \dfrac{c}{d}$, then $\dfrac{a}{b} = \dfrac{d}{c}$. false

8. If $\dfrac{a}{b} = \dfrac{c}{d}$, then $\dfrac{a+b}{b} = \dfrac{c+d}{d}$. true

The measures of corresponding sides of $\triangle ABC$ and $\triangle XYZ$ below are proportional. Find the indicated measures.

9. If $AB = 7$, $AC = 6$, and $XZ = 8$, find XY. $9\frac{1}{3}$

10. If $BC = 7$, $AC = 6$, and $XZ = 14$, find YZ. $16\frac{1}{3}$

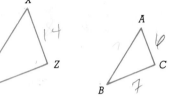

8-3 **For each of the following, write *yes* or *no*. Then explain your answer.**

11. All congruent triangles are similar. yes   12. All similar triangles are congruent. no

For reasons to Exercises 11–12, see the Teacher Guide.

For each of the following, find the measures x and y.

13. $\square QRST \sim \square MNOP$ $x = 9$; $y = 30$

14. $\triangle ABC \sim \triangle GFE$ $x = 8$; $y = 10$

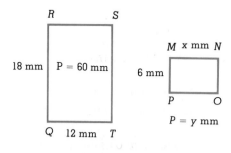

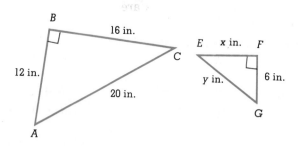

For Exercises 15–16, see the Teacher Guide.

Prove each of the following.

8-4 15. Given: $\dfrac{PR}{QS} = \dfrac{RS}{QP}$, $\overline{QR} \parallel \overline{PS}$, isosceles trapezoid $PQRS$

Prove: $\triangle PQR \sim \triangle SRQ$

16. Given: $\overline{QR} \parallel \overline{PS}$

Prove: $\dfrac{QT}{TS} = \dfrac{TR}{PT}$

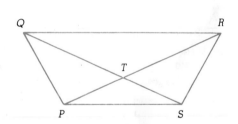

8-5 For each of the following, determine whether $\overline{BD} \parallel \overline{AE}$. Write *yes* or *no*.

17. $CB = 18$
$AC = 28$ $\frac{10}{18} \overset{?}{=} \frac{5}{9}$
$DE = 5$ yes
$CE = 14$

18. $EC = 48$
$BA = 4$ $\frac{4}{12} \overset{?}{=} \frac{14}{34}$
$CD = 34$ no
$CA = 16$

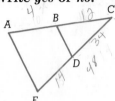

Use the figure and the given information to find the value of x.

19. $\overline{SV} \parallel \overline{PR}$
$TS = 5 + x$
$TV = 8 + x$
$VP = 4$
$SR = 3$

20. $\overline{RT} \parallel \overline{QV}$
$TV = 7.29$
$PV = x$
$PQ = 9$
$QR = 27$

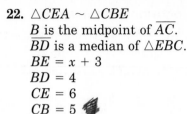

8-6 Use the figure and the given information to find the value of x.

21. $\triangle ABE \sim \triangle AEC$
$\overline{BE}$ bisects $\angle AEC$.
$\overline{BF}$ bisects $\angle ABE$.
$AB = 4$
$FB = 3$
$AE = x$
$EB = 4$

22. $\triangle CEA \sim \triangle CBE$
B is the midpoint of $\overline{AC}$.
$\overline{BD}$ is a median of $\triangle EBC$.
$BE = x + 3$
$BD = 4$
$CE = 6$
$CB = 5$

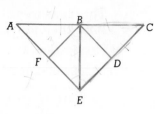

8-7 Answer each of the following.

23. A light pole casts a shadow 42 feet long. A man standing next to the pole casts a shadow 12 feet long. If the man is $5\frac{3}{4}$ feet tall, how tall is the light pole?

24. Before photographers make enlarged prints of negatives, they make small contact prints. Suppose a contact print is 50.8 mm wide and 58.4 mm high. If the enlargement is to be 190.5 mm wide, how high will it be?

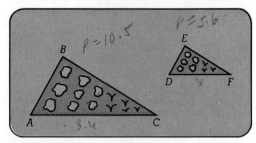

25. An attic window has a triangular shape as shown by $\triangle ACE$. A crossbar $\overline{BD}$ is parallel to the base $\overline{AE}$. Also, B and D are midpoints of their respective sides. The crossbar has a length of $3\frac{1}{2}$ feet. What is the length of the base $\overline{AE}$?

26. Two gardens are shaped like similar triangles. The perimeter of the larger garden is 10.5 m and the perimeter of the smaller garden is 5.6 m. If one side of the larger garden is 3.6 m long, find the measure of the corresponding side of the smaller garden.

Chapter Test

Solve each proportion.

1. $\dfrac{x}{28} = \dfrac{60}{16}$

2. $\dfrac{15}{33} = \dfrac{50}{x}$ 110

3. $\dfrac{1}{15} = \dfrac{x}{7}$ $\dfrac{7}{15}$

4. $\dfrac{5}{5x+4} = \dfrac{2}{3}$ $\dfrac{7}{10}$

5. $\dfrac{21}{1-x} = \dfrac{7}{x}$ $1\dfrac{1}{4}$

6. $\dfrac{x-1}{5-x} = \dfrac{3}{5}$ $2\dfrac{1}{2}$

Use the figure at the right and the given information to find the value of x.

7. $\triangle RWP \sim \triangle VST$
   PW = x
   QW = 1
   SU = 5
   ST = x + 5 $1\dfrac{1}{4}$

8. $\triangle WRS \sim \triangle VUS$
   SW = 3
   $RS = 1\dfrac{1}{3}$
   $SU = x + \dfrac{2}{3}$
   $SV = 2\dfrac{2}{9}$

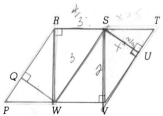

Exercises 7 and 8

Determine if the following pairs of triangles are similar. Write *yes* or *no*. If they are similar, give a reason.

9.

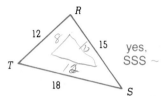

yes, SSS ~

10.

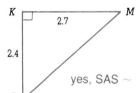

yes, SAS ~

Prove the following. See the Teacher Guide.

11. **Given:** $\triangle ABC \sim \triangle RSP$
    D is the midpoint of $\overline{AC}$.
    Q is the midpoint of $\overline{PR}$.
    $\overline{TP}$ bisects $\angle SPQ$.
    $\overline{EC}$ bisects $\angle BCD$.
    Prove: $\dfrac{QT}{DE} = \dfrac{SP}{BC}$

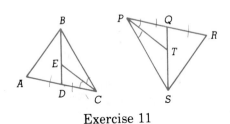

Exercise 11

Solve each of the following exercises.

12. Use similar triangles to find the distance AB across the river.   36 mi

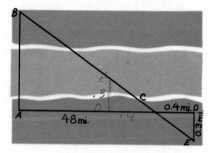

13. Fritz Gundlach measured the height of a building by sighting the top of the building in a mirror that was on the ground and facing up. The mirror was $17\dfrac{1}{2}$ ft from the building and Fritz was $2\dfrac{5}{8}$ ft from the mirror. If Fritz's eyes were 6 ft from the ground, how tall is the building?   40 ft

The test questions on these two pages deal with algebraic and geometric concepts. Read each problem carefully and select the best answer.

Most standardized tests have a time limit, so you must budget your time carefully. Some questions will be much easier than others. If you cannot answer a question within a few minutes, go on to the next one. If there is still time left when you get to the end of the test, go back to the ones that you skipped.

1. If $\triangle ACB \cong \triangle RQP$, then

   I. $\overline{AB} \cong \overline{RP}$.

D   II. $\angle C \cong \angle R$.

   III. $\overline{AC} \cong \overline{QR}$.

 (A) I only   **(B)** II only   **(C)** III only

 (D) I and III only   **(E)** I, II, and III

2. If two planes intersect, their intersection can be

   I. a line.

A   II. three noncollinear points.

   III. two intersecting lines.

 (A) I only   **(B)** II only   **(C)** III only

 (D) II and III only   **(E)** I and II only

3. If $\angle A$ and $\angle B$ are supplementary and $\angle A$ and $\angle C$ are complementary, then

   I. $m \angle A < 90$, $m \angle B > 90$, and $m \angle C < 90$.

C   II. $m \angle A < m \angle B$ and $m \angle C < 90$.

   III. $m \angle A > 90$ and $m \angle C < m \angle B$.

 (A) I only   **(B)** II only   **(C)** I and II only

 (D) III only   **(E)** I, II, and III

4. Skew lines are

   I. intersecting.

E   II. coplanar.

   III. noncoplanar.

 (A) I only   **(B)** II only   **(C)** I and II only

 (D) I and III only   **(E)** III only

5. If $\angle BAD$ is an exterior angle of $\triangle ABC$, then

   I. $m \angle BAD > m \angle C$.

E   II. $m \angle BAD > m \angle B$.

   III. $m \angle BAD = m \angle B + m \angle C$.

 (A) I only   **(B)** II only   **(C)** I and II only

 (D) III only   **(E)** I, II, and III

6. If $\overline{NL} \cong \overline{PR}$, $\angle M \cong \angle P$, and $\angle N \cong \angle Q$, then

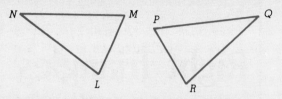

C   (A) $\triangle NML \cong \triangle QPR$ by AAS.

      (B) $\triangle NML \cong \triangle QPR$ by ASA.

      (C) the triangles may not be congruent.

7. The measure of one side of a regular hexagon is 10. What is the measure of a radius of the hexagon?

C   (A) 5   (B) $5\sqrt{3}$ (C) 10   (D) 20

8. What is the degree measure of an exterior angle of a regular nonagon?

B   (A) 36   (B) 40   (C) 140   (D) 360

9. In $\triangle ABC$, $m \angle A = 3x - 10$, $m \angle B = x + 10$, and $m \angle C = 4x - 20$. What is the degree measure of the smallest angle?

B   (A) 25   (B) 35   (C) 65   (D) 80

10. A person's salary is reduced by 20%. By what percent would the salary have to be increased to bring it back to the original amount?

D   (A) 20   (B) 80   (C) 100   (D) 25

11. In the figure at the right, find $c + d$ in terms of a.

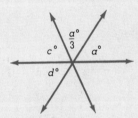

B   (A) $180 + \dfrac{a}{3}$ (B) $180 - \dfrac{a}{3}$

      (C) $2a + \dfrac{a}{3}$ (D) $180 - 2a - \dfrac{a}{3}$

12. In $\triangle DEF$, $DE = 8$ and $EF = 12$. Which of the following measures cannot equal DF?

D   (A) 5   (B) 6

      (C) 8   (D) 20

13. In $\triangle XYZ$, $m \angle X : m \angle Y : m \angle Z = 2{:}3{:}4$. Find $m \angle Z$.

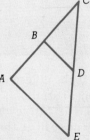

D   (A) 20   (B) 40

      (C) 60   (D) 80

14. In the figure shown at the right, $\overline{AE} \parallel \overline{BD}$. If $AB = 10$, $BC = x$, $ED = x + 3$, and $DC = x + 6$, find x.

D   (A) 3   (B) 7

      (C) 10   (D) 12

15. Triangle XYZ is isosceles with $\overline{XY} \cong \overline{XZ}$. If $m \angle Y = 65$, then find $m \angle X$.

A   (A) 50   (B) 65   (C) 115   (D) 130

16. What is the degree measure of the angle formed by the hands of a clock at one-thirty?

C   (A) 30   (B) 35   (C) 135   (D) 150

Right Triangles

Parallax is the difference in direction of an object when seen from two positions. Parallax is used in surveying to tell how far away a distant object is. Surveyors can measure the distance between two points on land, call it the baseline of an imaginary triangle, and using trigonometry, determine the distance to any third point within range.

A similar procedure is used in astronomy. Stellar parallax is used to find the distance to nearby stars.

9-1 Square Roots

Objectives: Find the square and square root of a number; simplify square roots; identify rational and irrational roots; find decimal approximations of roots using a table.

Suppose $\triangle ABD \sim \triangle BCD$ in the figure at the right. Then, the following proportion can be written.

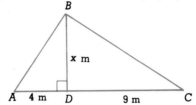

$$\frac{DC}{BD} = \frac{BD}{DA}$$

To find the value of x, make the appropriate substitutions in the proportion.

$$\frac{9}{x} = \frac{x}{4} \qquad DC = 9,\ BD = x,\ DA = 4$$

Then, cross multiply.

$$x \cdot x = 9 \cdot 4$$
$$x^2 = 36$$

Squaring a number means using that number as a factor two times. The inverse of squaring is finding the **square root.** To find the square root of 36, you must find two equal factors whose product is 36.

Since 6 times 6 is 36, one square root of 36 is 6. Since -6 times -6 is 36, another square root of 36 is -6.

What is the value of x in the problem above? 6

Since x represents a distance measure, only the nonnegative root has meaning.

For any numbers a and b, if $a^2 = b$, then a is a square root of b.	*Definition of Square Root*

The symbol $\sqrt{}$, called a **radical sign,** indicates a nonnegative square root. The expression under the radical sign is called the **radicand.** Emphasize that the principal square root is nonnegative.

$\sqrt{36} = 6 \qquad$ *$\sqrt{36}$ indicates the principal, or nonnegative, square root of 36.*

$-\sqrt{36} = -6 \qquad$ *$-\sqrt{36}$ indicates the negative square root of 36.*

$\pm\sqrt{36} = \pm 6 \qquad$ *$\pm\sqrt{36}$ indicates both square roots of 36.*

radical sign
$\downarrow$
$\sqrt{36} \leftarrow$ *radicand*

Examples

1 **Simplify:** $\sqrt{49}$

Since $7^2 = 49$, it follows that $\sqrt{49} = 7$.

2 **Simplify:** $-\sqrt{100}$

Since the square root of 100 is 10, it follows that $-\sqrt{100} = -10$.

To simplify a square root such as $\sqrt{196}$, find the square root of any perfect square factor of the radicand. Use the prime factorization of 196 to do this.

Use this opportunity to review prime factorization.

$$\sqrt{196} = \sqrt{2 \cdot 2 \cdot 7 \cdot 7} \qquad \textit{Find the prime factorization of 196.}$$
$$= \sqrt{2^2 \cdot 7^2}$$
$$= \sqrt{2^2} \cdot \sqrt{7^2}$$
$$= 2 \cdot 7 \text{ or } 14 \qquad \textbf{Check:} \quad 14^2 = 196$$

An important property of square roots was used to simplify $\sqrt{196}$.

For any nonnegative numbers a and b, $\sqrt{ab} = \sqrt{a} \cdot \sqrt{b}$.	***Postulate 9-1*** ***Product Property*** ***of Square Roots***

Point out that $\sqrt{(-6)(-7)} \ne \sqrt{-6} \cdot \sqrt{-7}$.

A similar property for quotients of square roots also can be used to simplify square roots.

For any nonnegative numbers a and b with $b \ne 0$, $\sqrt{\dfrac{a}{b}} = \dfrac{\sqrt{a}}{\sqrt{b}}.$	***Postulate 9-2*** ***Quotient Property*** ***of Square Roots***

Examples

3 **Simplify:** $\sqrt{300}$

$$\sqrt{300} = \sqrt{2 \cdot 2 \cdot 3 \cdot 5 \cdot 5} \qquad \textit{Find the prime factorization of 300.}$$
$$= \sqrt{2^2 \cdot 3 \cdot 5^2}$$
$$= \sqrt{2^2} \cdot \sqrt{3} \cdot \sqrt{5^2} \qquad \textit{Use the Product Property of Square Roots.}$$
$$= 2 \cdot \sqrt{3} \cdot 5$$
$$= 10\sqrt{3} \qquad \textit{Notice 3 remains under the radical sign.}$$
$$\textit{Why? } \sqrt{3} \textit{ is in simplest form.}$$

Check: $(10\sqrt{3})^2 = 100 \cdot 3 \text{ or } 300$

4 **Simplify:** $\sqrt{\dfrac{16}{9}}$

$$\sqrt{\frac{16}{9}} = \frac{\sqrt{16}}{\sqrt{9}} \qquad \textit{Use the Quotient Property of Square Roots.}$$
$$= \frac{4}{3}$$

Check: $\left(\dfrac{4}{3}\right)^2 = \dfrac{16}{9}$

The method used to simplify $\dfrac{\sqrt{5}}{\sqrt{2}}$ is called **rationalizing the denominator.** Notice that the denominator becomes a rational number.

$$\dfrac{\sqrt{5}}{\sqrt{2}} = \dfrac{\sqrt{5}}{\sqrt{2}} \cdot \dfrac{\sqrt{2}}{\sqrt{2}} \qquad \textit{Notice that } \dfrac{\sqrt{2}}{\sqrt{2}} \textit{ is equal to 1.}$$

$$= \dfrac{\sqrt{10}}{\sqrt{4}}$$

$$= \dfrac{\sqrt{10}}{2}$$

A square root is said to be simplified when the following conditions are met.

1. The radicand has no perfect square factor other than 1.
2. The radicand does *not* contain a fraction.
3. No radical appears in the denominator of a fraction.

Some numbers such as 5 and 13 have square roots that are *not* integers or rational numbers. These square roots are **irrational numbers.**

To compute with irrational numbers, you often use decimal approximations. Tables of square roots or calculators give approximations. Emphasize that these tables give approximations.

Such a table is given on page 580.

Example

5 **Use the table to find a decimal approximation for $\sqrt{5}$.**

Have students compare values in the table with values obtained from a calculator.

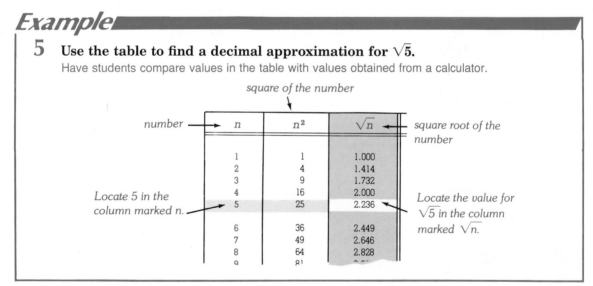

	number →	n	n^2 ← square of the number	$\sqrt{n}$ ← square root of the number
		1	1	1.000
		2	4	1.414
		3	9	1.732
Locate 5 in the		4	16	2.000
column marked n. →		5	25	2.236
		6	36	2.449
		7	49	2.646
		8	64	2.828
		9	81	

Locate the value for $\sqrt{5}$ in the column marked $\sqrt{n}$.

EN: 2–20 even, 2–48 even; **AV:** 1–20, 1–49 odd; **FD:** 1–20, 1–30

Exploratory Exercises

Find the square of each number.

1. 8 64

2. 12 144

3. −7 49

4. −11 121

5. 0.2 0.04

6. 0.1 0.01

7. $\dfrac{2}{5}$ $\dfrac{4}{25}$

8. $\dfrac{4}{9}$ $\dfrac{16}{81}$

9. 1.3 1.69

10. −2.5 6.25

Simplify.

11. $\sqrt{64}$ 8   **12.** $-\sqrt{144}$ −12   **13.** $-\sqrt{49}$ −7   **14.** $\sqrt{49}$ 7   **15.** $\sqrt{0.04}$ 0.2

16. $\sqrt{0.01}$ 0.1   **17.** $\pm\sqrt{1.69}$ ±1.3   **18.** $\sqrt{6.25}$ 2.5   **19.** $\sqrt{\dfrac{4}{25}}$ $\frac{2}{5}$ **20.** $\pm\sqrt{\dfrac{16}{81}}$ ±$\frac{4}{9}$

Written Exercises

Write the principal square root.

1. 1 1   **2.** 100 10   **3.** 0.25 0.5   **4.** 1.21 1.1   **5.** 0.09 0.3

6. $\dfrac{16}{121}$ $\frac{4}{11}$ **7.** $\dfrac{49}{4}$ $\frac{7}{2}$ **8.** 0.0025 0.05   **9.** 169 13   **10.** 16,900 130

Simplify and determine whether the answer is a rational or an irrational number.

11. $\sqrt{256}$ 16, r   **12.** $\sqrt{361}$ 19, r   **13.** $\sqrt{900}$ 30, r   **14.** $\sqrt{484}$ 22, r   **15.** $\sqrt{80}$ $4\sqrt{5}$, i

16. $\sqrt{72}$ $6\sqrt{2}$, i   **17.** $\sqrt{75}$ $5\sqrt{3}$, i   **18.** $\sqrt{54}$ $3\sqrt{6}$, i   **19.** $\sqrt{5}\sqrt{15}$ $5\sqrt{3}$, i   **20.** $\sqrt{8}\sqrt{2}$ 4, r

21. $\sqrt{\dfrac{5}{4}}$ $\frac{\sqrt{5}}{2}$, i   **22.** $\sqrt{\dfrac{2}{9}}$ $\frac{\sqrt{2}}{3}$, i   **23.** $\sqrt{\dfrac{1}{8}}$ $\frac{\sqrt{2}}{4}$, i   **24.** $\dfrac{1}{\sqrt{2}}$ $\frac{\sqrt{2}}{2}$, i   **25.** $\dfrac{5}{\sqrt{3}}$ $\frac{5\sqrt{3}}{3}$, i

26. $\sqrt{\dfrac{1}{3}}$ $\frac{\sqrt{3}}{3}$, i   **27.** $\sqrt{\dfrac{5}{3}}$ $\frac{\sqrt{15}}{3}$, i   **28.** $\sqrt{\dfrac{7}{2}}$ $\frac{\sqrt{14}}{2}$, i   **29.** $\dfrac{\sqrt{21}}{\sqrt{14}}$ $\frac{\sqrt{6}}{2}$, i   **30.** $\sqrt{\dfrac{2}{3}}\sqrt{\dfrac{5}{2}}$ $\frac{\sqrt{15}}{3}$ i

You may want to encourage students to use calculators for the following exercises.

Use the table on page 580 to find the approximate value of each expression.

−1.015

31. $\sqrt{76}$ 8.718   **32.** $\sqrt{21}$ 4.583   **33.** $\sqrt{17}$ 4.123   **34.** $\sqrt{61}$ 7.810   **35.** $\sqrt{6} - \sqrt{12}$

36. $\sqrt{15} + \sqrt{19}$ **37.** $\sqrt{\dfrac{7}{2}}$ 1.871   **38.** $\sqrt{\dfrac{5}{3}}$ 1.291   **39.** $\sqrt{200}$ 14.14   **40.** $\sqrt{175}$ 13.230

8.232

Solve for x. Approximate the values of x to three decimal places.

41. $x^2 - 40 = 0$ ±6.325   **42.** $x^2 = \dfrac{3}{2}$ ±1.225   **43.** $x^2 + 16 = 64$ ±6.928

44. $100 + x^2 = 121$ ±4.583   **45.** $x^2 + (\sqrt{5})^2 = (\sqrt{30})^2$ ±5   **46.** $(\sqrt{11})^2 + (4)^2 = x^2$ ±5.196

47. $\dfrac{3}{x} = \dfrac{x}{12}$ ±6   **48.** $\dfrac{3}{x} = \dfrac{x}{7}$ ±4.583   **49.** $\dfrac{5}{x} = \dfrac{x}{9}$ ±6.708

 **Using Calculators**   **Square Root Key**

The key labeled $\sqrt{x}$ on your calculator is the **square root key.** When this key is pressed, the calculator replaces the number in the display with its principal square root. If a square root is irrational, the calculator display will probably show as many decimal places as it can. The result can be rounded to the nearest hundredth or thousandth.

Exercises

1–9. Use a calculator to check your solutions for Written Exercises 41–49 above.

10. Choose any number and enter it on your calculator. Then press the square root key, followed by the x^2 key. What is the result? Why? The original number is displayed.

9-2 The Geometric Mean

Objectives: Find the geometric mean for a pair of numbers; solve problems using relationships between parts of a right triangle and the altitude.

When the altitude to the hypotenuse of a right triangle is drawn, two smaller triangles are formed. In the figure at the right, $\triangle PSQ$ and $\triangle PQR$ have $\angle P$ in common, and each triangle has a right angle. Therefore, the triangles are similar by Angle Angle Similarity. Similarly, $\triangle QSR \sim \triangle PQR$. The two smaller triangles are also similar to each other. These relationships are summarized in the following theorem. $\triangle PQR \sim \triangle PSQ \sim \triangle QSR$

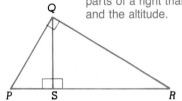

If the altitude is drawn from the vertex of the right angle to the hypotenuse of a right triangle, then the two triangles formed are similar to the given triangle and to each other.	*Theorem 9-1*

Example

1 Help students find the corresponding parts in these triangles.

Prove Theorem 9-1.

Given: $\angle PQR$ is a right angle.
$\overline{QS}$ is an altitude of right $\triangle PQR$.

Prove: $\triangle PQR \sim \triangle PSQ$
$\triangle PQR \sim \triangle QSR$
$\triangle PSQ \sim \triangle QSR$

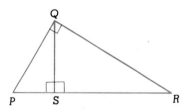

Proof:

STATEMENTS	REASONS
1. $\angle PQR$ is a right angle.	1. Given
2. $\overline{QS}$ is an altitude of right $\triangle PQR$.	2. Given
3. $\overline{QS} \perp \overline{PR}$	3. Definition of Altitude
4. $\angle PSQ$ is a right angle. $\angle QSR$ is a right angle.	4. Definition of Perpendicular Lines
5. $\angle PQR \cong \angle PSQ$ $\angle PQR \cong \angle QSR$ $\angle PSQ \cong \angle QSR$	5. If two angles are right angles, then the angles are congruent. (Theorem 3-6)
6. $\angle P \cong \angle P$ $\angle R \cong \angle R$	6. Congruence of angles is reflexive, symmetric, and transitive. (Theorem 3-1)
7. $\triangle PQR \sim \triangle PSQ$ $\triangle PQR \sim \triangle QSR$	7. AA Similarity (Postulate 8-1)
8. $\angle SQP \cong \angle QRP$	8. Definition of Similar Triangles
9. $\triangle PSQ \sim \triangle QSR$	9. AA Similarity (Postulate 8-1)

By Theorem 9-1, the two smaller triangles in the figure at the right are similar. Thus, corresponding sides are proportional, and the following proportion can be written.

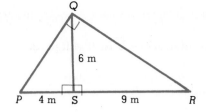

You may want to present Construction 14 on page 487 at this time.

$$\frac{4}{6} = \frac{6}{9}$$

Notice that the denominator of the first fraction is 6 and the numerator of the second fraction also is 6. This number, 6, is the **geometric mean** between 4 and 9.   The geometric mean is sometimes called the mean proportional.

For any positive numbers a and b, x is the geometric mean between a and b if and only if $\frac{a}{x} = \frac{x}{b}$ and x is positive.	*Definition of Geometric Mean*

The proportions also can be written $\frac{x}{b} = \frac{a}{x}$.

Examples

2 **Find the geometric mean between 4 and 10.**

Let x represent the geometric mean.

$\frac{4}{x} = \frac{x}{10}$ *Definition of geometric mean*

$x^2 = 40$ *Equality of cross products*

$x = \sqrt{40}$ *Definition of square root and the geometric mean is positive.*

$x = 2\sqrt{10}$

The geometric mean is $2\sqrt{10}$.   In general, the solution to $x^2 = 40$ is $\pm 2\sqrt{10}$.

3 **Show that the value of the geometric mean between a and b is $\sqrt{ab}$.**

Let x represent the geometric mean.

$\frac{a}{x} = \frac{x}{b}$ *Definition of geometric mean*

$x^2 = ab$ *Equality of cross products*

$x = \sqrt{ab}$ *Definition of square root and the geometric mean is positive.*

The proofs of the following theorems are based on the fact that the triangles formed are similar.

The measure of the altitude drawn from the right angle to the hypotenuse of a right triangle is the geometric mean between the measures of the two segments of the hypotenuse.	*Theorem 9-2*

Students will prove this theorem in Written Exercise 31.

4 **Find the measure of altitude $\overline{AE}$ in the figure.**

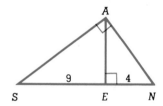

$$\frac{SE}{AE} = \frac{AE}{NE} \qquad \text{\textit{Theorem 9-2}}$$

$$\frac{9}{AE} = \frac{AE}{4} \qquad \text{\textit{Substitution}}$$

$$(AE)^2 = 36 \qquad \text{\textit{Equality of cross products}}$$

$$AE = 6 \qquad \text{\textit{Definition of square root and the geometric mean is positive.}}$$

If the altitude is drawn to the hypotenuse of a right triangle, then the measure of a leg of the triangle is the geometric mean between the measure of the hypotenuse and the measure of the segment of the hypotenuse adjacent to that leg.

Theorem 9-3

Students will prove this theorem in Written Exercise 32.

Example

5 **Find the measures of sides TS and SP in the figure.**

$TP = TO + OP$ *Definition of between*

Therefore, $TP = 25$.

$$\frac{OP}{SP} = \frac{SP}{TP} \text{ and } \frac{TO}{TS} = \frac{TS}{TP} \qquad \text{\textit{Theorem 9-3}}$$

$$\frac{5}{SP} = \frac{SP}{25} \text{ and } \frac{20}{TS} = \frac{TS}{25} \qquad \text{\textit{Substitution}}$$

$$(SP)^2 = 125 \text{ and } (TS)^2 = 500 \qquad \text{\textit{Equality of cross products}}$$

$$SP = 5\sqrt{5} \text{ and } TS = 10\sqrt{5}$$

Exploratory Exercises

ALL LEVELS: Algebra Review

Find the geometric mean for each pair of numbers.

1. 2 and 8 4
2. 3 and 12 6
3. 2 and 18 6
4. 5 and 20 10

5. 9 and 16 12
6. 2 and 50 10
7. 1 and 36 6
8. 16 and 1 4

Written Exercises

Find the geometric mean for each pair of numbers.

1. 3 and 5 $\sqrt{15}$
2. 4 and 6 $2\sqrt{6}$
3. 5 and 8 $2\sqrt{10}$
4. 2 and 10 $2\sqrt{5}$

5. $\frac{1}{4}$ and 9 $\frac{3}{2}$
6. 4 and $\frac{1}{9}$ $\frac{2}{3}$
7. $\frac{2}{5}$ and $\frac{5}{2}$ 1
8. $\frac{2}{3}$ and $\frac{1}{3}$ $\frac{\sqrt{2}}{3}$

9. $\frac{1}{4}$ and $\frac{3}{4}$ $\frac{\sqrt{3}}{4}$
10. $\frac{2}{3}$ and $\frac{1}{2}$ $\frac{\sqrt{3}}{3}$
11. $\frac{1}{2}$ and $\frac{1}{4}$ $\frac{\sqrt{2}}{4}$
12. $\frac{1}{3}$ and $\frac{1}{4}$ $\frac{\sqrt{3}}{6}$

Use the figure at the right to answer each of the following. Approximate each answer to three decimal places. A calculator is recommended for these exercises.

13. Find BD if $AD = 3$ and $DC = 10$. $\sqrt{30} \approx 5.477$
14. Find BD if $AD = 5$ and $DC = 9$. $\sqrt{45} \approx 6.708$
15. Find AB if $AC = 8$ and $AD = 3$. $\sqrt{24} \approx 4.899$
16. Find BD if $DC = 12$ and $AD = 3$. 6
17. Find BC if $AD = 3$ and $DC = 4$. $\sqrt{28} \approx 5.292$
18. Find BA if $DA = 4$ and $DC = 4$. $\sqrt{32} \approx 5.657$

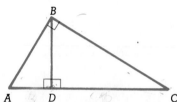

Find x and y. Simplify radicals whenever possible.

19.

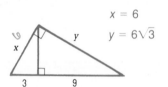

$x = 6$
$y = 6\sqrt{3}$

20.

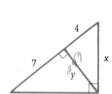

$x = 2\sqrt{11}$
$y = 2\sqrt{7}$

21.

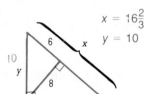

$x = 16\frac{2}{3}$
$y = 10$

22.

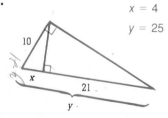

$x = 4$
$y = 25$

23.

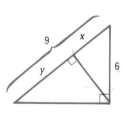

$x = 4$
$y = 5$

24.

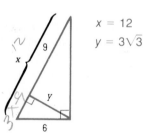

$x = 12$
$y = 3\sqrt{3}$

25.

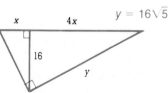

$x = 8$
$y = 16\sqrt{5}$

26.

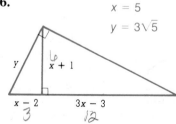

$x = 5$
$y = 3\sqrt{5}$

27.

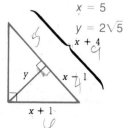

$x = 5$
$y = 2\sqrt{5}$

Complete each of the following exercises.

28. Given: $VQ = 6$, $QR = 4$
$\overline{RV} \perp \overline{PV}$, $\overline{VQ} \perp \overline{PR}$
Find: PQ, PR, PV, and VR
$PQ = 9$, $PR = 13$, $PV = 3\sqrt{13}$, $VR = 2\sqrt{13}$

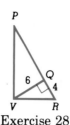

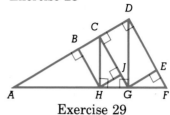

Exercise 28

A calculator is recommended for Exercise 29.

29. Given: $\overline{AD} \perp \overline{DF}$, $\overline{DG} \perp \overline{AF}$, $\overline{GE} \perp \overline{DF}$,
$\overline{GC} \perp \overline{AD}$, $\overline{CH} \perp \overline{AF}$, $\overline{BH} \perp \overline{AD}$,
$\overline{HJ} \perp \overline{CG}$
$AF = 15$, $AD = 12$, $DF = 9$
Find: AG, GF, DG, EF, CD, CG, and BC
$AG = 9.6$, $GF = 5.4$, $DG = 7.2$, $EF = 3.24$,
$CD = 4.32$, $CG = 5.76$, $BC = 2.7648$

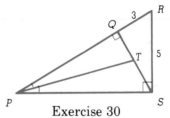

Exercise 29

30. Given: $QR = 3$, $RS = 5$
$\overline{RS} \perp \overline{PS}$, $\overline{SQ} \perp \overline{PR}$
$\angle QPT \cong \angle TPS$
Find: QP and PS
$QP = 5\frac{1}{3}$, $PS = 6\frac{2}{3}$

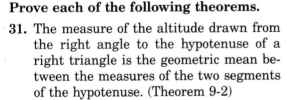

Exercise 30

For Exercises 31–32, see the Teacher Guide.

Prove each of the following theorems.

31. The measure of the altitude drawn from the right angle to the hypotenuse of a right triangle is the geometric mean between the measures of the two segments of the hypotenuse. (Theorem 9-2)

32. If the altitude is drawn to the hypotenuse of a right triangle, then the measure of a leg of the triangle is the geometric mean between the measure of the hypotenuse and the measure of the segment of the hypotenuse adjacent to that leg. (Theorem 9-3)

Algebra Review

Simplify.

1. $\sqrt{3} \cdot \sqrt{15}$ $3\sqrt{5}$

2. $(4 + \sqrt{3})(4 - \sqrt{3})$ 13

3. $\dfrac{5}{\sqrt{2} + \sqrt{3}}$ $5(\sqrt{3} - \sqrt{2})$

Solve.

4. $\sqrt{5x^2 - 9} = 2x$ 3

5. $\sqrt{4x + 1} = 5$ 6

Additional practice simplifying radicals can be found on pages 564–565.

Excursions in Geometry   Radical Sign

Ancient mathematicians commonly wrote the word for root to indicate square roots. Late medieval Latin writers commonly used ℞, a contraction of radix (root), to indicate a square root. The symbol $\sqrt{}$ first appeared in print in Rudolff's *Coss* (1525). It is uncertain whether Rudolff used the symbol because it resembled a small *r* for radix or whether he invented a new symbol.

9-3 The Pythagorean Theorem

Objectives: Recognize Pythagorean triples; use the Pythagorean Theorem or its converse as a test for right triangles; solve problems using the Pythagorean Theorem or its converse.

The **Pythagorean Theorem,** one of the most famous theorems in mathematics, has been studied and used for thousands of years. A Chinese manuscript from about 1000 B.C. illustrates this theorem. It is named after Pythagoras, a Greek mathematician from the sixth century. There are many proofs of the Pythagorean Theorem. President Garfield presented his own special proof of the theorem in 1876.

If a triangle is a right triangle, then the sum of the squares of the measures of the legs equals the square of the measure of the hypotenuse.	**Theorem 9-4** **Pythagorean Theorem**

If c is the measure of the hypotenuse, and a and b are the measures of the legs, then $a^2 + b^2 = c^2$.

Example

1 **Prove the Pythagorean Theorem.**

Given: $\triangle ABC$ is a right triangle.
Prove: $(BC)^2 + (CA)^2 = (AB)^2$

Proof:

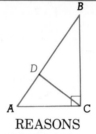

STATEMENTS	REASONS
1. Draw altitude $\overline{CD}$.	1. Given a line and a point *not* on the line, there is exactly one line through the point that is perpendicular to the given line. (Theorem 6-14)
2. $\triangle ABC$ is a right triangle.	2. Given
3. $\dfrac{AB}{BC} = \dfrac{BC}{BD}$ $\dfrac{AB}{CA} = \dfrac{CA}{DA}$	3. If the altitude is drawn to the hypotenuse of a right triangle, then the measure of a leg of the triangle is the geometric mean between the measure of the hypotenuse and the measure of the segment of the hypotenuse adjacent to that leg. (Theorem 9-3)
4. $(BC)^2 = AB \cdot BD$ $(CA)^2 = AB \cdot DA$	4. Equality of Cross Products (Theorem 8-1)
5. $(BC)^2 + (CA)^2 =$ $AB \cdot BD + AB \cdot DA$	5. Addition Property of Equality (Postulate 2-7)
6. $(BC)^2 + (CA)^2 =$ $AB(BD + DA)$	6. Distributive Property (Postulate 2-14)
7. $AB = BD + DA$	7. Definition of Between
8. $(BC)^2 + (CA)^2 = (AB)^2$	8. Substitution (Postulate 2-9)

If the square of the measure of the longest side of a triangle does *not* equal the sum of the squares of the measures of the other two sides, then the triangle is *not* a right triangle. Suppose $a^2 + b^2 = c^2$ is true for a given triangle. Can you conclude that the triangle is a right triangle?   *The answer is yes.*

The first sentence is the contrapositive of the Pythagorean Theorem. Recall that the contrapositive of a true statement also is a true statement.

If the sum of the squares of the measures of two sides of a triangle equals the square of the measure of the longest side, then the triangle is a right triangle.	*Theorem 9-5* *Converse of the* *Pythagorean Theorem*

Students will prove this theorem in Written Exercise 14.

Together, the Pythagorean Theorem and its converse provide a useful test for right triangles.

Examples

2   **Determine whether a triangle with sides measuring 11.5 meters, 16.1 meters, and 20.7 meters is a right triangle.**

Recall that if the measures of two angles of a triangle are unequal, then the measures of the sides opposite those angles are unequal in the same order. As a result, the hypotenuse of a right triangle is its longest side. Thus, it is only necessary to check one equation.

$$(20.7)^2 \overset{?}{=} (16.1)^2 + (11.5)^2$$
$$428.49 \overset{?}{=} 259.21 + 132.25$$
$$428.49 \neq 391.46$$

Since the equation is *not* true, the triangle is *not* a right triangle.

3   **Determine whether a triangle with sides measuring 4 inches, $5\frac{1}{3}$ inches, and $6\frac{2}{3}$ inches is a right triangle.**

The hypotenuse of a right triangle is its longest side. Thus, it is only necessary to check one equation.

$$\left(6\frac{2}{3}\right)^2 \overset{?}{=} (4)^2 + \left(5\frac{1}{3}\right)^2$$
$$\left(\frac{20}{3}\right)^2 \overset{?}{=} (4)^2 + \left(\frac{16}{3}\right)^2$$
$$\frac{400}{9} \overset{?}{=} 16 + \frac{256}{9}$$
$$\frac{400}{9} = \frac{400}{9}$$

Since the equation is true, the triangle is a right triangle.

The Pythagorean Theorem and its converse can be applied in many situations.

Example

4   The diagram shows a truss for a roof. The rise of the roof is 9 feet. The run is 18 feet on one part and 12 feet on the other. Find the lengths of both the long rafter and the short rafter, *not* counting the overhang. Round the answers to the nearest foot.

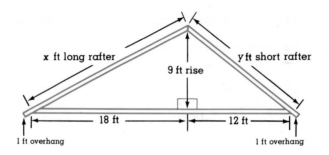

x ft long rafter

y ft short rafter

9 ft rise

18 ft   12 ft

1 ft overhang   1 ft overhang

Explore   Let x = the measure of the long rafter.
Let y = the measure of the short rafter.

Plan   Two right triangles are formed. One measures 18 feet by 9 feet by x feet. The other measures 12 feet by 9 feet by y feet. Use the Pythagorean Theorem.

$$x^2 = 18^2 + 9^2 \qquad y^2 = 12^2 + 9^2$$

Solve

$$
\begin{aligned}
x^2 &= 18^2 + 9^2 & y^2 &= 12^2 + 9^2 \\
x^2 &= 324 + 81 & y^2 &= 144 + 81 \\
x^2 &= 405 & y^2 &= 225 \\
x &= 9\sqrt{5} & y &= 15 \\
x &\approx 9 \cdot 2.236 \\
&\approx 20.124 \\
&\approx 20
\end{aligned}
$$

The length of the long rafter is about 20 feet and the short rafter is 15 feet.   *Examine this solution.*

Exploratory Exercises

Three integers that can be measures for the three sides of a right triangle are called a Pythagorean triple. Determine whether each of the following is a Pythagorean triple.

1. 5, 10, 12 no
2. 12, 16, 20 yes
3. 15, 20, 25 yes
4. 1.6, 3.0, 3.4 yes
5. 2.2, 2.4, 3.3 no
6. 3.87, 4.47, 5.91 no
7. 0.27, 0.36, 0.45 yes
8. 1, $\sqrt{2}$, $\sqrt{3}$ yes
9. $\sqrt{3}$, $\sqrt{4}$, $\sqrt{5}$ no
10. $\sqrt{5}$, $\sqrt{6}$, $\sqrt{7}$ no
11. 2, $2\frac{1}{3}$, $3\frac{2}{3}$ no
12. 2, $2\frac{2}{3}$, $3\frac{1}{3}$ yes

Written Exercises

Find the measure x. If necessary, round each answer to the nearest tenth.

1.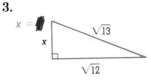

2.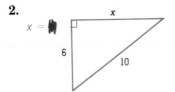

3.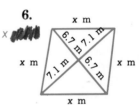

4.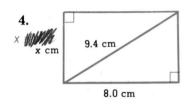

5.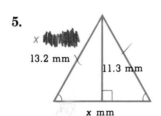

6.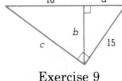

Solve each of the following exercises.

7. In a right triangle, the measures of the legs are 8 and $x + 7$, and the measure of the hypotenuse is $x + 9$. Find x.

8. In a right triangle, the measures of the sides are $x + 9$, $x + 2$, and $x + 10$. Find x.

9. Using the figure at the right, find $a + b + c$. 41

10. Find the perimeter of a rhombus whose diagonals are 30 cm and 16 cm 68 cm

11. The measure of a diagonal of a rhombus is 48 and the measure of a side is 26. Find the measure of the other diagonal. 20

12. $ABCD$ is an isosceles trapezoid. If $AB = 8$, $AC = 34$, and $EF = 30$, find the perimeter. $32 + 4\sqrt{241}$ units

13. In $\triangle PQS$, find RS such that $(QR)^2 - (RS)^2 = (PS)^2$ $\frac{41}{42}$

14. Prove the converse of the Pythagorean Theorem.
See the Teacher Guide.

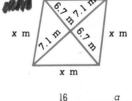

Exercise 9

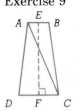

Exercise 12

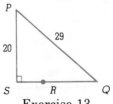

Exercise 13

Chapter 9 **321**

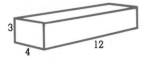

Exercise 17

15. A stair stringer is a board that supports stairs. Suppose a set of stairs is to rise 8 feet over a length of 15 feet. Find the length of the stair stringer to the nearest tenth of a foot. 17 ft

16. A picket fence is to have a gate 42 inches wide. The gate is 54 inches high. Find the length of a diagonal brace for the gate to the nearest inch. 68 in.

17. In a rectangular container all pairs of intersecting edges are perpendicular. What is the length of the longest rod that would fit inside the container shown at the left? 13 units

18. A plane flies 300 km due north, 400 km due east, and then 500 km due south. To the nearest kilometer, how far is the plane from its starting point? 447 km

19. The rafters of a roof truss are perpendicular to each other. The lengths are 24 ft and 32 ft. Find the rise of the roof. 19.2 ft

Statistics That Shape Your Life

You have studied how measures of dispersion describe data. Recall that the range is the difference between the greatest and least values in the set of data. The range is affected by unusually extreme values.

The chart below lists projected spending in billions of dollars for several states. Notice that the value for California is much greater than the other values in the set. In this case, the range is not a good measure of dispersion.

State	Expected '86 spending (in billions)
Ala.	$2.73
Alaska	$3.09
Ariz.	$2.34
Ark.	$1.67
Calif.	$28.36
Colo.	$1.90
Conn.	$4.01
Del.	$0.94
Fla.	$6.76
Ga.	$4.84

Copyright, 1985 USA Today.
Reprinted with permission.

A more representative measure of dispersion is called the **standard deviation.** This is an average measure of how much each value differs from the mean. The standard deviation is calculated by following these steps.

Encourage students to use calculators.

1. Find the mean.
2. Find the difference between each measurement and the mean.
3. Square each difference.
4. Find the mean of the squares.
5. Take the positive square root of this mean.

Exercise

Find the mean and the standard deviation to the nearest hundredth in projected state spending for the ten states listed in the chart above. 5.66; 7.73

9-4 Special Right Triangles

Objective: Find measures of parts of squares and equilateral triangles by using properties of 30°–60°–90° and 45°–45°–90° triangles.

The diagonal of a square and the sides of the square form two isosceles right triangles. By using the Pythagorean Theorem, it is possible to develop a formula relating the length of the diagonal to the length of a side.

Let s = the measure of each side of a square.
Let d = the measure of a diagonal of the square.

$$d^2 = s^2 + s^2$$
$$d^2 = 2s^2$$
$$d = s\sqrt{2}$$

Encourage students to learn how to derive these facts.

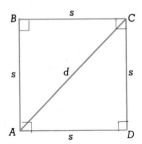

If each acute angle of a right triangle has a degree measure of 45, then the hypotenuse measures $\sqrt{2}$ times the measure of a leg.	*Theorem 9-6* *45°–45°–90° Theorem*	

The altitude of an equilateral triangle separates the triangle into two congruent right triangles. Using the Pythagorean Theorem, it is possible to develop a formula relating the length of the altitude to the length of a side of the equilateral triangle.

Let s = the measure of each side of an equilateral triangle.
Let a = the measure of an altitude of the triangle.

$$s^2 = a^2 + \left(\frac{s}{2}\right)^2$$
$$a^2 = s^2 - \left(\frac{s}{2}\right)^2$$
$$a^2 = \frac{3s^2}{4}$$
$$a = \frac{s\sqrt{3}}{2}$$

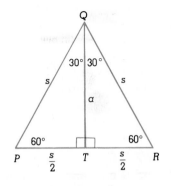

If the acute angles of a right triangle have degree measures of 30 and 60, then the measure of the hypotenuse is 2 times the measure of the shorter leg and the measure of the longer leg is $\sqrt{3}$ times the measure of the shorter leg.	*Theorem 9-7* *30°–60°–90° Theorem*	

Note that the shorter leg is opposite the angle of least degree measure.

The properties of the special right triangles can be used to solve a variety of problems.

Example

1 Consecutive bases of a square-shaped baseball diamond are 90 feet apart. Find the distance from home plate to second base. Round your answer to the nearest foot.

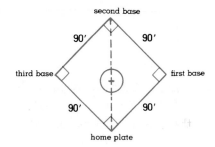

A line segment from home plate to second base is the diagonal of a square with sides measuring 90 feet.

$$d = s\sqrt{2}$$
$$= 90\sqrt{2}$$
$$\approx 90 \cdot 1.414 \text{ or } 127.26$$

The distance from home plate to second base is about 127 feet.

EN: 2–16 even, 2–16 even, 17–25; **AV:** 2–16 even, 1–23; **FD:** 1–16, 1–16, p. 322, 15–17;

Exploratory Exercises

ALL LEVELS: Mini Review

The length of each of the sides of a square is given. Find the length of the diagonals.

1. 1 ft

2. 3 cm

3. 2 in.

4. 12 in.

5. 31.2 m

6. $\frac{3}{4}$ ft

7. $4\frac{2}{3}$ yd

8. $1\frac{1}{2}$ ft

The length of each of the sides of an equilateral triangle is given. Find the length of the altitudes.

9. 1 in.

10. 1 m

11. 4 cm

12. 6 yd $3\sqrt{3}$ yd

13. $\frac{2}{3}$ yd $\frac{\sqrt{3}}{3}$ yd

14. $\frac{1}{4}$ ft $\frac{\sqrt{3}}{8}$ ft

15. $2\frac{3}{4}$ ft $\frac{11\sqrt{3}}{8}$ ft

16. $2\frac{1}{3}$ yd $\frac{7\sqrt{3}}{6}$ yd

Written Exercises

Find the measure x to the nearest tenth.

1.

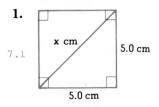

7.1

x cm

5.0 cm

5.0 cm

2.

5.2

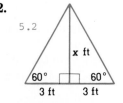

x ft

60° 60°

3 ft   3 ft

3.

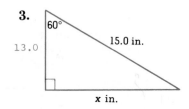

60°

13.0

15.0 in.

x in.

4.

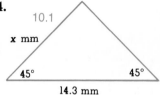

10.1
x mm
45°   45°
14.3 mm

5.

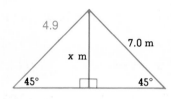

4.9
x m
7.0 m
45°   45°

6.

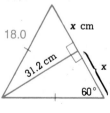

1.4
x cm
30°   30°
2.5 cm   2.5 cm

7.

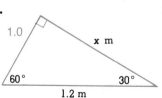

1.0
x m
60°   30°
1.2 m

8.

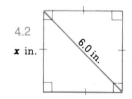

4.2
x in.
6.0 in.

9.

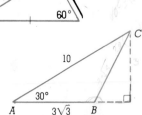

18.0
x cm
31.2 cm
x
60°

Solve each of the following. Unless specified otherwise, express answers in simplest radical form.

10. In the triangle at the right, $AC = 10$, $AB = 3\sqrt{3}$, and $m \angle A = 30$. Find BC. $\sqrt{37}$

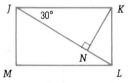

10
30°
A $3\sqrt{3}$ B
C
Exercise 10

11. Find the perimeter of $\triangle PQR$ shown at the right. $48 + 16\sqrt{3}$ units

8√3
30°
R   S   Q
P
Exercise 11

12. The sum of the squares of the lengths of all sides of a rectangle is 1458. Find the length of a diagonal of the rectangle.   27 units

13. In rectangle $JKLM$ shown at the right, $\overline{KN} \perp \overline{JL}$, $m \angle NJK = 30$, and $KN = 5$. Find the perimeter of $JKLM$. $\frac{60 + 20\sqrt{3}}{3}$ units

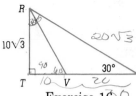

J   30°   K
N
M   L
Exercise 13

14. The perimeter of an equilateral triangle is 2.4 units. To the nearest tenth, find the measure of an altitude of the triangle.   0.7

15. The measure of an altitude of an equilateral triangle is 5.2. To the nearest tenth, find the perimeter of the triangle.   18.0 units

16. In $\triangle RST$ shown at the right, $RT = 10\sqrt{3}$. Find RS and VS. $RS = 20\sqrt{3}$, $VS = 20$

$10\sqrt{3}$
R
$10\sqrt{3}$
$20\sqrt{3}$
T   V   S
30°
Exercise 16

Use the figure at the right to find each measure.

17. u $\sqrt{2}$

18. v $\sqrt{3}$

19. w 2

20. x $\sqrt{5}$

21. y $\sqrt{6}$

22. z $\sqrt{7}$

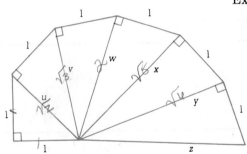

Exercises 17–22

Challenge Exercises

23. In $\triangle IJK$ below, $IJ = 18$, $m \angle I = 30$, and $m \angle K = 45$. Find JK.

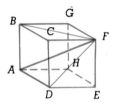

7-2

Suppose each edge of the cube below measures s units.

24. Develop a formula for the measure of the distance from A to F in terms of s. $AF = s\sqrt{3}$ 7-5

25. Find the degree measure of $\angle BFD$. 7-6
$m \angle BFD = 60$

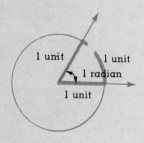

7-5

7-8

mini-review

1. What is the measure of one exterior angle of a regular heptagon? $51\frac{3}{7}°$

2. Name four quadrilaterals in which the diagonals bisect each other.

3. In which quadrilaterals are the diagonals perpendicular?

4. Given trapezoid $ABCD$ and median $\overline{PQ}$. Find DC if $AB = 42$ and $PQ = 51$. 60

5. How many faces are in an icosahedron? 20

2. square, rhombus, rectangle, parallelogram
3. rhombus, square

Excursions in Geometry _____ Radian Measure

One unit of angle measure is the degree. Another common unit of angle measure is the **radian**. This unit is defined using a circle.

Cut a piece of string that is the same length as the radius of a circle. Lay the string along the edge of the circle and mark the endpoints of the string on the circle. The angle formed by drawing two rays from the center of the circle through each point measures 1 radian.

Exercises

If a circle has a 1 unit radius, then the distance around the circle is 2π units. Use this information to solve each problem.

1. Find the radian measure of a right angle. $\frac{\pi}{2}$ radians

2. If the degree measures of two angles totals 180, find their total radian measure. π radians

9-5 Trigonometry

When the Egyptians first used a sun clock as early as 1500 B.C., they were using **trigonometry.** Trigonometry means *triangle measurement.*

The figure below represents a sun clock. A fixed staff, $\overline{GN}$, casts a shadow. $\overline{AN}$ represents the shadow and S represents the sun. Since $\overline{GN}$ is constant, the length of $\overline{AN}$ at any time varies with the measure of $\angle A$. The Egyptians understood that $\frac{GN}{AN}$ is a function of the measure of $\angle A$. Later, you will define this function as the tangent of $\angle A$.

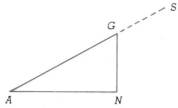

Extending this idea, consider the three overlapping triangles at the right. They are all right triangles and share a common angle, $\angle A$. Thus, the triangles are similar. How do the ratios $\frac{DE}{AE}$ and $\frac{FG}{AG}$ and $\frac{CB}{AB}$ compare? Because the triangles are similar, the ratios are equal.

In similar triangles, corresponding sides are proportional.

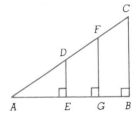

A ratio of the measures of two sides of a right triangle is called a **trigonometric ratio.** The value of a trigonometric ratio depends *only* on the measure of an acute angle. It does *not* depend on the size of the triangle.

The three most common trigonometric ratios are defined below.

Emphasize that these ratios are based on right triangles.

A ratio is the sine of an acute angle of a right triangle if and only if it is the ratio of the measure of the leg opposite the acute angle to the measure of the hypotenuse.	*Definition of Sine*
A ratio is the cosine of an acute angle of a right triangle if and only if it is the ratio of the measure of the leg adjacent to the acute angle to the measure of the hypotenuse.	*Definition of Cosine*
A ratio is the tangent of an acute angle of a right triangle if and only if it is the ratio of the measure of the leg opposite the acute angle to the measure of the leg adjacent to the acute angle.	*Definition of Tangent*

The sine of angle A is abbreviated sin A. The abbreviation cos A is used for cosine of angle A and tan A for tangent of angle A.

The trigonometric ratios for $\angle A$ of $\triangle ABC$ are as follows.

$$\sin A = \frac{BC}{AB}$$

$$\cos A = \frac{CA}{AB}$$

$$\tan A = \frac{BC}{CA}$$

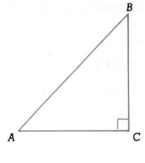

If the degree measure of $\angle A$ is 45, then you can write sin 45°, cos 45°, and tan 45°.

Given the measures of the sides of a triangle, the values of sine, cosine, and tangent can be calculated.

SOH-CAH-TOA is a helpful mnemonic device for remembering these ratios.

$$\sin = \frac{opposite}{hypotenuse}$$

$$\cos = \frac{adjacent}{hypotenuse}$$

$$\tan = \frac{opposite}{adjacent}$$

Point out that the tangent ratio never uses the hypotenuse.

Examples

1 **Find the sine, cosine, and tangent of angle A.**

$$\sin A = \frac{6}{10} \text{ or } 0.6000$$

$$\cos A = \frac{8}{10} \text{ or } 0.8000$$

$$\tan A = \frac{6}{8} \text{ or } 0.7500$$

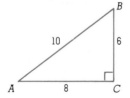

2 **Find sin 45°, cos 45°, and tan 45°.**

An isosceles right triangle has a 45° angle. According to Theorem 9-6, the hypotenuse measures $\sqrt{2}$ times the measure of a side.

$\sin 45° = \sin A$	$\cos 45° = \cos A$	$\tan 45° = \tan A$
$= \dfrac{BC}{AB}$	$= \dfrac{CA}{BA}$	$= \dfrac{BC}{CA}$
$= \dfrac{s}{s\sqrt{2}}$	$= \dfrac{s}{s\sqrt{2}}$	$= \dfrac{s}{s}$
$= \dfrac{s}{s\sqrt{2}} \cdot \dfrac{\sqrt{2}}{\sqrt{2}}$	$= \dfrac{\sqrt{2}}{2}$	$= 1$
$= \dfrac{\sqrt{2}}{2}$		

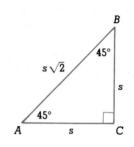

Thus, $\sin 45° = \dfrac{\sqrt{2}}{2}$, $\cos 45° = \dfrac{\sqrt{2}}{2}$, and $\tan 45° = 1$.

Exploratory Exercises

For the three triangles at the right, express each of the following as a fraction in simplest form.

1. $\sin A$ $\frac{21}{29}$
2. $\cos A$ $\frac{20}{29}$
3. $\tan A$ $\frac{21}{20}$
4. $\sin B$ $\frac{20}{29}$
5. $\cos B$ $\frac{21}{29}$
6. $\tan B$ $\frac{20}{21}$
7. $\sin E$ $\frac{4}{5}$
8. $\cos E$ $\frac{3}{5}$
9. $\tan E$ $\frac{4}{3}$
10. $\sin F$ $\frac{3}{5}$
11. $\cos F$ $\frac{4}{5}$
12. $\tan F$ $\frac{3}{4}$
13. $\sin G$ $\frac{15}{17}$
14. $\cos G$ $\frac{8}{17}$
15. $\tan G$ $\frac{15}{8}$
16. $\sin I$ $\frac{8}{17}$
17. $\cos I$ $\frac{15}{17}$
18. $\tan I$ $\frac{8}{15}$

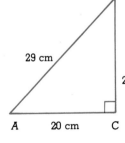

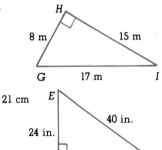

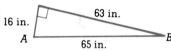

Written Exercises

A calculator may be helpful for these exercises.

For each of the following triangles, express the sine, cosine, and tangent of each acute angle to three decimal places. For Exercises 1–6, see the Teacher Guide.

1.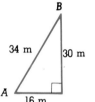

2.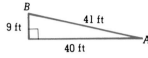

3.

4.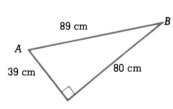

5.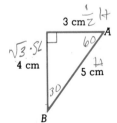

6.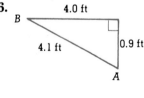

Find each of the following. Express answers in simplest radical form.

7. $\sin 30°$ $\frac{1}{2}$
8. $\cos 30°$ $\frac{\sqrt{3}}{2}$
9. $\tan 30°$ $\frac{\sqrt{3}}{3}$
10. $\sin 60°$ $\frac{\sqrt{3}}{2}$
11. $\cos 60°$ $\frac{1}{2}$
12. $\tan 60°$ $\sqrt{3}$

13. If $\angle A$ and $\angle B$ are complementary angles of a triangle, how are $\sin A$ and $\cos B$ related? They are equal.

Use the figures to state the trigonometric ratio for each of the angles and the value given.

14. $\frac{3}{5}$; $\angle Q$ $\sin Q$
15. $\frac{6}{4\sqrt{2}}$; $\angle W$ $\frac{1}{\sin W}$
16. $\frac{1}{\sqrt{3}}$; $\angle C$ $\tan C$
17. $\frac{5\sqrt{3}}{10}$; $\angle T$ $\sin T$
18. $\frac{3}{4}$; $\angle Q$ $\tan Q$
19. 3; $\angle W$ $\frac{1}{\cos W}$
20. 1.25; $\angle P$ $\frac{1}{\sin P}$
21. 2; $\angle C$ $\frac{1}{\sin C}$

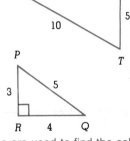

In Exercises 14–21, the reciprocals of trigonometric functions are used to find the solutions.

Problem Solving

One of the keys to solving problems using trigonometry is drawing a figure, or **model,** of the problem. Read the problem given below.

> Sandra is watching Johnny from a window 100 feet above the ground while Johnny plays 20 feet from the base of the building. What is the measurement of the angle Sandra's line of sight forms with the ground where Johnny is playing?

You can draw a figure to represent the problem above. The problem states that the window is 100 feet above the ground, so label that distance on your figure. The problem also states that Johnny is playing 20 feet from the base of the building, so label that distance. Finally, find the measurement of the angle Sandra's line of sight forms with the ground where Johnny is playing.

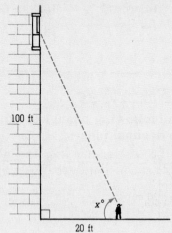

Write an equation for the problem. Since you are given the opposite and adjacent sides to the angle, use the tangent function to find x.

$$\tan x = \frac{100}{20}$$
$$\tan x = 5$$

As you learn more about trigonometry, you will be able to solve the equation and the problem.

Exercises See the Teacher Guide.

Draw a figure and write an equation that can be used to solve each problem. Do not solve.

1. The tortoise and the hare are 60 meters apart. A boy sitting in a tree at the finish line can see the hare as the tortoise crosses the line, winning the race. The measurement of the angle his line of sight forms with the tree is 75°. How far above the ground is the boy?

2. Patty, a basketball player, knows that the rim of the basket is 10 feet from the floor. From where she is standing, the angle of elevation to the rim is 33°. Find the distance from Patty's feet to the rim.

3. Two cars leave the same point at the same time. Car A goes east at 50 miles per hour, and car B goes south at 30 miles per hour. After one hour, what is the measurement of the angle the path of car A forms with the line between cars A and B?

4. A tent has a center pole that is 6 feet high, and a floor 8 feet wide. Find the measurement of the angle the tent side forms with the ground.

9-6 Trigonometric Tables

A weather team releases a weather balloon. The balloon's buoyancy accelerates it straight up at 15 m/s². A wind accelerates it horizontally at 6.5 m/s². What is the direction of the resulting acceleration? This problem can be represented graphically as shown below.

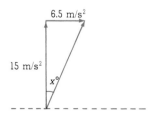

The direction of the acceleration, x, can be found by using the definition of a tangent. Recall that the tangent of an angle is the ratio of the length of the side opposite the angle to the length of the side adjacent to the angle. Therefore, the following equation can be written.

$$\tan x = \frac{6.5}{15}$$

$\tan x \approx 0.4333$
$x \approx 23°$

This equation can be solved by using trigonometric tables or a calculator with trigonometric functions. A table can be used to find decimal approximations for values of trigonometric ratios. Consider the following examples.

Example

1 **Find cos 48°.**   The complete table is given on page 581.

Locate 48° in the column marked Angle.

Angle	sin	cos	tan
45°	0.7071	0.7071	1.0000
46°	0.7193	0.6947	1.0355
47°	0.7314	0.6820	1.0724
48°	0.7431	0.6691	1.1106
49°	0.7547	0.6561	1.1504
50°	0.7660	0.6428	1.1918
51°	0.7771	0.6293	1.2349
52°	0.7880	0.6157	1.2799
53°	0.7986	0.6018	1.3270

Locate the value for cos 48° in the column marked cos.

An approximate value for cos 48° is 0.6691.

A table also can be used to find the measure of an angle, given a trigonometric ratio.

Examples

2 **Given cos A = 0.5446, find m ∠A.**

Locate 0.5446 in the column marked *cos*.

Locate the measure of the angle in the column marked Angle.

Angle	sin	cos	tan
54°	0.8090	0.5878	1.3764
55°	0.8192	0.5736	1.4281
56°	0.8290	0.5592	1.4826
57°	0.8387	0.5446	1.5399
58°	0.8480	0.5299	1.6003
59°	0.8572	0.5150	1.6643
60°	0.8660	0.5000	1.7321
61°	0.8746	0.4848	1.8040
62°	0.8829	0.4695	1.8807
63°	0.8910	0.4540	1.9626
64°	0.8988	0.4384	2.0503
65°	0.9063	0.4226	2.1445

The degree measure of ∠A is about 57.

3 **Given tan B = 0.1234, find m ∠B.**

Look in the column marked *tan*. Since the given value does *not* match any entry in a table, choose the closest value from the table.

As an additional example, you may wish to have students solve the weather balloon problem on the previous page.

Locate the measure of the angle in the column marked Angle.

Angle	sin	cos	tan
0°	0.0000	1.0000	0.0000
1°	0.0175	0.9998	0.0175
2°	0.0349	0.9994	0.0349
3°	0.0523	0.9986	0.0524
4°	0.0698	0.9976	0.0699
5°	0.0872	0.9962	0.0875
6°	0.1045	0.9945	0.1051
7°	0.1219	0.9925	0.1228
8°	0.1392	0.9903	0.1405
9°	0.1564	0.9877	0.1584
10°	0.1736	0.9848	0.1763
11°	0.1908	0.9816	0.1944
12°	0.2079	0.9781	0.2126

The value of 0.1234 is between 0.1228 and 0.1405. It is closer to 0.1228.

The degree measure of ∠B is about 7.

You may wish to discuss the Using Calculators feature on page 334 before assigning the exercises.

Exploratory Exercises

Use the table on page 581 to answer each of the following.

1. Name the least possible value for sine.
0.0000

2. Name the measurement of an angle for which the sine is at its minimum. 0°

3. Name the greatest possible value for sine.
1.0000

4. Name the measurement of an angle for which the sine is at its maximum. 90°

5. Name the least possible value for cosine.
0.0000

6. Name the measurement of an angle for which the cosine is at its minimum. 90°

7. Name the greatest possible value for cosine. 1.0000

8. Name the measurement of an angle for which the cosine is at its maximum. 0°

9. Name the least possible value for tangent. 0.0000

10. Name the greatest possible value for tangent. values go to infinity

11. Name the measurement of the angle for which sine and cosine are equal. 45°

12. Name the value of the tangent of the angle for which sine and cosine are equal. 1.0000

Written Exercises

Encourage students to use a calculator.

Find the value of the following ratios.

1. sin 0° 0.0000
2. sin 32° 0.5299
3. cos 0° 1.0000
4. tan 0° 0.0000

5. cos 69° 0.3584
6. tan 29° 0.5543
7. sin 58° 0.8480
8. cos 10° 0.9848

9. tan 38° 0.7813
10. sin 44° 0.6947
11. tan 45° 1.0000
12. tan 89° 57.2900

13. cos 22° 0.9272
14. tan 79° 5.1446
15. cos 36° 0.8090
16. cos 45° 0.7071

17. sin 13° 0.2250
18. cos 90° 0.0000
19. tan 50° 1.1918
20. sin 63° 0.8910

21. tan 84° 9.5144
22. sin 18° 0.3090
23. cos 16° 0.9613
24. tan 90° infinity

25. tan 51° 1.2349
26. cos 58° 0.5299
27. sin 89° 0.9998
28. sin 90° 1.0000

Find the measurement of each angle to the nearest degree.

29. sin A = 0.1045 6°
30. sin B = 0.5000 30°
31. cos C = 0.8988 26°

32. tan D = 0.3839 21°
33. tan E = 2.0503 64°
34. sin F = 0.7431 48°

35. cos P = 0.2588 75°
36. tan Q = 3.0777 72°
37. sin R = 0.9994 88°

38. tan S = 0.7002 35°
39. sin T = 0.8988 64°
40. sin V = 0.9205 67°

41. cos M = 0.3000 73°
42. tan N = 0.1500 9°
43. cos A = 0.7777 39°

44. cos P = 0.6 53°
45. tan L = 4.00 76°
46. tan T = 25 88°

47. sin X = 0.3 17°
48. tan Z = 0.15 9°
49. cos W = 0.65 49°

50. tan F = 1.75 60°
51. sin Q = 0.25 14°
52. cos E = 0.25 76°

53. tan R = 1.500 56°
54. cos G = 0.999 3°
55. sin H = 0.999 88°

56. sin A = $\frac{1}{2}$ 30°
57. cos T = $\frac{4}{5}$ 37°
58. tan Z = $\frac{3}{4}$ 37°

Find the value of each of the following to four decimal places.

59. cos 30° − sin 30° 0.3660
60. cos 60° − sin 30° 0.0000
61. sin 90° + cos 30° 1.8660

62. cos 30° + cos 60° 1.3660
63. tan 45° + tan 0° 1.0000
64. tan 0° + cos 90° 0.0000

65. 3 sin 30° − sin 90° 0.5000
66. cos 60° − 2 cos 30° −1.2320
67. 2 tan 30° − tan 60° −0.5773

68. tan 60° − 2 tan 30° 0.5773
69. 2 sin 45° − sin 90° 0.4142
70. 2 cos 45° − cos 90° 1.4142

71. $\frac{1}{2}$ sin 60° − sin 30° −0.0670

72. $\frac{1}{2}$ cos 60° + sin 30° 0.7500

73. tan 45° + tan 60° 2.7321

74. tan 45° − $\frac{1}{2}$ tan 60° 0.1340

75. $\frac{1}{2}$(sin 60° + sin 30°) 0.6830

76. $\frac{1}{2}$(tan 45° − tan 30°) 0.2113

77. sin 30° − cos 60° 0.0000

78. tan 45° + sin 0° 1.0000

79. sin 90° + cos 0° 2.0000

80. sin 90° − tan 0° 1.0000

81. sin 45° − cos 45° 0.0000

82. sin 45° − tan 45° −0.2929

83. cos 60° + 2 sin 90° 2.5000

84. cos 90° − 3 cos 30° −2.5980

Challenge Exercise

85. In △XYZ, Z is a right angle. If sin X = $\frac{3}{4}$, find tan Y. $\frac{\sqrt{7}}{3}$

Using Calculators

Trigonometric Function Keys

Some calculators have the $\boxed{\text{sin}}$, $\boxed{\text{cos}}$, and $\boxed{\text{TAN}}$ keys. To evaluate, enter the angle measure and then press the correct trigonometric function key.

Example Find sin 90°.

> Enter: 90 $\boxed{\text{sin}}$
>
> Display: 90   1
>
> Therefore, sin 90° = 1.

If your calculator has a degree/radian key, be sure the calculator is in the degree mode.

You can find angle measures using the $\boxed{\text{INV}}$ key. This key will provide the smallest angle whose function value has been given.

Example Find x if tan x = 1.

> Enter: 1 $\boxed{\text{INV}}$ $\boxed{\text{TAN}}$
>
> Display: 1   45
>
> Therefore, tan 45° = 1.

Some calculators have a key labeled TAN⁻¹ for this purpose.

Exercises
Find the value of each of the following.

1. cos 35° 0.819152

2. tan 120° −1.7320508

3. sin 45° 0.7071068

4. tan 225° 1

5. cos 315° 0.7071068

6. sin 27° 0.4539905

7. sin 30° − cos 60° 0

8. tan 45° + sin 0° 1

9. 4(sin 30°)(cos 60°) 1

Find x to the nearest degree.

10. tan x = 0 0

11. cos x = 1 0

12. sin x = 0.5 30

13. tan x = 5.1446 79

14. cos x = 0.3746 68

15. sin x = 0.2756 16

9-7 Application: Using Trigonometry

Objectives: Use trigonometric ratios to find missing measures of right triangles; recognize angles of depression or elevation; use trigonometry to solve problems.

Trigonometric ratios can be used to find missing measures of right triangles.

Examples

1 **For the triangle, find $m \angle A$ to the nearest degree.**

$$\tan A = \frac{BC}{AC}$$

$$\tan A = \frac{45}{55}$$

$$\tan A \approx 0.8182$$

$$m \angle A \approx 39$$

Show students that neither sin nor cos is helpful in this situation.

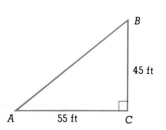

2 **For the triangle, find QR to the nearest tenth of a millimeter.**

$$\cos R = \frac{PR}{QR}$$

$$\cos 25° = \frac{42.0}{QR}$$

$$QR = \frac{42.0}{\cos 25°}$$

$$QR \approx \frac{42.0}{0.9063}$$

$$QR \approx 46.3$$

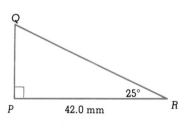

3 **For the triangle, find TV and VW to the nearest tenth of a centimeter.**

$$\sin W = \frac{TV}{TW} \qquad\qquad \cos W = \frac{VW}{TW}$$

$$\sin 40° = \frac{TV}{26.0} \qquad\qquad \cos 40° = \frac{VW}{26.0}$$

$$TV = 26.0 \sin 40° \qquad\qquad VW = 26.0 \cos 40°$$

$$TV \approx 26.0(0.6428) \qquad\qquad VW \approx 26.0(0.7660)$$

$$TV \approx 16.7 \qquad\qquad VW \approx 19.9$$

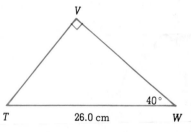

To see the top of a peak or an object in the sky, a person must look up rather than looking straight ahead. An **angle of elevation** is formed by the line of sight and a horizontal line.

A person in a tower or on a cliff must look down to see an object below. This person's line of sight forms an **angle of depression** with a horizontal line.

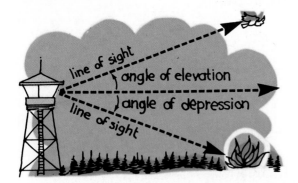

Example

4   A surveyor is 100.0 meters from a dam. The angle of elevation to the top of the dam is 26°. The surveyor's instrument is 1.73 meters above the ground. Find the height of the dam to the nearest hundredth.

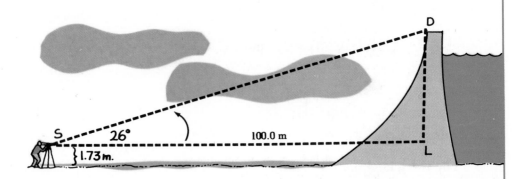

$$\tan 26° = \frac{DL}{100.0}$$

$$0.4877 \approx \frac{DL}{100.0}$$

$$48.77 \approx DL$$

The angle of elevation is from the horizontal line up to the line of sight.

The height of the dam is about 48.77 + 1.73 or 50.50 meters.

Exploratory Exercises

Name the angles of elevation and depression in each figure.

1. 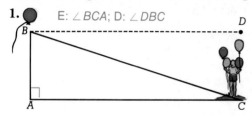 E: ∠BCA; D: ∠DBC

2. 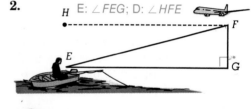 H E: ∠FEG; D: ∠HFE

3. 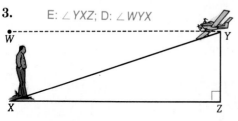 E: ∠YXZ; D: ∠WYX

4. 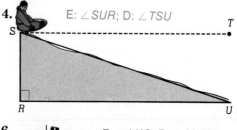 E: ∠SUR; D: ∠TSU

5. 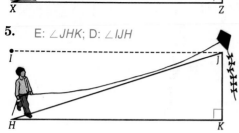 E: ∠JHK; D: ∠IJH

6. E: ∠LNO; D: ∠MLN

For each of the following, state an equation that would enable you to answer each problem. Use a triangle similar to $\triangle PRQ$.

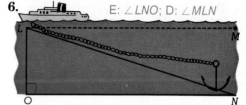

7. Given $m \angle P = 15$ and $PQ = 37$, find QR. $\sin 15° = \frac{QR}{37}$

8. Given $m \angle Q = 72$ and $PR = 13$, find QR. $\tan 72° = \frac{13}{QR}$

9. Given $m \angle P = 47$ and $QR = 10$, find PQ. $\sin 47° = \frac{10}{PQ}$

10. Given $QR = 21.5$ and $m \angle Q = 87$, find PR. $\tan 87° = \frac{PR}{21.5}$

11. Given $PR = 13.4$ and $m \angle P = 16$, find PQ.

12. Given $PR = 31.8$ and $m \angle P = 19$, find PQ.

11. $\cos 16° = \frac{13.4}{PQ}$ **12.** $\cos 19° = \frac{31.8}{PQ}$

Written Exercises

Using the figures at the right, find each of the following. Round all answers to the nearest whole number.

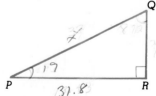

Exercises 1–5

Exercises 6–10

1. $m \angle X$ 27

2. $m \angle Y$ 63

3. $m \angle Z$ 90

4. XY 61

5. $(\sin X)^2 + (\cos X)^2$ 1

6. $m \angle U$ 90

7. $m \angle W$ 19

8. UV 2

9. WV 7

10. $(\sin W)^2 + (\cos W)^2$ 1

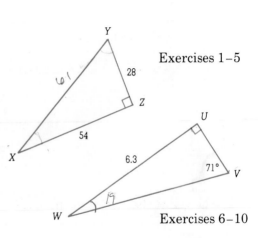

Answer each of the following. Round all answers to the nearest hundredth unless otherwise indicated.

11. A surveyor is 100.00 meters from a bridge. The angle of elevation to the top of the bridge is 35°. The surveyor's instrument is 1.45 meters above the ground. Find the height of the bridge. 71.47 m

12. A surveyor is 100.00 meters from a building. The angle of elevation to the top of the building is 23°. The surveyor's instrument is 1.55 meters above the ground. Find the height of the building. 44.00 m

13. To secure a 500-meter radio tower against high winds, guy wires are attached to a ring on the tower. The ring is 5 meters from the top. The wires form a 15° angle with the tower. Find the distance from the tower to the guy wire anchor in the ground. 132.61 m

14. In a parking garage, each level is 20 feet apart. Each ramp to a level is 130 feet long. Find the measure of the angle of elevation for each ramp. 9°

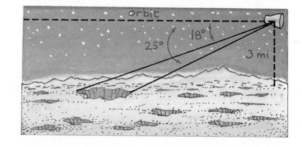

15. Before Apollo 11 descended to the surface of the moon, it made one orbit at a distance of 3 miles from the surface. At one point in its orbit, the onboard guidance system measured the angles of depression to the near and far edges of a huge crater. The angles measured 25° and 18°. Find the distance across the crater. 2.80 mi

16. A lighthouse built at sea level is 150 feet high. From its top, the angle of depression of a buoy is 25°. Find, to the nearest foot, the distance from the buoy to the foot of the lighthouse. 322 ft

17. A ladder is leaning against the side of a house and forms an angle of 65° with the ground. The foot of the ladder is 8 feet from the building. Find the length of the ladder to the nearest foot. 19 ft

18. At a certain time of day, the angle of elevation of the sun is 44°. Find, to the nearest meter, the shadow cast by a building 30 meters high. 31 m

19. A road rises vertically 40 feet over a horizontal distance of 630 feet. What is the angle of elevation of the road? 4°

20. A train in the mountains rises 10 feet for every 250 feet it moves along the track. Find the angle of elevation of the track. 2°

21. A plane rose from takeoff and flew at an angle of 11° with the ground. When it reached an altitude of 500 feet, what was the horizontal distance the plane had flown? 2572 ft

Applications in Surveying

Jan Takach is a surveyor. Part of her job with the U.S. National Geodetic Survey is to make maps of new territories. The theory of triangulation is used to measure and plot land and water surfaces.

Suppose Jan wants to find the distance to a mountain peak. First, Jan measures out one side of a triangle, called the baseline, on a flat terrain. The length of the baseline must be calculated with extreme care. She then erects marker poles at each end of the baseline where a survey instrument, usually a theodolite, is set up on a tripod. She can then measure the horizontal angle, or the bearing, between the baseline and the mountain peak. She then repeats the procedure at the other end of the baseline. Using trigonometry, it is possible to calculate the distance to the mountain peak without having to climb the mountain.

In these examples and exercises, the triangle will always be a right triangle. Later you will be able to solve problems in which the triangle is not a right triangle.

Example   During a preliminary survey of a future bridge site, an engineer measures the distance across the river by laying a baseline 30 m in length along the shoreline. One end of the baseline, A, is directly across from a tree on the opposite shoreline. Using a sighting instrument, the engineer finds that a line from the tree to the other end of the baseline, B, would form an angle of 76° with the baseline. What is the distance across the river?

$$\tan 76° = \frac{AC}{30} \qquad tan = \frac{opposite}{adjacent}$$

$$4.011 = \frac{AC}{30}$$

$$120.33 \approx AC$$

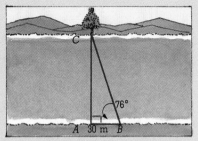

The distance across the river is approximately 120 m.

Exercise

Using the information in the figure at the right, find the distance across the pond to the nearest tenth of a meter.   92.4 m

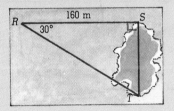

Vocabulary

square root (309)
radical sign (309)
radicand (309)
rationalizing the denominator (311)
irrational numbers (311)
geometric mean (314)
Pythagorean Theorem (318)

trigonometry (327)
trigonometric ratio (327)
sine (327)
cosine (327)
tangent (327)
angle of elevation (336)
angle of depression (336)

Chapter Summary

1. Definition of Square Root: For any numbers a and b, if $a^2 = b$, then a is a square root of b.   (309)

2. The radical sign indicates a nonnegative square root.   (309)

3. Product Property of Square Roots (Postulate 9-1):   For any nonnegative numbers a and b, $\sqrt{ab} = \sqrt{a} \cdot \sqrt{b}$.   (310)

4. Quotient Property of Square Roots (Postulate 9-2):   For any nonnegative numbers a and b with $b \neq 0$, $\sqrt{\dfrac{a}{b}} = \dfrac{\sqrt{a}}{\sqrt{b}}$.   (310)

5. A square root is said to be simplified when the following conditions are met.
   1. The radicand has no perfect square factor other than 1.
   2. The radicand does *not* contain a fraction.
   3. No radical appears in the denominator of a fraction.   (311)

6. Theorem 9-1:   If the altitude is drawn from the vertex of the right angle to the hypotenuse of a right triangle, then the two triangles formed are similar to the given triangle and to each other.   (313)

7. Definition of Geometric Mean: For any positive numbers a and b, x is the geometric mean between a and b if and only if $\dfrac{a}{x} = \dfrac{x}{b}$ and x is positive.   (314)

8. Theorem 9-2:   The measure of the altitude drawn from the right angle to the hypotenuse of a right triangle is the geometric mean between the measures of the two segments of the hypotenuse.   (314)

9. Theorem 9-3:   If the altitude is drawn to the hypotenuse of a right triangle, then the measure of a leg of the triangle is the geometric mean between the measure of the hypotenuse and the measure of the segment of the hypotenuse adjacent to that leg.   (315)

10. The Pythagorean Theorem (Theorem 9-4):   If a triangle is a right triangle, then the sum of the squares of the measures of the legs equals the square of the measure of the hypotenuse.   (318)

11. Converse of the Pythagorean Theorem (Theorem 9-5):   If the sum of the squares of the measures of two sides of a triangle equals the square of the measure of the longest side, then the triangle is a right triangle.   (319)

12. Theorem 9-6:   If each acute angle of a right triangle has a degree measure of 45, then the hypotenuse measures $\sqrt{2}$ times the measure of a leg.   (323)

13. Theorem 9-7:   If the acute angles of a right triangle have degree measures of 30 and 60, then the measure of the hypotenuse is 2 times the measure of the shorter leg and the measure of the longer leg is $\sqrt{3}$ times the measure of the shorter leg.   (323)

14. Definition of Sine: A ratio is the sine of an acute angle of a right triangle if and only if it is the ratio of the measure of the leg opposite the acute angle to the measure of the hypotenuse.   (327)

15. Definition of Cosine: A ratio is the cosine of an acute angle of a right triangle if and only if it is the ratio of the measure of the leg adjacent to the acute angle to the measure of the hypotenuse.   (327)

16. Definition of Tangent: A ratio is the tangent of an acute angle of a right triangle if and only if it is the ratio of the measure of the leg opposite the acute angle to the measure of the leg adjacent to the acute angle.   (327)

17. A table can be used to find decimal approximations for values of trigonometric ratios.   (331)

Chapter Review

9-1   **State the principal square root of each expression.**

1. 25 5   2. 0.04 0.2   3. $\dfrac{81}{16}$ $\dfrac{9}{4}$ 4. 75 $5\sqrt{3}$ 5. $\dfrac{5}{3}$ $\dfrac{\sqrt{15}}{3}$ 6. $\dfrac{1}{2}$ $\dfrac{\sqrt{2}}{2}$

Find the approximate value of each expression. Use the table of Squares and Approximate Square Roots on page 580.

7. $\sqrt{175}$ 13.23   8. $\sqrt{6} - \sqrt{15}$ −1.424   9. $\sqrt{\dfrac{7}{3}}$ 1.528

9-2   **Use the figure at the right to answer each of the following. Approximate each answer to the nearest tenth.**

10. Find BD if $AD = 4.0$ and $DC = 6.0$. $BD \approx 4.9$

11. Find AB if $AC = 18.0$ and $AD = 4.0$. $AB \approx 8.5$

12. Find BC if $AD = 4\dfrac{8}{9}$ and $DC = \dfrac{1}{9}$. $BC \approx 0.7$

13. Find BA if $AD = \dfrac{1}{3}$ and $DC = \dfrac{1}{4}$. $AB \approx 0.4$

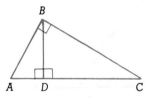

9-3 For each of the following, determine whether it is possible to draw a right triangle with sides of the given measures. Write *yes* or *no*.

14. 0.9, 2.1, 2.3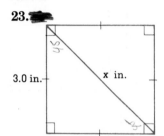

15. 0.9, 4.0, 4.1

16. 4, 4, $4\sqrt{2}$

17. 4, $7\frac{1}{2}$, $8\frac{1}{2}$

18. $\sqrt{5}$, $\sqrt{7}$, $\sqrt{12}$

19. $\sqrt{5}$, $\sqrt{6}$, $\sqrt{11}$

For each of the following, find the measure of the hypotenuse of a right triangle with legs of the given measure. Round each answer to the nearest tenth.

20. 9.4, 8.0

21. 7.1, 6.7

22. 8.0, 15.0

9-4 For each of the following, find the measure *x*. Round each answer to the nearest tenth.

23.

3.0 in.   *x* in.

24.

x cm   60°   60°   3.1 cm

25.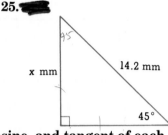

x mm   14.2 mm   45°

9-5 For each of the following triangles, express the sine, cosine, and tangent of each acute angle to the nearest tenth. For Exercises 26–27, see the Teacher Guide.

26.

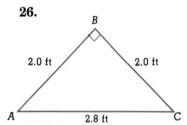

B   2.0 ft   2.0 ft   A   2.8 ft   C

27.

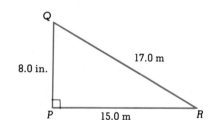

Q   17.0 m   8.0 in.   P   15.0 m   R

9-6 Find the approximate value of each expression.

28. sin 14° 0.2419

29. cos 33° 0.8387

30. tan 51° 1.2349

Find the measurement of each angle to the nearest degree.

31. sin A = 0.5000 30

32. cos B = 0.3200 71

33. tan C = 0.95 44

9-7 Use a triangle similar to △*ABC* to help answer each problem.

34. Given m ∠B = 25 and AB = 32, find AC. 13.5232

35. Given m ∠A = 52 and AB = 7.5, find BC. 5.91

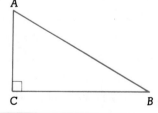

A   C   B

36. A surveyor is 350.0 m from a mountain peak. The angle of elevation to the top of the peak is 85°. The surveyor's instrument is 1.7 m above the ground. Find the height of the mountain peak to the nearest tenth of a meter. 4002.2 m

Chapter Test

For each of the following pairs of numbers, find the geometric mean. Approximate each answer to the nearest tenth.

1. 3.0 and 12.0 6.0

2. $\sqrt{2}$ and $2\sqrt{2}$ 2.0

3. 5.0 and 4.0 4.5

For each of the following, determine whether it is possible to draw a right triangle with sides of the given measures. Write *yes* or *no*.

4. 16, 30, 34 yes

5. 0.3, 0.4, 0.5 yes

6. $\sqrt{7}, 2\sqrt{6}, 5$ no

For each of the following, find the measure *x*. Round each answer to the nearest tenth.

7.
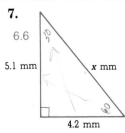
6.6
5.1 mm
x mm
4.2 mm

8. 5.9
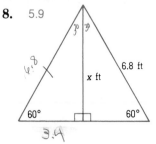
6.8 ft
x ft
60°   60°
3.4

9.
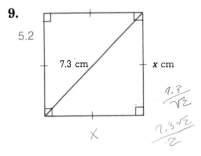
5.2
7.3 cm
x cm
$\frac{7.3}{\sqrt{2}}$
$\frac{7.3\sqrt{2}}{2}$
X

10. Using the figure at the right, find the measures *a*, *b*, and *c*. $a = 5\frac{5}{12}, b = 5, c = 13$

11. In an equilateral triangle, each side has a measure of 10. Find the measure of the altitude of the triangle. ▬▬

12. The figure at the right is a kite. It has right angles *BIK* and *BEK*. *SB* = 12 and *SK* = 3. Find *IE* and the perimeter of *BEKI*. *IE* = 12, perimeter = $18\sqrt{5}$

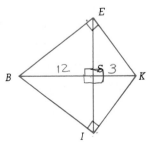

B
a   c
b
A $2\frac{1}{12}$ D   12   C

Exercise 10

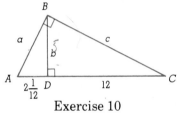

E
12   S 3
B   K
I

Exercise 12

Use the figure to answer each problem.

13. Find sin *A* to four decimal places. 0.7548

14. Find sin *C* to four decimal places. 0.6560

15. Find tan *A* to four decimal places. 1.1506

16. Find cos *C* to four decimal places. 0.7548

17. Find *m* ∠*A* to the nearest degree. 49

18. Find *m* ∠*C* to the nearest degree. 41

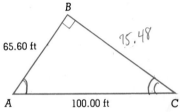

B
65.60 ft   75.48
A   100.00 ft   C

19. A flag pole casts a shadow 20 feet long when the angle of elevation of the sun measures 43°. Find the height of the pole to the nearest foot. 19 ft

State whether each of the following is *true* or *false*.

1. A point has only one dimension. false
2. A line contains at least two points. true
3. If two distinct planes intersect, then their intersection is exactly one point. false
4. The contrapositive of a statement is the same as the inverse of the converse of the statement. true
5. If P is between M and N, then P, M, and N are collinear. true
6. If $PM = MQ$, then M always is the midpoint of $\overline{PQ}$. false
7. An angle is defined as the union of two rays with a common endpoint. false
8. Vertical angles are equal in measure. true
9. Perpendicular lines form acute angles. false
10. The acute angles of a right triangle are supplementary. false
11. In an equilateral triangle all the medians and altitudes are congruent. true
12. The longest side of a right triangle is the hypotenuse. true
13. A triangle can have sides whose measures are 23, 7, and 16. false
14. Two parallel lines are everywhere equidistant. true
15. Regular polygons are always convex. true

Answer each of the following.

16. The degree measure of one angle of a regular polygon is 140. Name the polygon. nonagon (9 sides)

17. How many diagonals can be drawn in a regular heptagon? 14

18. An exterior angle of a regular polygon has a degree measure of 1. How many sides does the polygon have? 360

19. Find the measure of the other base of a trapezoid if the measures of a base and median are 12 and 29 respectively. 46

20. Find the perimeter of a regular polygon if one of its angles has a degree measure of 140 and one of its sides has a measure of 10. 9(10) or 90

21. How many faces does an icosahedron have? 20

22. In the figure at the right, $\overline{BC} \parallel \overline{DE}$, AB = 4, AC = 3, BC = 2, and CE = 4. Find BD and DE. $BD = \frac{16}{3}$, $DE = \frac{14}{3}$

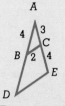

Exercise 22

23. In the figure at the right, DB = 5, AB = 4, AD = 3, and $\triangle ABD \sim \triangle DBC$. Find the perimeter of $\triangle DBC$. 15

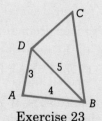

Exercise 23

Simplify each of the following expressions.

24. $\sqrt{80}$ $4\sqrt{5}$

25. $\sqrt{12a^2b^3c^4}$ $2abc^2\sqrt{3b}$

26. Find the geometric mean between 5 and 20. 10

27. Given $NT = 4$, $MT = 3$, $\angle MNR$ is a right angle, and $\angle NTR$ is a right angle, find MN, TR, and NR.
$MN = 5$, $TR = \frac{16}{3}$, $NR = \frac{20}{3}$

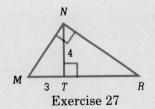

Exercise 27

28. Given $ST = 5\sqrt{2}$, $\overline{TO} \perp \overline{SP}$, $\overline{ST} \perp \overline{TP}$, and $m \angle TPO = 30$, find TO, OP, and TP.
$TP = 5\sqrt{6}$, $TO = \frac{5}{2}\sqrt{6}$, $OP = \frac{5}{2}\sqrt{18}$ or $\frac{15}{2}\sqrt{2}$

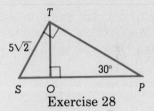

Exercise 28

29. Find the measure of the height, BC, in the diagram of the tree at the right.
49.99 ft or about 50 ft

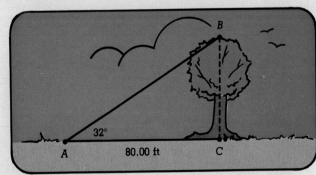

Complete each of the following exercises.

30. _Opposite_ angles of a parallelogram are congruent.

31. The diagonals of a parallelogram _bisect_ each other.

32. The diagonals of a rhombus _bisect_ the angles of the rhombus.

33. The median of a trapezoid is _parallel_ to the bases.

34. The mean proportional is also called the _geometric_ mean.

35. "For any right triangle, the square of the measure of the hypotenuse equals the sum of the squares of the measures of the legs," is called the _____ Theorem. Pythagorean

CHAPTER 10

Circles and Spheres

The most noted characteristic of the planet Saturn is the ring system that surrounds it. There are seven major rings around Saturn, although many smaller ones also exist. These rings, consisting of dust and ice particles, provide a graphic illustration of circles.

10-1 Parts of Circles

Objectives: Name parts of circles; determine relationships between lines and circles.

To irrigate the fields shown in the photograph, water is sprayed from pipes that rotate about central points. Circular patterns result. Notice that all the points along the edge of a field are the same distance from the center. Each edge forms a **circle.**

| A figure is a circle if and only if it is the set of all points in a plane that are a given distance from a given point in the plane, called the center. | *Definition of Circle* |

Usually, circles are named by their centers. For example, the circle at the right is called circle *P*. This is symbolized ⊙*P*.

The following figures show segments that are related to circles.

A **radius** of a circle is a segment whose endpoints are the center of the circle and a point on the circle. $\overline{CD}$ is a radius of ⊙*C*.

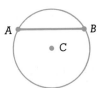

A **chord** of a circle is a segment whose endpoints are points on the circle. $\overline{AB}$ is a chord of ⊙*C*.

A **diameter** of a circle is a chord that contains the center of the circle. $\overline{EF}$ is a diameter of ⊙*C*.

Note that a diameter is also a chord.

It follows from the definition of a circle that all the radii of a circle are congruent. Also, all the diameters of a circle are congruent.

How are the measure of a radius and the measure of a diameter of a circle related? $d = 2r$

A circle separates a plane into three parts. The parts are the **interior,** the **exterior,** and the **circle** itself.

Suppose a point is in the *interior* of a circle. The measure of the segment joining the point to the center is *less than* the measure of the radius. *Since PI < PR, point I is in the interior of ⊙P.*

Suppose a point is in the *exterior* of a circle. The measure of the segment joining the point to the center is *greater than* the measure of the radius. *Point E is in the exterior of ⊙P because PE > PR.*

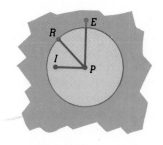

$\overline{PR}$ *is a radius of* ⊙P.

In a plane, a line can intersect a circle in one of two ways.

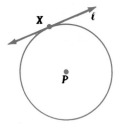

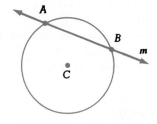

The line can intersect the circle in exactly one point. Such a line is a **tangent** to the circle. The point of intersection is the **point of tangency.** In the figure above, line ℓ is tangent to ⊙P at X.

The line can intersect the circle in exactly two points. Such a line is a **secant** of the circle. A secant of a circle contains a chord of the circle. In the figure above, line *m* contains the chord $\overline{AB}$ and is a secant of ⊙C.

The following theorem examines one of the ways lines can intersect circles.

In a plane, if a line contains a point in the interior of a circle, then the line intersects the circle in exactly two points.	*Theorem 10-1*

Example

1 All points of ⊙P are 4 units from P. Suppose *PA* = 5 and *PB* = 2. Determine whether $\overleftrightarrow{AB}$ intersects ⊙P in *zero points, one point,* or *two points.*

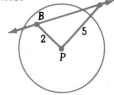

B must be in the interior of ⊙P because the measure of the distance from P to B is less than the measure of the radius of the circle. Thus, by Theorem 10-1, $\overleftrightarrow{AB}$ intersects the circle in exactly two points.

A line that is tangent to two circles in the same plane is called a **common tangent** of the two circles. There are two types of common tangents.

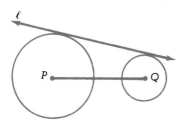

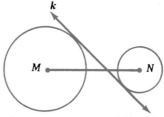

A common tangent that does not intersect the segment whose endpoints are the centers of the circles is a **common external tangent.** In the figure above, line ℓ is a common external tangent to ⊙P and ⊙Q.

A common tangent that intersects the segment whose endpoints are the centers of the circles is a **common internal tangent.** In the figure above, line k is a common internal tangent to ⊙M and ⊙N.

Example

2 **How many common tangents can be drawn to ⊙Q and ⊙P?**

There are 4 common tangents to ⊙Q and ⊙P.

Lines ℓ and m are common external tangents and lines j and k are common internal tangents.

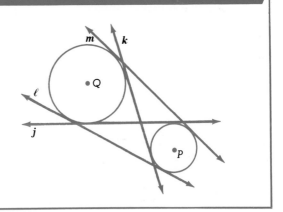

EN: 2–7, 2–12 even, 14–16, 18, 19; **AV:** 1–10, 1–14, 16; **FD:** 1–10, 1–10

Exploratory Exercises

Use the figure to answer each of the following.

1. Name the center of the circle. *P*
2. Name the circle. ⊙*P*
3. Name three radii of the circle. $\overline{PD}, \overline{PB}, \overline{PC}$
4. Name a diameter of the circle. $\overline{DB}$
5. Name a chord of the circle. $\overline{EA}$ or $\overline{DB}$
6. Name a tangent of the circle. $\overleftrightarrow{HB}$
7. Name a secant of the circle. $\overleftrightarrow{EA}$
8. Name two points in the interior of the circle. *G, P*
9. Name two points in the exterior of the circle. *F, H*
10. Name five points that lie on the circle. *A, B, C, D, E*

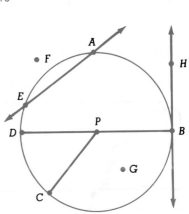

Written Exercises

Determine whether each statement is *true* or *false*.

1. A diameter of a circle is the longest chord of the circle. ▬▬

2. A radius of a circle is a chord of the circle. ▬▬

3. A chord of a circle is a secant of the circle. ▬▬

4. A secant of a circle is always a diameter of the circle. ▬▬

5. Two radii of a circle always form a diameter of the circle. ▬▬

6. A radius of a circle is tangent to the circle. ▬▬

Suppose all points of $\odot R$ are 6 units from R and $\overleftrightarrow{AB}$ and $\odot R$ are in the same plane. For each of the following, determine whether $\overleftrightarrow{AB}$ intersects $\odot R$ in *zero points, one point,* or *two points*. There may be more than one answer.

0, 1, or 2 points

7. $RA = 5.2$ 2 points
   $RB = 7.9$

8. $RA = 6.0$ 2 points
   $RB = 3.3$

9. $RA = 6.0$ 2 points
   $RB = 6.0$

10. $RA = 7.9$
    $RB = 9.7$

Draw two different circles that have the common tangents described in the following statements. For Exercises 11–13, see the Teacher Guide.

11. one common internal tangent and two common external tangents

12. no common internal tangents and two common external tangents

13. no common internal tangents and one common external tangent

Complete the following exercises.

14. Two parallel lines, ℓ and m, are tangent to $\odot P$. How many points are equidistant from ℓ, m, and $\odot P$? 3

15. If $n > 0$, draw $2n$ radii equally spaced in a circle. Let any secant cut the sections formed by the radii into non-overlapping regions. What will be the maximum number of such regions formed within the circle? Express your answer in terms of n.

$3n + 1$

Prove each of the following statements. See the Teacher Guide.

16. If the diameter of a circle measures d units and the radius of the circle measures r units, then $d = 2r$.

17. If X is a point in the interior of $\odot P$, then there are points A and B on $\odot P$ so that X is between A and B.

Challenge Exercises

Complete the following exercises.

18. Circles T and T', with radii 8 units and 18 units respectively, are tangent to each other and are tangent to the sides of $\angle MBI$ as shown in the figure. Find AB. 42

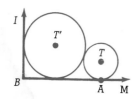

19. $\odot P$ is tangent to $\odot Q$ at A and $\odot R$ at B. $\odot Q$ and $\odot R$ are tangent at C. If $PQ = 18$, $PR = 15$, and $QR = 27$, find the radius of $\odot P$. 30

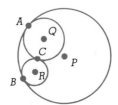

10-2 Angles and Arcs

Objectives: Recognize major or minor arcs, or semicircles; find the degree measures of arcs and central angles.

Two rays can be drawn from the center of a circle to form an angle. If the rays and the circle are in the same plane, such an angle is called a **central angle.**

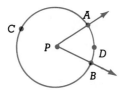

words	arc *ACB*	arc *AB*	*words*	
symbols	$\overparen{ACB}$	$\overparen{AB}$	*symbols*	

Emphasize that only two letters are necessary when naming a minor arc.

A central angle separates a circle into **arcs.** For example, in the figure above, $\angle APB$ is a central angle of $\odot P$. Points A and B and all points of the circle interior to $\angle APB$ form a **minor arc** called $\overparen{AB}$ or $\overparen{ADB}$. Points A and B and all points of the circle exterior to $\angle APB$ form a **major arc** called $\overparen{ACB}$. *Three letters are needed to name a major arc. Why?* Emphasize the need to use three letters in order to differentiate the major from the minor arc.

$\overparen{ADB}$ and $\overparen{BDA}$ name the same minor arc.

A line containing the diameter of a circle separates the circle into two **semicircles.** In the figure, $\overparen{XRY}$ and $\overparen{XSY}$ are semicircles.

Arcs are measured by their corresponding central angles.

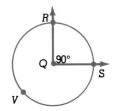

The degree measure of $\overparen{RS}$ is 90.   *words*

$$m\overparen{RS} = 90$$ *symbols*

The degree measure of a minor arc is the degree measure of its central angle. The degree measure of a major arc is 360 minus the degree measure of its central angle. The degree measure of a semicircle is 180.

Definition of Arc Measure

As with angles, measures of arcs can be added to find measures of other arcs. For example, $m\overparen{PQ} = 110$ and $m\overparen{QR} = 120$. Thus, $m\overparen{PQR} = 230$.

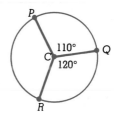

If Q is a point on $\overarc{PQR}$, then $m\overarc{PQ} + m\overarc{QR} = m\overarc{PQR}$.	*Postulate 10-1* *Arc Addition Postulate*

The sum of the degree measures of all of the arcs of a circle is 360. Why?
The sum of the degree measures of the central angles is 360.

Example

1   **In $\odot P$ at the right, $m \angle APB = 30$ and $\overline{AC}$ is a diameter. Find $m\overarc{AB}$, $m\overarc{ACB}$, $m\overarc{BC}$, and $m\overarc{BAC}$.**

The central angle of $\overarc{AB}$ and $\overarc{ACB}$ is $\angle APB$. Thus, $m\overarc{AB} = 30$. $\overarc{ACB}$ is a major arc for $\angle APB$. Thus, $m\overarc{ACB} = 360 - 30$ or 330.

By the Arc Addition Postulate, $m\overarc{AB} + m\overarc{BC} = m\overarc{ABC}$. Since $m\overarc{AB} = 30$ and $\overarc{ABC}$ is a semicircle, the following holds.

$$30 + m\overarc{BC} = 180$$
$$m\overarc{BC} = 180 - 30 \text{ or } 150$$

Finally, $\overarc{BAC}$ is a major arc for $\angle BPC$, which measures 150. Thus, $m\overarc{BAC} = 360 - 150$ or 210.

All circles have the same shape, but *not all* circles have the same size. Notice that the tree rings share a common center but have radii of different lengths. Circles that lie in the same plane and have the same center are called **concentric circles.**

All circles are similar.

As the tree rings show, circles with radii having different lengths are *not* congruent. For two circles to be congruent, their radii *must have* the same length.

Two circles are congruent if and only if their radii are congruent.	*Definition of* *Congruent Circles*

Two arcs of a circle are congruent if and only if they have the same measure.

In a circle or in congruent circles, two central angles are congruent if and only if their minor arcs are congruent.	*Theorem 10-2*

EN: 3, 6, 9, . . . 30, 3, 6, 9, . . . 42, 44, 47, 50; **AV:** 2–32 even, 2–50 even; **FD:** 1–32, 1–35, p. 350, 11–14;

Exploratory Exercises
ALL LEVELS: Algebra Review

For each of the following, determine whether it is a *minor arc*, a *major arc*, or a *semicircle* of ⊙M.

3. semicircle **4.** semicircle

1. $\widehat{AB}$ minor   **2.** $\widehat{ECA}$ major **3.** $\widehat{BAE}$ **4.** $\widehat{BDE}$
5. $\widehat{DCE}$ major **6.** $\widehat{CBD}$ major **7.** $\widehat{DAB}$ major **8.** $\widehat{AE}$ minor
9. $\widehat{BC}$ minor   **10.** $\widehat{BCD}$ minor **11.** $\widehat{BDC}$ major **12.** $\widehat{AD}$ minor
13. $\widehat{CBA}$ **14.** $\widehat{DC}$ minor **15.** $\widehat{ACD}$ major **16.** $\widehat{CAE}$ major
  semicircle

17–32. Estimate, to the nearest ten degrees, the measures of the arcs in Exercises 1–16. See the Teacher Guide.

Written Exercises

Find the following measures if in ⊙P, $m \angle WPX = 28$, $m \angle ZPY = 38$, and $\overline{WZ}$ and $\overline{XV}$ are diameters.

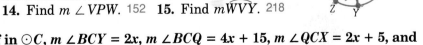

1. Find $m\widehat{YZ}$. 38   **2.** Find $m\widehat{WX}$ 28   **3.** Find $m \angle VPZ$. 28
4. Find $m\widehat{VZ}$. 28   **5.** Find $m\widehat{VWX}$. 180   **6.** Find $m\widehat{ZVW}$. 180
7. Find $m\widehat{WYZ}$. 180   **8.** Find $m\widehat{ZXW}$. 180   **9.** Find $m \angle XPY$. 114
10. Find $m\widehat{XY}$. 114   **11.** Find $m\widehat{XWY}$. 246   **12.** Find $m\widehat{WZX}$. 332
13. Find $m\widehat{VW}$. 152   **14.** Find $m \angle VPW$. 152   **15.** Find $m\widehat{WVY}$. 218

Answer the following if in ⊙C, $m \angle BCY = 2x$, $m \angle BCQ = 4x + 15$, $m \angle QCX = 2x + 5$, and $\overline{XY}$ and $\overline{AB}$ are diameters.

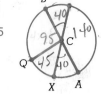

16. Find x. 20   **17.** Find $m\widehat{BY}$. 40   **18.** Find $m\widehat{BQ}$. 95
19. Find $m\widehat{QX}$. 45   **20.** Find $m\widehat{YQ}$. 135   **21.** Find $m \angle YCQ$. 135
22. Find $m\widehat{BX}$. 140   **23.** Find $m \angle BCX$. 140 **24.** Find $m\widehat{XA}$. 40
25. Find $m\widehat{QA}$. 85   **26.** Find $m \angle QCA$. 85   **27.** Find $m\widehat{XYA}$. 320

Determine whether each of the following statements is *true* or *false*.

28. If $m\widehat{AB} = 32$ and $m\widehat{XY} = 32$, then $\widehat{AB} \cong \widehat{XY}$.   **29.** If $\widehat{AB} \cong \widehat{XY}$, and $m\widehat{AB} = 32$, then $m\widehat{XY} = 64$.

30. Two congruent circles have congruent radii.   **31.** All radii of a circle are congruent.

32. Two concentric circles never have congruent radii.   **33.** If two circles have the same center, they are congruent.

34. If two central angles are congruent, then their corresponding minor arcs are congruent.   **35.** If two minor arcs are congruent, then their corresponding central angles are congruent.

In the figure, A is the center of two concentric circles with radii $\overline{AQ}$ and $\overline{AR}$. Also, $m\angle SAR = 32$, and $m\angle RAW = 112$.

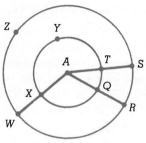

36. Find $m\widehat{SR}$. 32
37. Find $m\widehat{TX}$. 144
38. Find $m\widehat{XQ}$. 112
39. Find $m\widehat{WR}$. 112
40. Find $m\widehat{SW}$. 144
41. Find $m\widehat{TQ}$. 32
42. Find $m\widehat{TYX}$. 216
43. Find $m\widehat{SZW}$. 216
44. Can two arcs have the same measure but not be congruent? yes

Exercises 36–44

Complete the following exercises.

45. If $m\widehat{PQ} = 120$, find $m\angle Q$.

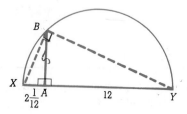

46. $ABCDEF$ is a regular hexagon inscribed in $\odot O$. Find $m\widehat{ACE}$.

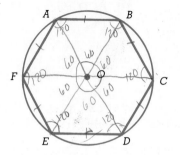

47. If B is a point on a semicircle $\widehat{XBY}$ with $\overline{AB} \perp \overline{XY}$ at point A, $\overline{XB} \perp \overline{BY}$, $XA = 2\frac{1}{12}$, and $AY = 12$, find BY.

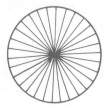

48. Suppose a wheel has 30 spokes evenly spaced and numbered consecutively from 1 through 30. Find the degree measure of the central angle formed by spokes 1 and 14. 156

For Exercises 49–50, see the Teacher Guide.

Prove the following statements.

49. In two congruent circles, if two minor arcs are congruent, then their corresponding central angles are congruent.

50. In two congruent circles, if two central angles are congruent, then their corresponding minor arcs are congruent.

Algebra Review

Solve each equation.

1. $\sqrt{x} = 6$
2. $4 + \sqrt{2y} = 6$
3. $\sqrt{5a + 6} = 11$
4. $2\sqrt{10} = \sqrt{x}$
5. $8 = 4\sqrt{6x - 8}$

For additonal practice solving radical equations, see page 566 of the Diagnostic Skills Review.

10-3 Arcs and Chords

Objective: Recognize and use the relationships between arcs, chords, and other parts of circles.

When a minor arc and a chord have the same endpoints, we call the arc the **arc of the chord.** For example, in the figure at the right, $\overset{\frown}{PQ}$ is the arc of $\overline{PQ}$.

Chords and their arcs are related in the following way.

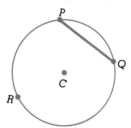

In a circle or in congruent circles, two minor arcs are congruent if and only if their corresponding chords are congruent.	*Theorem 10-3*

The proof of this theorem is based on congruent triangles. The following example shows how they are used to prove one part of the theorem. Students will complete the second part of Theorem 10-3 in Written Exercise 18.

Example

1   Prove that if two arcs of a circle are congruent, then their corresponding chords are congruent.

Given: In $\odot C$,
$\overset{\frown}{AB} \cong \overset{\frown}{PQ}$.

Prove: $\overline{AB} \cong \overline{PQ}$

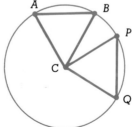

Proof:

STATEMENTS	REASONS
1. Draw radii $\overline{AC}$, $\overline{BC}$, $\overline{PC}$, and $\overline{QC}$ and chords $\overline{AB}$ and $\overline{PQ}$.	1. Through any two points there is exactly one line. (Postulate 1-1)
2. $\overline{AC} \cong \overline{PC}$ $\overline{BC} \cong \overline{QC}$	2. Definition of Circle
3. $\overset{\frown}{AB} \cong \overset{\frown}{PQ}$, $\odot C$	3. Given
4. $\angle ACB \cong \angle PCQ$	4. In a circle or in congruent circles, if two minor arcs are congruent, then their central angles are congruent. (Theorem 10-2)
5. $\triangle ACB \cong \triangle PCQ$	5. SAS (Postulate 4-3)
6. $\overline{AB} \cong \overline{PQ}$	6. Definition of Congruent Triangles *CPCTC*

The midpoint of an arc separates the arc into two congruent arcs. In $\odot C$, point M is the midpoint of $\overset{\frown}{AB}$ because $\overset{\frown}{AM} \cong \overset{\frown}{MB}$, and we say that $\overline{CM}$ bisects $\overset{\frown}{AB}$. By using congruent triangles, it can be shown that $\overline{CM}$ also bisects $\overline{AB}$. In addition, $\overline{CM} \perp \overline{AB}$.

Suppose a diameter or radius of a circle is perpendicular to a chord. Does it appear to bisect the chord and its arc? yes

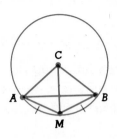

Students will prove this theorem in Written Exercise 20.

In a circle, if a diameter is perpendicular to a chord, then it bisects the chord and its arcs.	*Theorem 10-4*

Example

2 Suppose a chord of a circle is 24 centimeters long and is 9 centimeters from the center of the circle. Find the length of the radius.

Let $\overline{AD}$ represent the chord, and draw $\overline{BC}$ perpendicular to $\overline{AD}$. Then, $BC = 9$.

By Theorem 10-4, $\overline{BC}$ bisects $\overline{AD}$. Thus, AC and $CD = \frac{24}{2}$ or 12.

$\overline{AB}$ is a radius of the circle and the hypotenuse of a right triangle with sides measuring 12 and 9 centimeters, respectively.

$$(AB)^2 = 12^2 + 9^2$$
$$= 225$$
$$AB = 15$$

Thus, the radius is 15 centimeters long.

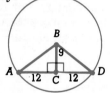

Suppose $\odot C$ and $\odot R$ are congruent, and $\overline{AB} \cong \overline{PQ}$. Are the chords the same distance from the centers of the circles? yes

Suppose, instead, that you know the chords to be equidistant from the centers of the circles. Could you conclude that the chords are congruent? yes

Remember, the distance from a point to a line is always the measure of the perpendicular segment.

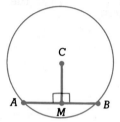
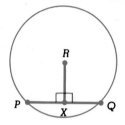

In a circle or in congruent circles, two chords are congruent if and only if they are equidistant from the center.	*Theorem 10-5*

Students will prove this theorem in Written Exercises 21 and 22.
356 *Circles and Spheres*

Exploratory Exercises

For the following exercises, name the theorem or theorems that justify the statement.

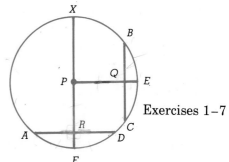

1. If $\overline{BC} \cong \overline{AD}$, then $\widehat{BC} \cong \widehat{AD}$. Theorem 10-3
2. If $\widehat{BC} \cong \widehat{AD}$, then $\overline{BC} \cong \overline{AD}$. Theorem 10-3
3. If $\overline{BC} \cong \overline{AD}$, then $PQ = PR$. Theorem 10-5
4. If $\overline{PF} \perp \overline{AD}$, then $\widehat{AF} \cong \widehat{FD}$. Theorem 10-4
5. If $\overline{PQ} \perp \overline{BC}$, then $\overline{BQ} \cong \overline{QC}$. Theorem 10-4
6. If $PQ = PR$, then $\overline{CB} \cong \overline{DA}$. Theorem 10-5
7. If $\overline{FX} \perp \overline{AD}$, then $\widehat{AX} \cong \widehat{XD}$. Theorem 10-4

Exercises 1–7

Written Exercises

For $\odot A$ answer the following if $\overline{SY} \perp \overline{QT}$, and $\overline{YS}$ and $\overline{ZR}$ are diameters.

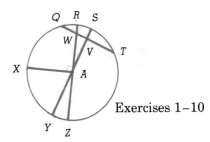

1. Name a segment congruent to $\overline{VT}$. QV
2. Name the midpoint of $\widehat{QT}$. S
3. Name the midpoint of $\widehat{TQ}$. V
4. Name an arc congruent to $\widehat{ST}$. QS
5. Name an arc congruent to $\widehat{QY}$. YT
6. Name a segment congruent to $\overline{RZ}$. SY
7. Which segment is longer, $\overline{WA}$ or $\overline{VA}$? WA
8. Which segment is longer, $\overline{QT}$ or $\overline{YS}$? YS
9. If W is the midpoint of $\widehat{QV}$, then R is the midpoint of $\widehat{QS}$. Write *yes* or *no*. no
10. If X is the midpoint of $\widehat{ZXR}$, how is $\overline{XA}$ related to $\overline{ZR}$? They are perpendicular.

Exercises 1–10

Answer each of the following exercises.

11. Suppose a chord of a circle is 10 inches long and is 12 inches from the center of the circle. Find the length of the radius.

12. Suppose a chord of a circle is 18 centimeters long and is 12 centimeters from the center of the circle. Find the length of the radius.

13. Suppose the diameter of a circle is 20 centimeters long and a chord is 16 centimeters long. Find the distance between the chord and the center of the circle.

14. Suppose the diameter of a circle is 10 inches long and a chord is 6 inches long. Find the distance between the chord and the center of the circle. 4 in.

15. In $\odot O$, $\overline{MN} \cong \overline{PQ}$, $MN = 7x + 13$, and $PQ = 10x - 8$. Find PS.

16. Find the distance from the center of $\odot O$, with radius 12 units, to a side in regular hexagon $ABCDEF$. 6√3 units

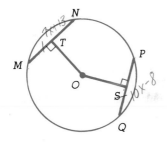

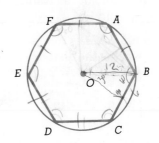

Prove each of the following exercises. For Exercises 17–27, see the Teacher Guide.

17. If two chords of a circle are congruent, then their corresponding arcs are congruent.

18. If two congruent circles each contain a chord that is congruent to the other chord, then the corresponding arcs are congruent.

19. If a radius of a circle bisects an arc of the circle, then it bisects the corresponding chord.

20. In a circle, if a diameter is perpendicular to a chord, then it bisects the chord and its arcs. (Theorem 10-4)

21. If two chords of a circle are congruent, then they are equidistant from the center of the circle.

22. If two chords of a circle are equidistant from the center of the circle, then the two chords are congruent.

23. In a circle, if a chord is a perpendicular bisector of another chord, then the first chord is a diameter of the circle.

24. In a circle, if one chord is longer than another chord, then the longer chord is closer to the center of the circle.

25. Given: $\overline{AC}$ is a diameter.
  $\overline{AC} \perp \overline{BD}$
  Prove: $\triangle EBC \cong \triangle EDC$

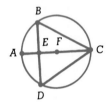

26. Given: $\overset{\frown}{PTS} \cong \overset{\frown}{QST}$
  $\overline{RS} \cong \overline{RT}$
  Prove: $\triangle PQR$ is isosceles.

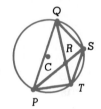

27. Given: $\overline{FE}$ is a diameter of $\odot A$.
  $\overline{UT}$ is a diameter of $\odot P$.
  $\overline{FE} \perp \overline{BD}$
  $\overline{UT} \perp \overline{QS}$
  $\odot A$ and $\odot P$ are congruent.
  $\overline{BC} \cong \overline{QR}$
  Prove: $\overset{\frown}{BD} \cong \overset{\frown}{QS}$

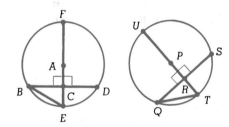

Challenge Exercises

Complete the following exercises.

28. Find the length of a chord that is the perpendicular bisector of a radius of length 20 units in a circle. $20\sqrt{3}$ units

29. Circles O and P, with radii 20 and 34 units respectively, intersect at points A and B. If the length of $\overline{AB}$ is 32 units, find OP.
42 units

30. Regular pentagon *IJKLM* is inscribed in $\odot P$. If $ML = 20$, what is the distance from $\overline{ML}$ to the center of $\odot P$? What is the length of the radius of $\odot P$? Round answers to the nearest hundredth.

distance ≈ 13.76 units
radius ≈ 17.01 units

10-4 Inscribed Angles

Objectives: Recognize intercepted arcs and inscribed angles; find the measures of inscribed angles; use properties of inscribed figures to solve problems.

In each of the figures below, the angles intercept arcs of the circles. The **intercepted arcs** are shown in red.

The intercepted arc is always in the interior of the angle.
Note that one angle intercepts two arcs.

$\stackrel{\frown}{PQR}$ is not an intercepted arc.

$\stackrel{\frown}{STU}$ is not an intercepted arc.

You may wish to identify $\stackrel{\frown}{STU}$ as the arc that inscribes $\angle STU$.

An angle intercepts an arc if and only if each of the following conditions hold.	*Definition of Intercepted Arc*
1. The endpoints of the arc lie on the angle. 2. All points of the arc, except the endpoints, are in the interior of the angle. 3. Each side of the angle contains an endpoint of the arc.	

In the figure at the right, $\angle ABC$ intercepts an arc of a circle, and the vertex of the angle lies on the circle. Such an angle is called an **inscribed angle**. We say that $\angle ABC$ intercepts $\stackrel{\frown}{AC}$ and is inscribed in $\stackrel{\frown}{ABC}$.

An angle is an inscribed angle if and only if its vertex lies on a circle and its sides contain chords of the circle.	*Definition of Inscribed Angle*

The measures of inscribed angles are related to the measures of their intercepted arcs.

In the figure at the right, $\angle QPR$ is an inscribed angle that intercepts $\overset{\frown}{QR}$. By using the Isosceles Triangle Theorem and the Exterior Angle Theorem, you can show $m\angle QPR = \frac{1}{2}(m\angle QCR)$.

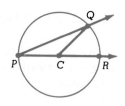

Since $\angle QCR$ is a central angle of $\odot C$, $m\angle QCR = m\overset{\frown}{QR}$. Thus, $m\angle QPR = \frac{1}{2}(m\overset{\frown}{QR})$.

Point out that an inscribed angle could intercept a major arc just as well as a minor arc.

The following deductions show how to find the measures of inscribed angles whose sides do *not* contain diameters of a circle.

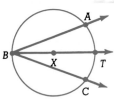

$m\angle ABC = m\angle ABT + m\angle TBC$
$= \frac{1}{2}(m\overset{\frown}{AT}) + \frac{1}{2}(m\overset{\frown}{TC})$
$= \frac{1}{2}(m\overset{\frown}{AT} + m\overset{\frown}{TC})$
$= \frac{1}{2}m\overset{\frown}{AC}$

$m\angle LMN = m\angle LMD - m\angle NMD$
$= \frac{1}{2}(m\overset{\frown}{LD}) - \frac{1}{2}(m\overset{\frown}{ND})$
$= \frac{1}{2}(m\overset{\frown}{LD} - m\overset{\frown}{ND})$
$= \frac{1}{2}m\overset{\frown}{LN}$

If an angle is inscribed in a circle, then the measure of the angle equals one-half the measure of its intercepted arc.	*Theorem 10-6*

Example

1 In the figure at the right, $m\overset{\frown}{PQ} = 112$, $m\overset{\frown}{QS} = 54$, and $m\overset{\frown}{ST} = 88$. Find $m\angle 1$, $m\angle 2$, and $m\angle 3$.

$m\overset{\frown}{PQ} + m\overset{\frown}{QS} + m\overset{\frown}{ST} + m\overset{\frown}{TP} = 360$
$112 + 54 + 88 + m\overset{\frown}{TP} = 360$
$m\overset{\frown}{TP} = 106$

$m\angle 1 = \frac{1}{2}(m\overset{\frown}{QS})$
$= \frac{1}{2}(54)$
$= 27$

$m\angle 2 = \frac{1}{2}(m\overset{\frown}{TP})$
$= \frac{1}{2}(106)$
$= 53$

$m\angle 3 = m\angle 1 + m\angle 2$ *Exterior Angle Theorem*
$= 27 + 53$
$= 80$

The proofs of the following theorems are based on Theorem 10-6.

Students will prove the following theorem in Written Exercise 34.

If two inscribed angles of a circle or congruent circles intercept congruent arcs, then the angles are congruent.	*Theorem 10-7*
If an angle is inscribed in a semicircle, then the angle is a right angle.	*Theorem 10-8*

Example

2   Prove Theorem 10-8.

Given: $\overarc{PQR}$ is a semicircle of $\odot C$.

Prove: $\angle PQR$ is a right angle.

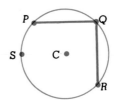

Proof:

STATEMENTS	REASONS
1. $\overarc{PQR}$ is a semicircle of $\odot C$.	1. Given
2. $\overarc{PSR}$ is a semicircle of $\odot C$.	2. Definition of Semicircle
3. $m\overarc{PSR} = 180$	3. Definition of Arc Measure
4. $m\angle PQR = \frac{1}{2}(m\overarc{PSR})$	4. The measure of an inscribed angle of a circle equals one-half the measure of its intercepted arc. (Theorem 10-6)
5. $m\angle PQR = \frac{1}{2}(180)$ or 90	5. Substitution (Postulate 2-9)
6. $\angle PQR$ is a right angle.	6. Definition of Right Angle

A polygon is an **inscribed polygon** if and only if each of its vertices lies on a circle. The polygon is said to be *inscribed* in the circle. In the figure, quadrilateral $PQRS$ is inscribed in $\odot C$.

Since the measures of the arcs of a circle total 360, the opposite angles of an inscribed quadrilateral are related in a special way.

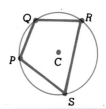

If the angles of a quadrilateral are inscribed in a circle, then each pair of opposite angles are supplementary.	*Theorem 10-9*

Students will prove this theorem in Written Exercise 35.

EN: 1–7 odd, 3, 6, 9, . . . 30, 32, 34–36; AV: 1–8, 2–34; FD: 1–8, 1–25, p. 358, 18, 25

Exploratory Exercises

For each of the following, name the arc or arcs intercepted by the given angle. Then, determine whether each angle is an inscribed angle. Write *yes* or *no*.

1. $\overset{\frown}{BC}$, yes

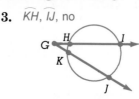

2. $\overset{\frown}{DF}$, no

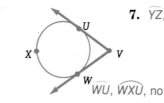

3. $\overset{\frown}{KH}$, $\overset{\frown}{IJ}$, no

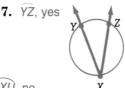

4. $\overset{\frown}{LN}$, $\overset{\frown}{LTO}$, no

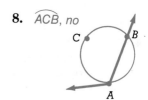

5.

$\overset{\frown}{QT}$, $\overset{\frown}{RS}$, no

6.

$\overset{\frown}{WU}$, $\overset{\frown}{WXU}$, no

7. $\overset{\frown}{YZ}$, yes

8. $\overset{\frown}{ACB}$, no

Written Exercises

Find the measure for each of the following angles if in $\odot X$, $\overline{AB} \parallel \overline{DC}$, $m\overset{\frown}{BC} = 94$, and $m \angle AXB = 104$.

1. $\overset{\frown}{AB}$ ▨
2. $\angle BAC$ ▨
3. $\angle BDC$ ▨

4. $\angle BCA$ ▨
5. $\angle ADB$ ▨
6. $\angle ADC$ ▨

7. $\angle XAB$ ▨
8. $\angle ABX$ ▨
9. $\angle ACD$ ▨

10. $\angle BCD$ ▨
11. $\angle DEC$ ▨
12. $\angle AED$ ▨

13. $\angle EAD$ ▨
14. $\overset{\frown}{DC}$ ▨
15. $\angle BAD$ ▨

16. $\angle DBC$ ▨
17. $\overset{\frown}{AD}$ ▨
18. $\angle ABD$ ▨

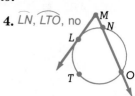

Exercises 1– 18

The figure shows a regular hexagon inscribed in $\odot P$ with radius measuring 12 units. Answer each of the following.

19. Find the length of each side. ▨ units
20. Find the distance of each side from the center of the circle. ▨ units
21. Find $m \angle FBC$. ▨
22. Find $m \angle ADB$. ▨

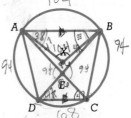

Exercises 19–22

The figure shows an equilateral triangle inscribed in $\odot Q$ with radius measuring 12 units. Answer each of the following.

23. Find the length of each side. ▨ units
24. Find the distance from each side of the triangle to the center of the circle. ▨ units
25. Find $m\overset{\frown}{AB}$. ▨

In the figure at the right, regular hexagon *ABCDEF* is inscribed in $\odot O$. Find the measure for each of the following angles.

26. $m \angle BDC$ ▓▓

27. $m \angle BCD$ ▓▓

Exercises 26–31

28. $m \angle PCD$ ▓▓

29. $m \angle CPD$ ▓▓

30. $m \angle ABD$ ▓▓

31. $m \angle FEC$ ▓▓

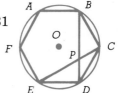

Prove the following exercises. For Exercises 32–35, see the Teacher Guide.

32. The measure of an inscribed angle that has a side that contains a diameter is one-half the measure of its intercepted arc.

33. The bisector of an inscribed angle separates the intercepted arc into two congruent arcs.

34. If two inscribed angles of a circle or congruent circles intercept congruent arcs, then the angles are congruent. (Theorem 10-7)

35. If the angles of a quadrilateral are inscribed in a circle, then each pair of opposite angles are supplementary. (Theorem 10-9)

*Challenge Exercise*_____

Complete the following exercise.

36. In the figure at the right, $\overline{AB}$ is a diameter of $\odot O$. If $AB = 7$, find the exact value of AP. $\dfrac{7\sqrt{3}}{2}$

Exercise 36

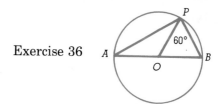

*Statistics That Shape Your Life*_____

Listening to music is a popular pastime for young and old alike. Today, recorded music can be purchased in many different forms. The adjacent circle graph demonstrates how music is purchased today.

Exercises

1. What is the most popular way to buy music today?

2. Is the table based on total dollar sales or on total number of items sold?

3. If the table is based on total dollar sales, how many dollars in 12-inch singles were sold, assuming the total industry sales to be one billion dollars?

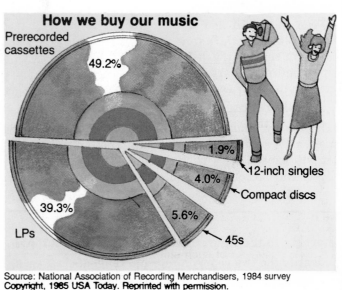

Source: National Association of Recording Merchandisers, 1984 survey
Copyright, 1985 USA Today. Reprinted with permission.

1. Prerecorded Cassettes **2.** We can't be sure based on information given. It is probably total dollar sales.
3. $19,000,000

Applications in Astronomy

A natural phenomenon that is both fascinating and terrifying is an **eclipse.** An eclipse occurs when the shadow of one object in space falls across another object, or an object moves in front of another to block its light. Those that are most familiar are the lunar and solar eclipses.

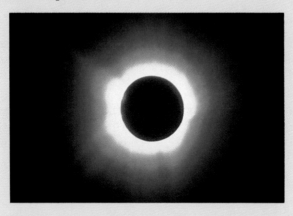

In a solar eclipse, the shadow of the moon blocks the light of the sun.

A *lunar eclipse* takes place when the earth is between the sun and the moon. The earth casts a shadow over the moon, either causing it to darken or appear reddish in color.

Most impressive is the *solar eclipse*. This occurs when the moon passes between the sun and the earth to block the sun. Only certain areas of the earth will experience a total eclipse; other areas, a partial eclipse. Some areas will experience no eclipse at all.

In the figure, the moon is between the earth and the sun. The lines that are tangent to the sun and the moon help to outline the areas affected by the solar eclipse.

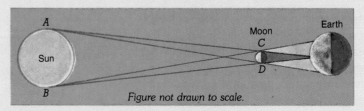

Figure not drawn to scale.

The darkly shaded region in the figure is the area of the earth that will experience a total eclipse of the sun. The lightly shaded region indicates the area that will experience a partial eclipse of the sun. Other areas will experience no eclipse. The darkened portion of the earth is the area that is experiencing night.

Exercises

Referring to the figure above, complete the following exercises.

1. Identify the two common internal tangents. $\overleftrightarrow{AD}$ and $\overleftrightarrow{BC}$
2. Identify the two common external tangents. $\overleftrightarrow{AC}$ and $\overleftrightarrow{BD}$
3. Realizing the sun and the moon are not coplanar, can additional common tangents be drawn to the figures? Explain your answer. Because of the (spherical) shape of these figures, many other common tangents can be drawn.

10-5 Tangents

In a plane, a line that intersects a circle in exactly one point is called a **tangent.** Also, segments and rays that are contained in the tangent and intersect the circle are said to be tangent to the circle.

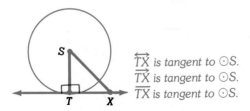

$\overleftrightarrow{TX}$ is tangent to $\odot S$.
$\overrightarrow{TX}$ is tangent to $\odot S$.
$\overline{TX}$ is tangent to $\odot S$.

In the figure, S is the center of the circle, and T is the **point of tangency.** X is in the exterior of the circle and $\overline{ST}$ is a radius. Thus, $SX > ST$. A similar inequality holds for any point in the exterior of the circle.

The shortest segment from a point to a line is the perpendicular segment. Thus, $\overline{ST} \perp \overleftrightarrow{TX}$.

If a line is tangent to a circle, then it is perpendicular to the radius drawn to the point of tangency.	*Theorem 10-10*

Example

1 In $\odot C$, $\overline{QR}$ and $\overline{QP}$ are tangents and $m \angle RPC = 15$. Find $m \angle Q$.

Since $\overline{CR}$ and $\overline{CP}$ are radii, they are congruent. Thus, by the Isosceles Triangle Theorem, $\angle RPC \cong \angle PRC$, and $m \angle PRC = 15$.

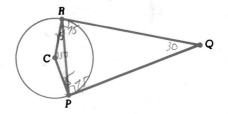

Since $\overline{QR}$ and $\overline{QP}$ are tangents, they are perpendicular to the radii. Therefore, $m \angle CPQ = 90$ and $m \angle CRQ = 90$.
Thus, $m \angle PRQ = 90 - 15$ or 75 and $m \angle QPR = 90 - 15$ or 75.

The sum of the degree measures of the angles of a triangle is 180.

$$m \angle Q + m \angle PRQ + m \angle QPR = 180$$
$$m \angle Q + 75 + 75 = 180$$
$$m \angle Q = 30$$

The converse of Theorem 10-10 also holds and provides one method for identifying tangents to a circle.

In a plane, if a line is perpendicular to a radius of a circle at its endpoint on the circle, then the line is a tangent.	*Theorem 10-11*

Students will prove this theorem in Written Exercise 23.

In the picture at the right, the ball bearing game demonstrates that it is possible to have two tangents to a circle from the same exterior point.

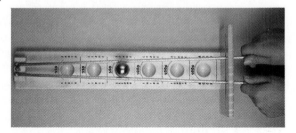

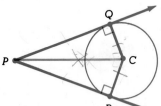

Note that $\overrightarrow{PQ}$ and $\overrightarrow{PR}$ are both tangent to $\odot C$. Also, $\overline{PQ}$ and $\overline{PR}$ are **tangent segments.**

By drawing $\overline{PC}$, two right triangles are formed. These triangles are congruent by HL, and thus the following conclusion can be made.

If two segments from the same exterior point are tangent to a circle, then they are congruent.	*Theorem 10-12*

Students will prove this theorem in Written Exercise 24.

Example

2 In the figure, both $\overline{AB}$ and $\overline{AC}$ are tangent to $\odot P$. Suppose $PB = 10$ and $AP = 26$. Find AC.

By Theorem 10-10, if a line is tangent to a circle, then it is perpendicular to the radius drawn to the point of tangency. Thus, $\overline{PB} \perp \overline{AB}$ and $\overline{PC} \perp \overline{AC}$, and $\triangle ABP$ and $\triangle ACP$ are right triangles.

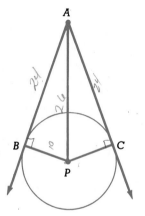

$$(AB)^2 + (PB)^2 = (AP)^2 \qquad \textit{Pythagorean Theorem}$$
$$(AB)^2 + 10^2 = 26^2 \qquad \textit{Substitution}$$
$$(AB)^2 = 26^2 - 10^2 \qquad \textit{Subtraction Property of Equality}$$
$$AB = \sqrt{576} \text{ or } 24$$

By Theorem 10-12, the two tangent segments, $\overline{AB}$ and $\overline{AC}$, are congruent. Thus, $AC = AB = 24$.

A polygon is a **circumscribed polygon** if and only if each side of the polygon is tangent to a circle.

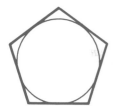

The circle is inscribed in the polygon.

The polygon is said to be circumscribed about the circle.

Must a circumscribed polygon be regular? The answer is *no.* But, it is possible to show that a polygon is regular if and only if it can be inscribed in and circumscribed about two concentric circles.

EN: 5–7, 2–30 even; AV: 1–7, 1–21, 23, 24–28 even; FD: 1–7, 1–21, p. 363, 26–31, 34;

Exploratory Exercises

ALL LEVELS: Mini Review

Answer each of the following.

1. How many tangents can be drawn to a circle through a point outside the circle?

2. How many tangents can be drawn to a circle through a point inside the circle?

3. How many tangents can be drawn to a circle through a point on the circle?

4. Can a radius of a circle be a tangent of the circle? State *yes* or *no.*

Identify the following polygons as *circumscribed*, *inscribed*, or *neither*.

5.

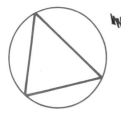

6.

7.

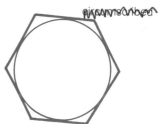

Written Exercises

For each of the following exercises, find the measure *x*. Assume *C* is the center of the circle.

1.

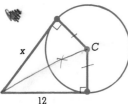

2.

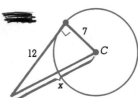

3.

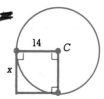

4.

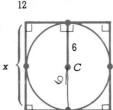

5.

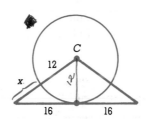

6.

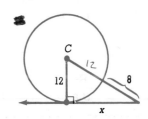

In the figure, $\overline{AB}$ and $\overline{CD}$ both are tangent to $\odot P$ and $\odot Q$. Also, $AP = 8$, $BQ = 5$, and $m\angle CPE = 45$. Find the measures for each of the following.

7. $\overset{\frown}{CE}$
8. $\angle PCG$
9. $\angle CGP$

10. $\overline{CG}$
11. $\angle QDC$
12. $\angle FGD$

13. $\angle FQD$
14. $\overset{\frown}{DF}$
15. $\overline{DQ}$

16. $\overline{DG}$
17. $\overline{DC}$
18. $\overline{PG}$

19. $\overline{GQ}$
20. $\overline{PQ}$
21. $\overline{AB}$

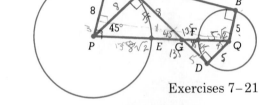

Point out that $\overline{AB}$ is *externally* tangent and that $\overline{CD}$ is *internally* tangent.

Exercises 7–21

Prove each of the following exercises. For Exercises 22–27, see the Teacher Guide.

22. If a line is tangent to a circle, then it is perpendicular to the radius drawn to the point of tangency. (Theorem 10-10)

23. In a plane, if a line is perpendicular to a radius of a circle at its endpoint on the circle, then the line is a tangent. (Theorem 10-11)

24. If two segments from the same exterior point are tangent to a circle, then they are congruent. (Theorem 10-12)

25. If a hexagon can be inscribed in and circumscribed about two concentric circles, then the polygon is regular.

26. **Given:** $\overleftrightarrow{AC}$ is a tangent to $\odot P$.
    $\overset{\frown}{DB} \cong \overset{\frown}{BE}$
    Prove: $\overline{AB} \cong \overline{BC}$

27. **Given:** $\overleftrightarrow{AF}$ and $\overleftrightarrow{CF}$ are tangent to $\odot B$.
    Prove: $\triangle ADF \cong \triangle CDF$

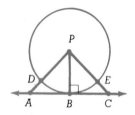

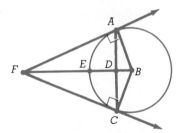

Challenge Exercises

Complete the following exercises.

28. A circle is inscribed in a triangle whose sides are 9 cm, 14 cm, and 17 cm. If P divides the side of length 14 cm into segments whose ratio is $x{:}y$ with $x < y$, find the ratio $x{:}y$. 3:11

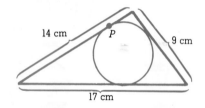

29. In a rectangle with width of 10 units and length of 24 units, a diagonal is drawn. A circle is inscribed in each triangle. Find the distance between the centers of the inscribed circles. Express your answer in radical form. $2\sqrt{65}$

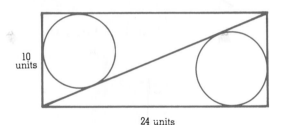

30. In the figure, line ℓ is tangent to $\odot O$ and $\odot O'$ at T and T'. If $AB = 4$, $OB = 20$, and $O'A = 10$, find TT'. 24

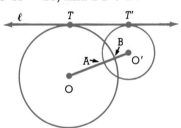

31. In 30°–60°–90° $\triangle ABC$, $AB = 42\sqrt{3}$. Find the measure of the radius of inscribed circle P. $\dfrac{63 - 21\sqrt{3}}{2}$

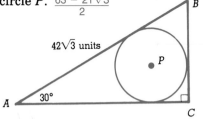

9-2

9-2

9-3

9-4

10-1

1. Name the triangles in the figure that are similar to $\triangle MIT$. ~~[scribbled out]~~

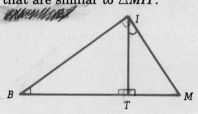

2. Find the geometric mean for 1 and 4. ✗

3. In a right triangle, the measure of the sides are $x - 1$, $x + 16$, and $x + 17$. Find x. ✗

4. In right triangle KMN, $\angle M$ is a right angle. If $m\ \angle K = 60$, find the ratio $KM{:}MN{:}NK$. ✗

5. Draw two circles that have no internal tangents. See students' work.

Excursions in Geometry _____ Centers of Circles

The following procedure can be used to find the center of a circle.

Place a sheet of paper over the circle so one corner touches the circle at point C.

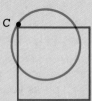

The paper intersects the circle at two other points, A and B. Draw chord $\overline{AB}$.

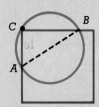

Place the paper so the corner touches the circle at a different point, D. Draw $\overline{EF}$.

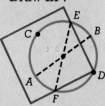

The intersection of $\overline{AB}$ and $\overline{EF}$ is the center of the circle.

Exercises

Find the center and the length of the radius to the nearest millimeter.

1.

7 mm

2.

9 mm

3.

6 mm

4.

8 mm

Objective: Find the measure of angles formed by the intersection of secants and tangents in relation to intercepted arcs.

10-6 Measuring Angles

Lines intersecting the circular patterns on a radar screen demonstrate that many different angle relationships exist. The location of the vertex of the angle determines the relationship between the measure of the angle and its intercepted arcs.

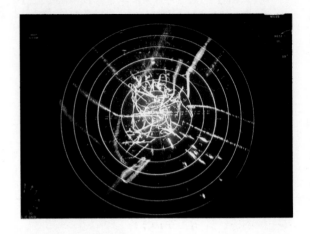

Two secants intersect to form angles that intercept arcs in three different ways.

intersect on circle   *intersect inside circle*   *intersect outside circle*

Emphasize the importance of identifying the location of the vertex of each angle.

In each case, the measure of the angle formed is related to the measures of the intercepted arcs. If the secants intersect on the circle, an inscribed angle is formed. Its measure is one-half the measure of the intercepted arc. The following theorems describe the other two cases.

Students will prove the following theorem in Written Exercise 36.

If two secants intersect in the interior of a circle, then the measure of an angle formed is one-half the sum of the measures of the arcs intercepted by the angle and its vertical angle.	*Theorem 10-13*
If two secants intersect in the exterior of a circle, then the measure of an angle formed is one-half the positive difference of the measures of the intercepted arcs.	*Theorem 10-14*

Examples

1　In $\odot P$, $m\angle CBD = 52$, $m\overset{\frown}{CD} = 39$, and $\overline{AD}$ is a diameter. Find $m\overset{\frown}{DE}$.

$$m\angle CBD = \tfrac{1}{2}(m\overset{\frown}{AE} + m\overset{\frown}{CD})$$

$$52 = \tfrac{1}{2}(m\overset{\frown}{AE} + 39)$$

$$104 = m\overset{\frown}{AE} + 39$$

$$65 = m\overset{\frown}{AE}$$

$$m\overset{\frown}{AED} = 180$$
$$m\overset{\frown}{DE} + m\overset{\frown}{AE} = 180$$
$$m\overset{\frown}{DE} + 65 = 180$$
$$m\overset{\frown}{DE} = 115$$

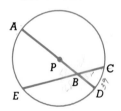

2　**Prove Theorem 10-14.**

Given:　$\overline{AC}$ and $\overline{AD}$ intersect at A.
　　　　A is exterior to a circle.

Prove:　$m\angle BAD = \tfrac{1}{2}(m\overset{\frown}{CD} - m\overset{\frown}{BE})$

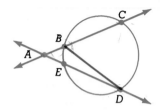

Proof:

STATEMENTS	REASONS
1. Draw chord $\overline{BD}$.	1. Through any two points there is exactly one line. (Postulate 1-1)
2. $m\angle BAD + m\angle ADB = m\angle CBD$	2. Exterior Angle Theorem (Theorem 5-1)
3. $m\angle BAD = m\angle CBD - m\angle ADB$	3. Subtraction Property of Equality (Postulate 2-7)
4. $\angle CBD$ and $\angle BDA$ are inscribed angles.	4. Definition of Inscribed Angles
5. $m\angle CBD = \tfrac{1}{2}m\overset{\frown}{CD}$ $m\angle ADB = \tfrac{1}{2}m\overset{\frown}{BE}$	5. If an angle is inscribed in a circle, then the measure of the angle equals one-half the measure of its intercepted arc. (Theorem 10-6)
6. $m\angle BAD = \tfrac{1}{2}m\overset{\frown}{CD} - \tfrac{1}{2}m\overset{\frown}{BE}$	6. Substitution (Postulate 2-9)
7. $m\angle BAD = \tfrac{1}{2}(m\overset{\frown}{CD} - m\overset{\frown}{BE})$	7. Distributive Property (Postulate 2-14)

A tangent and a secant, or two tangents, intercept arcs in several ways. In each case, the measure of the angle formed is related to the measures of the intercepted arcs.

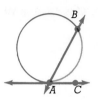

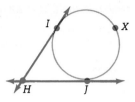

$m \angle BAC = \frac{1}{2}m(\widehat{BA})$ $m \angle FDG = \frac{1}{2}(m\widehat{FG} - m\widehat{GE})$ $m \angle IHJ = \frac{1}{2}(m\widehat{IXJ} - m\widehat{IJ})$

Students will prove
Theorem 10-15 in Written
Exercise 37, and Theorem
10-16 in Written Exercises
38 and 39.

If a secant and a tangent intersect at the point of tangency, then the measure of each angle formed is one-half the measure of its intercepted arc.	*Theorem 10-15*
If a secant and a tangent, or two tangents, intersect in the exterior of a circle, then the measure of the angle formed is one-half the positive difference of the measures of the intercepted arcs.	*Theorem 10-16*

EN: 1–3, 6, 1, 2, 4, 7, 16–33, 35, 36, 40; **AV:** 1–6, 1–36, 41; **FD:** 1–6, 1–33, p. 368, 26, 27

Exploratory Exercises

For each of the following circles, measurements of certain arcs are given. Find the degree measure of each numbered angle. Assume lines that appear tangent are tangent.

1.
63
1
126°

2.
59   117°
2
125°

3.
35
100°   120°
50°
3
90°

4.
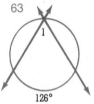
105
150°
4

5.
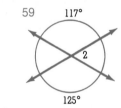
$17\frac{1}{2}$ 175°
110°
5

6.
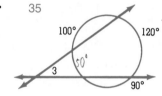
40
220°
6

Written Exercises

In the figure, $m\widehat{BC} = 84$, $m\widehat{CD} = 38$, $m\widehat{DE} = 64$, $m\widehat{EF} = 60$, and $\overleftrightarrow{AB}$ and $\overleftrightarrow{AF}$ are tangents. Find each of the following measures.

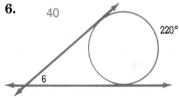

1. $m\widehat{BF}$ ▆▆   2. $m\widehat{BDF}$ ▆▆   3. $m \angle 1$ ▆▆
4. $m\widehat{BFC}$ ▆▆   5. $m \angle 2$ ▆▆   6. $m \angle GBC$ ▆▆
7. $m\widehat{BFE}$ ▆▆   8. $m \angle 3$ ▆▆   9. $m \angle 4$ ▆▆
10. $m \angle 5$ ▆▆   11. $m\widehat{FBC}$ ▆▆   12. $m \angle 6$ ▆▆
13. $m\widehat{FBD}$ ▆▆   14. $m \angle 7$ ▆▆   15. $m \angle 8$ ▆▆

372   *Circles and Spheres*

In the figure, $m\angle 1 = 2x$, $m\angle 1 = m\angle 2$, $m\widehat{RYT} = 4x + 4$, $m\widehat{YT} = 3x - 20$, $m\angle 4 = 3x + 14$, and $\overleftrightarrow{ST}$ and $\overleftrightarrow{SR}$ are tangents. Find each of the following measures.

16. the value of x
17. $m\angle 1$
18. $m\widehat{RV}$
19. $m\angle 2$
20. $m\widehat{RYT}$
21. $m\widehat{TRV}$
22. $m\widehat{YT}$
23. $m\widehat{YR}$
24. $m\angle 5$
25. $m\widehat{TW}$
26. $m\widehat{RW}$
27. $m\angle 6$
28. $m\angle 4$
29. $m\widehat{TWV}$
30. $m\widehat{YV}$
31. $m\widehat{VW}$
32. $m\angle 3$
33. $m\angle 7$

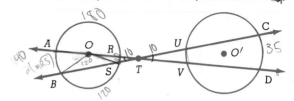

In the following exercises, find the indicated measures.

34. In the figure below, find $m\angle CED$.

35. In the figure, $\overleftrightarrow{AD}$ passes through the center of $\odot O$. If $m\widehat{SB} = 120$, $m\widehat{AB} = 2(m\widehat{RS})$, and $m\widehat{CD} = 35$, find $m\widehat{UV}$.

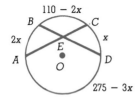

$110 - 2x$

$2x$

x

$275 - 3x$

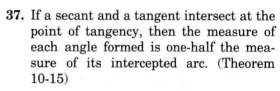

Prove each of the following exercises. For Exercises 36–41, see the Teacher Guide.

36. If two secants intersect in the interior of a circle, then the measure of an angle formed is one-half the sum of the measures of the arcs intercepted by the angle and its vertical angle. (Theorem 10-13)

37. If a secant and a tangent intersect at the point of tangency, then the measure of each angle formed is one-half the measure of its intercepted arc. (Theorem 10-15)

38. If a secant and a tangent intersect in the exterior of a circle, then the measure of the angle formed is one-half the positive difference of the measures of the intercepted arcs.

39. If two tangents intersect in the exterior of a circle, then the measure of the angle formed is one-half the positive difference of the measures of the intercepted arcs.

40. **Given:** $\overleftrightarrow{FA}$ is tangent to $\odot P$ and $\odot E$ at A.

   Prove: $m\angle CAF = \frac{1}{2}m\angle CEA$

41. **Given:** $\overline{RP} \perp \overline{QT}$
   $\overline{RT} \perp \overline{QS}$

   Prove: $m\widehat{PT} = m\widehat{ST}$

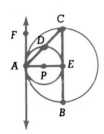

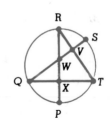

10-7 Segments

Objectives: Use properties of segments of chords, secants, and tangents to solve problems.

Angles formed by intersecting chords are related to arcs of the circle. In addition, the segments formed by the intersecting chords are related.

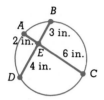

In the figure, the segments of $\overline{AC}$ are $\overline{AE}$ and $\overline{EC}$. The segments of $\overline{BD}$ are $\overline{BE}$ and $\overline{ED}$.

$$AE \cdot EC = 2 \cdot 6 \qquad BE \cdot ED = 3 \cdot 4$$
$$= 12 \qquad\qquad = 12$$

If two chords intersect in a circle, then the product of the measures of the segments of one chord equals the product of the measures of the segments of the other chord.	*Theorem 10-17*

The proof of the theorem is based on properties of similar triangles.

Example

1 **Prove Theorem 10-17.**

Given: $\overline{AC}$ and $\overline{BD}$ intersect at E.
Prove: $AE \cdot EC = BE \cdot ED$

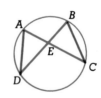

Proof:

STATEMENTS	REASONS
1. Draw $\overline{AD}$ and $\overline{BC}$.	1. Through any two points there is exactly one line. (Postulate 1-1)
2. $\angle A \cong \angle B$ $\angle D \cong \angle C$	2. If two inscribed angles of a circle intercept congruent arcs, then the angles are congruent. (Theorem 10-7)
3. $\triangle DAE \sim \triangle CBE$	3. AA Similarity (Postulate 8-1)
4. $\dfrac{AE}{BE} = \dfrac{ED}{EC}$	4. Definition of Similar Polygons
5. $AE \cdot EC = BE \cdot ED$	5. Equality of Cross Products (Theorem 8-1)

In the figure, both $\overline{RP}$ and $\overline{RT}$ are called **secant segments.** They contain chords of the circle. The parts of these segments that are exterior to the circle are called **external secant segments.** In the figure, $\overline{RQ}$ and $\overline{RS}$ are external secant segments.

The measures of the segments of the figure are related in an interesting way.

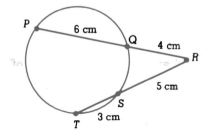

$$RQ \cdot RP \qquad RS \cdot RT$$
$$4 \cdot 10 \qquad\quad 5 \cdot 8$$
$$40 \quad = \quad 40$$

To prove the following theorem, draw a figure like the one shown above. Connect P and S, and T and Q. Show that $\triangle PSR \sim \triangle TQR$. Then, write a proportion and find its cross product.

If two secant segments are drawn to a circle from an exterior point, then the product of the measures of one secant segment and its external secant segment equals the product of the measures of the other secant segment and its external secant segment.	*Theorem 10-18*

Students will prove this theorem in Written Exercise 21.

The figure shows a tangent segment and a secant segment drawn to a circle from an exterior point. By drawing $\overline{XW}$ and $\overline{XZ}$ several triangles are formed.

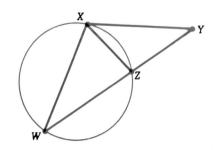

$\overline{XY}$ is a tangent segment.

$\triangle YXZ \sim \triangle YWX$ *AA Similarity*

$\dfrac{XY}{YW} = \dfrac{YZ}{XY}$ *Definition of Similarity*

$XY^2 = YW \cdot YZ$ *Equality of Cross Products*

Have students identify the two pairs of congruent angles in the similar triangles.

If a tangent segment and a secant segment are drawn to a circle from an exterior point, then the square of the measure of the tangent segment equals the product of the measures of the secant segment and its external secant segment.	*Theorem 10-19*

Students will prove this theorem in Written Exercise 22.

Example

2
In the figure, $\overline{BC}$ is a tangent segment. Find the measure x.

$$AC \cdot DC = (BC)^2$$
$$(x + 6.6)(x) = (8)^2$$
$$x^2 + 6.6x = 64$$
$$x^2 + 6.6x - 64 = 0$$

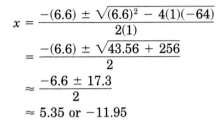

B

8 units

C

x units

6.6 units

D

A

$$x = \frac{-(6.6) \pm \sqrt{(6.6)^2 - 4(1)(-64)}}{2(1)}$$

Use the quadratic formula.

$$= \frac{-(6.6) \pm \sqrt{43.56 + 256}}{2}$$

a is 1,
b is 6.6,

$$\approx \frac{-6.6 \pm 17.3}{2}$$

and c is −64.

$$\approx 5.35 \text{ or } -11.95$$

Why is −11.95 not used?

x is approximately equal to 5.35.

EN: 2, 3, 5, 2–20 even, 21, 22; **AV:** 1–6, 1–22; **FD:** 1–6, 1–18, p. 373, 34, 35, 41

Exploratory Exercises

For each exercise, state the equation you would use to find the measure x. Assume segments that appear tangent are tangent.

1.
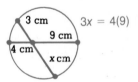
3 cm
9 cm
4 cm
x cm

$3x = 4(9)$

2.
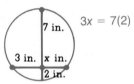
7 in.
3 in. | x in.
2 in.

$3x = 7(2)$

3.
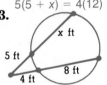
x ft
5 ft
4 ft
8 ft

$5(5 + x) = 4(12)$

4.
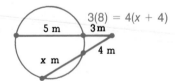
5 m
3m
4 m
x m

$3(8) = 4(x + 4)$

5.
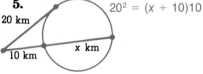
20 km
10 km
x km

$20^2 = (x + 10)10$

6.
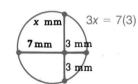
x mm
7 mm | 3 mm
3 mm

$3x = 7(3)$

Written Exercises

For each of the following, find the measure x. Assume segments that appear tangent are tangent.

1.

4
x
3
9

2.

3
7
2
x

3.
0.9   3.6
x
1.2

376 *Circles and Spheres*

4.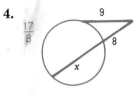
$\frac{17}{8}$

5.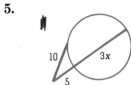

6.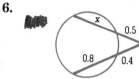

7.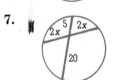

8.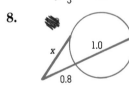

9.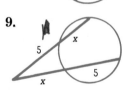

10.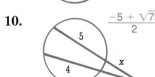
$\frac{-5 + \sqrt{73}}{2}$

11.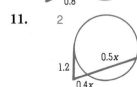
2

12.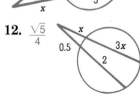
$\frac{\sqrt{5}}{4}$

In the figure, $\overline{AB}$ is a tangent segment. Use the figure to solve each problem. Round each answer to the nearest tenth.

13. Suppose $FH = 6$, $HD = 2$, and $HE = 3$. Find CH. 4

14. Suppose $AD = 16$, $FD = 8$, and $AG = 6$. Find GC. 15.3

15. Suppose $AC = 21$, $AF = 8$, and $FD = 8$. Find AG. 6.1

16. Suppose $CH = 20$, $EH = 10.5$, and $DH = 8$. Find FH. 26.3

17. Suppose $AF = 16$, $FH = 6$, and $DH = 2$. Find BA. 19.6

18. Suppose $GC = 15.3$ and $GA = 6.0$. Find AB. 11.3

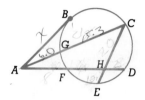

Exercises 13–18

Find the indicated lengths in the following exercises.

19. In $\odot O$, the ratio of QT to TO is 5:6, RT is twice TQ, and TS is $4\frac{1}{2}$ less than RT. Find PQ.

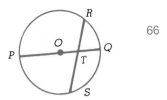

66

20. An arch over a door is 50 cm high and 180 cm wide. Find the length of the radius of the arch.

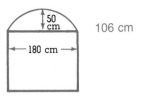

106 cm

Prove each of the following exercises. For Exercises 21–22, see the Teacher Guide.

21. If two secant segments are drawn to a circle from an exterior point, then the product of the measures of one secant segment and its external secant segment equals the product of the measures of the other secant segment and its external secant segment. (Theorem 10-18)

22. If a tangent segment and a secant segment are drawn to a circle from an exterior point, then the square of the measure of the tangent segment equals the product of the measures of the secant segment and its external secant segment. (Theorem 10-19)

10-8 Spheres

Objective: Recognize and define basic properties of spheres.

A globe is a physical representation of the earth. A globe, although round, is not contained in a plane. The globe has the shape of a **sphere.**

In space, many congruent circles can be drawn using the same center. Considered together, all these circles form a sphere.

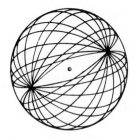

Emphasize that a sphere is a hollow shell and not solid.

In space, a figure is a sphere if and only if it is the set of all points that are a given distance from a given point, called the center.	*Definition of Sphere*

Point out the common characteristics of a circle and sphere.

A **radius** of a sphere is a segment whose endpoints are the *center* and *a point on the sphere.* In the figure above, $\overline{CR}$ is a radius.

A **chord** of a sphere is a segment whose endpoints are *points on the sphere.* In the figure above, $\overline{TS}$ is a chord.

A **diameter** of a sphere is a segment that *contains the center,* and whose *endpoints are points on the sphere.* In the figure above, $\overline{PQ}$ is a diameter. A diameter could be defined as a chord containing the center.

A **tangent** to a sphere is a line that *intersects the sphere in exactly one point.* In the figure above, $\overleftrightarrow{AB}$ is tangent to the sphere at X.

A plane can intersect a sphere in one of three ways.

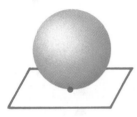

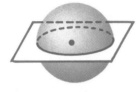

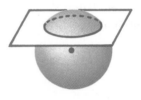

A plane may be tangent to the sphere.

A plane may intersect the sphere and contain the center of the sphere.

A plane may intersect the sphere but *not* contain the center of the sphere.

Example

1

Prove that the intersection of a sphere and a plane is a circle if the intersection contains more than one point.

Suppose X and Y are two points in the intersection of sphere P and plane $\mathscr{A}$. Draw $\overline{PQ}$ so that $\overline{PQ} \perp \mathscr{A}$ and Q lies in $\mathscr{A}$. Next, draw $\overline{QX}, \overline{QY}, \overline{PX},$ and $\overline{PY}$. $\overline{PQ} \perp \overline{QX}$ and $\overline{PQ} \perp \overline{QY}$, since $\overline{PQ} \perp \mathscr{A}$. Thus, $\angle PQX \cong \angle PQY$ because they are right angles.

Since $\overline{PX}$ and $\overline{PY}$ are both radii of the sphere, $\overline{PX} \cong \overline{PY}$. Also, $\overline{PQ} \cong \overline{PQ}$. So, $\triangle PQX \cong \triangle PQY$ by HL.

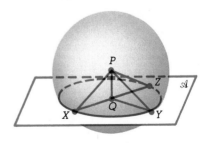

As a result, $\overline{QX} \cong \overline{QY}$, and X and Y are equidistant from Q. They lie on the circle with Q as a center and radius measuring QY. In addition, any point on the circle is in $\mathscr{A}$.

Suppose Z is a point on $\odot Q$. Then, $\overline{QZ} \cong \overline{QY}$. Also, $\overline{PQ} \perp \overline{QZ}$ because $\overline{PQ} \perp \mathscr{A}$. Since $\overline{PQ} \cong \overline{PQ}$, the two right triangles, $\triangle PQY$ and $\triangle PQZ$, are congruent. Thus, $\overline{PY} \cong \overline{PZ}$ and Z must be on the sphere.

If a plane intersects a sphere in more than one point, then the intersection is a circle.	*Theorem 10-20*

Suppose a plane intersects a sphere in more than one point and contains the center of the sphere. The intersection is called a **great circle.** A great circle has the same center as the sphere and its radii are also radii of the sphere.

Each great circle separates a sphere into two hemispheres.

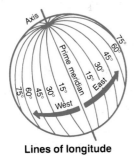

Lines of longitude

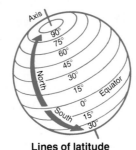

Lines of latitude

Why is each line of longitude a great circle, but for lines of latitude, only the equator is a great circle?

Lines of longitude always have as their center the center of the earth. The lines of latitude have only the equator whose center is the center of the earth.

The surface of a globe is a model of a sphere. Each north-south meridian represents a great circle. Of the parallels of latitude, only the equator represents a great circle.

EN: 2–12 even, 3, 6, 9, . . . 39, 41; **AV:** 1–12, 2–40 even; **FD:** 1–12, 1–39 odd, p. 377, 19, 20

Exploratory Exercises

Describe each of the following as a model of a *circle*, a *sphere*, or *neither*.

1. ball bearing sphere
2. basketball hoop circle
3. Jupiter sphere
4. basketball sphere
5. car tire circle
6. corona of eclipse circle
7. orbit of electron circle
8. cross section of pipe circle
9. telephone dial circle
10. ping pong ball sphere
11. helicopter pad circle
12. record circle

Written Exercises

Determine whether each of the following statements is *true* or *false*.

1. A diameter of a sphere is a chord of the sphere. true
2. A radius of a sphere is a chord of the sphere. false
3. All radii of a sphere are congruent. true
4. All diameters of a sphere are congruent. true
5. All great circles of a sphere are congruent. true
6. A plane and a sphere may intersect in exactly two points. false
7. A diameter of a great circle is a diameter of the sphere. true
8. A diameter of a sphere is a diameter of a great circle of the sphere. true
9. A secant of a sphere intersects the sphere in exactly one point. false
10. A radius of a sphere intersects the sphere in exactly one point. true
11. Two spheres may intersect in exactly one point. true
12. Two great circles of a sphere may intersect in exactly one point. false
13. Two great circles of a sphere intersect in exactly two points. true
14. Two spheres may intersect in exactly two points. false

Write *if and only if* definitions for each of the following.

For Exercises 15–26, see the Teacher Guide.

15. radius of a sphere

Have students draw a figure to illustrate each situation.

16. chord of a sphere

17. great circle of a sphere

18. diameter of a sphere

19. interior of a sphere

20. exterior of a sphere

21. line tangent to a sphere

22. plane tangent to a sphere

23. secant of a sphere

24. hemisphere

25. congruent spheres

26. arc of a sphere

Suppose C is the center of a sphere, I is in the interior of the sphere, and E is in the exterior of the sphere. Answer each of the following questions about the sphere.

27. In how many points does $\overline{IE}$ intersect the sphere? one

28. In how many points does $\overleftrightarrow{IE}$ intersect the sphere? two

29. In how many points does $\overrightarrow{IE}$ intersect the sphere? one

30. In how many points does $\overrightarrow{EI}$ intersect the sphere? two

31. In how many points does $\overline{CE}$ intersect the sphere? one

32. In how many points does $\overline{CI}$ intersect the sphere? none

33. How many chords contain I? infinitely many

34. How many radii contain I? one

In the figure, P is the center of the sphere and the plane, $\mathcal{B}$, intersects the sphere in $\odot R$.

35. Suppose $PS = 25$ and $PR = 7$. Find RS. 24

36. Suppose $PS = 15$ and $PR = 9$. Find RS. 12

37. Suppose $PS = 13$ and $RS = 12$. Find PR. 5

38. Suppose $PS = 26$ and $RS = 24$. Find PR. 10

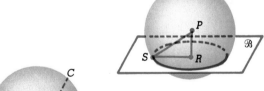

Complete the following exercises.

39. Chords $\overline{AB}$ and $\overline{CD}$ of a sphere intersect at point E. If $CE = x + 6$, $ED = x + 1$, $AE = x + 4$, and $EB = x + 2$, find x. 2

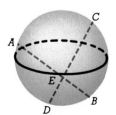

Exercise 39

40. In the figure, a sphere has tangent segment $\overline{PQ}$ and secant segment $\overline{PS}$ intersecting the sphere at points R and S. If $PQ = 10$ and $PS = 50$, find RS. 48

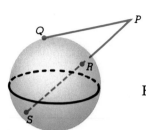

Exercise 40

41. Prove that if $\overline{PR}$ and $\overline{QS}$ are diameters of a sphere, then $PQRS$ is a rectangle.

See the Teacher Guide.

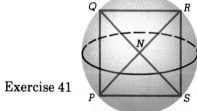

Exercise 41

On the surface of a sphere such as the earth, the shortest distance between two points is an arc of a great circle. Therefore, navigators consider great circles as "lines" in a special kind of two-dimensional geometry called **spherical geometry.**

The giant step of extending this geometry from two dimensions to three or more was taken by the German mathematician Bernhard Riemann in the latter half of the 19th century. The new type of non-Euclidean geometry that Riemann developed was called **Riemannian** or **elliptic geometry.**

Two postulates of elliptic geometry contradict two important Euclidean postulates. One of Euclid's postulates states that a straight line extends indefinitely. Elliptic geometry replaces this postulate with the idea that if a line is extended it will meet itself.

Euclidean Postulate   *Elliptic Postulate*

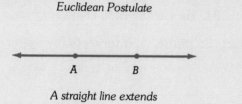

A straight line extends
indefinitely.

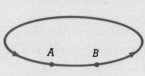

If a line is extended, it will
meet itself.

In elliptic geometry lines are finite, yet unbounded. Suppose you were to walk the "line" of the earth's equator. You would be walking in a straight line and yet if you were to map your journey it would appear as a circle. The distance you walked would be a finite length. Yet, you could travel around the earth forever in that line and never reach an end. Thus, the lines are finite, yet unbounded.

The other Euclidean postulate that elliptic geometry does *not* satisfy is the parallel postulate. In elliptic geometry the Euclidean parallel postulate is replaced by: In a plane, given a line ℓ and a point P *not* contained in ℓ, there exists *no* line through P and parallel to ℓ.

Elliptic geometry includes most of Euclid's postulates. One of these postulates states that when two lines intersect they intersect in just one point. To satisfy this postulate in elliptic geometry the concept of "point" must be changed. If two lines intersect in elliptic geometry they intersect in what appears to be two points. By the new definition what appears to be two points is really only one.

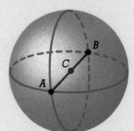

A and B are considered one point.

Exercises

Answer each of the following using a reference.

1. Write a brief biographical sketch of Bernhard Riemann.

For Exercises 1–2, see the Teacher Guide.

2. Draw a diagram depicting why parallel lines do *not* exist in elliptic geometry.

Vocabulary

circle (347)
radius (347, 378)
chord (347, 378)
diameter (347, 378)
interior of a circle (348)
exterior of a circle (348)
tangent (348, 378)
point of tangency (348)
secant (348)
common external tangent (349)
common internal tangent (349)
central angle (351)
minor arc (351)

major arc (351)
semicircle (351)
concentric circles (352)
arc of a chord (355)
intercepted arc (359)
inscribed angle (359)
inscribed polygon (361)
tangent segment (366)
circumscribed polygon (367)
secant segment (375)
external secant segment (375)
sphere (378)
great circle (380)

Chapter Summary

1. **Definition of Circle:** A figure is a circle if and only if it is the set of all points in a plane that are a given distance from a given point in the plane, called the center. (347)

2. **Theorem 10-1:** In a plane, if a line contains a point in the interior of a circle, then the line intersects the circle in exactly two points. (348)

3. **Definition of Arc Measure:** The degree measure of a minor arc is the degree measure of its central angle. The degree measure of a major arc is 360 minus the degree measure of its central angle. The degree measure of a semicircle is 180. (351)

4. **Arc Addition Postulate (Postulate 10-1):** If Q is a point on $\overset{\frown}{PQR}$, then $m\overset{\frown}{PQ} + m\overset{\frown}{QR} = m\overset{\frown}{PQR}$. (352)

5. **Definition of Congruent Circles:** Two circles are congruent if and only if their radii are congruent. (352)

6. **Theorem 10-2:** In a circle or in congruent circles, two central angles are congruent if and only if their minor arcs are congruent. (353)

7. **Theorem 10-3:** In a circle or in congruent circles, two minor arcs are congruent if and only if their corresponding chords are congruent. (355)

8. **Theorem 10-4:** In a circle, if a diameter is perpendicular to a chord, then it bisects the chord and its arcs. (356)

9. Theorem 10-5:   In a circle or in congruent circles, two chords are congruent if and only if they are equidistant from the center.   (356)

10. Theorem 10-6:   If an angle is inscribed in a circle, then the measure of the angle equals one-half the measure of its intercepted arc.   (360)

11. Theorem 10-7:   If two inscribed angles of a circle or congruent circles intercept congruent arcs, then the angles are congruent.   (361)

12. Theorem 10-8:   If an angle is inscribed in a semicircle, then the angle is a right angle.   (361)

13. Theorem 10-9:   If the angles of a quadrilateral are inscribed in a circle, then each pair of opposite angles are supplementary.   (361)

14. Theorem 10-10:   If a line is tangent to a circle, then it is perpendicular to the radius at the point of tangency.   (365)

15. Theorem 10-11:   In a plane, if a line is perpendicular to a radius of a circle at its endpoint on the circle, then the line is a tangent.   (366)

16. Theorem 10-12:   If two segments from the same exterior point are tangent to a circle, then they are congruent.   (366)

17. Theorem 10-13:   If two secants intersect in the interior of a circle, then the measure of an angle formed is one-half the sum of the measures of the arcs intercepted by the angle and its vertical angle.   (370)

18. Theorem 10-14:   If two secants intersect in the exterior of a circle, then the measure of an angle formed is one-half the positive difference of the measures of the intercepted arcs.   (370)

19. Theorem 10-15:   If a secant and a tangent intersect at the point of tangency, then the measure of each angle formed is one-half the measure of its intercepted arc.   (372)

20. Theorem 10-16:   If a secant and a tangent, or two tangents, intersect in the exterior of a circle, then the measure of the angle formed is one-half the positive difference of the measures of the intercepted arcs.   (372)

21. Theorem 10-17:   If two chords intersect in a circle, then the product of the measures of the segments of one chord equals the product of the measures of the segments of the other chord.   (374)

22. Theorem 10-18:   If two secant segments are drawn to a circle from an exterior point, then the product of the measures of one secant segment and its external secant segment equals the product of the measures of the other secant segment and its external secant segment.   (375)

23. Theorem 10-19:   If a tangent segment and a secant segment are drawn to a circle from an exterior point, then the square of the measure of the tangent segment equals the product of the measures of the secant segment and its external secant segment.   (375)

24. Definition of Sphere: In space, a figure is a sphere if and only if it is the set of all points that are a given distance from a given point, called the center.   (378)

25. Theorem 10-20:   If a plane intersects a sphere in more than one point, then the intersection is a circle.   (379)

Chapter Review

10-1 **Complete each of the following exercises.**

1. A radius of a circle is a chord of the circle. Write *yes* or *no*. no

2. A diameter of a circle is a chord of the circle. Write *yes* or *no*. yes

3. Write an if and only if definition for the diameter of a circle.
For Exercises 3 and 4, see the Teacher Guide.

4. Draw two distinct circles that have no common tangents.

10-2 **In $\odot P$, $\overline{XY}$ and $\overline{AB}$ are diameters.**

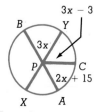

5. Find x. 21
7. Find $m\widehat{YAX}$. 180
9. Find $m\angle BPC$. 123
11. Find $m\angle CPA$. 57
13. Find $m\widehat{CA}$. 57

6. Find $m\angle BPY$. 63
8. Find $m\angle YPC$. 60
10. Find $m\widehat{BX}$. 117
12. Find $m\angle XPA$. 63
14. Find $m\widehat{BC}$. 123

Exercises 5 –14

10-3 **Answer each of the following.**

15. A chord is 5 centimeters from the center of a circle with radius 13 centimeters. Find the length of the chord. 24 cm

16. Suppose a chord of a circle is 16 centimeters long and is 6 centimeters from the center of the circle. Find the length of the radius. 10 cm

17. **Given:** $\overline{AB}$ is a diameter of $\odot E$.
$\overline{AB} \perp \overline{CD}$

Prove: $\widehat{CB} \cong \widehat{DB}$
See the Teacher Guide.

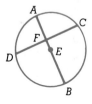

Exercise 17

10-4 **In $\odot P$, $\overline{AB} \parallel \overline{CD}$, $m\widehat{BD} = 72$, and $m\angle CPD = 144$. Find the degree measure for each of the following.**

18. $\angle DPB$ 72
20. $\widehat{CD}$ 144
22. $\widehat{CA}$ 72
24. $\widehat{AB}$ 72

19. $\angle DAB$ 36
21. $\angle CPA$ 72
23. $\angle CDA$ 36
25. $\angle APB$ 72

10-5 For each of the following exercises, find the value of x. Assume C is the center of each circle and that segments that appear tangent are tangent.

26.

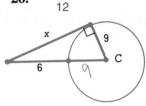

27.

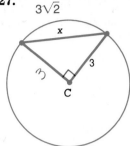

28.

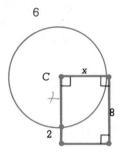

29. Determine whether the sides of a circumscribed polygon are chords or tangents of the circle. tangents

10-6 In $\odot P$, $m\widehat{AB} = 29$, $m\angle AEB = 42$, $m\widehat{BG} = 18$, and $\overline{AC}$ is a diameter. Find each of the following measures.

30. $m\angle DEC$ 42

31. $m\widehat{CD}$ 55

32. $m\angle GFD$ $18\frac{1}{2}$

33. $m\widehat{AD}$ 125

34. $m\angle AED$ 138

35. $m\widehat{GC}$ 133

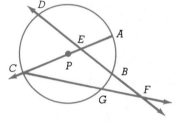

10-7 For each of the following, find the measure x. Assume the segment in Exercise 37 is tangent.

36.

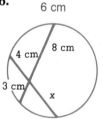

37. ≈ 0.806 ft

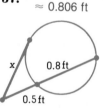

38.

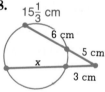

10-8 Answer each of the following.

39. A radius of a sphere is a chord of the sphere. Write *yes* or *no*. no

40. All great circles of a sphere are congruent. Write *yes* or *no*. yes

Suppose C is the center of a sphere, I is in the interior of the sphere, and E is in the exterior of the sphere. Solve each problem about the sphere.

41. In how many points does $\overrightarrow{EI}$ intersect the sphere? two

42. How many chords contain E? none

43. In how many points does $\overleftrightarrow{IC}$ intersect the sphere? none

44. In how many points does $\overline{EC}$ intersect the sphere? one

Chapter Test

1. Write an if and only if definition for the radius of a circle. A segment is a radius of a circle if and only if its endpoints are the center of the circle and a point on the circle.

For each of the following, find the measure of *x*. Assume *C* is the center of each circle and that segments that appear tangent are tangent.

2.

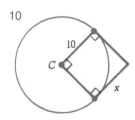

3.

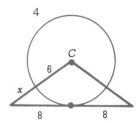

4.

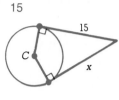

5.

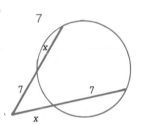

6.

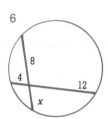

7.

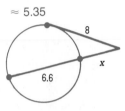

Answer each of the following.

8. Suppose the diameter of a circle is 10 inches long and a chord is 6 inches long. Find the distance between the chord and the center of the circle. 4 in.

9. Determine whether the sides of an inscribed polygon are chords or tangents of the circle. chords

10. Two spheres may intersect in exactly two points. Write *yes* or *no*. no

In ⊙*P*, $\overline{AB} \parallel \overline{CD}$, $m\widehat{BD} = 42$, $m\widehat{BE} = 12$, and $\overline{CF}$ and $\overline{AB}$ are diameters. Find each of the following measures.

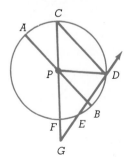

11. $m \angle BPD$ 42

12. $m\widehat{AC}$ 42

13. $m \angle APC$ 42

14. $m\widehat{CD}$ 96

15. $m \angle BPF$ 42

16. $m\widehat{FB}$ 42

17. $m\widehat{AF}$ 138

18. $m\widehat{FE}$ 30

19. $m \angle FCD$ 42

20. $m \angle EDC$ 105

21. Secant segments $\overline{PQ}$ and $\overline{PR}$ intersect sphere *S* at *M* and *N*, and *Q* and *R*. If $PM = 5$, $PN = 6$, and $NR = 4$, find MQ. 7

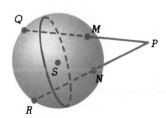

CHAPTER 11

Area and Volume

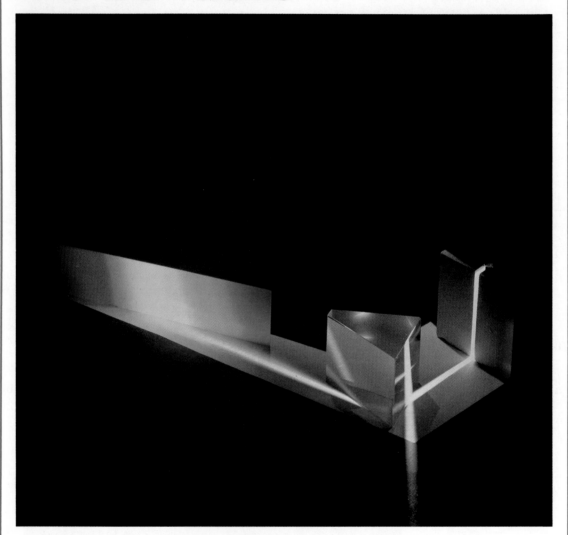

Sir Isaac Newton made some of the first studies of the relationship between light and color. Newton observed that light was dispersed into an orderly arrangement of colors after passing through a glass prism.

In this chapter you will find the surface area and volume of several right prisms.

11-1 Defining Area

Objectives: Find the area and perimeter of a rectangle; find the width of a rectangle given its length and area.

If you were driving from Memphis, Tennessee to the Great Smoky National Park in Gatlinburg, Tennessee, you might use a road map similar to the one shown below. The map has been separated into congruent, nonoverlapping squares to aid you in finding certain cities. Intuitively you know that the amount of surface that each square covers is called the **area** of the surface. If you know the measure of the area represented by one square, you can estimate to find the measure of the area of the state of Tennessee.

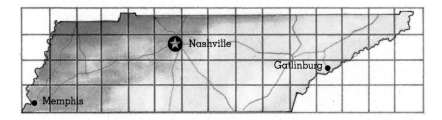

In geometry, a polygon separates the planes into three parts, the polygon, the interior, and the exterior. Together, a polygon and its interior are called a **polygonal region.** Area will mean the amount of surface covered by a polygonal region.

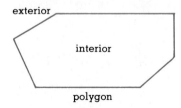

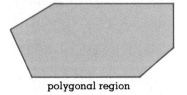

In this text, the area of a polygonal region will be referred to as the area of a polygon.

Just as you have used positive real numbers to compare the length of line segments or the size of angles, there is a positive real number that can be used to compare the size of polygonal regions. This number is called the measure of the area.

For any polygonal region and a given unit of measure, there is a unique positive real number called the measure of the area of the region.	*Postulate 11-1* *Area Postulate*

Two commonly-used units of area are the square centimeter and the square inch.

The area is 1 square centimeter.

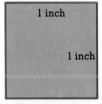

The area is 1 square inch.

Emphasize that area is measured in square units.

Using the following postulates, it is possible to find the areas of various polygonal regions.

If two polygons are congruent, then they have equal areas.	*Postulate 11-2*
If a polygonal region is separated into nonoverlapping regions, then the sum of the areas of these regions equals the area of the entire region.	*Postulate 11-3* *Area Addition* *Postulate*

The rectangular region at the right is separated into 12 congruent squares whose sides are 1 centimeter long. Thus, the area of each square is 1 square centimeter. By the Area Addition Postulate, the area of the rectangle is 12 square centimeters.

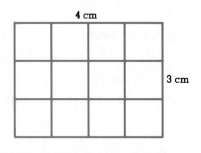

Nonoverlapping regions are regions that have no interior points in common.

This and many similar examples suggest the following postulate.

If a rectangle has an area of A square units, a length of ℓ units, and a width of w units, then $A = \ell w$.	*Postulate 11-4* *Area of a Rectangle*

Examples

1 Find the area of a rectangle that has a length of 6.1 m and a width of 3.7 m.

$A = \ell w$ *Postulate 11-4*
   $= 6.1 \times 3.7$
   $= 22.57$

The area of the rectangle is 22.57 square meters (m²).

2 Find the area of the figure below. Assume all angles are right angles.

The area of the figure is equal to the sum of the areas of the two rectangles.

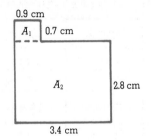

$A_1 = 0.9 \times 0.7$ $A_2 = 2.8 \times 3.4$
     $= 0.63$ $= 9.52$

$A = A_1 + A_2$
   $= 0.63 + 9.52$
   $= 10.15$

The area of the figure is 10.15 square centimeters (cm²).

If the measures of the length and width are equal, the rectangle is also a square.

If a square has an area of A square units, and each side is s units long, then $A = s^2$.	*Theorem 11-1* *Area of a Square*

EN: 1, 4, 8, 16, 3, 6, 9, . . . 27, 28, 29; AV: 1–16, 2–26 even, 28, 29; FD: 1–16, 1–10, 11–27, odd;

Exploratory Exercises

ALL LEVELS: Algebra Review

Answer each of the following.

1. Draw as many rectangles as you can that are separated into 24 unit squares. Name the dimensions for each rectangle.
   For Exercises 1–2, see the Teacher Guide.

2. Draw as many rectangles as you can that are separated into 36 unit squares. Name the dimensions for each rectangle.

Estimate the area of each figure. The area of each square is 1 square unit.

3.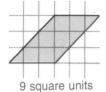
9 square units

4.
5 square units

5.
6 square units

6.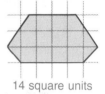
14 square units

Find the measure of the area and perimeter of each rectangle described below.

7. 6 units by 6 units $A = 36, P = 24$

8. 9 units by 4 units $A = 36, P = 26$

9. 12 units by 3 units $A = 36, P = 30$

10. 18 units by 2 units $A = 36, P = 40$

11. 5 units by 5 units $A = 25, P = 20$

12. 6 units by 4 units $A = 24, P = 20$

Determine whether each of the following is *true* or *false*.

13. If two rectangles have the same area, then they have the same perimeter. false

14. If two rectangles have the same perimeter, then they have the same area. false

15. If two squares have the same area, then they have the same perimeter. true

16. If two squares have the same perimeter, then they have the same area. true

Written Exercises

Complete each table from the information given about a rectangle.

	length	width	area
1.	5 cm	4 cm	20 cm²
3.	53.4 cm	42.5 cm	2269.5 cm²
5.	$5\frac{1}{2}$ mi	$3\frac{1}{3}$ mi	$18\frac{1}{3}$ mi²
7.	30.5 ft	20 ft	610 ft²
9.	$(x + 3)$ ft	x ft	$(x^2 + 3x)$ ft²

	length	width	area
2.	7 in.	4 in.	28 in²
4.	10 in.	- 3.5 in.	35 in²
6.	$\frac{3}{4}$ ft	$\frac{1}{4}$ ft	$\frac{3}{16}$ ft²
8.	y cm	$2y$ cm	$2y^2$ cm²
10.	$2k$ cm	$(k + 1)$ cm	$(2k^2 + 2k)$ cm²

Find the area of each shaded region. Assume that the same unit is used for all measures and all angles that appear to be right angles are right angles.

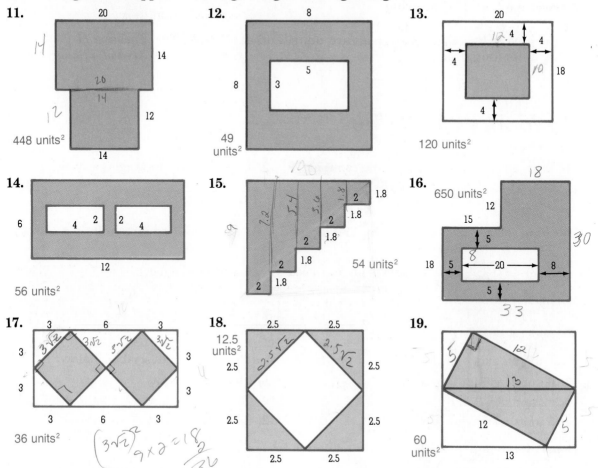

11.

20

14

14

26

14

12

12

448 units²

14

12.

8

5

8   3

49
units²

13.

20

12.4   4

4   4

4   10   18

4

120 units²

14.

6 | 2 | 2 |
    | 4 | | 4 |

12

56 units²

15.

1.2   5.4   5.6   1.8

2   1.8

2   1.8

2   1.8

2   1.8

2   1.8

2   1.8

9

54 units²

16.   650 units²

18

12

15

5

8

18   5   20   8

5

33

30

17.

3   6   3

3   3√2 3√2 3√2 3√2

3

3

3   6   3

36 units²

$(3\sqrt{2})^2$
$9 \times 2 = 18$
$\frac{}{30}$

18.

2.5   2.5

12.5
units²

2.5   2.5√2   2.5√2   2.5

2.5   2.5

2.5   2.5

19.

5   12

5

13

12   13

60
units²

5

5

Solve each of the following problems.

20. Find the area of a square whose diagonal is $3\sqrt{2}$ cm. 9 cm²

21. Find the area of a square whose diagonal is 5. 12.5 units²

22. The diagonal of a rectangle is $\sqrt{61}$ in. and the width is 5 in. Find the area. 30 in²

23. The diagonal of a rectangle makes a 30° angle with the length. If the diagonal is 2 m, find the area. $\sqrt{3}$ m²

24. The length of a rectangle is 4 cm greater than its width. The area of the rectangle is 117 cm². Find the length and width. 13 cm, 9 cm

25. If the length of each side of a square is doubled, the area is increased by 363 in². Find the length of each side of the original square. 11 in.

26. A rectangular piece of glass is twice as long as it is wide. If the length and width are both reduced by 1 cm, the area of the glass becomes 10 cm². What are the original dimensions of the glass? 3 cm, 6 cm

27. A rectangular piece of sheet metal is 3 in. longer than it is wide. If the length and width are both increased by 2 in., the area increases by 34 in². What are the original dimensions of the sheet metal? 6 in., 9 in.

Application Exercises

Answer each of the following.

28. A rectangular field to be planted with grain is 150 meters wide and 160 meters long. One bushel of grain plants 100 square meters of land. How many bushels are needed to plant the field? 240 bushels

29. A rectangular window is $5\frac{1}{2}$ feet by 4 feet. The window is to be filled with stained glass. Most stained glass costs about $12 per square foot. Estimate the cost of stained glass for the window. $264

Excursions in Geometry

Pick's Theorem

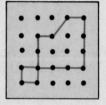

A geoboard usually is a square piece of wood with an arrangement of nails on its surface. If the nails are in rows and columns of 5 each for a total of 25 nails, then a 5 × 5 geoboard is formed.

A variety of geometric figures can be formed by looping rubber bands around the nails on a geoboard. The diagram at the right shows two such figures. The area of the region outlined in green is 1 square unit.

Pick's Theorem gives a formula for the area of a region outlined on a geoboard or grid.

> If the area of a region on a geoboard is A square units, the borders of the region touch x nails, and there are y nails in the interior, then $A = \frac{x}{2} + y - 1$.

Example   **Find the area of the region outlined in red in the figure shown above.**

$$A = \frac{x}{2} + y - 1 \qquad \text{x is 11 and y is 3.}$$

$$= \frac{11}{2} + 3 - 1$$

$$= 7\frac{1}{2}$$

Exercises

Find the area for each of the following regions. Use Pick's Theorem.

1.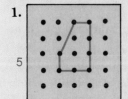
5

2.
8

3.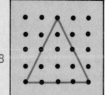
8

4.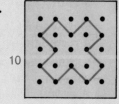
10

11-2 Area Formulas

Objectives: Recognize the base(s) and altitude(s) of parallelograms, triangles, and trapezoids; find the areas of parallelograms, triangles, and trapezoids.

Any side of a parallelogram may be called the **base** of the parallelogram. For each base there is a corresponding **altitude.** An altitude of a parallelogram is a segment that is perpendicular to the line containing the base and which has its endpoints on the lines containing the base and the opposite side.

For each parallelogram shown below, one base is 10 units long, and its corresponding altitude is 7 units long.

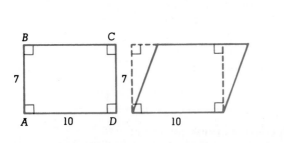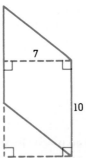

By using the Area Addition Postulate and congruence, it is possible to show that each region has the same area, 7 × 10 or 70 square units.

These and many similar examples suggest the following theorem.

If a parallelogram has an area of *A* square units, a base of *b* units, and a corresponding altitude of *h* units, then *A = bh*.	*Theorem 11-2 Area of a Parallelogram*

Example

1 **Prove Theorem 11-2.**

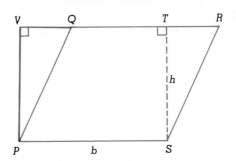

Given: □*PQRS*
   PS = b   Locate *T* between *R* and *Q*
   TS = h   and draw altitude $\overline{ST}$.
   The area of □*PQRS* is *A* square units.

Prove: *A = bh*

Proof:

Extend $\overline{RQ}$ and draw $\overline{PV}$ so that $\overline{PV} \perp \overleftrightarrow{RQ}$. Then *PV = h* and quadrilateral *PVTS* is a rectangle with a length of *h* units and a width of *b* units.

Since $\overline{PQ} \cong \overline{SR}$, show $\triangle PVQ \cong \triangle STR$ by HL. Thus, by the Area Addition Postulate, show that the area of the parallelogram is the same as the area of the rectangle. Thus, *A = bh*.

The area of a triangle is related to the area of a parallelogram. For example, consider □PQRS.

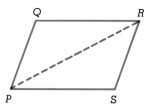

Have students identify the base and altitude for a variety of triangles including obtuse, acute, and right triangles.

Draw the diagonal $\overline{PR}$ to form $\triangle PQR$ and $\triangle RSP$. We know $\triangle PQR$ and $\triangle RSP$ are congruent by SAS. If the area of □$PQRS$ is A square units, then the sum of the areas of $\triangle PQR$ and $\triangle RSP$ is A square units. Therefore it follows that each triangle has half the area of the parallelogram. This conclusion suggests the following theorem.

If a triangle has an area of A square units, a base of b units, and a corresponding altitude of h units, then $A = \frac{1}{2}bh.$	*Theorem 11-3* *Area of a Triangle*

Students will prove this theorem in Written Exercise 16.

A diagonal of a trapezoid separates the trapezoid into two triangles. The formula for the area of a trapezoid can be found by finding the areas of triangles.

An altitude of the trapezoid is a segment perpendicular to the lines containing the bases of the trapezoid, and with its endpoints on the bases. Notice that the measure h of $\overline{QT}$ is the measure of the altitudes of both triangles.

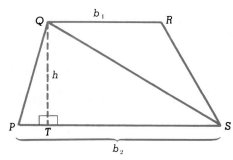

Provide examples of trapezoids in a variety of positions and have students identify bases and altitude.

area of trapezoid $PQRS$=area $\triangle PQS$ + area $\triangle QRS$

$$= \frac{1}{2}b_2h + \frac{1}{2}b_1h$$

$$= \frac{1}{2}h(b_2 + b_1)$$

Emphasize in the trapezoid above that $\overline{QT}$ is an altitude of both triangles.

If a trapezoid has an area of A square units, bases of b_1 units and b_2 units, and an altitude of h units, then $A = \frac{1}{2}h(b_1 + b_2).$	*Theorem 11-4* *Area of a Trapezoid*

Students will prove this theorem in Written Exercise 17.

Example 2

Find the area of the isosceles trapezoid whose bases are 20 units and 32 units, and whose legs measure 10 units each.

Draw the altitudes shown at the right. Two right triangles are formed with a leg of 6 units and hypotenuse of 10 units. Use the Pythagorean Theorem to find the length of the altitude.

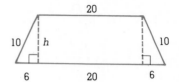

$$h^2 + 6^2 = 10^2$$
$$h^2 = 10^2 - 6^2$$
$$= 100 - 36$$
$$= 64$$
$$h = 8$$

Then, use the formula to find the area of the trapezoid.

$$A = \frac{1}{2}h(b_1 + b_2)$$

$$= \frac{1}{2}(8)(20 + 32)$$

$$= \frac{1}{2}(8)(52)$$

$$= 208 \qquad \text{The area is 208 square units.}$$

EN: 3, 6, 9, . . . 18, 4–6, 8–18 even; AV: 2–18 even, 1–9, 10–14 even, 18; FD: 1–18, 1–10, p. 393, 28, 29

Exploratory Exercises

Complete each of the following tables. Exercises 1–6 refer to a parallelogram, Exercises 7–12 refer to a triangle, and Exercises 13–18 refer to a trapezoid.

	base	altitude	area
1.	12 in.	8 in.	96 in²
3.	2 cm	9 cm	18 cm²
5.	21 mm	12 mm	252 mm²

	base	altitude	area
2.	6 ft	2 ft	12 ft²
4.	4 yd	5 yd	20 yd²
6.	9 m	4 m	36 m²

	base	altitude	area
7.	7 cm	12 cm	42 cm²
9.	4.5 in.	2 in.	4.5 in²
11.	4.95 ft	1.02 ft	2.5245 ft²

	base	altitude	area
8.	11 mi	10 mi	55 mi²
10.	9 m	2.6 m	11.7 m²
12.	120 mm	63.5 mm	3810 mm²

	base	base	altitude	area
13.	9 cm	2 cm	7 cm	38.5 cm²
15.	30 mi	20 mi	34 mi	850 mi²
17.	12 in.	4 in.	8 in.	64 in²

	base	base	altitude	area
14.	16 m	11 m	11 m	148.5 m²
16.	55.0 m	40 cm	21 cm	997.5 cm²
18.	7 ft	5 ft	5 ft	30 ft²

Written Exercises

Find the area of each of the following regions. Assume that all lines that appear parallel are parallel.

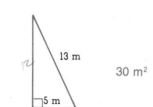
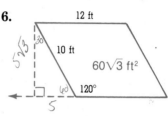
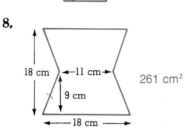
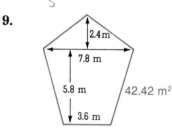

1. 25 cm, 12 cm, 6 cm, 150 cm²

2. $7\frac{1}{2}$ in², 8 in., 3 in., 4 in., 5 in.

3. 12 ft, 135 ft², 12 ft, 10 ft, 15 ft

4. 15 cm, 45°, 20 cm, $43\frac{3}{4}$ cm²

5. 13 m, 30 m², 5 m

6. 12 ft, 10 ft, 60√3 ft², 120°

7. 2.1 m, 1.8 m, 0.6 m, 1.2 m, 3.78 m²

8. 18 cm, 11 cm, 9 cm, 261 cm², 18 cm

9. 2.4 m, 7.8 m, 5.8 m, 3.6 m, 42.42 m²

Using the information given, complete the following exercises.

10. The areas of a parallelogram and a rectangle are equal. The rectangle has a length of 8 centimeters and a diagonal of 10 centimeters. Find the altitude of the parallelogram whose base is 12 centimeters. 4 cm

11. In a triangle, a side and its corresponding altitude are 7 inches and 4 inches respectively. Find the length of the corresponding altitude of another side of the triangle whose length is 8 inches. $3\frac{1}{2}$ in.

12. Find the area of an equilateral triangle whose side measures 20 inches. 100√3 in²

13. The lengths of the bases of an isosceles trapezoid are 14 and 22 centimeters. If a base angle is 60°, find the area of the trapezoid. 72√3 cm²

14. The base of an isosceles triangle measures 16 centimeters. If each leg of the triangle measures 20 centimeters, find the area of the triangle. 32√21 cm²

15. The area of a parallelogram is $(2x^2 + 9x + 4)$ cm². If the length of the base is $(x + 4)$ cm, find the length of its corresponding altitude. $(2x + 1)$ cm

Prove each of the following statements. For Exercises 16–17, see the Teacher Guide.

16. If a triangle has an area of A square units, a base of b units, and a corresponding altitude of h units, then $A = \frac{1}{2}bh$. (Theorem 11-3)

17. If a trapezoid has an area of A square units, bases b_1 and b_2 units, and an altitude of h units, then $A = \frac{1}{2}h(b_1 + b_2)$. (Theorem 11-4)

Complete the following exercise.

18. David Laing wants to fertilize his lawn. A diagram of his lot, which is in the shape of a trapezoid, is shown at the right. Before he purchases the fertilizer, he needs to know the area of the lawn. Calculate the number of square feet of lawn to be covered with fertilizer if the dimensions of the lot, house, and driveway are given in the figure. 9200 ft²

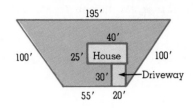

Using Calculators ——————— Heron's Formula

In the first century A.D. a Greek mathematician of Alexandria named Heron (or Hero) developed a formula for computing the area of a triangle if the lengths of its sides are known.

If a triangle has an area of A square units and sides of a units, b units, and c units, then $A = \sqrt{s(s - a)(s - b)(s - a)}$ where $s = \frac{1}{2}(a + b + c)$.

The Store and Recall keys on a calculator can be very useful when computing an area using Heron's Formula. Notice that the value of s is used four times in the formula. When you enter the value of s and then press the key labeled STO, the value of s is stored in the memory of the calculator.

The key labeled RCL is the Recall key. When you press this key, the calculator retrieves the value of s from the memory and displays it.

Example Using Heron's Formula, find the area of a triangle with sides of 6 cm, 8 cm, and 10 cm.

First, find the value of s and store it.

ENTER: 6 [+] 8 [+] 10 [=] [÷] 2 [=] [STO]

DISPLAY: 6   6   8   14   10   24   24   2   12   12

> Since this triangle is a right triangle with base 8 cm and height 6 cm, have students check the answer using the formula $A = \frac{1}{2}bh$.

Then compute the area.

ENTER: [RCL] [×] [(] [RCL] [−] 6 [)] [×] …. [×] [√]

DISPLAY: 12   12   12   12   12   6   6   72   576   24

The area is 24 cm².

Exercises
Find the area of each triangle with the given sides. Round answers to the nearest hundredth.

1. 5 in., 12 in., 13 in. 30 in²   **2.** 8 cm, 8 cm, 8 cm 27.71 cm² **3.** 10 ft, 11 ft, 12 ft 51.52 ft²

11-3 Regular Polygons

Objectives: Find the degree measure of a central angle of a regular polygon; determine the radius, apothem, center, and area of a regular polygon.

In the figure at the right, $\odot X$ is circumscribed about the regular hexagon. Notice that $\overline{XP}$, $\overline{XQ}$, $\overline{XR}$, $\overline{XS}$, $\overline{XT}$, and $\overline{XV}$ are radii of the circle. They also are called **radii of the regular hexagon.**

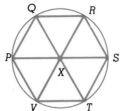

In the figure at the left, $\odot Y$ is inscribed in the regular hexagon. Notice that $\overline{YA}$, $\overline{YB}$, $\overline{YC}$, $\overline{YD}$, $\overline{YE}$, and $\overline{YF}$ are radii of the circle with endpoints at points where the hexagon is tangent to the circle. They are called **apothems of the regular hexagon.**

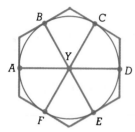

A segment is a radius of a regular polygon if and only if it is a radius of a circle circumscribed about the polygon.	*Definition of Radius of a Regular Polygon*
A segment is an apothem of a regular polygon if and only if it is a radius of a circle inscribed in the polygon.	*Definition of Apothem of a Regular Polygon*

For a regular polygon, a circle inscribed in the polygon and a circle circumscribed about the polygon have the same center. This point is also called the **center of the regular polygon.**

Point out that this theorem is a biconditional statement.

A polygon is regular if and only if a circle inscribed in the polygon and a circle circumscribed about the polygon have the same center.	*Theorem 11-5*

The circles are concentric.

A point is a center of a regular polygon if and only if it is the common center of its inscribed and circumscribed circles.	*Definition of Center of a Regular Polygon*

If a polygon is *not* regular, then the inscribed circle and the circumscribed circle may *not* exist. If the circles do exist, they may *not* have the same center.

Each side of a regular polygon is tangent to a circle inscribed in the polygon. A radius of a circle drawn to a point of tangency is perpendicular to the tangent. Thus, each apothem of a regular polygon is perpendicular to one side of the polygon.

If a segment is an apothem of a regular polygon, then it is perpendicular to a side of the polygon at the point of tangency with the inscribed circle.	*Theorem 11-6*

Students will prove this theorem in Written Exercise 20.

Given the length of the apothem and one side of a regular polygon, the area can be found.

Examples

1   **Find the area of a regular hexagon if the apothem is *a* units long and one side is *s* units long.**

By drawing all the radii of the hexagon, 6 triangles such as $\triangle XYZ$ are formed. Each apothem of a regular polygon is perpendicular to a side of the polygon. Thus, the altitude of each triangle is an apothem of *a* units. The base of each triangle is a side of the hexagon, and is *s* units long.

By the Area Addition Postulate, the area of the hexagon equals the sum of the areas of the triangles.

$$A = \frac{1}{2}sa + \frac{1}{2}sa + \frac{1}{2}sa + \frac{1}{2}sa + \frac{1}{2}sa + \frac{1}{2}sa$$

$$= 6\left(\frac{1}{2}sa\right) \quad \text{Note that } 6 \cdot s \text{ is the perimeter.}$$

$$= 3sa \quad \text{The area is } 3sa \text{ square units.}$$

2   **Find the area of a regular octagon if the apothem is *a* units long and one side is *s* units long.**

By drawing all the radii of the hexagon, 8 triangles such as $\triangle ABC$ are formed. By the Area Addition Postulate, the area of the octagon equals the sum of the areas of the triangles.

$$A = 8\left(\frac{1}{2}sa\right) \quad \begin{array}{l} s \text{ represents the base of } \triangle ABC. \\ a \text{ represents the altitude of } \triangle ABC. \end{array}$$

$$= 4sa \quad \text{The area is } 4sa \text{ square units.}$$

Point out that $8 \cdot s$ is the perimeter.

These and other similar examples suggest the following theorem.

If a regular polygon has an area of *A* square units, a perimeter of *p* units, and an apothem of *a* units, then $A = \frac{1}{2}ap$.	*Theorem 11-7* *Area of a Regular Polygon*

Students will prove this theorem in Written Exercise 21.

A central angle of a regular polygon is formed by two radii drawn to consecutive vertices.

The central angles of the polygon also are central angles of a circle. The sum of their degree measures must be 360. *Why?*

A regular hexagon has 6 central angles. Thus, the degree measure of each is $\frac{360}{6}$ or 60.

If a regular polygon has *n* sides, then the degree measure of each central angle is $\frac{360}{n}$.	*Theorem 11-8*

Students will prove specific cases of this theorem in Written Exercises 22–23.

Example

3 **Find the area of a regular hexagon having 6-inch sides.**

Since $\angle ACB$ is a central angle its degree measure is $\frac{360}{6}$ or 60. Also, $\overline{AC} \cong \overline{BC}$, so the triangle must be equilateral. Thus, AC and BC are 6 inches.

Since the apothem $\overline{CD}$ also is an altitude, it bisects $\overline{AB}$. Thus AD and DB are 3 inches.

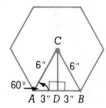

The length of the apothem can be found using either trigonometry or the Pythagorean Theorem. Since $\triangle ACD$ is a 30°–60°–90° right triangle and $\overline{CD}$ is opposite the 60° angle, CD can be found by multiplying the measure of $\overline{AD}$ by $\sqrt{3}$. Thus, $CD = 3\sqrt{3}$ inches. Now, the area of the hexagon can be found as follows.

$$A = \frac{1}{2}ap$$
$$= \frac{1}{2}(3\sqrt{3})(6)(6) \quad \text{\textit{p = s · n, where s is the length of one side}}$$
$$\text{\textit{and n is the number of sides of the polygon.}}$$
$$= 54\sqrt{3}$$
$$\approx 93.5 \quad \text{The area is about 93.5 square inches.}$$

EN: 7–9, 3, 6, 9, . . . 30, 31, 35–36; **AV:** 1–9 odd, 2–30 even, 34, 35; **FD:** 1–9, 1–26, p. 397, 11–13

Exploratory Exercises   ALL LEVELS: Mini Review

Find the degree measure of a central angle of each regular polygon with the given number of sides.

1. 3 120   **2.** 4 90   **3.** 5 72

4. 6 60   **5.** 8 45   **6.** 9 40

7. 10 36   **8.** 12 30   **9.** 14 $25\frac{5}{7}$

Written Exercises

Complete the charts from the information given about a regular polygon.

	n	s	p	a	A
1.	3	4	12	$2\sqrt{3}/3$	$4\sqrt{3}$
3.	3	$12\sqrt{3}$	$36\sqrt{3}$	6	$108\sqrt{3}$
5.	4	3	12	3/2	9
7.	4	10	40	5	100

	n	s	p	a	A
2.	4	5	20	5/2	25
4.	6	8	48	$4\sqrt{3}$	$96\sqrt{3}$
6.	6	$4\sqrt{3}/3$	$8\sqrt{3}$	2	$8\sqrt{3}$
8.	6	3.4	20.4	$1.7\sqrt{3}$	$17.34\sqrt{3}$

Find the area of each regular polygon with the following measurements. Round answers to the nearest tenth.

9. equilateral triangle
apothem 5.8 centimeters
side 20 centimeters 174 cm²

10. square
apothem 8 inches
side 16 inches 256 in²

11. pentagon
apothem 8.9 miles
side 13.0 miles 289.3 mi²

12. hexagon
apothem 16.5 millimeters
side 19.1 millimeters 945.5 mm²

13. hexagon
apothem 8.7 meters
side 10 meters 261 m²

14. octagon
apothem 7.5 feet
side 6.2 feet 186 ft²

Complete each of the following exercises. Express answers in simplest radical form.

15. Find the radius of an equilateral triangle with a side of 16 centimeters. $\frac{16\sqrt{3}}{3}$ cm

16. Find the radius of a square with a perimeter of 24 inches. $3\sqrt{2}$ in.

17. Find the radius of a regular hexagon with an apothem of 16 inches. $\frac{32\sqrt{3}}{3}$ in.

18. Find the apothem of a regular hexagon with radius of 6 centimeters. $3\sqrt{3}$ cm

19. Find the area of an equilateral triangle with a radius of $4\sqrt{3}$ units. $36\sqrt{3}$ units²

20. Find the area of an equilateral triangle with a radius of 6 units. $27\sqrt{3}$ units²

21. Find the area of a regular hexagon with an apothem of 12 centimeters. $288\sqrt{3}$ cm²

22. Find the area of a regular hexagon with a side of 12 centimeters. $216\sqrt{3}$ cm²

23. Find the area of a square inscribed in a circle with a radius of 10 feet. 200 ft²

24. Find the area of a square circumscribed about a circle with a radius of 10 feet. 400 ft²

25. Find the area of a regular pentagon with a perimeter of 16.5 inches and an apothem of 4 inches. 33 in²

26. Find the area of a regular pentagon with a perimeter of 68.3 meters and an apothem of 5 meters. 170.75 m²

Find the area of each shaded region. Assume the polygons are regular polygons.

27. $42\sqrt{3}$ units²

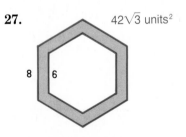

8   6

28. $12 + 4\sqrt{3}$ units²

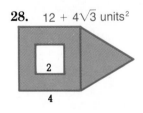

2

4

29. 88 units²

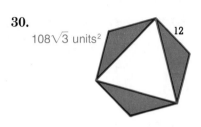

30. $108\sqrt{3}$ units²

Prove each of the following statements. For Exercises 31–33, see the Teacher Guide.

31. If a segment is an apothem of a regular polygon, then it is perpendicular to a side of the polygon at the point of tangency with the inscribed circle. (Theorem 11-6)

32. If a regular polygon has an area of A square units, a perimeter of p units, and an apothem of a units, then $A = \frac{1}{2}ap$. (Theorem 11-7)

33. If a regular polygon has n sides, then the degree measure of each central angle is $\frac{360}{n}$. (Theorem 11-8)

Application Exercises

Complete the following exercises. Round answers to the nearest tenth.

34. Dolores Smith wants to add a triangular deck in the yard behind her house. Each side is to be 18 feet long. Find the length of the railing that will fit completely around the deck. Then, find the area of the deck. $P = 54$ ft, $A = 140.3$ ft²

35. The City of Medina is building a gazebo on the city square. The gazebo will be in the shape of a regular hexagon with length of sides being 6 meters. Find the area the gazebo will cover. 93.5 m²

Challenge Exercises

Using the figures given, complete the following exercises.

36. *ABCDEF* is a regular hexagon. Find the length of a side.

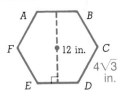

9-4
9-4

9-4
9-3

9-4

37. Find the ratio of the area of square *ABCD* to the area of square *BFCE*.

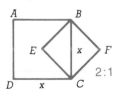

mini-review

Find the measure x. Express answers in simplest radical form.

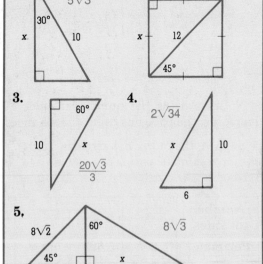

11-4 Circles

Suppose a wheel, such as a bicycle wheel, makes one complete revolution. The distance it travels is the same as the **circumference** of the wheel.

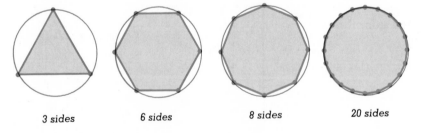

Start   *Turning*   *All the way around*

The circumference of a circle is related to the perimeter of regular polygons. The sequence of figures below suggests the relationship.

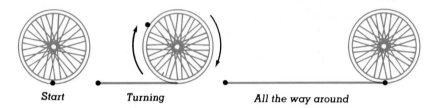

3 sides   *6 sides*   *8 sides*   *20 sides*

You may want to have students create circles in Logo by drawing polygons with many sides. See page 542.

Notice that as the number of sides of the inscribed polygons increases, the polygons begin to look more and more like a circle.

Emphasize that as the number of sides increase, the polygon approaches the shape of a circle.

Suppose the radius of a circle is r units. The following chart gives the approximate perimeter and area of each regular polygon inscribed in the circle.

Number of sides	3	4	5	6	8	10	20	50	100
Perimeter	$5.20r$	$5.66r$	$5.88r$	$6.00r$	$6.12r$	$6.18r$	$6.27r$	$6.28r$	$6.28r$
Area	$1.30r^2$	$2.00r^2$	$2.38r^2$	$2.60r^2$	$2.83r^2$	$2.94r^2$	$3.09r^2$	$3.13r^2$	$3.14r^2$

Notice that as the number of sides increases, the perimeter approaches some limiting number. This number is called the circumference of the circle. Similarly, the area approaches some limiting number. This number is called the area of the circle.

You may wish to discuss the idea of limit in more detail.

The circumference of a circle is the limit of the perimeter of the inscribed regular polygons as the number of sides increases.	*Definition of Circumference of a Circle*
The area of a circle is the limit of the area of the inscribed polygons as the number of sides increases.	*Definition of Area of a Circle*

The number 3.14 seems to occur in the approximations of the area and perimeter of the inscribed regular polygon. This number is an approximation for π.

The Greek letter π (pronounced pi) stands for a number that cannot be named exactly by a decimal or fraction. One decimal approximation for π is 3.14159265 and one fractional approximation for π is $\frac{22}{7}$. Both the circumference and area of a circle are related to π.

Another fractional approximation for π is $\frac{355}{113}$.

For large values of n, the perimeter values in the chart are approximately $2\pi r$ and the area values in the chart are approximately πr^2. These values suggest the following formulas.

If a circle has a circumference of C units and a radius of r units, then $C = 2\pi r$.	*Theorem 11-9 Circumference of a Circle*
If a circle has an area of A square units and a radius of r units, then $A = \pi r^2$.	*Theorem 11-10 Area of a Circle*

Example

1 **Find the circumference and area of a circle with a radius of 5.6 centimeters. Use 3.14 to approximate π. Round answers to the nearest tenth.**

$$C = 2\pi r \qquad\qquad A = \pi r^2$$
$$\approx 2(3.14)(5.6) \qquad \approx (3.14)(5.6)^2$$
$$\approx 35.2 \qquad\qquad \approx 98.5$$

The circumference is about 35.2 centimeters.

The area is about 98.5 square centimeters.

Example

2

Find the area of a circle inscribed in an equilateral triangle whose sides are 5 centimeters. Use 3.14 to approximate π and round to the nearest hundredth.

By using a theorem about tangent segments and properties of congruence, it is possible to conclude that $\overline{AD} \cong \overline{DC}$. Thus, AD is 2.5 centimeters. Also, $\overline{PA}$ bisects $\angle EAD$. Thus, $m \angle PAD = 30$. Finally $\overline{PD} \perp \overline{AD}$. Since $\triangle APD$ is a 30°–60°–90° triangle, $(PD)\sqrt{3} = AD$.

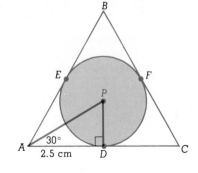

$$PD = \frac{AD}{\sqrt{3}} \qquad \overline{PD} \text{ is the radius of } \odot P.$$

$$PD = \frac{2.5\sqrt{3}}{3} \qquad \text{Note } AD = 2.5.$$

Then, find the area of the circle.

$$A = \pi r^2$$

$$\approx (3.14)\left(\frac{2.5\sqrt{3}}{3}\right)^2 \qquad \text{Note } \frac{2.5\sqrt{3}}{3} \approx 1.4.$$

$$\approx (3.14)(1.4)^2$$

$$\approx 6.15$$

The area of the circle is about 6.15 square centimeters.

A **sector** of a circle is a region bounded by a central angle and its intercepted arc.

The sum of the degree measures of the central angles of a circle is 360. The region bounded by a circle can be separated into exactly three sectors whose central angles measure 120°. Since the boundaries of the sectors are congruent, the sectors have the same area. As a result, the area of each sector is $\frac{1}{3}$ the area of the circle or, if the radius is r units, $\frac{1}{3}\pi r^2$.

$$\frac{120}{360} = \frac{1}{3}$$

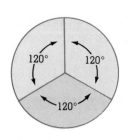

In general, the area of a sector of a circle is the fraction of the area of the circle times the area of the circle.

If a sector of a circle has an area of A square units, a central angle measurement of N degrees, and a radius of r units, then $A = \dfrac{N}{360}\pi r^2$.	*Definition of Area of a Sector of a Circle*

Exploratory Exercises

Complete the following charts from the information given about a circle. Express answers, when necessary, in terms of π.

	r	d	C	A
1.	7 cm	14 cm	14π cm	49π cm²
3.	8 ft	16 ft	16π ft	64π ft²
5.	2.4 km	4.8 km	4.8π km	5.76π km²
7.	$5\sqrt{2}$ cm	$10\sqrt{2}$ cm	$10\sqrt{2}\pi$ cm	50π cm²
9.	$4\sqrt{3}$ in.	$8\sqrt{3}$ in.	$8\sqrt{3}\pi$ in.	48π in²
11.	$4\frac{2}{3}$ yd	$9\frac{1}{3}$ yd	$9\frac{1}{3}\pi$ yd	$21\frac{7}{9}\pi$ yd²

	r	d	C	A
2.	10 m	20 m	20π m	100π m²
4.	5 m	10 m	10π m	25π m²
6.	9.6 m	19.2 m	19.2π m	92.16π m²
8.	$3\sqrt{6}$ cm	$6\sqrt{6}$ cm	$6\sqrt{6}\pi$ cm	54π cm²
10.	$3\sqrt{2}$ in.	$6\sqrt{2}$ in.	$6\sqrt{2}\pi$ in.	18π in²
12.	$5\frac{3}{4}$ ft	$11\frac{1}{2}$ ft	$11\frac{1}{2}\pi$ ft	$33\frac{1}{16}\pi$ ft²

Written Exercises

Find the circumference of each circle with the given radius. Use 3.14 to approximate π and round answers to the nearest tenth.

1. 7 centimeters 44.0 cm
2. 10 meters 62.8 m
3. 4 inches 25.1 in.
4. 8 feet 50.2 ft
5. 7.4 centimeters 46.5 cm
6. 9.6 meters 60.3 m
7. 2.4 kilometers 15.1 km
8. 1.5 miles 9.4 mi
9. $\frac{1}{2}$ foot 3.1 ft

Find the area of each circle with the given radius. Use $\frac{22}{7}$ to approximate π.

10. $3\frac{1}{3}$ yards $34\frac{58}{63}$ yd²
11. $4\frac{2}{3}$ yards $68\frac{4}{9}$ yd²
12. $5\frac{3}{4}$ feet $103\frac{51}{56}$ ft²
13. $5\sqrt{2}$ centimeters $157\frac{1}{7}$ cm²
14. $4\sqrt{3}$ inches $150\frac{6}{7}$ in²
15. $3\sqrt{2}$ inches $56\frac{4}{7}$ in²

Each of the following is a measurement for a central angle of a circle. The area of the corresponding sector is what fraction of the area of its circle?

16. 40° $\frac{1}{9}$
17. 60° $\frac{1}{6}$
18. 30° $\frac{1}{12}$
19. 2° $\frac{1}{180}$
20. 45° $\frac{1}{8}$
21. 15° $\frac{1}{24}$
22. 18° $\frac{1}{20}$
23. 72° $\frac{1}{5}$

Use the information given to find the area of the sector in each of the following figures. Express answers in terms of π.

24.
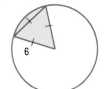
6π units²

25.
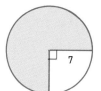
$36\frac{3}{4}\pi$ units²

26.
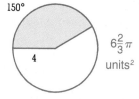
$6\frac{2}{3}\pi$ units²

Complete the following exercises. Express answers in terms of π.

27. A circle with radius $3\sqrt{2}$ contains a sector with area 6π. Find the degree measure of the sector. 120°

28. Find the degree measure of a sector whose area is 15π and is contained in a circle with radius 5. 216°

29. A circle contains a 210° sector with an area of 21π. Find the radius of the circle. 6

30. The area of a 60° sector of a circle is 10π. Find the radius of the circle. $2\sqrt{15}$

31. Find the area of a circle inscribed in a square whose sides are 6 meters. 9π m²

32. Find the area of a circle inscribed in a square whose diagonal is 8 feet. 8π ft²

Find the area of the shaded regions. Assume the polygons are regular polygons. Express answers in terms of π.

33.

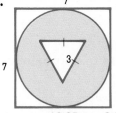

$18\pi - 36$ units²

34.

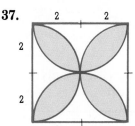

$144\pi - 216\sqrt{3}$ units²

35.

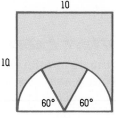

$4\frac{1}{6}\pi$ units²

36.

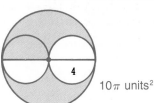

$12.25\pi - 2.25\sqrt{3}$ units²

37.

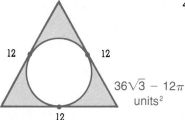

$8\pi - 16$ units²

38.

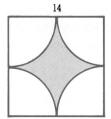

$100 - \frac{25}{3}\pi$ units²

39.

10π units²

40.

$36\sqrt{3} - 12\pi$ units²

41.

$196 - 49\pi$ units²

Application Exercises

Complete each exercise. Use 3.14 to approximate π and round answers to the nearest tenth.

42. Find the distance a bike travels if its tire makes 50 revolutions. The diameter of the tire is approximately 27 inches. 4239 in.

43. A town has installed a Public Alert System to notify residents in the event of tornado warnings. The sound emitted will travel a radius of $5\frac{1}{2}$ miles. Find the area that will benefit from the new system. 95.0 mi²

The ratio of the circumference to the diameter of a circle is a constant, π. The number π is **irrational**. That is, the value is an infinite, non-repeating decimal. It has been proven that π is also **transcendental**. That is, π cannot be the root of a polynomial equation with rational coefficients.

In the history of mathematics, many expressions have been found that represent the value of π.

In 1593 a French mathematician, François Viète, found an infinite irrational product for π.

$$\frac{\pi}{2} = \frac{1}{\sqrt{\frac{1}{2}} \cdot \sqrt{\frac{1}{2} + \frac{1}{2}\sqrt{\frac{1}{2}}} \cdot \sqrt{\frac{1}{2} + \frac{1}{2}\sqrt{\frac{1}{2} + \frac{1}{2}\sqrt{\frac{1}{2}}}} \ldots}$$

In 1655 an English mathematician, John Wallis, found an infinite rational product for π.

$$\frac{\pi}{2} = \frac{2}{1} \cdot \frac{2}{3} \cdot \frac{4}{3} \cdot \frac{4}{5} \cdot \frac{6}{5} \cdot \frac{6}{7} \cdot \frac{8}{7} \cdot \frac{8}{9} \ldots$$

One of the simplest expressions for π was discovered by Wilhelm von Leibniz, a German mathematician and philosopher. In 1674 Leibniz expressed π as the limit of an infinite series.

$$\frac{\pi}{4} = 1 - \frac{1}{3} + \frac{1}{5} - \frac{1}{7} + \frac{1}{9} - \frac{1}{11} + \frac{1}{13} \cdots$$

Each of the expressions given above can be used to approximate π to any given number of decimal places. However, an accurate approximation requires lengthy calculations. More recently, other expressions have been found that can be used to approximate π more quickly.

Computers have been used to calculate over a million decimal places for π. The first 100 decimal places for π are given below.

π = 3.1415926535 8979323846 2643383279 5028841971 6939937510
　　　5820974944 5923078164 0628620899 8628034825 3421170679 $\cdots$

Exercises
Use a calculator for each approximation.

1. Use the first 3 products in Viète's expression to approximate π. 3.1214452

2. Use the first 4 products in Viète's expression to approximate π. 3.1365485

3. Use the first 10 products in Wallis's expression to approximate π. 3.002176

4. Use the first 20 products in Wallis's expression to approximate π. 3.0677038

5. Use the first 5 terms of Leibniz's series to approximate π. 3.3396825

6. Use the first 10 terms of Leibniz's series to approximate π. 3.0418396

11-5 Defining Surface Area

Objective: Find the lateral areas and the total surface areas of right prisms and right cylinders.

Solids are boundaries that enclose a part of space. Recall that solids with flat surfaces that form polygons are called polyhedrons. Perhaps the most common regular polyhedron is the hexahedron, or cube.

If a cube was cut apart at its edges and unfolded, it would resemble the figure below. The area of the figure is called the *total* **surface area** of the cube.

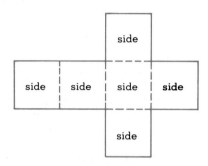

One type of solid is called a **prism.** A cube and a rectangular box are both prisms. Prisms have the following characteristics.

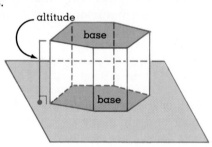

1. Two faces, called **bases,** are formed by congruent polygons that lie in parallel planes.
2. The faces that are *not* bases, called **lateral faces,** are formed by parallelograms.
3. The intersections of two adjacent lateral faces are called **lateral edges** and are parallel segments.

The length of an altitude is also called the height of the prism.

An **altitude** of a prism is a segment perpendicular to the base planes with an endpoint in each plane. If the lateral edges of a prism are also altitudes, then the prism is a **right prism.** Otherwise, the prism is an **oblique prism.**

Prisms can be classified by the shape of the base.

The lateral faces of right prisms are rectangles.

Right triangular
prism

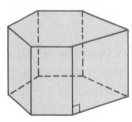

Right hexagonal
prism

Oblique pentagonal
prism

One way to find the surface area of a prism is to add the area of each face. Another way is to use a formula.

The **lateral area** of a prism is the area of all the lateral faces. As a result of the Distributive Property, the lateral area of a right prism can be found by multiplying the height by the perimeter of a base.

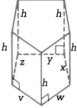

Does this hold for oblique prisms? See Cavalieri's Principle on page 424.

$$A = vh + wh + xh + yh + zh$$
$$= (v + w + x + y + z)h \text{ Point out that } v + w + x + y + z \text{ is the perimeter of the base.}$$

This and many similar examples suggest the following theorem.

If a right prism has a lateral area of L square units, a height of h units, and each base has a perimeter of p units, then $L = ph$.	*Theorem 11-11* *Lateral Area of a* *Right Prism*

The total surface area of a prism is found by adding the lateral area to the areas of both bases. Since the bases of a prism are congruent, they have the same area.

If the total surface area of a right prism is T square units, each base has an area of B square units, a perimeter of p units, and a height of h units, then $T = ph + 2B$.	*Theorem 11-12* *Total Surface Area* *of a Right Prism*

Example

1 Find the total surface area of a right prism whose base is a right triangle with legs of 5 inches and 12 inches, and whose height is 20 inches.

First, use the Pythagorean Theorem to find the measure of the hypotenuse.

$$a^2 = 5^2 + 12^2$$
$$= 169$$
$$a = 13$$

Then, find the total surface area.

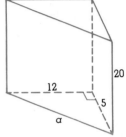

$$T = ph + 2B$$
$$= (5 + 12 + 13)20 + 2\left(\frac{1}{2} \cdot 5 \cdot 12\right)$$
$$= (30)20 + 2(30)$$
$$= 660$$

The total surface area is 660 square inches.

Another type of solid is a **cylinder.** The **bases** of a cylinder are formed by two congruent circles that lie in parallel planes. The segment whose endpoints are centers of these circles is called the **axis** of the cylinder.

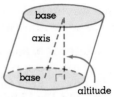

Right cylinder   Oblique cylinder

The **altitude** of a cylinder is a segment perpendicular to the base planes with an endpoint in each plane. If the axis of a cylinder also is an altitude of the cylinder, then the cylinder is called a **right cylinder.** Otherwise, the cylinder is an **oblique cylinder.**

The length of the altitude is called the height of the cylinder.

If a cylinder was cut apart and unfolded, it would resemble the figure below. The lateral area of a cylinder is the area of the curved surface. The total surface area is the lateral area and the area of the bases.

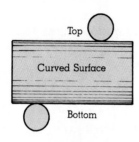

Top

Curved Surface

Bottom

Emphasize that the width of the curved surface is the height of the cylinder. The length of the curved surface is the circumference of the base.

If a right cylinder has a lateral area of L square units, a height of h units, and the bases have radii of r units, then $L = 2\pi rh$.	*Theorem 11-13* *Lateral Area of a* *Right Cylinder*
If a right cylinder has a total surface area of T square units, a height of h units, and the bases have radii of r units, then $T = 2\pi rh + 2\pi r^2$.	*Theorem 11-14* *Total Surface Area* *of a Right Cylinder*

Example

2   **Find the total surface area of a cylinder with a diameter of 4 cm and a height of 5 cm. Use 3.14 to approximate π.**

$$T = 2\pi rh + 2\pi r^2$$
$$\approx 2(3.14)(2)(5) + 2(3.14)(2^2)$$
$$\approx 62.8 + 25.12$$
$$\approx 87.92$$

The radius of the cylinder is 2 cm since $2r = d$.

The total surface area is about 87.92 square centimeters.

Exploratory Exercises

Use the prism at the right to answer each of the following.

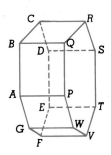

1. Name each base. heptagon *RSTVWPQ*, heptagon *CDEFGAB*
2. Tell how many sides to each base. 7
3. Tell how many lateral faces to the figure. 7
4. Name the lateral faces. *CRQB, CRSD, STED, TVFE, PWGA, QPAB, WVFG*
5. Suppose each polygon forming a base is regular with side of s units. Suppose the height is h units and the lateral area is L square units. Write a formula for the lateral area of the prism. $L = 7sh$

Determine whether each figure can be folded into a cube. Write *yes* or *no*.

6.   yes
7.   no
8.   yes
9.   yes
10.   no

Written Exercises

Find the lateral area and total surface area of each right prism.

1. 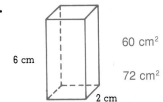 60 cm² 72 cm²
   6 cm   2 cm   3 cm

2. 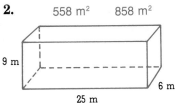 558 m²   858 m²
   9 m   6 m   25 m

3. 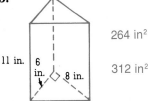 264 in² 312 in²
   11 in.   6 in.   8 in.

Find the lateral area of each right cylinder. Use 3.14 to approximate π and round answers to the nearest tenth.

4. 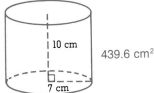 10 cm   7 cm   439.6 cm²

5. 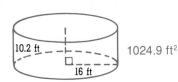 10.2 ft   16 ft   1024.9 ft²

6. 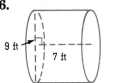 9 ft   7 ft   197.8 ft²

Find the total surface area of each right prism described below. Round answers to the nearest hundredth.

7. square base with sides of 4 in. and height of 4 in. 96 in²

8. square base with sides of x ft and height of x ft $6x^2$ ft²

9. right triangular base with legs of 16 mm and 12 mm, height of 15 mm 912 mm²

10. triangular base with height of 12.25 cm, sides of 10 cm, 10 cm, and 12 cm 488 cm²

11. equilateral triangular base with sides of 2.7 m, height of 5 m 46.81 m²

12. regular hexagonal base with height of 6 in., sides of 11.1 in. 1039.82 m²

Find the total surface area of each right cylinder. Use $\frac{22}{7}$ to approximate π.

13.

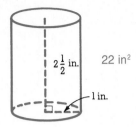

$2\frac{1}{2}$ in.   22 in²

1 in.

14.

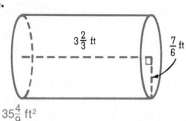

$3\frac{2}{3}$ ft $\frac{7}{6}$ ft

$35\frac{4}{9}$ ft²

15.

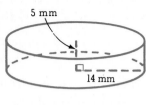

5 mm

14 mm

1672 mm²

Application Exercises

Solve each problem. Use 3.14 to approximate π and round answers to the nearest tenth.

16. Find the surface area of a cylindrical gas tank that is 25 feet tall and has a radius of 30 feet. 10,362 ft²

17. Find the surface area of a cylindrical water tank that is 8 meters tall and has a diameter of 8 meters. 301.4 m²

18. A diagram of a shed is shown at the right. The outside walls and the roof are to be painted. Find the area that will be painted. 1668 ft²

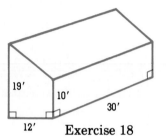

19'   10'   30'

12'   **Exercise 18**

19. Find the number of square feet of cardboard needed to make the sides of 30,000 orange juice cans if they each are 6 inches tall and are 3 inches in diameter. 11,775 ft²

20. Suppose two different crystals occur in the shape of right prisms. One crystal has a rectangular base of 2 units by 3 units with a height of 2.5 units. The other crystal has regular hexagonal bases with sides of 2.1 units and height 2.3 units. Which crystal has the greater surface area?

rectangular prism surface area = 37 units²,
hexagonal prism surface area = 51.9 units²
The hexagonal prism has the greater surface area.

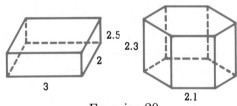

2.5   2.3

2

3   2.1

Exercise 20

Challenge Exercises

Find the total surface area of each of the following oblique rectangular prisms.

21.

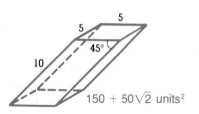

5

5

45°

10

$150 + 50\sqrt{2}$ units²

22.

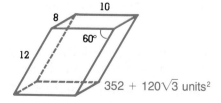

10

8

60°

12

$352 + 120\sqrt{3}$ units²

11-6 More About Surface Area

The design of the Transamerica Tower in San Francisco is based on the solid called a **pyramid.** A pyramid has the following characteristics.

1. All the faces, except one face, intersect at a point called the **vertex.**
2. The face that does not intersect at the vertex is called the **base** and forms a polygon.
3. The faces meeting at the vertex are called **lateral faces** and form triangles.

A prism has two bases. A pyramid has only one.

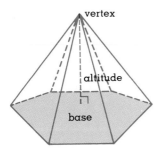

A pyramid is a **regular pyramid** if and only if its base is a regular polygon and the segment whose endpoints are the center of the base and the vertex is perpendicular to the base. This segment is called the **altitude.**

All the lateral faces of a regular pyramid form congruent isosceles triangles. The height of each lateral face is called the **slant height,** ℓ, of the pyramid.

Emphasize the difference between altitude and slant height.

The figure at the right is a regular hexagonal pyramid. Its lateral area can be found in the following way.

Point out the six triangles.

$$L = \frac{1}{2}s\ell + \frac{1}{2}s\ell + \frac{1}{2}s\ell + \frac{1}{2}s\ell + \frac{1}{2}s\ell + \frac{1}{2}s\ell$$
$$= \frac{1}{2}(s + s + s + s + s + s)\ell$$

This and many similar examples suggest the following theorem.

If a regular pyramid has a lateral area of L square units, a slant height of ℓ units, and its base has a perimeter of p units, then $L = \frac{1}{2}p\ell$.	*Theorem 11-15* *Lateral Area for a* *Regular Pyramid*

Example

1 Find the total surface area of a regular square pyramid in which the slant height is 10 inches and the sides of the base are 7 inches.

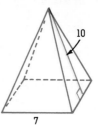

total surface area = lateral area + base area

$$= \frac{1}{2}p\ell \quad + \quad s^2$$

$$= \frac{1}{2}(4 \cdot 7)(10) + \quad (7)^2$$

$$= 189$$

The total surface area is 189 square inches.

The figure shown at the right is a **right circular cone.** It has a circular **base,** and a **vertex** at T. Its **axis,** $\overline{TC}$, is the segment whose endpoints are the vertex and the center of the base.

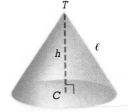

In a right circular cone, the axis is perpendicular to the base. Thus, it is the **altitude** of the cone. The length of any segment joining the vertex to the circle is called the **slant height.** In the cone at the right, the slant height is ℓ units.

Finding the lateral area and total surface area of a right circular cone is similar to finding those same measurements for a regular pyramid.

Emphasize the similarities between a regular pyramid and a circular cone.

If a right circular cone has a lateral area of L square units, a total surface area of T square units, a slant height of ℓ units, and the radius of the base is r units, then $L = \pi r \ell$ and $T = \pi r \ell + \pi r^2$.	*Theorem 11-16* *Lateral and Total Surface Area of a Right Circular Cone*

Example

2 A right circular cone has a radius of 7.6 centimeters. Its altitude is 11.9 centimeters. Find the total surface area of the cone. Use 3.14 to approximate π and round your answer to the nearest tenth.

First, use the Pythagorean Theorem to find the slant height.

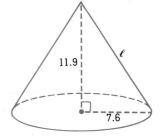

$$\ell^2 = 11.9^2 + 7.6^2$$
$$= 141.61 + 57.76$$
$$= 199.37$$
$$\ell = \sqrt{199.37}$$
$$\approx 14.1$$

Then, find the total surface area.

$$T = \pi r \ell + \pi r^2$$
$$\approx (3.14)(7.6)(14.1) + (3.14)(7.6)^2$$
$$\approx 336.5 + 181.4$$
$$\approx 517.9 \qquad \text{The total surface area is about 517.9 square centimeters.}$$

A formula for the surface area of a sphere is given in the following theorem.

If a sphere has a surface area of A square units and a radius of r units, then $A = 4\pi r^2$.	**Theorem 11-17** *Surface Area of a Sphere*

EN: 2–12 even, 2, 3, 5, 9, 15, 16–20 even; **AV:** 1–12, 2–14 even, 16–20; **FD:** 1–12, 1–15, p. 414, 15, 17, 18

Exploratory Exercises

Determine whether the condition given is characteristic of a pyramid or a prism, both, or neither.

1. It has only one base. pyramid
2. It has two bases. prism
3. Its lateral faces are parallelograms. prism
4. Its lateral faces are triangles. pyramid
5. It has the same number of faces as vertices. neither
6. It can have as few as three faces. neither
7. It can have as few as four faces. pyramid
8. It can have as few as five faces. both
9. One or more of its faces must be a parallelogram. prism
10. It always has an even number of vertices. prism
11. It always has an even number of faces. neither
12. It always has an even number of edges. pyramid

Written Exercises

Find the lateral area of each regular pyramid.

1.
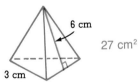
6 cm
27 cm²
3 cm

2.
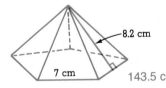
8.2 cm
7 cm
143.5 cm²

3.
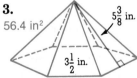
$5\frac{3}{8}$ in.
56.4 in²
$3\frac{1}{2}$ in.

Find the lateral area of each right circular cone. Use 3.14 to approximate π and round answers to the nearest tenth.

4.
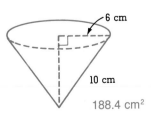
6 cm
10 cm
188.4 cm²

5.
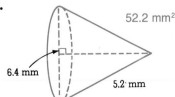
52.2 mm²
6.4 mm
5.2 mm

6.
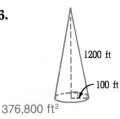
1200 ft
100 ft
376,800 ft²

Find the total surface area of each right circular cone in terms of π.

7.

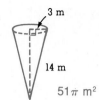

3 m

14 m

51π m²

8.

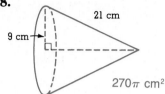

21 cm

9 cm

270π cm²

9.

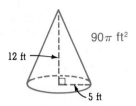

90π ft²

12 ft

5 ft

Find the surface area of each sphere given the following radii. Use 3.14 for π and round answers to the nearest tenth.

10. 10 centimeters 1256 cm²

11. 2 inches 50.2 in²

12. 2000 feet 50,240,000 ft²

13. 3.8 meters 181.4 m²

14. 372 miles 1,738,103 mi²

15. 75.3 centimeters 71,216.3 cm²

Solve each problem.

16. Find the lateral area for a regular pentagonal pyramid if each side of the base is 5 cm and the slant height is 6 cm. 75 cm²

17. Find the perimeter of the base of a regular pyramid with a slant height of 6 cm and a lateral area of 72 cm². 24 cm

18. If the area of the base of a right cone is 25π mm² and the height is 12 mm, find the lateral area in terms of π. 65π mm²

19. The radius of the earth is about 4000 mi. Find its surface area to the nearest square mile. Use 3.14 to approximate π. 200,960,000 mi²

20. Determine which of the right circular cones shown at the right has the greater lateral area. The cone with height 6 cm.

8 cm

6 cm

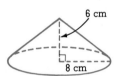

6 cm

8 cm

Statistics That Shape Your Life

By the year 2005 there will be two cars for every three people in the United States. The chart below shows the number of cars in the United States for 1980 and 1985 as well as the projected number of cars for following years.

More cars to people		
Year	Number of cars	People per car
1980	114.9 million	2.0
1985	125.3 million	1.9
1990	137.4 million	1.8
1995	150.9 million	1.7
2000	165.1 million	1.6
2005	179.6 million	1.5

Even though the population of the United States is not listed, you can use your knowledge of ratio to calculate the population.

Exercises

1. According to the chart, what was the population of the United States in 1980? 229.8 million

2. What is the projected population for 2005?

3. According to the chart, is car production or population increasing at a greater rate between 1980 and 2005?

2. 269.4 million **3.** Car production

11-7 Defining Volume

The construction of a hot air balloon requires an understanding of the property of gases. The **volume** of the balloon varies inversely with the applied pressure. That is, the volume of the balloon decreases as the pressure exerted on the outer surface of the balloon increases.

Volume is used to measure space. When each edge of a cube is 1 unit long, we say that the volume of the cube is 1 cubic unit. Thus, a cube one centimeter by one centimeter by one centimeter has a volume of one cubic centimeter (cm^3).

The volume is
1 cubic centimeter.

Emphasize that volume is expressed in cubic units.

Just as you have used positive real numbers to compare the area of polygonal regions, there is a positive real number that can be used to compare the amount of space enclosed by a solid figure. This number is called the measure of the volume.

For any solid region and a given unit of measure, there is a unique positive number called the measure of the volume of the region.	*Postulate 11-5* *Volume Postulate*

Using the following postulates, it is possible to find the volumes of various solid regions.

If two solid regions are congruent, then they have equal volumes.	*Postulate 11-6*
If a solid region is separated into nonoverlapping regions, then the sum of the volumes of these regions equals the volume of the given region.	*Postulate 11-7* *Volume Addition Postulate*

The rectangular box below is separated into 24 congruent cubes whose sides are 1 unit each. Thus, the volume of each cube is 1 cubic unit. Notice that the box has three layers, each with 2 × 4 or 8 cubes. By the Volume Addition Postulate, the volume of the box is 24 cubic units.

The base of the figure is a rectangle where A = ℓw.

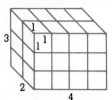

$$V = (2 \times 4) \times 3$$
$$= \text{Base area} \times \text{height}$$

In a similar manner, any right prism can be separated into layers to find its volume. The example shown and many others suggest the following.

If a right prism has a volume of V cubic units, a base with an area of B square units, and a height of h units, then $V = Bh$.	*Postulate 11-8*

You may want to review finding the area of a regular polygon.

Example

1 **Find the volume of a right hexagonal prism that has a base with sides of 8 centimeters and a height of 20 centimeters. Round your answer to the nearest unit.**

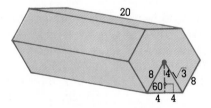

$$V = Bh$$
$$= \left(\frac{1}{2}ap\right)h$$
$$= \frac{1}{2}(4\sqrt{3})(48)(20)$$
$$\approx 3325.54$$

The volume is about 3326 cubic centimeters.

The stack of coins shown at the right represents a right cylinder that has been separated into circular layers. The volume of the cylinder is the area of each layer times the height of the stack.

Volume = Base area × height
= πr^2 × h

The base of the cylinder is a circle where A = πr².

If a right cylinder has a volume of V cubic units, a height of h units, and a radius of r units, then $V = \pi r^2 h$.	*Theorem 11-18* *Volume of a Right Cylinder*

Example

2 Hexagonal metal bars are made by cutting the sides from cylindrical bars. The radii of the hexagonal and cylindrical bars are 2.5 centimeters. Find the volume of waste metal from making a bar 60 centimeters long. Use 3.14 to approximate π and round your answer to the nearest hundredth.

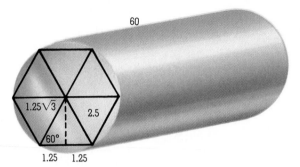

volume waste metal = volume cylindrical bar − volume hexagonal bar

$$= \pi r^2 h \quad - \quad Bh$$

$$= \pi r^2 h \quad - \quad \frac{1}{2}aph$$

$$\approx (3.14)(2.5)^2(60) \quad - \frac{1}{2}(1.25\sqrt{3})(15)(60)$$

$$\approx 203.22$$

You may want to encourage students to use calculators.

About 203.22 cubic centimeters of metal are wasted.

EN: 3, 6, 2–10 even, 13, 16, 18; AV: 2–6 even; 2–18 even; FD: 1–5 odd, 1–10, p. 418, 16–18

Exploratory Exercises

Find the volume of each right prism described below.

1. area of base: 12 m²
height: 3.5 m 42 m³

2. area of base: 17.5 cm²
height: 14 cm 245 cm³

3. area of base: 16 ft²
height: 4.2 ft 67.2 ft³

Find the volume of each right cylinder described below. Use 3.14 to approximate π and round answers to the nearest tenth.

4. radius: 2 m
height: 8 m 100.5 m³

5. radius: 3.2 cm
height: 10.5 cm 337.6 cm³

6. radius: $1\frac{1}{2}$ ft
height: 4 ft 28.3 ft³

Written Exercises

Find the volume of each figure. Use 3.14 to approximate π and round answers to the nearest tenth.

1.

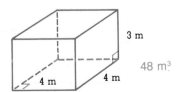

48 m³

2.

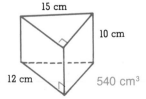

540 cm³

3.

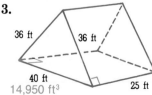

14,950 ft³

4.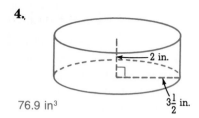

76.9 in³

5.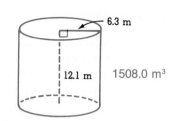

6.3 m

12.1 m   1508.0 m³

6.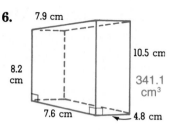

7.9 cm

10.5 cm

8.2 cm

341.1 cm³

7.6 cm   4.8 cm

2 in.

3½ in.

Solve each problem. Round answers to the nearest tenth.

7. In a regular triangular right prism, the radius of the triangle is 2 cm. If the height of the prism is 27 cm, find the total surface area and volume. 290.5 cm², 140.4 cm³

8. The figure at the right is a regular hexagonal right prism. Find the total surface area and volume. 1329.9 in², 2598.1 in³

9. Find the effect on the volume of a cube if the length of each edge is doubled. 8 times larger

10. Find the effect on the volume of a cube if the length of each edge is tripled. 27 times larger

11. In a certain cube, the measure of the volume is equal to the measure of the total area. Find the length of the edge of the cube. 6 units

12. Find the total surface area of a cylinder inscribed in a cube with edges of 10 in. 471 in²

13. A hole with a diameter of 4 mm is drilled through a block of metal as shown at the right. Find the remaining volume and the total surface area of the resulting solid. Use 3.14 to approximate π. 1011.6 mm³, 863.3 mm²

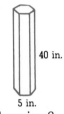

40 in.

5 in.

Exercise 8

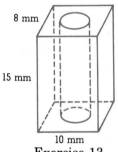

8 mm

15 mm

10 mm

Exercise 13

Application Exercises

14. Suppose a classroom is 30 ft long, 24 ft wide, and 10 ft high. If each person in the room must have 300 ft³ of air, find the maximum capacity of the room. 24 people

15. The drawing at the right represents a driveway. Blacktop will be spread over the driveway at an average depth of 3 inches. If the blacktop costs $7 per cubic foot, find the cost of blacktopping the driveway. $1102.50

16. A pipe is 100 ft long and has an inside diameter of 0.5 ft. Find the number of cubic feet of oil that it can hold. Use 3.14 to approximate π. 19.6 ft³

17. A cube of aluminum with edges of 15 in. is melted and then rolled into a wire with a diameter of 0.2 in. Find the length of the wire. 107,484.1 in.

18. The figure at the right represents concrete steps. If concrete costs $60 per cubic yard, how much did it cost to construct the steps? $100

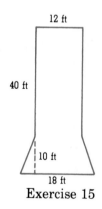

12 ft

40 ft

10 ft

18 ft

Exercise 15

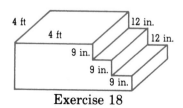

4 ft

4 ft

9 in.

12 in.

12 in.

9 in.

9 in.

Exercise 18

11-8 More About Volume

In the figures at the right, the pyramid and prism have the same base and height, and the cone and cylinder have the same base and height. You can see that the volume of the pyramid is less than the volume of the prism, and the volume of the cone is less than the volume of the cylinder.

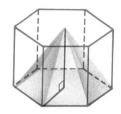 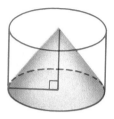

If a right pyramid has a volume of V cubic units, a height of h units, and the area of the base is B square units, then $V = \frac{1}{3}Bh$.	*Theorem 11-19* *Volume of a Right* *Pyramid*
If a right circular cone has a volume of V cubic units, a height of h units, and the area of the base is B square units, then $V = \frac{1}{3}Bh$.	*Theorem 11-20* *Volume of a Right* *Circular Cone*

Similarly, the volume of a sphere is less than the volume of a right circular cylinder in which it is inscribed.

If a sphere has a volume of V cubic units and a radius of r units, then $V = \frac{4}{3}\pi r^3$.	*Theorem 11-21* *Volume of a Sphere*

Example

1 Find the total volume of the two cones inside the right circular cylinder shown.

$$\begin{aligned}
\text{Total Volume} &= \text{Volume Top Cone} + \text{Volume Bottom Cone} \\
&= \tfrac{1}{3}Bh + \tfrac{1}{3}Bh \\
&= \tfrac{1}{3}(\pi r^2)\left(\tfrac{1}{2}a\right) + \tfrac{1}{3}(\pi r^2)\left(\tfrac{1}{2}a\right) \\
&= \tfrac{1}{3}\pi r^2 a
\end{aligned}$$

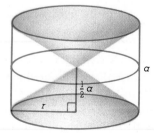

Example

2

Find the volume of the right circular cone with a radius of 3 cm and a slant height of 5 cm. Use 3.14 to approximate π and round your answer to the nearest tenth.

First use the Pythagorean Theorem to find the height.

$$h^2 + r^2 = \ell^2$$
$$h^2 + 9 = 25$$
$$h = 4$$

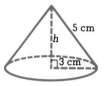

Then, find the volume.

$$V = \frac{1}{3}Bh$$

$$\approx \frac{1}{3}(3.14)(3^2)(4)$$

$$\approx 37.7 \qquad \text{The volume is about 37.7 cubic centimeters.}$$

So far only the formulas for the volume of *right* prisms, cylinders, pyramids, and cones have been considered. You may have wondered if the same formulas can be applied to *oblique* solids. The photograph at the right shows two matching decks of cards. One resembles a right prism and the other resembles an oblique prism. The photograph suggests that the two prisms have the same volume.

A **cross section** of a solid is the intersection of the solid with a plane that is parallel to the base of the solid. In the photograph, each card represents a plane parallel to the base of the deck. Thus, the area of each card represents the area of a cross section of the prism. Notice at each level, the decks of cards have the same cross-sectional area. The number of cards in a stack represents the measure of the height of that stack. Thus, the two decks have the same height.

If two solids have the same cross-sectional area at every level, and the same height, then they have the same volume.	*Postulate 11-9 Cavalieri's Principle*

As a result of Cavalieri's Principle, if a prism has a base with an area of B square units and a height of h units, then its volume is Bh cubic units, whether it is right or oblique. Similarly, the volume formulas for cylinders, cones, and pyramids hold whether they are right or oblique.

Example

3 Find the volume of the cone. Use 3.14 to approximate π and round your answer to the nearest cubic meter.

$$V = \frac{1}{3}Bh$$
$$= \frac{1}{3}[\pi \cdot (6)^2](13)$$
$$= 156\pi$$
$$\approx 489.84 \text{ or } 490$$

The volume is about 490 cubic meters.

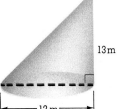

13 m

12 m

EN: 2, 6, 7, 12, 1, 2, 6, 8, 12, 14, 18, 20; **AV:** 2–12 even, 1–10 even, 13, 14, 16, 18;

Exploratory Exercises

FD: 1–12, 1–10, p. 422, 12–15

Find the volume of each pyramid given below. Round answers to the nearest tenth.

1. area of base: 15 ft²
   height: 7 ft 35 ft³

2. area of base: 24 cm²
   height: 5 cm 40 cm³

3. area of base: 10 ft²
   height: 3 ft 10 ft³

4. area of base: 17 m²
   height: 9 m 51 m³

5. area of base: 31.2 cm²
   height: 11.6 cm 120.6 cm³

6. area of base: 27.9 mm²
   height: 18.5 mm 172.1 mm³

Find the volume of each right circular cone given below. Use 3.14 to approximate π and round answers to the nearest tenth.

7. base radius: 5 ft
   height: 16 ft 418.7 ft³

8. base radius: 4 m
   height: 11 m 184.2 m³

9. base radius: 5 m
   height: 13 m 340.2 m³

10. base radius: 9 yd
    height: 16 yd 1356.5 yd³

11. base radius: 8.6 cm
    height: 12.0 cm 928.9 cm³

12. base radius: 4.2 m
    height: 10.3 m 190.2 m³

Written Exercises

Find the volume of each figure. Use 3.14 to approximate π and round answers to the nearest tenth.

1.
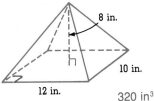
8 in.
10 in.
12 in.
320 in³

2.
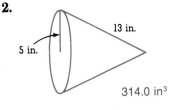
13 in.
5 in.
314.0 in³

3.
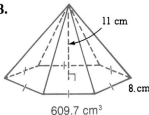
11 cm
8. cm
609.7 cm³

4.
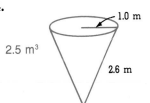
1.0 m
2.5 m³
2.6 m

5.
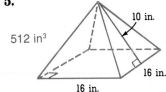
10 in.
512 in³
16 in.
16 in.

6.
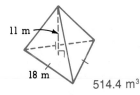
11 m
18 m
514.4 m³

Find the volume of each sphere. Use 3.14 to approximate π and round answers to the nearest tenth.

7. radius: 6 inches
904.3 in³

8. area of great circle:
50.24 square centimeters
267.9 cm³

9. circumference of great circle:
18.84 meters 113.0 m³

12. No. Volume of the cone is 41.9 cm³ and volume of the scoop is 33.5 cm³.

Solve each problem. Use 3.14 to approximate π and round answers to the nearest tenth.

10. Using the figure at the right, find the volume remaining if the smaller cone is removed from the larger cone. 535.9 in³

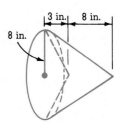

3 in. 8 in.
8 in.

Exercise 10

11. In the figure at the right, the eight faces of this regular octahedron are congruent equilateral triangles. If each edge is 12 cm, find the volume. 814.6 cm³

12. An ice cream cone is 10 cm deep and has a diameter of 4 cm. A scoop of ice cream that is 4 cm across rests on top of the cone. If all the ice cream melts into the cone, will the cone overflow? Justify your answer.

Exercise 11

13. Find the volume of a sphere whose total surface area is $256\,\pi$ cm². 2143.6 cm³

14. The diagram at the right represents a silo. If the height of the wall is 20 m and the silo is 10 m across, find the total surface area and volume of the silo. 863.5 m², 1831.7 m³

15. The radii of two spheres are in a ratio of 3:5. Find the ratio of their volumes. 27:125

16. A cone-shaped cup has a mark halfway up the side. If the cup is filled to the mark, what portion of the total volume of the cup is filled? $\frac{1}{8}$

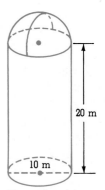

20 m

10 m

Exercise 14

17. Find the volume of the largest sphere that can be inscribed in a cube whose edges are 10 cm. 523.3 cm³

18. Find the volume of the smallest sphere that can be circumscribed about the cube in Exercise 17. 1480.2 cm³

19. A sphere is inscribed in a cylinder whose height is the same as the sphere's diameter. Find the ratio of the surface area of the sphere to the lateral area of the cylinder. 2:1

20. A right circular cone and a hemisphere have congruent bases and equal heights. Determine the ratio of the volume of the cone to the volume of the hemisphere. 1:2

Applications in Real Estate

Rich Danko is a real estate broker. His primary responsibility is to negotiate the sale of homes. Other responsibilities include managing apartment buildings, renting office buildings, and developing parcels of land.

Real estate brokers are licensed by the state in which they are employed. All brokers must pass the real estate broker's examination, which contains a section on real estate mathematics.

The following exercises are typical problems in real estate mathematics. Note how many problems involve concepts of area and volume.

Exercises

1. What is the cost of a lot 264 feet wide by 660 feet deep at a price of $880 per acre? The area of one acre is 43,560 square feet. $3520

2. How many square feet of concrete would be needed to construct a walk 7 feet wide around the outside corner of a corner lot measuring 50 × 120 feet? 1239 ft²

3. A broker has a problem of subdividing a 13-acre tract of land into 80 × 110 foot lots. After allowing 38,280 square feet for necessary roads, into how many lots could the tract be subdivided? 60

4. A retaining wall is being poured into a form which is 9 feet high, 110 feet long, and 18 inches wide. The concrete costs $60.00/cubic yard. How much will the concrete for the wall cost? $3300

5. A 7% commission was charged on a $90,000 home sale. The sales associate received 25% of the commission, the listing sales associate received 40% of the commission, and the broker retained the balance. How much did the broker receive? $2205

6. A broker purchased a vacant lot with a frontage of 50 feet at $215 per foot and made arrangements with a contractor to erect a building 40 feet long, 24 feet wide, and 16 feet deep for $50 per cubic foot. What would you charge your client for the property, figuring 10% profit and excluding any other charges? $856,625

Vocabulary

area (389)
polygonal region (389)
radius of a regular polygon (399)
apothem of a regular polygon (399)
center of a regular polygon (399)
circumference (404)
sector (406)
surface area (410)
prism (410)
bases (410, 412, 415, 416)
lateral faces (410, 415)
lateral edges (410)
altitude (410, 412, 415, 416)
right prism (410)
oblique prism (410)
lateral area (411)
cylinder (412)
axis (412, 416)
right cylinder (412)
oblique cylinder (412)
pyramid (415)
vertex (415, 416)
regular pyramid (415)
slant height (415, 416)
right circular cone (416)
volume (419)
cross section (424)

Chapter Summary

1. Area Postulate (Postulate 11-1): For any polygonal region and a given unit of measure, there is a unique real positive number called the measure of the area of the region. (389)
2. Postulate 11-2: If two polygons are congruent, then they have equal areas. (390)
3. Area Addition Postulate (Postulate 11-3): If a region is separated into nonoverlapping regions, then the sum of the areas of these regions equals the area of the given region. (390)
4. Formulas for areas of polygons and circles:

   Rectangle $A = \ell w$ (390)
   Square $A = s^2$ (391)
   Parallelogram $A = bh$ (394)
   Triangle $A = \frac{1}{2}bh$ (395)
   Trapezoid $A = \frac{1}{2}h(b_1 + b_2)$ (395)
   Regular Polygon $A = \frac{1}{2}ap$ (400)
   Circle $A = \pi r^2$ (405)

5. Theorem 11-5: A polygon is regular if and only if a circle inscribed in the polygon and a circle circumscribed about the polygon have the same center. (399)
6. Theorem 11-6: If a segment is an apothem of a regular polygon, then it is perpendicular to a side of the polygon at the point of tangency with the inscribed circle. (400)

7. Theorem 11-8:   If a regular polygon has n sides, then the degree measure of each central angle is $\frac{360}{n}$.   (401)
8. Circumference of a Circle (Theorem 11-9):   If a circle has a circumference of C units and a radius of r units, then $C = 2\pi r$.   (405)
9. Definition of Area of a Sector of a Circle: If a sector of a circle has an area of A square units, a central angle measurement of N degrees, and a radius of r units, then $A = \frac{N}{360}\pi r^2$.   (406)
10. Volume Postulate (Postulate 11-5):   For any solid region and a given unit of measure, there is a unique positive number called the measure of the volume of the region.   (419)
11. Postulate 11-6:   If two solid regions are congruent, then they have equal volumes.   (419)
12. Volume Addition Postulate (Postulate 11-7):   If a solid region is separated into nonoverlapping regions, then the sum of the volumes of these regions equals the volume of the given region.   (419)
13. Cavalieri's Principle (Postulate 11-9):   If two solids have the same cross-sectional area at every level, and the same height, then they have the same volume.   (424)
14. Formulas for areas and volumes of solids:

Prism	Cylinder	Circular Cone
$L = ph$ (411)	$L = 2\pi rh$ (412)	$L = \pi r\ell$ (416)
$T = ph + 2B$ (411)	$T = 2\pi rh + 2\pi r^2$ (412)	$T = \pi r\ell + \pi r^2$ (416)
$V = Bh$ (420)	$V = \pi r^2 h$ (420)	$V = \frac{1}{3}Bh$ (423)

Regular Pyramid	Sphere
$L = \frac{1}{2}p\ell$ (415)	$A = 4\pi r^2$ (417)
$V = \frac{1}{3}Bh$ (423)	$V = \frac{4}{3}\pi r^3$ (423)

Chapter Review

Answers to the following exercises have been rounded at the final step.

Find the area for each of the following. Round answers to the nearest tenth.

11-1
1. a rectangle with length of 6 feet and width of 4 feet 24 ft²
2. a parallelogram with height of 4 feet and base of 10 feet 40 ft²

11-2
3. a right triangle with a base of 6 meters and a hypotenuse of 10 meters 24 m²
4. an equilateral triangle with each side 16 centimeters long 110.9 cm²
5. a trapezoid with bases of 14 feet and 12 feet, and a height of 10 feet 130 ft²
6. a rhombus with diagonals of 12 inches and 20 inches 120 in²

11-3
7. a square inscribed in a circle with radius of 25 centimeters 1250 cm²
8. a regular hexagon with an apothem of 20 centimeters 1385.6 cm²
9. a regular hexagon with a side of 32 centimeters 2660.4 cm²
10. a square circumscribed about a circle with radius of 8 inches 256 in²

Solve each problem. Use 3.14 to approximate π and round answers to the nearest tenth.

11-4

11. Find the circumference of a circle with a radius of 9.6 meters. 60.3 m

12. Find the area of a circle with a radius of 9.6 meters. 289.4 m²

13. Find the area of a sector of a circle, if the measurement of the central angle is 72° and the radius of the circle is 5 inches. 15.7 in²

14. Find the area of a circle inscribed in a square whose diagonal is 5.7 cm. 12.8 cm²

11-5

15. Find the lateral area of a regular octagonal prism if its base has sides of 2 centimeters and its height is 3 centimeters. 48 cm²

16. Find the surface area of a right cylindrical gas tank if it is 7 meters tall and has a diameter of 11 meters. 431.8 m²

11-6

17. Find the total surface area of a square pyramid, if each side is 3 centimeters long and its slant height is 6 centimeters. 45 cm²

18. Find the total surface area of a right circular cone with a radius of 5 feet and a slant height of 13 feet. 282.6 ft²

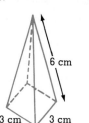

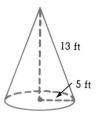

19. Find the surface area of the moon if its diameter is approximately 2160 miles. 14,649,984 mi²

11-7

20. Find the volume of a hexagonal prism if its radius is 10 centimeters and its height is 20 centimeters. 5196.2 cm³

21. Find the volume of a right circular cone if its radius is 10 centimeters and its height is 20 centimeters. 2093.3 cm³

11-8

22. Find the volume of a triangular pyramid if its base is an equilateral triangle with sides 9 centimeters long and its height is 15 centimeters. 175.4 cm³

23. Find the volume of a right circular cone if its height is 22 centimeters and its radius is 11 centimeters. 2786.2 cm³

24. Find the volume of the sphere shown below. 33,493.3 ft³

25. Find the volume of a right circular cone if the circumference of the base is 62.8 millimeters and the height is 15 millimeters. 1570 mm³

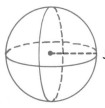

Sphere with radius of 20 feet

Chapter Test

Answers to the following exercises have been rounded at the final step.

Find the area for each of the following. Round answers to the nearest tenth. Use 3.14 to approximate π.

1.

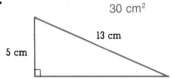

7.1 mm

9.2 mm   65.3 mm²

2.

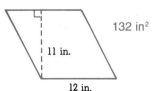

132 in²

11 in.

12 in.

3.

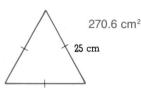

270.6 cm²

25 cm

4.

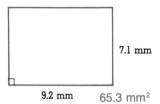

30 cm²

13 cm

5 cm

5.

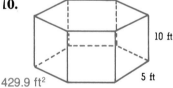

15 ft

584.6 ft²

6.

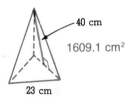

21.7 in²

2.5 in.

7. a circle with a diameter of 4 inches   12.6 in²

8. a circle inscribed in a square with a diagonal of 21.5 centimeters   181.4 cm²

9. a sector of a circle, if the measurement of the central angle is 30° and the radius of the circle is 3 feet   2.4 ft²

Find the total surface area for each figure. Round answers to the nearest tenth. Use 3.14 to approximate π. Assume that the bases of each pyramid or prism are regular.

10.

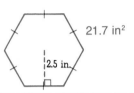

10 ft

5 ft

429.9 ft²

11.

471 ft²

10 ft

5 ft

12.

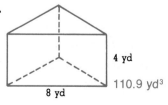

40 cm

1609.1 cm²

23 cm

13. a right circular cone with a radius of 27 millimeters and a height of 30 millimeters   5710.9 mm²

14. a regular square pyramid with base sides of 4 inches and a height of 6 inches   66.6 in²

Find the volume for each figure. Round answers to the nearest tenth. Use 3.14 to approximate π. Assume that the bases of each pyramid or prism are regular.

15.

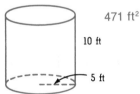

4 yd

8 yd   110.9 yd³

16.

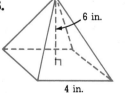

6 in.

32 in³

4 in.

17.

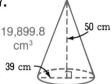

19,899.8 cm³

50 cm

39 cm

18. a right cylinder with a diameter of 39 centimeters and a height of 50 centimeters   59,699.3 cm³

19. a sphere with radius of 18 millimeters   24,416.6 mm³

The following questions each consists of two quantities, one in Column A and one in Column B. Compare the two quantities and write your answer as follows:

Write A if the quantity in Column A is greater.

Write B if the quantity in Column B is greater.

Write C if the two quantities are equal.

Write D if there is not enough information.

All variables represent real numbers. A symbol appearing in both columns represents the same quantity in Column A as it does in Column B.

In some questions, information concerning one or both of the quantities to be compared is centered above the two columns. Geometric figures may *not* be drawn to scale.

Example	
Column A	**Column B**

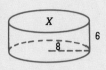

| volume of cylinder *A* | volume of cylinder *B* |

The formula for the volume of a cylinder is $V = \pi r^2 h$.

cylinder *X*	cylinder *Y*
$V = \pi \cdot 8^2 \cdot 6$	$V = \pi \cdot 6^2 \cdot 8$
$= 384\pi$	$= 288\pi$

Thus, the answer is **A**. Note it was not necessary to compute π.

Column A	Column B

1. C

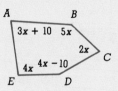

$m \angle A$ | | $m \angle G$

---

2. B

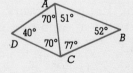

BC | | DC

---

3. D the area of a circle with diameter 10 | the area of a right triangle with hypotenuse 10

---

4. D

In $\triangle ABC$, $AB = 23$ and $AC = 7$.
In $\triangle DEF$, $DE = 17$ and $DF = 13$.

EF | | BC

	Column A		Column B

5. C

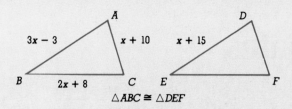

$3x - 3$	$x + 10$ $x + 15$
$2x + 8$	

$\triangle ABC \cong \triangle DEF$

FE	BC

---

6. C

The average of four
numbers is 21.

the sum of the four numbers	84

---

7. C

The area of a square
is 288 square inches.

the length of the diagonal	24 inches

---

8. A

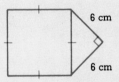

6 cm

6 cm

the area of the figure	54 in^2

---

9. D

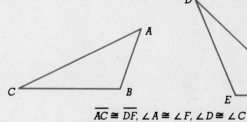

DE	$\overline{AC} \cong \overline{DF}, \angle A \cong \angle F, \angle D \cong \angle C$	AB

---

10. C

r $2r$

the lateral area of the cylinder	the surface area of the sphere

---

11. D

a given chord in a given circle	the radius of the same circle

---

12. C

$a:b = c:d$

ad	bc

CHAPTER 12

Coordinates

Maps are used by cross country skiers to determine the route they will take. Coordinates describe the skiers' route.

12-1 Graphing

Objectives: Name the ordered pair for a point on a graph; identify a linear equation; graph points and linear equations.

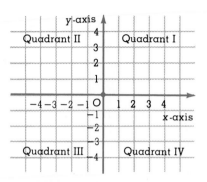

Ordered pairs of real numbers can be used to locate points in a plane. Two perpendicular number lines separate the plane into four regions called **quadrants.** The horizontal number line is called the **x-axis.** The vertical number line is called the **y-axis.** Their point of intersection is called the **origin** and named *O.* The plane is called the **coordinate plane.**

The two axes do not lie in any quadrant.
Emphasize this point.

Each ordered pair of numbers corresponds to exactly one point in the coordinate plane. The point is the **graph** for the ordered pair.

The figure at the right shows the graph of the ordered pair $(4, 2)$. The first component, 4, is called the **x-coordinate.** It tells the number of units the point lies to the left or right of the origin. The second component, 2, is called the **y-coordinate.** It tells the number of units the point lies above or below the origin.

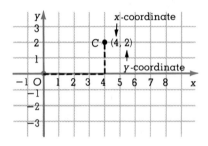

Emphasize the order of x and y in the ordered pair.

The origin has coordinates (0, 0).

Example

1 **Graph point *A* at $(2, -3)$.**

Start at *O.* Move 2 units to the right. Then, move 3 units down.

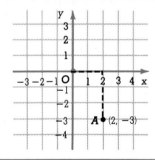

When graphing points, the following is true.

Each point in a coordinate real plane corresponds to exactly one ordered pair of real numbers. Each ordered pair of real numbers corresponds to exactly one point in a coordinate plane.	*Postulate 12-1* *Completeness Property for Points in the Real Plane*

You may want to have students graph ordered pairs of numbers using Logo. See page 545 for a discussion.

You may recall from your study of algebra that the solutions of $y = 2x - 1$ are ordered pairs of real numbers. By substituting different values for x in the equation you can find the corresponding values for y. Some of the solutions are shown in the table below.

x	$2x - 1$	y	(x, y)
-2	$2(-2) - 1$	-5	$(-2, -5)$
-1	$2(-1) - 1$	-3	$(-1, -3)$
0	$2(0) - 1$	-1	$(0, -1)$
1	$2(1) - 1$	1	$(1, 1)$
2	$2(2) - 1$	3	$(2, 3)$

For each value of x you choose, there is a corresponding value of y that satisfies the equation.

The solutions of $y = 2x - 1$ can also be shown by a graph. The figure at the left shows points for some of the solutions of $y = 2x - 1$. The figure at the right shows the line containing all the points whose ordered pairs are solutions of $y = 2x - 1$.

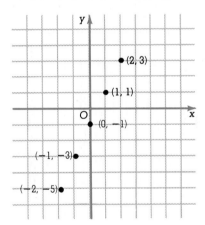
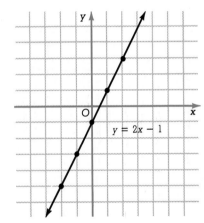

When you graph a set of ordered pairs, make sure all points can be shown on the same grid. When there are no labels on the axes, each unit is understood to represent an increment of one.

Point out the difference between the B in Ax + By = C and the b in y = mx + b.

An equation whose graph is a straight line is called a **linear equation**.

Tell students that $Ax + By = C$ is called the *standard form* of a linear equation.

An equation is linear if and only if it can be written in the form $Ax + By = C$, where A, B, and C are any real numbers, and A and B are not both 0.	*Definition of Linear Equation*

Students should understand that the equation need not appear in the form $Ax + By = C$.

The equations $5x + 6y = 8$, $3x = 4y + 9$, $5x - y = \dfrac{1}{2}$, and $x = 4$ are linear equations. Each can be written in the form $Ax + By = C$. The equations $4x + 5y^2 = 7$ and $\dfrac{1}{y} + x = 3$ are *not* linear equations. Why?

$Ax + By = C$ is called standard form.

The first is a second degree equation. The second equation has the $\dfrac{1}{y}$ or y^{-1} term.

436 *Coordinates*

Example

2 Graph $y = 3x - 3$.

Make a table of values of x and y. Graph the ordered pairs and connect them with a line.

x	y
-2	-9
-1	-6
0	-3
1	0
2	3

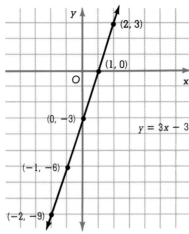

The equation $y = 3x - 3$ can be written in the form $3x - y = 3$. Therefore, it is a linear equation and the graph is a line.

According to Postulate 1-1, two points determine a line. Therefore, to graph any equation, simply find two ordered pairs that satisfy the linear equation. Then, graph the ordered pairs and connect the points with a line.

Students should be encouraged to find a third ordered pair as a check.

Example

3 Graph $3x + 2y = 4$.

First transform the equation so that y is on one side by itself.

$$3x + 2y = 4$$
$$2y = 4 - 3x$$
$$y = \frac{4 - 3x}{2}$$

The equation $3x + 2y = 4$ is a linear equation. The graph is a line.

Then, make a table of values of x and y. Graph the ordered pairs and connect them with a line.

x	y
0	2
2	-1
4	-4

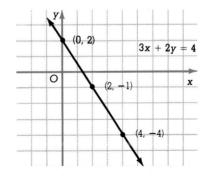

Exploratory Exercises

Name the ordered pair for each point on the graph below.

1. A $(-6, 4)$
2. I $(-1, -4)$
3. F $(-6, -5)$
4. W $(8, 4)$
5. P $(1, 5)$
6. X $(8, -5)$
7. Q $(3, 3)$
8. S $(0, -5)$
9. B $(-4, -3)$
10. C $(-5, 0)$
11. M $(4, 0)$
12. N $(3, -3)$

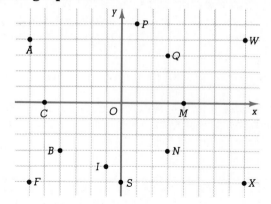

Determine whether each of the following is a linear equation. Write *yes* or *no*.

13. $3x + 2y = 6$ yes
14. $y = 2x - 1$ yes
15. $y = 8$ yes
16. $3x + 4y^2 = 1$ no
17. $9x + 4y = -2$ yes
18. $\dfrac{1}{x} + \dfrac{3}{4}y = 7$ no

Written Exercises

Graph each of the following linear equations. For Exercises 1–18, see the Teacher Guide.

1. $y = 2x$
2. $x + y = 5$
3. $x + 2y = 6$
4. $4x - 3y = 0$
5. $y = 4x$
6. $x + y = -4$
7. $x - 4y = -8$
8. $5x + 2y = 0$
9. $y = -x + 2$
10. $2x + y = 6$
11. $4x + 2y = 6$
12. $2x - 3y = 4$

Each of the following are the coordinates of three vertices of a rectangle. Graph them. Then, find each fourth vertex.

13. $(3, 1)$, $(3, -3)$, $(-5, -3)$ $(-5, 1)$
14. $(1, 0)$, $(3, 0)$, $(3, 3)$ $(1, 3)$
15. $(-3, 4)$, $(5, 4)$, $(5, -3)$ $(-3, -3)$
16. $(2, -2)$, $(-2, -2)$, $(-2, -5)$ $(2, -5)$
17. $(2, 0)$, $(0, 2)$, $(-4, -2)$ $(-2, -4)$
18. $(-1, 0)$, $(1, 1)$, $(0, 3)$ $(-2, 2)$

State which of the ordered pairs given are *not* solutions of the equation.

19. $y = 4x - 8$ b, d   **a.** $(2, 0)$ **b.** $(-2, 0)$ **c.** $(1, -4)$ **d.** $(3, 6)$
20. $3x + 4y - 2 = 0$ a, c   **a.** $(1, 1)$ **b.** $\left(4, -2\frac{1}{2}\right)$ **c.** $\left(4, -3\frac{1}{2}\right)$ **d.** $\left(0, \frac{1}{2}\right)$
21. $x = 5$ b, d   **a.** $(5, 2)$ **b.** $(3, 1)$ **c.** $(5, -10)$ **d.** $(4, 5)$
22. $y = -3$ b, d   **a.** $(0, -3)$ **b.** $(-3, 0)$ **c.** $(-4, -3)$ **d.** $(-3, -4)$
23. $y = -2x - 3$ b   **a.** $(0, -3)$ **b.** $(2, 1)$ **c.** $(-2, 1)$ **d.** $\left(-\frac{1}{2}, -2\right)$
24. $2x - y + 2 = 0$ a, c, d   **a.** $(1, 1)$ **b.** $(2, 6)$ **c.** $(-2, 2)$ **d.** $(0, 1)$

Challenge Exercise

25. If a convex area of 12 square units is bounded by the lines $x = 2$, $x = 5$, $y = 0$, and $y = mx + 5$, find the value for m. $-\frac{2}{7}$

12-2 Distances and Midpoints

Objectives: Find the distance between points; find the midpoint of a segment.

In a coordinate plane consider two points A and C with coordinates $(-3, -1)$, and $(1, -1)$. These points lie on a horizontal line. You use *absolute value* to find the distance between points A and C.

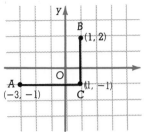

$AC = |-3 - 1| = |-4|$ or 4   *Find the difference of the x-coordinates.*

The points B and C with coordinates $(1, 2)$ and $(1, -1)$ lie on a vertical line. The distance between points B and C is 3 units.

$BC = |2 - (-1)| = |3|$ or 3   *Find the difference of the y-coordinates.*

Notice that the segment connecting A and B is neither horizontal nor vertical. The distance between A and B can be found by using the Pythagorean Theorem.   A review of absolute value may be helpful.

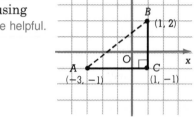

$$(AB)^2 = (AC)^2 + (BC)^2$$
$$= |-3 - 1|^2 + |2 - (-1)|^2$$
$$= 4^2 + 3^2$$
$$= 16 + 9$$
$$= 25$$
$$AB = \sqrt{25} \text{ or } 5 \qquad \textit{Distance is positive.}$$

Emphasize that distance is always positive.

Example

1 **Find the distance between the points with coordinates $(-2, 3)$ and $(5, -3)$.**

A vertical line through $(-2, 3)$ and a horizontal line through $(5, -3)$ intersect at $(-2, -3)$. These three points are the vertices of a right triangle, $\triangle ABC$. The length of the hypotenuse is the distance between $(-2, 3)$ and $(5, -3)$.
Now, use the Pythagorean Theorem.

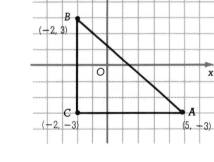

$$(AB)^2 = (AC)^2 + (BC)^2$$
$$(AB)^2 = |5 - (-2)|^2 + |3 - (-3)|^2$$
$$= 7^2 + 6^2$$
$$= 49 + 36$$
$$= 85$$
$$AB = \sqrt{85} \qquad \textit{This is approximately 9.22.}$$

The Pythagorean Theorem can be used to develop a general formula for finding the distance between two points in a plane.

Suppose (x_1, y_1) and (x_2, y_2) are coordinates of the endpoints of $\overline{BA}$. Form a right triangle, $\triangle ABC$, by drawing a vertical line through (x_1, y_1) and a horizontal line through (x_2, y_2). These lines intersect at (x_1, y_2).

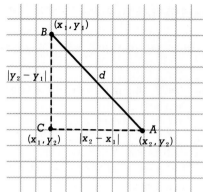

Point out that the right triangle could also be formed by locating point C at (x_2, y_1).

$(BA)^2 = (AC)^2 + (CB)^2$
$\quad d^2 = |x_2 - x_1|^2 + |y_2 - y_1|^2$
$\quad d^2 = (x_2 - x_1)^2 + (y_2 - y_1)^2$
$\quad\ d = \sqrt{(x_2 - x_1)^2 + (y_2 - y_1)^2}$

x_1 is read "x sub one."
y_1 is read "y sub one."

The distance between two points with coordinates (x_1, y_1) and (x_2, y_2) is given by the following formula.
$$d = \sqrt{(x_2 - x_1)^2 + (y_2 - y_1)^2}$$

Theorem 12-1
Distance Formula

Compare the Distance Formula with the Pythagorean Theorem.

Example

2 **Use the Distance Formula to find the distance between the points with coordinates $(-1, 6)$ and $(5, -4)$.**

$d = \sqrt{(x_2 - x_1)^2 + (y_2 - y_1)^2}$ *Let $x_2 = 5$, $x_1 = -1$, $y_2 = -4$, and $y_1 = 6$.*
$\ = \sqrt{[5 - (-1)]^2 + (-4 - 6)^2}$
$\ = \sqrt{(6)^2 + (-10)^2}$
$\ = \sqrt{36 + 100}$
$\ = \sqrt{136}$
$\ = 2\sqrt{34}$ *The distance is $2\sqrt{34}$ units.*

The Distance Formula can be used to show that a given point on a segment is the midpoint of that segment.

Example 3 assumes that $(3, 1)$ is on the line segment.

Example

3 **Show that the point represented by $(3, 1)$ is the midpoint of a segment having endpoints whose coordinates are $(6, -1)$ and $(0, 3)$.**

distance between $(3, 1)$ and $(6, -1)$
$d = \sqrt{(6 - 3)^2 + (-1 - 1)^2}$
$\ = \sqrt{(3)^2 + (-2)^2}$
$\ = \sqrt{9 + 4}$
$\ = \sqrt{13}$

distance between $(3, 1)$ and $(0, 3)$
$d = \sqrt{(0 - 3)^2 + (3 - 1)^2}$
$\ = \sqrt{(-3)^2 + (2)^2}$
$\ = \sqrt{9 + 4}$
$\ = \sqrt{13}$

The Distance Formula also can be used to find the coordinates of the midpoint of a segment.

Example

4 **Find the coordinates of M, the midpoint of a segment having endpoints whose coordinates are (2, 3) and (6, 7).**

Form trapezoid $ABQP$ by drawing vertical segments through A, through B, and through M to the x-axis. Since $\overline{MR}$ is the median of the trapezoid, R is the midpoint of $\overline{PQ}$. Thus, the x-coordinate of R is also the x-coordinate of M. Use the Definition of Midpoint to find the x-coordinate of M.

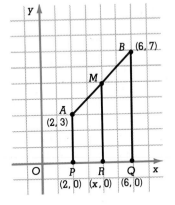

$$PR = RQ$$
$$x - 2 = 6 - x$$
$$2x = 2 + 6$$
$$x = \frac{2 + 6}{2}$$

Point out that the x-coordinate of the midpoint is the sum of the x-coordinates divided by 2.

$x = \dfrac{8}{2}$ or 4   *The x-coordinate of M is 4.*

To find the y-coordinate of M, form trapezoid $ABCD$ by drawing horizontal segments through A, through B, and through M to the y-axis. Since $\overline{MG}$ is the median of the trapezoid, G is the midpoint of $\overline{CD}$. Thus, the y-coordinate of G is also the y-coordinate of M. Use the Definition of Midpoint to find the y-coordinate of G.

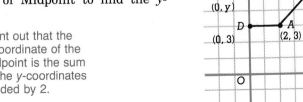

$$CG = GD$$
$$7 - y = y - 3$$
$$7 + 3 = 2y$$
$$\frac{7 + 3}{2} = y$$

Point out that the y-coordinate of the midpoint is the sum of the y-coordinates divided by 2.

$y = \dfrac{10}{2}$ or 5   *The y-coordinate of M is 5.*

The coordinates of M are (4, 5).

Example 4 and many other similar examples suggest the following theorem.

If the coordinates of A and B are (x_1, y_1) and (x_2, y_2) respectively, then the midpoint M of $\overline{AB}$ has coordinates $\left(\dfrac{x_1 + x_2}{2}, \dfrac{y_1 + y_2}{2}\right)$.	*Theorem 12-2* *Midpoint Formula*

Exploratory Exercises

Find the distance between each of the following pairs of points.

1. (5, 0), (12, 0) 7

2. (0, 3), (0, 6) 3

3. (−6, 0), (−2, 0) 4

4. (1, 2), (3, 4) $2\sqrt{2}$

5. (2, 3), (5, 7) 5

6. (−1, −2), (−3, −4) $2\sqrt{2}$

Find the coordinates of the midpoint of each segment that has endpoints with the following coordinates.

7. (0, 4), (0, 0) (0, 2)

8. (6, 0), (13, 0) $\left(\frac{19}{2}, 0\right)$

9. (−3, 2), (−5, 6) (−4, 4)

10. (−1, −2), (−3, −6) (−2, −4)

11. (4, 6), (−2, −3) $\left(1, \frac{3}{2}\right)$

12. (−1, −7), (6, 1) $\left(\frac{5}{2}, −3\right)$

Written Exercises

In each of the following the coordinates of the endpoints of a segment are given. Find the distance between each pair of points and the coordinates of the midpoint of each segment. For Exercises 1–12, see the Teacher Guide.

1. (2, 3), (8, 9)

2. (15, 0), (0, 15)

3. (1, 1), (8, 8)

4. (−7, −5), (−10, −9)

5. (0, 3), (5, 7)

6. (4, 6), (0, −4)

7. (6, 0), (−4, −8)

8. (0, 0), (p, q)

9. (a, c), (c, a)

10. (0, r), (0, −r)

11. (4, a), (−8, b)

12. (0.2, 0.7), (0.4, 0.9)

Answer each of the following.

13. The vertices of a rectangle have the coordinates (4, 1), (−5, 1), (−5, −3), and (4, −3). Find the perimeter and area of the rectangle. 26, 36

14. Find the measure of each diagonal of the rectangle in Exercise 13. $\sqrt{97}$ for each diagonal

15. Find the coordinates of the center of a circle whose diameter has endpoints with coordinates (−6, −8), and (5, 7). (−0.5, −0.5)

16. The center of a circle has coordinates (−8, 3). One endpoint of a diameter has coordinates (5, 4). Find the coordinates of the other endpoint of the diameter. (−21, 2)

17. The coordinates of two of the vertices of an equilateral triangle are (0, 0) and (0, 5). Find the coordinates of the third vertex. $\left(\frac{5}{2}\sqrt{3}, \frac{5}{2}\right)$ or $\left(−\frac{5}{2}\sqrt{3}, \frac{5}{2}\right)$

18. In △ABC, A(2, 4), B(−3, 6), and C(−8, −7) are coordinates of the vertices. Find the coordinates of the point of intersection of each median with its corresponding side and the measure of each median. $\left(−\frac{1}{2}, 5\right), \frac{3}{2}\sqrt{89}; \left(−\frac{11}{2}, −\frac{1}{2}\right), \frac{3}{2}\sqrt{34}; \left(−3, −\frac{3}{2}\right), \frac{15}{2}$

19. Find the coordinates of the points that trisect a segment whose endpoints have coordinates (−4, 5) and (5, −1). (−1, 3), (2, 1)

Excursions in Geometry _____ Polar Coordinates

Points in a real plane can also be identified using **polar coordinates**. A fixed point in the plane is called the **pole** or origin. The polar axis is a ray whose initial point is the pole. Every point P in the plane can be located using polar coordinates of the form (r, θ), in which r represents the distance from the pole to P and θ is the angle of rotation of $\overrightarrow{OP}$ from the polar axis.

θ is a Greek letter pronounced "thay-ta."

The figure at the right shows the graph of point P that has polar coordinates (2, 60°).

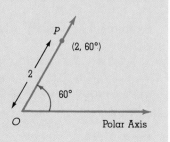

12-3 Slope

Objectives: Describe the slope of a line; determine the slope of a line from a table and pairs of points; find the coordinate of a point if given the slope and a point.

A staircase has two parts, the stringers and the steps. The stringers slope from one floor to the next and support the steps. The vertical and horizontal measurements of the stairs affect the steepness of the stringers.

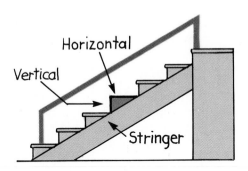

The measure of the **slope,** or steepness, of a line is found by comparing the change in vertical units to the change in horizontal units. For example, in the graph of $y = 2x$, a vertical change of 2 units is accompanied by a horizontal change of 1 unit.

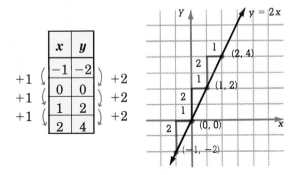

Notice that the vertical change is the difference of the y-coordinates and the horizontal change is the difference of the corresponding x-coordinates. A ratio is used to compare the two differences.

Students may refer to the vertical and horizontal changes as the rise and the run respectively.

$$\text{slope} = \frac{\text{difference of the } y\text{-coordinates}}{\text{difference of the corresponding } x\text{-coordinates}}$$

$$= \frac{2}{1} \text{ or } 2$$

Emphasize that the difference of corresponding coordinates must be found.

The slope of a line containing two points with coordinates (x_1, y_1) and (x_2, y_2) is given by the following formula.

$$m = \frac{y_2 - y_1}{x_2 - x_1} \text{ where } x_2 \neq x_1$$

Definition of Slope

Point out that $m = \frac{y_1 - y_2}{x_1 - x_2}$ is true also.

Example

1 Determine the slope of each of the following lines.

a.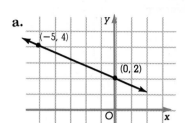

b.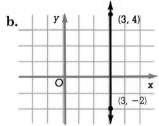

c.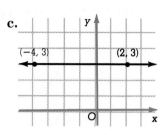

a. $m = \dfrac{y_2 - y_1}{x_2 - x_1}$

$= \dfrac{2 - 4}{0 - (-5)}$

$= \dfrac{-2}{5}$

$= -\dfrac{2}{5}$

The slope is $-\dfrac{2}{5}$.

b. $m = \dfrac{y_2 - y_1}{x_2 - x_1}$

$= \dfrac{-2 - 4}{3 - 3}$

$= \dfrac{-6}{0}$

The slope is undefined.

c. $m = \dfrac{y_2 - y_1}{x_2 - x_1}$

$= \dfrac{3 - 3}{2 - (-4)}$

$= \dfrac{0}{6}$

$= 0$

The slope is 0.

These and many other similar examples suggest that the following conclusions about slope can be made.

If the line *rises* from the left to the right, then the slope of the line is *positive*.

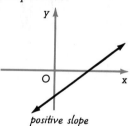

positive slope

If the line *falls* from the left to the right, then the slope of the line is *negative*.

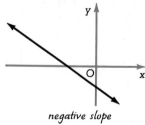

negative slope

Several chalkboard examples can be used to reinforce these concepts and aid in the recognition of these cases by students.

If the line is *vertical*, then the slope of the line is *undefined*.

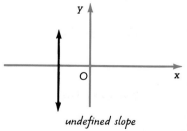

undefined slope

If the line is *horizontal*, then the slope of the line is *0*.

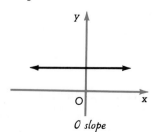

0 slope

Emphasize the difference between an undefined slope and a slope of 0.

Examples

2 The following lines are parallel. Determine the slope of each line.

slope of $\ell = \dfrac{0 - (-4)}{-2 - (-3)}$

$\qquad = \dfrac{4}{1}$ or 4

slope of $m = \dfrac{4 - 0}{4 - 3}$

$\qquad = \dfrac{4}{1}$ or 4

Notice that the slopes are the same.

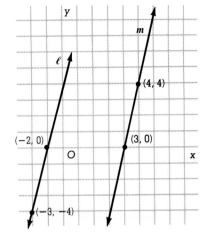

3 The following lines are perpendicular. Determine the slope of each line.

slope of $a = \dfrac{4 - (-3)}{1 - (-1)}$

$\qquad = \dfrac{7}{2}$

slope of $b = \dfrac{3 - 1}{-4 - 3}$

$\qquad = \dfrac{2}{-7}$ or $-\dfrac{2}{7}$

$\dfrac{7}{2} \cdot \left(-\dfrac{2}{7}\right) = -1$

Notice that the product of their slopes is -1.

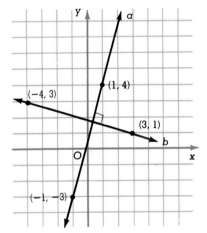

Discuss why nonvertical is part of Theorem 12-4.

In general, the following theorems can be stated.

Remind students that the slope of vertical lines is undefined.

Two lines have the same slope if and only if they are parallel and nonvertical.	*Theorem 12-3*
Two nonvertical lines are perpendicular if and only if the product of their slopes is -1.	*Theorem 12-4*

Illustrate these theorems with other examples similar to Examples 2 and 3.

Exploratory Exercises

Describe the slope of each of the following lines.

1. vertical lines undefined slope
2. horizontal lines zero slope
3. nonvertical perpendicular lines
4. nonvertical parallel lines
5. lines that rise to the right positive slope
6. lines that fall to the right negative slope

3. The product of their slopes is -1.
4. The slopes are equal.

For each table, state the change in y and the change in x. Then, determine the slope of the line passing through the points whose coordinates are listed in each table.

7.
x	0	1	2	3
y	0	2	4	6

8.
x	-2	-1	0	1
y	2	1	0	-1

9.
x	6	3	0	-3
y	-8	-4	0	4

10.
x	4	3	2	1
y	4	3	2	1

For Exercises 7–10, see the Teacher Guide.

State the slope of a line parallel to a line passing through each pair of points.

11. $(1, 2)$, $(4, -6)$ $-\frac{8}{3}$
12. $(3, -1)$, $(4, 2)$ 3
13. $(-7, 5)$, $(1, 1)$ $-\frac{1}{2}$
14. $(1, 6)$, $(-2, -2)$ $\frac{8}{3}$

State the slope of a line perpendicular to a line passing through each pair of points.

15. $(3, 2)$, $(1, 5)$ $\frac{2}{3}$
16. $(-1, -1)$, $(3, 2)$ $-\frac{4}{3}$
17. $(1, 8)$, $(-2, -3)$ $-\frac{3}{11}$
18. $(5, 6)$, $(2, 1)$ $-\frac{3}{5}$

Written Exercises

Find the slope of the lines passing through the pairs of points whose coordinates are listed below.

1. $(4, 6)$, $(3, 4)$ 2
2. $(-7, 4)$, $(2, 9)$ $\frac{5}{9}$
3. $(6, 3)$, $(-7, 3)$ 0
4. $(-4, 11)$, $(-6, 3)$ 4
5. $(6, 9)$, $(4, 6)$ $\frac{3}{2}$
6. $(4, 8)$, $(4, 6)$ undefined slope
7. $(-8, 1)$, $(-5, -8)$ -3
8. $(3, -2)$, $(5, -9)$ $-\frac{7}{2}$

Determine the value of r so that a line through the points with the given coordinates has the slope listed.

9. $(r, -5)$, $(5, 3)$; slope $= \frac{2}{3}$ -7
10. $(9, r)$, $(6, 3)$; slope $= -\frac{1}{3}$ 2
11. $(8, r)$, $(12, 6)$; slope $= \frac{1}{2}$ 4
12. $(r, 3)$, $(5, 9)$; slope $= 2$ 2

Answer each of the following for $\triangle ABC$ whose vertices are $A(3, 2)$, $B(6, -3)$, and $C(1, -2)$.

13. Find the slope of the median to $\overline{AC}$. $-\frac{3}{4}$
14. Find the slope of the median to $\overline{BC}$. -9
15. Find the slope of the median to $\overline{AB}$. $\frac{3}{7}$
16. Change the coordinates for B so that $\triangle ABC$ is a right triangle. See the Teacher Guide.

Answer each of the following.

17. Find the value of y if the points $A(1, 4)$, $B(3, 2)$, and $C(8, y)$ are collinear. (Hint: Use slope.) -3

18. Find the slope of any line parallel to a line passing through points with coordinates of $(4, -3)$ and $(-8, 10)$. $-\frac{13}{12}$

19. Find the slope of any line perpendicular to the line passing through points with coordinates $(3, 8)$ and $(-7, -12)$. $-\frac{1}{2}$

20. $\overline{AB}$: $\frac{4}{3}$, $\overline{CD}$: $\frac{4}{3}$, $\overline{BC}$: $-\frac{3}{4}$, $\overline{AD} = -\frac{3}{4}$

20. Find the slope of each side of quadrilateral $ABCD$ to determine if it is a rectangle. The vertices are $A(2, 4)$, $B(5, 8)$, $C(13, 2)$, and $D(10, -2)$.

21. Are the graphs of $3x + 4y = 7$ and $6x + 8y = 10$ parallel?

   Yes, the slopes are both $-\frac{3}{4}$.

22. Are the graphs of $2x + 5y = 15$ and $5x + 2y = 2$ perpendicular?

   No, since $-\frac{2}{5} \cdot -\frac{5}{2} \neq -1$.

Topics in Geometry

When a marching band performs a half-time show at a football game, the members often march the same distance. But to completely describe their change in position, it is necessary to give the direction of the marching as well as the distance moved. This can be represented on the coordinate plane as shown below.

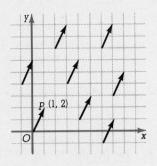

Point out that a vector is not a ray.

The vector from O to P may be represented by $\overrightarrow{OP}$.

A change in position can be described mathematically using a vector. A vector is a quantity that possesses both magnitude and direction. Geometrically, a vector is represented as a directed line segment. Since vectors having the same magnitude and direction are equal, all of the vectors in the graph above are equal.

Algebraically, a vector is represented using ordered pairs of real numbers. In the graph above, the ordered pair $(1, 2)$ represents the vector from the origin $(0, 0)$ to the point $(1, 2)$ because $(1, 2) = (1 - 0, 2 - 0)$. How should the other vectors be represented? The following definition will help you decide.

Suppose $P_1(x_1, y_1)$ is the initial point of a vector, and $P_2(x_2, y_2)$ is the terminal point. A single ordered pair that represents $\overrightarrow{P_1P_2}$ is given by the following.

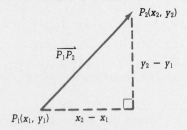

$$\overrightarrow{P_1P_2} = (x_2 - x_1, y_2 - y_1)$$

Note the similarity between this ordered pair and the definition of slope.

For each vector represented in the graph above, the difference in x-coordinates is 1, and the difference in y-coordinates is 2. Therefore, each vector on the graph can be represented by the ordered pair $(1, 2)$.

Exercises
You may want to ask students if $\overrightarrow{AB}$ and $\overrightarrow{BA}$ are equal.

For each pair of points A and B, find an ordered pair that represents $\overrightarrow{AB}$.

1. $A(1, 3)$; $B(-2, 5)$ $(-3, 2)$ **2.** $A(7, 7)$; $B(-2, -2)$ $(-9, -9)$ **3.** $A(5, 0)$; $B(7, 6)$ $(2, 6)$

4. $A(0, 5)$; $B(-5, 0)$ $(-5, -5)$ **5.** $A(5, -6)$; $B(6, -5)$ $(1, 1)$ **6.** $A(-4, -3)$; $B(-9, 2)$ $(-5, 5)$

12-4 Equations for a Line

Objectives: Determine the slope and y-intercept from the equation of a line; rewrite an equation in slope-intercept form; write the equation of a line satisfying certain given conditions.

The graph of $y = 3x + 2$ is shown below.

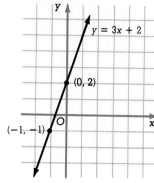

Notice that $(0, 2)$ and $(-1, -1)$ represent points on the line. The coordinates can be used to find the slope of the line.

$$m = \frac{-1 - 2}{-1 - 0}$$

$$= \frac{-3}{-1} \text{ or } 3$$

Compare the slope of the line to the coefficient of x in $y = 3x + 2$. The graph of $y = 3x + 2$ crosses the y-axis when y is 2. This value, 2, is called the **y-intercept** of the line.

In general, most linear equations can be written in the form $y = mx + b$. The slope of the line is m and its y-intercept is b. This form is called the **slope-intercept form**.

Emphasize that "m" represents the slope and "b" represents the y-intercept.

The equation of the line having a slope m and y-intercept b is $y = mx + b$.	*Theorem 12-5* *Slope-Intercept Form*

Point out the difference between the b in $y = mx + b$ and the B in $Ax + By = C$.

Examples

1 Write the equation of the line having a slope of 4 and y-intercept −3.

Substitute the values for slope and y-intercept into the slope-intercept form.

$$y = mx + b$$
$$= 4x + (-3) \qquad \text{Substitute 4 for m and } -3 \text{ for b.}$$
$$= 4x - 3$$

The equation is $y = 4x - 3$.

2 Name the slope and y-intercept of $5x + 3y = 6$.

Rewrite the equation in slope-intercept form.

$$5x + 3y = 6$$
$$3y = -5x + 6 \qquad \text{Subtraction Property of Equality}$$
$$y = -\frac{5}{3}x + 2 \qquad \text{Division Property of Equality}$$

The slope is $-\frac{5}{3}$. The y-intercept is 2.

Suppose the slope and the coordinates of one point of a line are known. For example, in the figure at the right, the slope of the line is 4 and the coordinates of one point on the line are (2, 3). Using this information, it is possible to determine the equation of the line. Let (x, y) be the coordinates of another point on the line. Substitute the known values into the following expression.

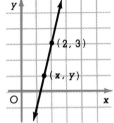

$$m = \frac{y_2 - y_1}{x_2 - x_1} \qquad m = 4, x_1 = 2, y_1 = 3$$

$$4 = \frac{y - 3}{x - 2} \qquad \text{Substitution}$$

$$y - 3 = 4(x - 2) \qquad \text{Multiplication Property of Equality}$$

y-coordinate   slope x-coordinate

Point out that it is possible to rewrite the equation in slope-intercept form or standard form.

This equation is said to be in **point-slope form.** Notice where the slope and coordinates of the point appear in this form.

The equation of the line passing through the point whose coordinates are (x_1, y_1) and which has a slope m is $y - y_1 = m(x - x_1)$.	*Theorem 12-6* *Point-Slope Form*

Examples

3 **Find the equation of the line passing through the point whose coordinates are (−3, 2) and having a slope of 5. Write the equation in the point-slope form.**

Substitute −3, 2, and 5 into the point-slope form.

$$y - y_1 = m(x - x_1) \qquad \text{Point-Slope Form}$$
$$y - 2 = 5[x - (-3)] \qquad \text{Substitution}$$

4 **Find the equation of the line passing through points whose coordinates are (3, −6) and (−2, 1).**

Find the slope of the line.

$$m = \frac{y_2 - y_1}{x_2 - x_1} \qquad \text{Definition of Slope}$$
$$m = \frac{1 - (-6)}{-2 - 3} \qquad \text{Substitution}$$
$$= \frac{7}{-5}$$

Substitute either (3, −6) or (−2, 1) and $-\frac{7}{5}$ into the point-slope form.

$$y - y_1 = m(x - x_1) \qquad \text{Point-Slope Form} \qquad \text{Using the other point, } y - 1 = -\frac{7}{5}[x - (-2)].$$
$$y - (-6) = -\frac{7}{5}(x - 3) \qquad \text{Substitution}$$

This equation can also be written in standard form as $7x + 5y = -9$ or in slope-intercept form as $y = -\frac{7}{5}x - \frac{9}{5}$.

Demonstrate how these equations can be derived.

Exploratory Exercises   ALL LEVELS: Mini Review

Determine the slope and y-intercept of the graph of each equation.

1. $y = -\frac{3}{4}x + 2$ $m = -\frac{3}{4}$, $b = 2$

2. $y = -3x + 5$ $m = -3$, $b = 5$

3. $y = 4x - 3$ $m = 4$, $b = -3$

4. $y = \frac{1}{2}x + 6$ $m = \frac{1}{2}$, $b = 6$

5. $y = 3x - 5$ $m = 3$, $b = -5$

6. $y = mx + b$ slope $= m$, y-intercept $= b$

7. $y = 6$ $m = 0$, $b = 6$

8. $x = -3$ undefined slope, no y-intercept

Write an equation of the line satisfying the given conditions.

9. $m = 6$, y-intercept is -5 $y = 6x - 5$

10. $m = -2$, y-intercept is 3 $y = -2x + 3$

11. $m = 4$, through a point at $(1, 3)$
    $y - 3 = 4(x - 1)$ or $y = 4x - 1$

12. $m = -7$, through a point at $(2, 4)$
    $y - 4 = -7(x - 2)$ or $y = -7x + 18$

Written Exercises

6. $y = 7x - 73$ 7. $y = -\frac{2}{3}x - \frac{10}{3}$ 8. $y = \frac{1}{5}x - \frac{13}{30}$

Write an equation of the line satisfying the given conditions.

1. $m = 2$, y-intercept is -3 $y = 2x - 3$

2. $m = -\frac{1}{3}$, y-intercept is 0.4 $y = -\frac{1}{3}x + 0.4$

3. $m = -4$, y-intercept is 7 $y = -4x + 7$

4. $m = 0$, y-intercept is -5 $y = -5$

5. $m = 0$, through a point at $(-4, 8)$ $y = 8$

6. $m = 7$, through a point at $(10, -3)$

7. $m = -\frac{2}{3}$, through a point at $(-2, -2)$

8. $m = \frac{1}{5}$, through a point at $\left(\frac{1}{2}, -\frac{1}{3}\right)$

9. parallel to the graph of $y = 3x + 4$, through a point at $(3, 7)$ $y = 3x - 2$

10. parallel to the y-axis, through a point at $(3, 9)$ $x = 3$

11. parallel to the x-axis, through a point at $(-3, -6)$ $y = -6$

12. parallel to the y-axis, through a point at $(2, 6)$ $x = 2$

13. perpendicular to the graph of $y = -2x + 1$, through a point $(3, -7)$ $y = \frac{1}{2}x - \frac{17}{2}$

14. perpendicular to the graph of $3x - 5y = 6$, through a point $(-4, -5)$ $y = -\frac{5}{3}x - \frac{35}{3}$

15. passing through points at $(-7, 4)$ and $(-7, -5)$ $x = -7$

16. passing through points at $(-3, -7)$ and $(6, -1)$ $y = \frac{2}{3}x - \frac{15}{3}$

Determine the slope and y-intercept of the graph of each equation.

17. $y = 5x - 3$ $m = 5$, $b = -3$

18. $y = \frac{1}{2}x + 6$ $m = \frac{1}{2}$, $b = 6$

19. $2x - y = 4$ $m = 2$, $b = -4$

20. $-9x + 3y = 6$ $m = 3$, $b = 2$

21. $4x - 3y = 5$ $m = \frac{4}{3}$, $b = -\frac{5}{3}$

22. $-6x + 5y = 7$ $m = \frac{6}{5}$, $b = \frac{7}{5}$

Answer each of the following.

23. Write the equation of a line that has a slope of -5 and bisects a segment whose endpoints have coordinates $(-4, 10)$ and $(5, -7)$. $y = -5x + 4$

24. Write the equation of a line that is the perpendicular bisector of a segment whose endpoints have coordinates $(-3, -7)$ and $(12, 14)$. $y = -\frac{5}{7}x + \frac{47}{7}$.

25. Write the equation of a line that bisects two segments, one whose endpoints have coordinates $(-2, -3)$ and $(-6, 5)$, and the other whose endpoints have coordinates $(1, 4)$ and $(-8, 7)$. $y = 9x + 37$

26. If a line passes through points at $(3, 6)$ and $(-4, 9)$, an equation of the line can be written as $y - 6 = -\frac{3}{7}(x - 3)$ or $y - 9 = -\frac{3}{7}(x + 4)$. Show that the two equations are equivalent.   See the Teacher Guide.

27. Two perpendicular lines meet at the point $(-3, 2)$. The equation of one line is $2x + 5y - 4 = 0$. Find the equation of the other line and express it in standard form. $5x - 2y = -19$

28. Find the y-intercept of the line through $(-5, 4)$ and $(1, -8)$. -6

29. Write an equation for the set of all points in a plane equidistant from $(3, -5)$ and $(-7, -3)$. $y = 5x + 6$

30. Find the coordinates of a point on the graph of $x + 2y = 11$ if the y-coordinate is 5 less than the x-coordinate. $(7, 2)$

Challenge Exercises

31. A line through the point $(-8, 0)$ cuts from the second quadrant a triangular region of area 120 square units. Find the equation of the line. $y = \frac{15}{4}x + 30$

32. Lines ℓ and m are symmetric to each other with respect to the line $y = x$. If the equation of line ℓ is $y = 3x - 5$, then find the equation of m. $y = \frac{1}{3}x + \frac{5}{3}$

mini-review

State the formula for each of the following.

11-6   **1.** surface area of a sphere $A = 4\pi r^2$

11-4   **2.** area of a circle $A = \pi r^2$

11-3   **3.** area of any regular polygon $A = \frac{1}{2}ap$

11-2   **4.** area of a trapezoid $A = \frac{1}{2}h(b_1 + b_2)$

11-2   **5.** area of a parallelogram $A = bh$

Statistics That Shape Your Life

Line graphs are often used to plot changes in data over a period of time. For example, the graph below shows the Dow Jones Industrial Average from August 2 to November 22.

You can use your knowledge of slope to quickly analyze the data. If the segment slopes up to the right, it indicates that the Average increased. The steeper the segment, the greater the increase. Similarly, if the segment slopes down to the right, it indicates that the Average decreased. If the segment is horizontal, it indicates no change.

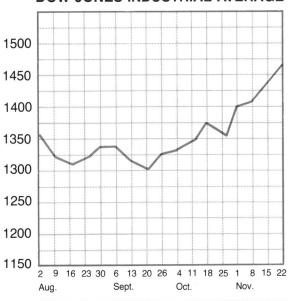

DOW JONES INDUSTRIAL AVERAGE

Exercises

1. During which week did the greatest increase in the Dow Jones Average take place? Oct. 25–Nov. 1

2. How many weeks did the Average decrease? 5

3. Name a week in which the Average did not change. Aug. 30–Sept. 6

4. What was the Dow Jones Industrial Average on November 1? 1400

12-5 Systems of Equations

Straight lines are used in architecture to create a pleasing design. In mathematics, graphs of lines are representations of relationships between two variables.

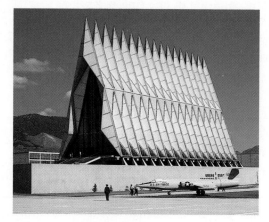

The graphs of $y = 2x + 1$ and $y = -2x + 5$ are shown below.

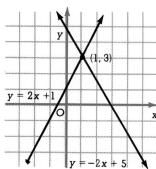

Notice that the graphs intersect at the point with coordinates $(1, 3)$. Since this point lies on the graph of each equation, its coordinates satisfy both $y = 2x + 1$ and $y = -2x + 5$. The equations $y = 2x + 1$ and $y = -2x + 5$ together are called a **system of equations.** The solution of this system of equations is $(1, 3)$.

You can check this algebraically by substituting $x = 1$ and $y = 3$ into both equations.

Example

1 **Graph the equations $x + y = 6$ and $y = 2x$. Then, find the solution of the system of equations.**

The graphs intersect at $(2, 4)$. Therefore, $(2, 4)$ is the solution of the system of equations $x + y = 6$ and $y = 2x$.

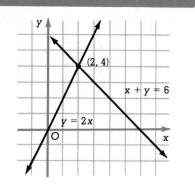

A system of equations can be solved by algebraic methods as well as by graphing. Two algebraic methods are the **substitution method** and the **elimination method.**

2 **Use substitution to solve the system of equations $y = x - 3$ and $3x + 5y = 9$.**

By the first equation, y is equal to $x - 3$. Therefore, $x - 3$ can be substituted for y in the second equation.

$$3x + 5y = 9$$
$$3x + 5(x - 3) = 9 \qquad \textit{Substitute } x - 3 \textit{ for y.}$$

The resulting equation has only one variable, x. Solve the equation.

$$3x + 5x - 15 = 9$$
$$8x - 15 = 9$$
$$8x = 24$$
$$x = 3 \qquad \textit{The x-coordinate is 3.}$$

Now, find y by substituting 3 for x in the first equation.

$$y = x - 3$$
$$y = 3 - 3 \qquad \textit{Substitute 3 for x.}$$
$$y = 0 \qquad \textit{The y-coordinate is 0.}$$

The solution is $(3, 0)$.   *Check in the original equations.*

3 **Use elimination to solve the system of equations $3x + 4y = 6$ and $2x + 3y = 5$.**

Sometimes adding or subtracting two equations will eliminate a variable. In this case, adding or subtracting the two equations will not eliminate a variable. If both sides of the first equation are multiplied by 2, and both sides of the second equation are multiplied by -3, the system can be solved by adding the equations.

$3x + 4y = 6$ *Multiply by 2.* $6x + 8y = 12$

$2x + 3y = 5$ *Multiply by -3.* $-6x - 9y = -15$

Now, add to eliminate x. Then, solve for y.

$$\begin{array}{r} 6x + 8y = 12 \qquad \textit{Add} \\ -6x - 9y = -15 \\ \hline -y = -3 \qquad \textit{The variable x is eliminated.} \\ y = 3 \end{array}$$

Point out that there is more than one way to solve a system of equations. This system could be solved by multiplying the first equation by 3 and the second equation by 4, then subtracting the two equations.

Finally, substitute 3 for y in the first equation. Then, solve for x.

$$3x + 4y = 6$$
$$3x + 4(3) = 6$$
$$3x + 12 = 6 \qquad$$
$$3x = -6$$
$$x = -2$$

3 could also be substituted for y in the second equation.

The solution is $(-2, 3)$.   *Check in the original equations.*

Exploratory Exercises

ALL LEVELS: Algebra Review

State the coordinates of the point of intersection of each pair of lines.

1. *a* and *b*   (−10, 6)

2. *a* and *c*   (−2, 2)

3. *a* and *d*   (2, 0)

4. *b* and *d*   (6, 2)

5. *b* and *c*   (−2, 4)

6. *d* and the *y*-axis   (0, −1)

7. *c* and the *x*-axis   (−2, 0)

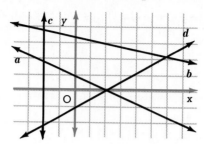

State the letter of the ordered pair(s) that satisfies each equation.

8. $x + 3y = 6$ a, c, d   **a.** (0, 2)   **b.** (−1, 4)   **c.** (6, 0)   **d.** (−3, 3)

9. $2x − 5y = −1$ b, c   **a.** (0, 5)   **b.** (2, 1)   **c.** (−0.5, 0)   **d.** (−2, −1)

10. $3x = 15$ a, b, d   **a.** (5, 1)   **b.** (5, 0)   **c.** (0, 5)   **d.** (5, 8)

Written Exercises

For graphs to Exercises 1–6, see the Teacher Guide.

Graph each pair of equations. Then, state the solution of each system of equations.

1. $x + y = 6$ (4, 2)
   $x − y = 2$

2. $y = x − 1$ (6, 5)
   $x + y = 11$

3. $3x − 2y = 10$ (2, −2)
   $x + y = 0$

4. $x + 2y = 7$ (1, 3)
   $y = 2x + 1$

5. $y = x + 3$ (−1, 2)
   $3y + x = 5$

6. $y = 4x$ (1, 4)
   $x + y = 5$

Solve each system of equations by an algebraic method.

7. $x − y = −5$ (10, 15)
   $x + y = 25$

8. $x − y = 6$ $\left(5\frac{1}{2}, −\frac{1}{2}\right)$
   $x + y = 5$

9. $x + 2y = 5$ (3, 1)
   $2x + y = 7$

10. $y = 3x$ (−3, −9)
    $x + 2y = −21$

11. $3x + 4y = −7$ (−1, −1)
    $2x + y = −3$

12. $y = x − 1$ (6, 5)
    $4x − y = 19$

13. $x = y + 10$ (14, 4)
    $2y = x − 6$

14. $12 − 3y = −4x$ (0, 4)
    $40 + 4x = 10y$

15. $9x + y = 20$ (2, 2)
    $3x + 3y = 12$

Solve the following exercises.

16. The graphs of $y = 2$, $x − y = 0$, and $3y = −2x + 30$ intersect to form a triangle. Find the coordinates of the vertices of the triangle. Then, find the area of the triangle. (2, 2), (6, 6), (12, 2); 20

17. In $\triangle IBM$, $I(−8, 6)$, $B(5, 6)$, and $M(−1, −6)$ are coordinates of the vertices. Find the coordinates of the intersection of the altitude from I and $\overline{MB}$. $\left(\frac{12}{5}, \frac{4}{5}\right)$

Challenge Exercise

18. Find the distance between the parallel lines $y = 3x + 1$ and $y = 3x − 8$. $\frac{9\sqrt{10}}{10}$

Algebra Review

Solve each equation using the quadratic formula. Express answers in simplest radical form. See the Teacher Guide.

$$x = \frac{−b \pm \sqrt{b^2 − 4ac}}{2a}$$

1. $x^2 + 4x − 1 = 0$

2. $3x^2 + 6x + 1 = 0$

3. $−2x^2 − 7x + 5 = 0$

4. $10 = x^2 − 4x$

5. $x^2 + x = 3$

Additional practice in solving equations can be found on page 566 of the Diagnostic Skills Review.

Applications in Business

In producing and selling a product, the amount of goods or services that must be sold in order to make a zero profit is called the *break-even point*. Business analysts often determine this point by writing an equation that represents the cost of producing the product and an equation that represents the income from selling the product. These equations form a system of equations that can be solved graphically or algebraically.

Example The Murphy Company, a leading gadget maker, has a fixed cost of $200 per week. If each item costs $4 per unit to produce and can be sold for $5 per unit, what is the break-even point?

First determine the cost equation and the income equation.
Let x = the number of items.
The cost equation is $y = 4x + 200$.
The income equation is $y = 5x$.

Then graph the system of equations.

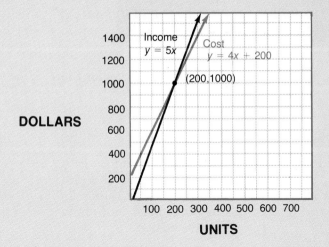

The graphs intersect at (200, 1000). Therefore the Murphy Company must sell 200 gadgets to break even. At 200 units, there is a cost of $1000 and an income of $1000. To make a profit, the Murphy Company must sell more than 200 gadgets.

Check by solving the system algebraically.

Exercises

Find the cost and profit equations. Then, graph the system to find the break-even point. Use algebra to check. For Exercises 1–2, see the Teacher Guide.

1. The Westerville Corporation has a weekly fixed cost of $5,000. It costs $16,000 to produce 400 units. The units can be sold for $60 a piece.

2. The City Corporation has a weekly fixed cost of $260,000. To produce 100 units of a product it costs $130,000. The selling price is $1,800 per unit.

12-6 Circles

Objectives: Determine the center and the measure of the radius from the equation of a circle; write the equation for a circle using the center and the measure of the radius.

Meteorologists often track the path of severe storms using radar. The photo below is a radar image of a storm. Circles are used to locate points on a radar scope.

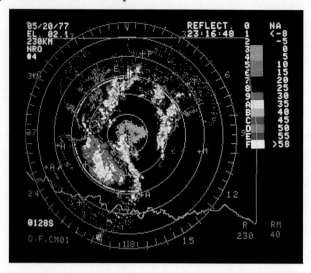

The distance formula can be used to develop an equation for the graph of the circle.

This concept may be new to students and may require more in-depth explanation.

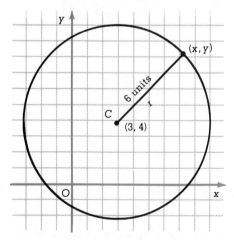

The circle at the left has its center at $(3, 4)$. The length of the radius is 6 units. Suppose (x, y) represents any point on the circle. This point must be 6 units from the center.

Review the definition of a circle.

The distance between (x, y) and (3, 4) is 6 units.

$$\sqrt{(x - 3)^2 + (y - 4)^2} = 6$$
$$(x - 3)^2 + (y - 4)^2 = 6^2$$
$$(x - 3)^2 + (y - 4)^2 = 36$$

Square both sides.

The equation of a circle with center at $(3, 4)$ and radius measuring 6 units is $(x - 3)^2 + (y - 4)^2 = 36$.

The equation of a circle can be written in the form given below.

The equation of a circle with center at (h, k) and radius measuring r units is $(x - h)^2 + (y - k)^2 = r^2$.

Theorem 12-7
General Equation
of a Circle

Examples

1 **Find the equation of a circle whose center is at (0, 0) and whose radius is 4 inches long.**

The distance between (0, 0) and a point on the circle (x, y) is 4 units.

$$\sqrt{(x-0)^2 + (y-0)^2} = 4$$
$$x^2 + y^2 = 4^2$$
$$x^2 + y^2 = 16$$

The equation of the circle is $x^2 + y^2 = 16$.

It may be desirable with Enriched classes to use the completing the square method for finding $(x - h)^2 + (y - k)^2 = r^2$.

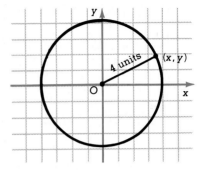

2 **Graph the circle whose equation is $(x + 1)^2 + (y - 4)^2 = 25$.**

First rewrite the equation in the form
$(x - h)^2 + (y - k)^2 = r^2$.

$$(x + 1)^2 + (y - 4)^2 = 25$$
$$[x - (-1)]^2 + (y - 4)^2 = 5^2$$

Therefore, $h = -1$, $k = 4$, and $r = 5$.
The center is $(-1, 4)$.
The radius is 5 units long.

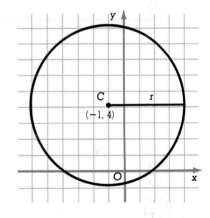

EN: 6–10 even, 3, 6, 9, . . . 42, 44–46; **AV:** 1–10, 2–42 even; **FD:** 1–10, 2–32 even, p. 454, 13–15

Exploratory Exercises

Determine the center and measure of the radius for each circle whose equation is given below.

1. $x^2 + y^2 = 16$ (0, 0), $r = 4$

2. $(x + 2)^2 + (y + 7)^2 = 81$ (−2, −7), $r = 9$

3. $x^2 + y^2 - 25 = 0$ (0, 0), $r = 5$

4. $\left(x + \frac{1}{2}\right)^2 + \left(y + \frac{1}{3}\right)^2 = \frac{16}{25}$ $\left(-\frac{1}{2}, -\frac{1}{3}\right)$, $r = \frac{4}{5}$

5. $(x - 4)^2 + (y - 6)^2 = 9$ (4, 6), $r = 3$

6. $(x - 2)^2 + (y - 5)^2 = 49$ (2, 5), $r = 7$

7. $(x - 3)^2 + (y - 12)^2 - 36 = 0$ (3, 12), $r = 6$

8. $(x + 5)^2 + (y - 7)^2 = 100$ (−5, 7), $r = 10$

9. $(x + 8)^2 + (y - 9)^2 = 81$ (−8, 9), $r = 9$

10. $(x + 4)^2 + y^2 - 121 = 0$ (−4, 0), $r = 11$

Written Exercises

For each of the following, write the equation of the circle. The coordinates of the center and measure of the radius are given. For Exercises 1–33, see the Teacher Guide.

1. $(0, 0)$, 5

2. $(0, 0)$, 7

3. $(3, 4)$, 6

4. $(1, 2)$, 3

5. $(-1, -1)$, $\frac{1}{4}$

6. $(-4, 3)$, $\frac{4}{3}$

7. $(-2, 8)$, $\sqrt{2}$

8. $(-5, 9)$, $\sqrt{20}$

9. $(0, 0)$, $\sqrt{14}$

10. $(0, 0)$, $\frac{1}{2}$

11. $(6, 0)$, 12

12. $(0, -5)$, 9

13. $\left(3, \frac{1}{2}\right)$, $\frac{4}{5}$

14. $\left(-\frac{3}{4}, 6\right)$, $\sqrt{18}$

15. $\left(-\frac{2}{5}, -\frac{1}{2}\right)$, $2\sqrt{3}$

Determine the center and measure of the radius for each circle whose equation is given.

16. $(x - 9)^2 + (y - 10)^2 = 1$

17. $x^2 + (y - 3)^2 - 4 = 0$

18. $0 = -y^2 - x^2 + 10$

19. $(x + 3)^2 + (y - 4)^2 = 20$

20. $(x + 7)^2 + (y + 3)^2 = 50$

21. $(x - 7)^2 + (y + 5)^2 = 4$

22. $x^2 + y^2 = 64$

23. $y^2 = 16 - x^2$

24. $(x + 1)^2 = 11 - y^2$

25. $(x + 7)^2 + (y + 3)^2 = 3$

26. $x^2 + (y - 3)^2 = 25$

27. $(x + 4)^2 + \left(y - \frac{1}{2}\right)^2 = 6$

28. $(x - 4)^2 + y^2 = \frac{16}{25}$

29. $(x + 5)^2 + (y - 2)^2 = \frac{3}{4}$

30. $x^2 + (y + 5)^2 = \frac{81}{64}$

31. $x^2 - 4x + 4 + y^2 - 6y + 9 = 25$

32. $x^2 + 6x + 9 + y^2 + 12y + 36 = 49$

33. $x^2 - 2x + y^2 + 6y = 111$

Solve each system of equations.

34. $x^2 + y^2 = 36$ $(3\sqrt{2}, 3\sqrt{2})$
$y = x$ $(-3\sqrt{2}, -3\sqrt{2})$

35. $x^2 + y^2 = 25$ $(3, 4)$
$y = x + 1$ $(-4, -3)$

36. $x^2 + y^2 = 49$ $(3, 2\sqrt{10})$
$x = 3$ $(3, -2\sqrt{10})$

37. $x^2 + y^2 = 100$ $(5\sqrt{3}, 5)$
$y = 5$ $(-5\sqrt{3}, 5)$

38. $x^2 + y^2 = 36$ $(4, \pm 2\sqrt{5})$
$x^2 - y^2 = -4$ $(-4, \pm 2\sqrt{5})$

39. $(x + 3)^2 + y^2 = 25$ $(0, 4)$
$(x - 3)^2 + y^2 = 25$ $(0, -4)$

Complete each of the following.

40. Write the equation of the circle that has a diameter whose endpoints are at $(2, 7)$ and $(-6, 15)$. $(x + 2)^2 + (y - 11)^2 = 32$

41. Write the equation of the circle that has a diameter of 12 units and a center at $(-4, -7)$. $(x + 4)^2 + (y + 7)^2 = 36$

42. The x-axis and the y-axis are both tangent to a circle that has its center in the second quadrant and a radius of 5. Write the equation of the circle. $(x + 5)^2 + (y - 5)^2 = 25$

43. The graphs of $x = 4$ and $y = -1$ are both tangent to a circle that has its center in the fourth quadrant and a diameter of 14. Write the equation of the circle. $(x - 11)^2 + (y + 8)^2 = 49$

Challenge Exercises

44. Find the equation of the circle whose center is in the third quadrant and is tangent to the lines $y = 7$, $y = -14$, and $x = 2$. $\left(x + \frac{17}{2}\right)^2 + \left(y + \frac{7}{2}\right)^2 = \left(\frac{21}{2}\right)^2$

45. A circle with center $(2, 8)$ intersects another circle with center $(8, 8)$ at the point $(-2, 11)$. Find the coordinates of the other point of intersection. $(-2, 5)$

46. If the line $x - y = -k$ is tangent to the circle whose equation is $x^2 + y^2 = k$, then find k. 2

12-7 Coordinate Proofs

Objectives: Position and label figures in a coordinate plane; plan and write a coordinate proof.

Theorems can be proven using coordinate geometry.

Example

1 **Prove that the diagonals of a square are perpendicular.**

Given: Square $PQRS$
Prove: $\overleftrightarrow{PR} \perp \overleftrightarrow{QS}$

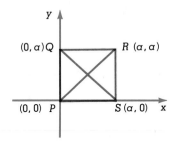

Proof:

By Theorem 12-4, the product of the slopes of perpendicular lines is -1.
First, find the slope of $\overleftrightarrow{PR}$ and of $\overleftrightarrow{QS}$.

$$\text{slope of } \overleftrightarrow{PR} = \frac{a - 0}{a - 0}$$

$$= \frac{a}{a} \text{ or } 1$$

$$\text{slope of } \overleftrightarrow{QS} = \frac{0 - a}{a - 0}$$

$$= \frac{-a}{a} \text{ or } -1$$

Then, find the product of the slopes.

$$\text{slope of } \overleftrightarrow{PR} \cdot \text{slope of } \overleftrightarrow{QS} = 1 \cdot -1 \text{ or } -1$$

Therefore, the diagonals are perpendicular.

Point out that students should minimize the number of variables introduced.

Placing the geometric figure in a coordinate plane is an important part of planning a coordinate proof. In most cases, the following suggestions will help you place figures for your proofs.

1. **Use the origin as a vertex or center.** 2. **Place at least one side of a polygon on a coordinate axis.** 3. **Keep the figure within the first quadrant.**	*Placing Figures on a Coordinate Plane*

Step 3 may not always be possible but should be attempted.

Example

2 Position and label a right triangle on the coordinate plane.

Use the origin as the vertex of the right angle. Place the legs of the triangle on the positive axes.

Label the vertices P, Q, and R. Since Q is on the y-axis, its x-coordinate is 0. Since R is on the x-axis, its y-coordinate is 0. Since P is at the origin, both coordinates are 0.

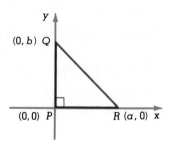

The Exploratory Exercises can be used in conjunction with a discussion of positioning and labeling figures in the coordinate plane.

Some common ways of positioning and labeling several figures on the coordinate plane are shown below.

Discuss how these coordinates were determined from the properties of the figures.

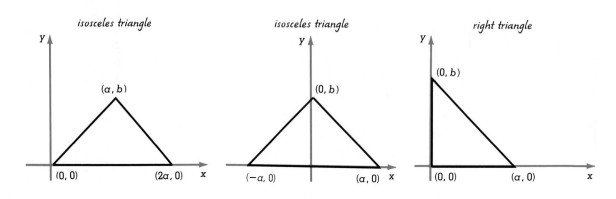

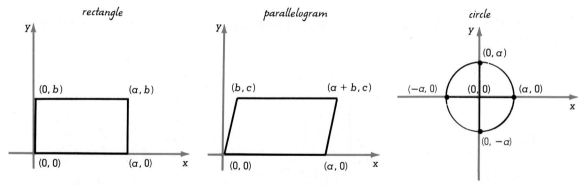

The Written Exercises on page 548 of the Logo Appendix will provide students with additional practice positioning figures on the coordinate plane.

Example

3 Prove that the midpoint of the hypotenuse of a right triangle is equidistant from the vertices.

Given: $\angle QPR$ is a right angle.

M is the midpoint of $\overline{QR}$.

Prove: M is equidistant from Q, P, and R.

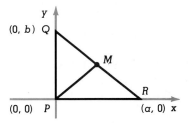

Proof:

By the Midpoint Formula, the coordinates of M are $\left(\dfrac{a}{2}, \dfrac{b}{2}\right)$.

Use the Distance Formula to find MR and PM.

$$MR = \sqrt{\left(\frac{a}{2} - a\right)^2 + \left(\frac{b}{2} - 0\right)^2} \qquad PM = \sqrt{\left(\frac{a}{2} - 0\right)^2 + \left(\frac{b}{2} - 0\right)^2}$$

$$= \sqrt{\left(\frac{-a}{2}\right)^2 + \left(\frac{b}{2}\right)^2} \qquad\qquad = \sqrt{\left(\frac{a}{2}\right)^2 + \left(\frac{b}{2}\right)^2}$$

$$= \sqrt{\frac{a^2 + b^2}{4}} \qquad\qquad\qquad = \sqrt{\frac{a^2 + b^2}{4}}$$

Therefore, $MR = PM$. Also, by the definition of midpoint, $QM = MR$. Thus, $QM = MR = PM$ and M is equidistant from Q, P, and R.

EN: 1–6, 1–6, 8, 9, 12, 14; **AV:** 1–6, 1–10; **FD:** 1–6, 1–8, p. 458, 34, 36, 39

Exploratory Exercises

For each of the following figures, name the missing coordinates without introducing new variables.

1.

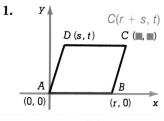

parallelogram

2.

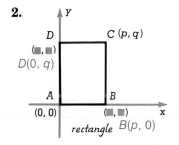

rectangle $B(p, 0)$

3. $R(-b, 2b)$

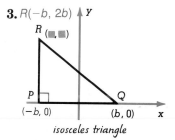

isosceles triangle

4.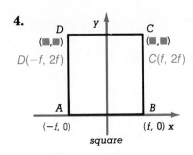

D
(■,■)
D(−f, 2f)

C
(■,■)
C(f, 2f)

A
(−f, 0)

B
(f, 0) x

square

5.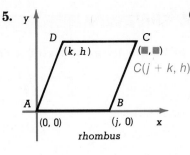

D
(k, h)

C
(■,■)
C(j + k, h)

A
(0, 0)

B
(j, 0) x

rhombus

6.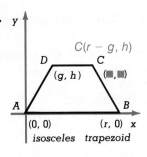

C(r − g, h)

D
(g, h)

C
(■,■)

A
(0, 0)

B
(r, 0) x

isosceles trapezoid

Written Exercises

For each of the following figures, name the missing coordinates without introducing new variables.

1.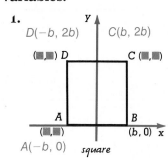

D(−b, 2b) C(b, 2b)

(■,■) D   C (■,■)

A
(■,■)

B
(b, 0) x

A(−b, 0)   square

2.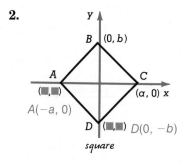

B (0, b)

A
(■,■)
A(−a, 0)

C
(a, 0) x

D (■,■) D(0, −b)

square

3.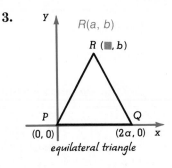

R(a, b)

R (■, b)

P
(0, 0)

Q
(2a, 0) x

equilateral triangle

4.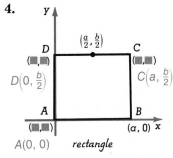

$(\frac{a}{2}, \frac{b}{2})$

D
(■,■)
D$(0, \frac{b}{2})$

C
(■,■)
C$(a, \frac{b}{2})$

A
(■,■)
A(0, 0)

B
(a, 0) x

rectangle

5.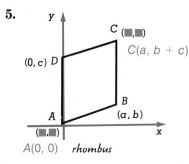

C (■,■)
C(a, b + c)

(0, c) D

B
(a, b)

A
(■,■)
A(0, 0)

rhombus

6.

R(−a, a)

R (■,■)

P
(−a, 0)

Q
(■,■) x

Q(0, 0)

isosceles right triangle

For Exercises 7–14, see the Teacher Guide.

For each of the following theorems, name the given, the prove statement, and draw a diagram you would use in a formal proof. Then, prove the theorem.

7. The diagonals of a rectangle are congruent.

8. The diagonals of a rhombus are perpendicular.

9. The diagonals of an isosceles trapezoid are congruent.

10. The diagonals of a parallelogram bisect each other.

11. Opposite sides of a parallelogram are congruent.

12. The segments that join the midpoints of consecutive sides of a rectangle form a rhombus.

13. The length of the median of a trapezoid is one-half the sum of the lengths of the bases.

14. The segments that join the midpoints of consecutive sides of an isosceles trapezoid form a rhombus.

12-8 Coordinates in Space

Objectives: Determine the distance between a pair of points in space; determine the midpoint of a segment in space; determine the center and the measure of the radius of a sphere; write the equation of a sphere given the center and the radius.

The two-dimensional coordinate system can be extended to a three-dimensional coordinate system in space. The x-axis, the y-axis, and the z-axis are perpendicular to each other.

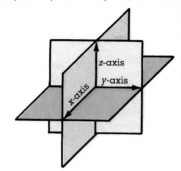

Emphasize that the axes are perpendicular.

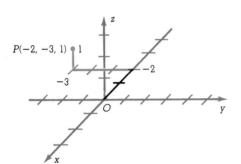

A point in space is represented by an ordered triple of real numbers (x, y, z). In the figure at the left, the ordered triple $(-2, -3, 1)$ represents point P.

The graph of all ordered triples of real numbers is space.

Just as the Pythagorean Theorem can be used to find the distance between two points in a plane, it can also be used to find the distance between two points in space.

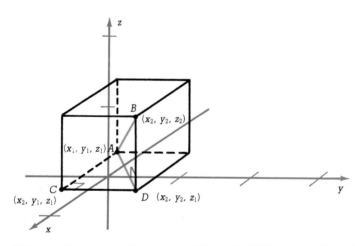

The distance between points A and B on $\triangle ABD$ can be found as follows.

$(AB)^2 = (AD)^2 + (BD)^2$ *Pythagorean Theorem* $\overline{AD}$ is the hypotenuse of $\triangle ACD$.

$\quad\quad = (AC)^2 + (CD)^2 + (BD)^2$ *Substitute $(AC)^2 + (CD)^2$ for $(AD)^2$.*

$AB = \sqrt{(AC)^2 + (CD)^2 + (BD)^2}$ *Find the square root of both sides.*

But, $AC = |x_2 - x_1|$, $CD = |y_2 - y_1|$, and $BD = |z_2 - z_1|$.

$AB = \sqrt{(x_2 - x_1)^2 + (y_2 - y_1)^2 + (z_2 - z_1)^2}$ *Substitution*

Given two points A (x_1, y_1, z_1) and B $(x_2, y_2 z_2)$ in space, the distance between A and B is given by the following equation.

$$AB = \sqrt{(x_2 - x_1)^2 + (y_2 - y_1)^2 + (z_2 - z_1)^2}$$

Theorem 12-8
This formula is an extension of the Distance Formula in the two-dimensional coordinate system.

Example

1   **Find the distance between $P(6, -1, 3)$ and $Q(2, 3, 5)$.**

Let $(2, 3, 5)$ be (x_1, y_1, z_1) and $(6, -1, 3)$ be (x_2, y_2, z_2).

$$
\begin{aligned}
PQ &= \sqrt{(x_2 - x_1)^2 + (y_2 - y_1)^2 + (z_2 - z_1)^2} \\
&= \sqrt{(6 - 2)^2 + (-1 - 3)^2 + (3 - 5)^2} \\
&= \sqrt{4^2 + (-4)^2 + (-2)^2} \\
&= \sqrt{16 + 16 + 4} \\
&= \sqrt{36} \\
&= 6 \qquad \text{The distance between P and Q is 6 units.}
\end{aligned}
$$

Suppose M is the midpoint of $\overline{PQ}$, a segment in space. The midpoint is represented by the following.

$$\left(\frac{x_1 + x_2}{2}, \frac{y_1 + y_2}{2}, \frac{z_1 + z_2}{2}\right)$$

This formula is an extension of the Midpoint Formula in the two-dimensional coordinate system.

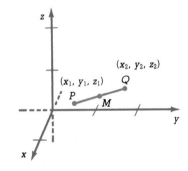

Example

2   **Find the coordinates of the midpoint of a segment in space whose endpoints P and Q have coordinates $(3, -7, 0)$ and $(5, 1, 7)$.**

Let $(3, -7, 0)$ be (x_1, y_1, z_1) and $(5, 1, 7)$ be (x_2, y_2, z_2).

$$\left(\frac{x_1 + x_2}{2}, \frac{y_1 + y_2}{2}, \frac{z_1 + z_2}{2}\right)$$

$$\left(\frac{3 + 5}{2}, \frac{-7 + 1}{2}, \frac{0 + 7}{2}\right)$$

$$\left(\frac{8}{2}, \frac{-6}{2}, \frac{7}{2}\right)$$

$$\left(4, -3, \frac{7}{2}\right) \qquad \text{The midpoint of } \overline{PQ} \text{ is represented by } \left(4, -3, \frac{7}{2}\right).$$

The formula for the equation of a sphere is an extension of the formula for the equation of a circle.

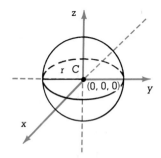

The equation of a sphere whose center is at $(0, 0, 0)$ and whose radius is r units in length is as follows.

$$x^2 + y^2 + z^2 = r^2$$

The equation of a sphere whose center is at (i, j, k) and that has a radius measuring r units is as follows.

$$(x - i)^2 + (y - j)^2 + (z - k)^2 = r^2$$

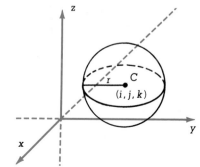

Example

3   **Write the equation of a sphere whose center is at $(3, -2, 4)$ and that has a radius measuring 6 units.**

Let $i = 3, j = -2, k = 4$, and $r = 6$.

$$(x - i)^2 + (y - j)^2 + (z - k)^2 = r^2$$
$$(x - 3)^2 + [y - (-2)]^2 + (z - 4)^2 = 6^2$$
$$(x - 3)^2 + (y + 2)^2 + (z - 4)^2 = 36$$

The equation of the sphere is $(x - 3)^2 + (y + 2)^2 + (z - 4)^2 = 36$.

Exploratory Exercises

Find the distance between each of the following pairs of points.

1. $A(0, 0, 0)$, $B(0, 4, 0)$ 4

2. $P(0, 0, 0)$, $Q(3, 4, 0)$ 5

3. $R(0, 0, 0)$, $S(2, 1, 1)$ $\sqrt{6}$

4. $C(2, 4, 5)$, $D(2, 4, 7)$ 2

Determine the midpoint of the segment whose endpoints are given.

5. $A(1, 3, -2)$, $B(7, -3, 2)$ $(4, 0, 0)$

6. $C(-5, 4, -2)$, $D(5, -4, 2)$ $(0, 0, 0)$

7. $P(0, 0, 6)$, $Q(-1, 8, 10)$ $\left(-\frac{1}{2}, 4, 8\right)$

8. $R(14, -10, -8)$, $S(-4, 2, 6)$ $(5, -4, -1)$

Determine the center and the measure of the radius for each sphere whose equation is given below.   **9.** $c = (3, 8, 2)$, $r = 7$

9. $(x - 3)^2 + (y - 8)^2 + (z - 2)^2 = 49$

10. $x^2 + y^2 + z^2 = 7$ $c = (0, 0, 0)$, $r = \sqrt{7}$

11. $(x + 4)^2 + (y - 2)^2 + (z + 1)^2 = 25$
$c = (-4, 2, -1)$, $r = 5$

12. $x^2 + y^2 + (z - 2)^2 = 2$
$c = (0, 0, 2)$, $r = \sqrt{2}$

Written Exercises

Find the distance between each of the following pairs of points.

1. $A(0, 0, 0)$, $B(3, 0, 2)$ $\sqrt{13}$

2. $S(0, 4, 0)$, $T(2, 0, 0)$ $2\sqrt{5}$

3. $P(3, 4, \sqrt{11})$, $Q(0, 0, 0)$ 6

4. $E(3, 7, -1)$, $F(4, 8, 9)$ $\sqrt{102}$

5. $R(-1, -4, 3)$, $S(2, -5, 1)$ $\sqrt{14}$

6. $H(-2, -4, -3)$, $J(-3, -4, -2)$ $\sqrt{2}$

7. $M(2, 2, 2)$, $N(-5, 1, 7)$ $5\sqrt{3}$

8. $P(6, 1, 3)$, $Q(10, 8, 6)$ $\sqrt{74}$

Determine the midpoint of the segment whose endpoints are given.

9. $A(0, -4, 2)$, $B(3, 0, 2)$ $\left(\frac{3}{2}, -2, 2\right)$

10. $S(-6, 3, -1)$, $T(6, 3, 1)$ $(0, 3, 0)$

11. $C(2, -5, 1)$, $D(3, 2, 4)$ $\left(\frac{5}{2}, -\frac{3}{2}, \frac{5}{2}\right)$

12. $R(2, 7, 4)$, $S(0, 8, -4)$ $\left(1, \frac{15}{2}, 0\right)$

13. $P(-1, 8, 10)$, $Q(0, 0, 0)$ $\left(-\frac{1}{2}, 4, 5\right)$

14. $H(4, -4, 2)$, $J(8, -4, 6)$ $(6, -4, 4)$

Determine the center and the measure of the radius for each sphere whose equation is given below.   **15.** $c = (6, 5, -1)$, $r = 9$ **16.** $c = (-2, -3, 2)$, $r = 10$

15. $(x - 6)^2 + (y - 5)^2 + (z + 1)^2 = 81$

16. $(x + 2)^2 + (y + 3)^2 + (z - 2)^2 = 100$

17. $x^2 + (y - 3)^2 + z^2 = 4$ $c = (0, 3, 0)$, $r = 2$

18. $(x + 1)^2 + (y - 8)^2 + z^2 = 11$
$c = (-1, 8, 0)$, $r = \sqrt{11}$

Write the equation of the sphere having the coordinates of the center and the measure of the radius given below.

19. $(0, 0, 0)$, 3 $x^2 + y^2 + z^2 = 9$

20. $(0, 3, 1)$, 1 $x^2 + (y - 3)^2 + (z - 1)^2 = 1$

21. $(-1, 2, 4)$, 4 $(x + 1)^2 + (y - 2)^2 + (z - 4)^2 = 16$

22. $(6, -2, 3)$, 12 $(x - 6)^2 + (y + 2)^2 + (z - 3)^2 = 144$

23. $\left(2, \frac{1}{2}, 1\right)$, $\frac{1}{3}$ $(x - 2)^2 + \left(y - \frac{1}{2}\right)^2 + (z - 1)^2 = \frac{1}{9}$

24. $\left(-5, 0, \frac{2}{3}\right)$, $\frac{3}{5}$ $(x + 5)^2 + y^2 + \left(z - \frac{2}{3}\right)^2 = \frac{9}{25}$

Answer each of the following.

25. Find the perimeter of a triangle whose vertices are $A(6, 4, 1)$, $B(4, 6, 0)$, and $C(3, -2, 3)$. $P = 10 + \sqrt{74}$ or about 18.6

26. Find the perimeter of a triangle whose vertices are $P(0, 0, 0)$, $Q(3, 4, \sqrt{11})$, and $R(0, 5, 0)$. $P = 11 + \sqrt{21}$ or about 15.6

The diameter of a sphere has endpoints $A(-3, 5, 7)$ and $B(5, -1, 5)$. Use this information to answer each of the following. $\sqrt{26}$ or about 5.1

27. Determine the center. $(1, 2, 6)$

28. Determine the measure of the radius.

29. Write the equation of the sphere.
$(x - 1)^2 + (y - 2)^2 + (z - 6)^2 = 26$

30. Sketch the graph of the sphere.
See students' work.

466 *Coordinates*

Vocabulary▬

ordered pair (435)
quadrant (435)
axis (435)
origin (435)
coordinate plane (435)
graph (435)
x-coordinate (435)

y-coordinate (435)
linear equation (436)
slope (443)
slope-intercept form (448)
point-slope form (449)
system of equations (452)

Chapter Summary▬

1. **Completeness Property for Points in the Real Plane (Postulate 12-1):** Each point in a coordinate real plane corresponds to exactly one ordered pair of numbers. Each ordered pair of real numbers corresponds to exactly one point in a coordinate plane. (435)

2. **Definition of Linear Equation:** An equation is linear if and only if it can be written in the form $Ax + By = C$, where A, B, and C are any real numbers and A and B are not both 0. (436)

3. **Distance Formula (Theorem 12-1):** The distance between two points with coordinates (x_1, y_1) and (x_2, y_2) is given by the following formula. (440)

$$d = \sqrt{(x_2 - x_1)^2 + (y_2 - y_1)^2}$$

4. **Midpoint Formula (Theorem 12-2):** If the coordinates of A and B are (x_1, y_1) and (x_2, y_2) respectively, then the midpoint of M of $\overline{AB}$ has coordinates $\left(\dfrac{x_1 + x_2}{2}, \dfrac{y_1 + y_2}{2}\right)$. (441)

5. **Definition of Slope:** The slope of a line containing two points with coordinates (x_1, y_1) and (x_2, y_2) is given by the following formula. (443)

$$m = \frac{y_2 - y_1}{x_2 - x_1} \quad \text{where } x_2 \neq x_1$$

6. If the line is vertical, then the slope is undefined; if the line is horizontal, then the slope is zero. (444)

7. **Theorem 12-3:** Two lines have the same slope if and only if they are parallel and nonvertical. (445)

8. **Theorem 12-4:** Two nonvertical lines are perpendicular if and only if the product of their slopes is -1. (445)

9. **Slope-Intercept Form (Theorem 12-5):** The equation of the line having a slope m, and y-intercept b is $y = mx + b$. (448)

10. **Point-Slope Form (Theorem 12-6):** The equation of the line passing through the point whose coordinates are (x_1, y_1) and which has a slope m is $y - y_1 = m(x - x_1)$. (449)

11. A system of equations can be solved by three methods: graphing, the substitution method, and the elimination method. (452)

12. General Equation of a Circle (Theorem 12-7): The equation of a circle with center at (h, k) and radius measuring r units is $(x - h)^2 + (y - k)^2 = r^2$. (456)

13. Placing figures in a coordinate plane: (459)
    1. Use the origin as a vertex or center.
    2. Place at least one side of a polygon on a coordinate axis.
    3. Keep the figure within the first quadrant.

14. In a three-dimensional coordinate system in space, the x-axis, the y-axis, and the z-axis are perpendicular to each other. A point in space is represented by an ordered triple of real numbers (x, y, z). (463)

15. Theorem 12-8: Given two points $A(x_1, y_1, z_1)$ and $B(x_2, y_2, z_2)$ in space, the distance between A and B is given by the following equation. (464)

$$AB = \sqrt{(x_2 - x_1)^2 + (y_2 - y_1)^2 + (z_2 - z_1)^2}$$

16. Given two points $P(x_1, y_1, z_1)$ and $Q(x_2, y_2, z_2)$ in space, the midpoint of $\overline{PQ}$ is represented by the following. (464)

$$\left(\frac{x_1 + x_2}{2}, \frac{y_1 + y_2}{2}, \frac{z_1 + z_2}{2} \right)$$

17. The equation of a sphere whose center is at (i, j, k) and that has a radius measuring r units is as follows. (465)

$$(x - i)^2 + (y - j)^2 + (z - k)^2 = r^2$$

Chapter Review

12-1 **Graph each linear equation.** For Exercises 1–10, see the Teacher Guide.

1. $x = 4$
2. $3x + y = 5$
3. $5x + 2y = 0$
4. $3x - 6y = 9$
5. $y = -x + 1$
6. $2x = y - 1$

Each of the following are the coordinates of three vertices of a rectangle. Graph them. Then, determine each fourth vertex.

7. $(-2, 2)$, $(1, 2)$, $(1, -4)$ $(-2, -4)$
8. $(0, 0)$, $(1, -1)$, $(-3, -5)$ $(-4, -4)$
9. $(-6, 4)$, $(-4, 6)$, $(-2, 4)$ $(-4, 2)$
10. $(1, 0)$, $(5, 0)$, $(5, 6)$ $(1, 6)$

12-2 **Find the distance between each of the following pairs of points.**

11. $(0, 3)$, $(4, 0)$ 5
12. $(-3, -5)$, $(3, 5)$ $2\sqrt{34}$
13. $(6, r)$, $(4, r)$ 2
14. $\left(\frac{2}{5}, \frac{3}{5} \right)$, $\left(\frac{1}{10}, \frac{3}{10} \right)$ $\frac{3}{10}\sqrt{2}$
15. (a, b), (b, a) $|a - b|\sqrt{2}$
16. $(0.1, 0.3)$, $(0.2, 0.4)$ $\frac{\sqrt{2}}{10}$

Determine the coordinates of the midpoints of each segment that has endpoints with the following coordinates.

17. $(-4, 2)$, $(-4, 5)$ $\left(-4, \frac{7}{2}\right)$ **18.** $(5, 0)$, $(12, 0)$ $\left(\frac{17}{2}, 0\right)$ **19.** $(-2, -3)$, $(-4, -7)$ $(-3, -5)$

20. $(0, 0)$, $(0, 5)$ $\left(0, \frac{5}{2}\right)$ **21.** $\left(\frac{1}{2}, \frac{1}{3}\right)$, $\left(1, \frac{2}{3}\right)$ $\left(\frac{3}{4}, \frac{1}{2}\right)$ **22.** $(4, 6)$, $(5, 7)$ $\left(\frac{9}{2}, \frac{13}{2}\right)$

23. The center of a circle has coordinates $(-6, -8)$. One endpoint of a diameter has coordinates $(0, 0)$. Determine the coordinates of the other endpoint of the diameter. $(-12, -16)$

12-3 Determine the slope of the lines passing through the following pairs of points whose coordinates are listed below.

24. $(5, 2)$, $(-6, 2)$ 0 **25.** $(-2, 1)$, $(-5, 3)$ $-\frac{2}{3}$ **26.** $(3, 6)$, $(9, -6)$ -2

27. $(3, 8)$, $(3, 6)$ undefined **28.** $(2, 6)$, $(5, 2)$ $-\frac{4}{3}$ **29.** $(-3, 10)$, $(-7, 2)$ 2

Determine the value of r so that a line through the points with the given coordinates has the slope listed.

30. $(r, 6)$, $(1, 5)$; slope $= \frac{1}{5}$ 6 **31.** $(4, r)$, $(-2, 4)$; slope $= \frac{1}{2}$ 7

32. $(5, 3)$, $(8, r)$; slope $= 0$ 3 **33.** $(r, -2)$, $(5, r)$; slope $= 1$ $\frac{3}{2}$

34. Find the value of x if the points $A(x, 4)$, $B(0, 2)$, and $C(2, 0)$ are collinear. -2

12-4 Determine the slope and y-intercept of the graphs of each equation.

35. $y = 4x + 6$ $m = 4$, $b = 6$ **36.** $y = -8$ $m = 0$, $b = -8$

37. $x = 7$ m undefined, no y-intercept **38.** $4x - 6y = 8$ $m = \frac{2}{3}$, $b = -\frac{4}{3}$

Write an equation of the line satisfying the given conditions.

39. $m = 3$, y-intercept is -1 $y = 3x - 1$ **40.** $m = 0$, through a point at $\left(\frac{1}{2}, \frac{1}{3}\right)$ $y = \frac{1}{3}$

41. m is undefined; through a point at $(4, 6)$ $x = 4$ **42.** $m = \frac{2}{3}$, y-intercept is -5 $y = \frac{2}{3}x - 5$

43. Write the equation of a line passing through points whose coordinates are $(-2, -6)$ and $(5, 0)$. $y = \frac{6}{7}x - \frac{30}{7}$

For graphs to Exercises 44–45, see the Teacher Guide.

12-5 Graph each pair of equations. Then, state the solution of each system of equations.

44. $x + y = 4$
$x - y = 2$ $(3, 1)$

45. $y = x - 2$
$2x + y = 13$ $(5, 3)$

Solve each system of equations by an algebraic method.

46. $y = 2x - 1$
$x + y = 7$ $\left(\frac{8}{3}, \frac{13}{3}\right)$

47. $3x - 4y = -1$
$-2x + y = -1$ $(1, 1)$

48. $3x + y = 5$
$2x + 3y = 8$ $(1, 2)$

49. $4x + 5y = 29$
$3x - 2y = 16$ $(6, 1)$

12-6 Determine the center and the measure of the radius for each circle whose equation is given below.

50. $x^2 + y^2 = 36$ $c = (0, 0), r = 6$

51. $(x + 2)^2 + y^2 = 12$ $c = (-2, 0), r = 2\sqrt{3}$

52. $(x + 3)^2 + (y - 6)^2 = 16$
$c = (-3, 6), r = 4$

53. $x^2 + (y - 5)^2 = \dfrac{64}{121}$ $c = (0, 5), r = \dfrac{8}{11}$

For each of the following, write the equation of the circle. The center and measure of the radius are given.

54. $(2, 3), 8$ $(x - 2)^2 + (y - 3)^2 = 64$

55. $(0, 0), 0.3$ $x^2 + y^2 = 0.09$

56. $(-7, 8), 5$ $(x + 7)^2 + (y - 8)^2 = 25$

57. $\left(-\dfrac{2}{3}, 5\right), \dfrac{6}{7}$ $\left(x + \dfrac{2}{3}\right)^2 + (y - 5)^2 = \dfrac{36}{49}$

58. Find the equation of a circle with a diameter of 12 units and a center at $(-5, -6)$.
$(x + 5)^2 + (y + 6)^2 = 36$

12-7 For each of the following figures, name the missing coordinates without introducing new letters.

59.

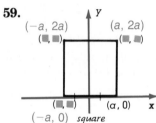

square

60.

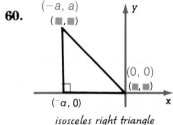

isosceles right triangle

61. Using the methods of coordinate geometry, name the given and the prove statement and then draw a diagram you would use to prove that the diagonals of a rhombus are perpendicular. See the Teacher Guide.

12-8 Find the distance between each of the following pairs of points.

62. $(0, 0, 0), (0, -3, 7)$ $\sqrt{58}$

63. $(3, 3, 3), (-6, 0, 6)$ $3\sqrt{11}$

64. $(0, 8, 0), (4, 0, 0)$ $4\sqrt{5}$

65. $(5, 0, 2), (9, 7, 5)$ $\sqrt{74}$

Determine the midpoint of the segment whose endpoints are given.

66. $(-5, 2, 0), (5, 2, 0)$ $(0, 2, 0)$

67. $(1, 6, 4), (0, 7, -3)$ $\left(\dfrac{1}{2}, \dfrac{13}{2}, \dfrac{1}{2}\right)$

68. $(3, -3, 1), (7, -3, 5)$ $(5, -3, 3)$

69. $(2, 4, 6), (0, 2, 4)$ $(1, 3, 5)$

Determine the center and the measure of the radius for each sphere whose equation is given below. $c = (4, 1, -2), r = 10$

70. $(x - 4)^2 + (y - 1)^2 + (z + 2)^2 = 100$

71. $x^2 + y^2 + z^2 = 144$ $c = (0, 0, 0), r = 12$

72. $(x + 1)^2 + y^2 + (z - 5)^2 = 4$
$c = (-1, 0, 5), r = 2$

73. $(x + 3)^2 + (y + 4)^2 + (z - 1)^2 = 13$
$c = (-3, -4, 1), r = \sqrt{13}$

Write the equation of the sphere having the center and the measure of the radius given below.

$(x - 9)^2 + (y + 6)^2 + (z - 4)^2 = 64$

74. $(0, 0, 0), 5$ $x^2 + y^2 + z^2 = 25$

75. $(9, -6, 4), 8$

76. $(-1, 2, -3), 4$
$(x + 1)^2 + (y - 2)^2 + (z + 3)^2 = 16$

77. $\left(-2, 1, \dfrac{2}{5}\right), \dfrac{2}{7}$
$(x + 2)^2 + (y - 1)^2 + \left(z - \dfrac{2}{5}\right)^2 = \dfrac{4}{49}$

Chapter Test

Graph each of the following linear equations. For Exercises 1–2, see the Teacher Guide.

1. $x + 2y = 6$

2. $x = -3$

Find the distance between each of the following pairs of points.

3. $(2, 3), (6, 7)$ $4\sqrt{2}$

4. $\left(\frac{2}{3}, \frac{4}{5}\right), \left(\frac{1}{3}, \frac{2}{5}\right)$ $\frac{\sqrt{61}}{15}$

Determine the coordinates of the midpoint of each segment that has endpoints with the coordinates given below.

5. $(0, 4), (6, 8)$ $(3, 6)$

6. $(-5, 7), (-5, 9)$ $(-5, 8)$

Determine the slope of the lines passing through the following pairs of points whose coordinates are given below.

7. $(-4, 11), (-6, 3)$ 4

8. $(5, 2), (8, 2)$ 0

9. $(3, 7), (3, -6)$ undefined

10. Determine the value of r so that a line through $(r, 3)$ and $(5, 9)$ has a slope of 2. 2

11. Write the equation of a line passing through points whose coordinates are $(-2, -6)$ and $(8, -2)$. $y = \frac{2}{5}x - \frac{26}{5}$

Solve each system of equations.

12. $y = 4x$
    $x + y = 5$ $(1, 4)$

13. $3x - 2y = 10$
    $x + y = 0$ $(2, -2)$

14. $3x + 4y = -7$
    $2x + y = -3$ $(-1, -1)$

Determine the center and the measure of the radius for each circle whose equation is given below.

15. $x^2 + y^2 = 49$ $c = (0, 0), r = 7$

16. $(x + 7)^2 + (y - 3)^2 = 3$ $c = (-7, 3), r = \sqrt{3}$

For each of the following, write the equation of the circle. The center and the measure of the radius are given.

17. $(0, 0), 2$ $x^2 + y^2 = 4$

18. $(-5, -6), \sqrt{8}$
    $(x + 5)^2 + (y + 6)^2 = 8$

19. $(2, -3), 12$
    $(x - 2)^2 + (y + 3)^2 = 144$

Answer each of the following. For Exercise 20, see the Teacher Guide.

20. Using the methods of coordinate geometry, name the given, the prove statement, and draw a diagram you would use to prove that the diagonals of a rectangle are congruent.

21. Determine the distance between $(2, 4, 5)$ and $(2, 4, 7)$. 2

22. Determine the midpoint of the segment whose endpoints are $(0, -4, 2)$ and $(3, 0, 2)$. $\left(\frac{3}{2}, -2, 2\right)$

Determine the center and the measure of the radius for each sphere whose equation is given below.

23. $(x - 4)^2 + (y - 5)^2 + (z + 2)^2 = 81$ $c = (4, 5, -2), r = 9$

24. $x^2 + y^2 + z^2 = 7$ $c = (0, 0, 0), r = \sqrt{7}$

25. Write the equation of the sphere whose diameter has endpoints at $(-3, 5, 7)$ and $(5, -1, 5)$. $(x - 1)^2 + (y - 2)^2 + (z - 6)^2 = 26$

Draw and label a diagram to show each of the following.

1. Points R, S, and T are coplanar.

For Exercises 1–4, see the Teacher Guide.

2. Points L, M, and N are collinear.

Write the inverse and the contrapositive of each of the following statements.

3. If three points are coplanar, then they lie in the same plane.

4. If it snows, then you may ski.

Change each fraction to a decimal form.

5. $-\dfrac{7}{8}$ −0.875

6. $4\dfrac{2}{3}$ $4.\overline{6}$

Change each decimal to fractional form.

7. $2.\overline{54}$ $2\dfrac{6}{11}$

8. $0.\overline{324}$ $\dfrac{12}{37}$

Determine whether each of the following is *true* or *false*.

9. $\overrightarrow{BA}$ and $\overrightarrow{BC}$ are opposite rays. true

10. $\angle ABE$ and $\angle EBC$ form a linear pair. true

11. F is in the interior of $\angle DBC$. false

12. $\angle ABE$ and $\angle DBC$ are adjacent angles. false

Exercises 9–12

Answer each of the following.

13. The measure of the supplement of an angle is three times the measure of the complement of the angle. What is the measure of the angle? 45

14. If $\triangle BCD$ is isosceles with $\overline{BD} \cong \overline{DC}$ and $BD = 2x - 5$ and $DC = x + 3$, then find the value of x. 8

In the figure, $\overline{AB} \cong \overline{CB}$ and $m \angle 2 = 40$. Find each of the following.

15. $m \angle 4$ 40

16. $m \angle 5$ 140

17. $m \angle 3$ 100

18. $m \angle 1$ 140

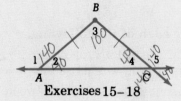

Exercises 15–18

Answer the following.

19. Using the information in the figure at the right, find the measures x, y, and z.

$x = 4$, $y = 2\sqrt{21}$, $z = 5\sqrt{21}$

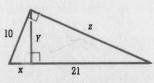

Exercise 19

Answer each of the following.

20. Draw a diagram showing a ray and a segment that are *not* parallel.
See the Teacher Guide.

21. Find the number of diagonals that can be drawn in a pentagon. 5

22. Find the sum of the degree measures of the angles of a 12-gon. 1800

23. If the length of a rectangle is 21 ft and the width is 16 ft, find the perimeter. 74 ft

Solve each proportion.

24. $\dfrac{x}{8} = \dfrac{13}{40}$ $\dfrac{13}{5}$

25. $\dfrac{4}{3x+2} = \dfrac{2}{3}$ $\dfrac{4}{3}$

26. $\dfrac{x-1}{5-x} = \dfrac{3}{5}$ $\dfrac{5}{2}$

27. Find the geometric mean between $\dfrac{3}{4}$ and $\dfrac{4}{3}$. 1

In $\odot O$, $\overline{AB} \parallel \overline{CD}$, $m \angle ABO = 50$, $m\widehat{EC} = 70$, and $\overline{CB}$ is a diameter. Find each of the following.

28. $m\widehat{AEC}$ 100

29. $m \angle 3$ 80

30. $m \angle D$ 35

31. $m \angle 1$ 50

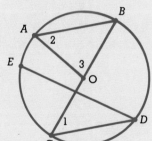

Answer each of the following.

32. Find the area of an equilateral triangle with sides measuring 20 cm. $100\sqrt{3}$ cm²

33. Find the area of a regular hexagon with an apothem measuring 3 inches. $18\sqrt{3}$ in²

34. Find the total surface area of a right cylinder with height of 10 ft and a radius of the base of 6 ft. Use 3.14 for π. 602.88 ft²

35. Find the volume of a regular square pyramid with a height of 12 inches and a base with sides of 6 inches. 144 in³

36. Find the distance between the points with coordinates (4, 7) and (−8, 6) $\sqrt{145}$

37. Find the coordinates of the midpoint of a segment whose endpoints are (3, 7) and (7, −11). (5, − 2)

38. Write the equation of a circle with center at (−3, 9) and radius of 13 units.
$(x + 3)^2 + (y − 9)^2 = 169$

39. Determine r so that the line through $(r, 3)$ and (5, 9) has a slope of 2. 2

Loci and Constructions

Designers must be accurate as they prepare plans of projects. Among other instruments, designers use compasses, protractors, and computers to construct design layouts. Their work involves the basic constructions included in this chapter.

13-1 Basic Constructions

Objectives: Construct congruent line segments, congruent angles, and the bisector of an angle; translate a problem into the given statement, construct statement- and diagram.

It is possible to construct many geometric figures without making measurements. Two instruments are used, a **straightedge** and a **compass.**

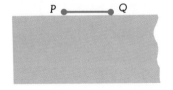

A straightedge is like an unmarked ruler. It is used to draw lines and segments. Two points, such as P and Q, lie on exactly one line. A straightedge is used to draw that line.

A ruler may be used as a straightedge for constructions, as long as the measurement marks are not used.

A compass is used to draw circles and arcs of circles. In a plane there is exactly one circle with a given center and radius. A compass is used to draw such a circle. You may wish to demonstrate the correct way to use a compass.

Emphasize that geometric constructions are done without measuring with a ruler or protractor.

The following **construction** shows how to construct a segment congruent to a given segment. *Notice the parts of the construction: given statement, construct statement, diagram, method, and justification.* The justification explains why the construction is valid.

Construction

Construction 1: Construct a segment congruent to a given segment.

Given: $\overline{AB}$

Construct: $\overline{CD}$ so that $\overline{CD} \cong \overline{AB}$

Method:

1. Use a straightedge to draw a line. Call it ℓ.
2. Choose any point on ℓ. Label it C.
3. Place the compass point on A and the pencil on B. The compass radius now has measure AB.
4. With the same compass setting, place the compass point on C. Mark an arc intersecting ℓ. Label the point D. Then, $\overline{CD} \cong \overline{AB}$.

   Labeling parts of the construction is important for reference as well as for the justification.

Justification: The radius for a circle with center C has the same measure as a circle with center A and radius AB. Thus, $\overline{CD} \cong \overline{AB}$ since the radii are congruent.

Construction 2:   Construct an angle congruent to a given angle.

Given: $\angle ABC$

Construct: $\angle DEF$ so that $\angle DEF \cong \angle ABC$

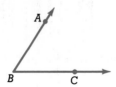

Emphasize to students
that neat, accurate
work is important for
all constructions.

Method:

1. Draw $\overrightarrow{EF}$.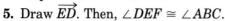

2. Using B as center, draw an arc that intersects both sides of $\angle ABC$. Call the intersection points X and Y.

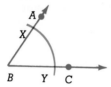

3. Keep the compass at the same setting. Using E as a center, draw an arc intersection $\overrightarrow{EF}$. Call the intersection R.
   The arc may intersect on either side of F or on F.

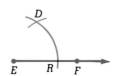

4. Using R as a center and radius setting XY, draw an arc that intersects the arc drawn in Step 3. Call the intersection D.

5. Draw $\overrightarrow{ED}$. Then, $\angle DEF \cong \angle ABC$.

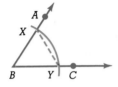

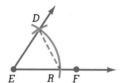

Emphasize the justification.

Justification: Draw $\overline{XY}$ and $\overline{DR}$. Then, $\overline{DR} \cong \overline{XY}$ because radii of a circle are congruent. Also, by construction, $\overline{ED} \cong \overline{BX}$ and $\overline{ER} \cong \overline{BY}$. Thus, $\triangle DER \cong \triangle XBY$ by SSS. Then, $\angle DEF \cong \angle ABC$ by the definition of congruent triangles.   *CPCTC*

Construction 3: Construct the bisector of a given angle.

    Given: $\angle ABC$

Construct: $\overrightarrow{BD}$ so that $\overrightarrow{BD}$ bisects $\angle ABC$

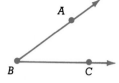

    Method:

1. Using B as a center, draw an arc that intersects both sides of $\angle ABC$. Call the intersection points X and Y.

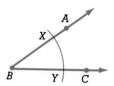

2. Keep the same compass setting. Using X as a center, draw an arc in the interior of $\angle ABC$.

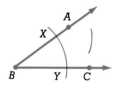

3. Keep the same compass setting. Using Y as a center, draw an arc that intersects the arc drawn in Step 2. Call the intersection D.

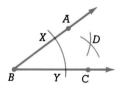

4. Draw $\overrightarrow{BD}$. Then, $\overrightarrow{BD}$ bisects $\angle ABC$.

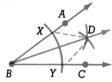

Justification: Draw $\overline{XD}$ and $\overline{YD}$. By construction, $\overline{XD} \cong \overline{YD}$ and $\overline{BX} \cong \overline{BY}$. Also, $\overline{BD} \cong \overline{BD}$. Thus, $\triangle BXD \cong \triangle BYD$ by SSS. By the definition of congruent triangles, $\angle XBD \cong \angle YBD$. Thus $\overrightarrow{BD}$ bisects $\angle ABC$.

Exploratory Exercises   For Exercises 1–4, see the Teacher Guide.

For each of the following, state the given and the construct statements, and provide a diagram for the given. Then, complete the construction.

1. Construct a segment whose measure is twice the measure of a given segment.

2. Construct a triangle congruent to a given triangle.

3. Construct an angle whose measure is one-half the measure of a given angle.

4. Construct an angle whose measure is the sum of the measures of two given angles.

Written Exercises

On a piece of paper, draw and label two segments like the segments shown below. Then, construct segments for each of the following measures.

1. $AB + CD$ **2.** $CD - AB$ **3.** $2AB$

4. $3CD$ **5.** $4AB - CD$ **6.** $2AB - CD$

7. $3(CD - AB)$ **8.** $2(AB + CD)$

For Exercises 1–29, see the Teacher Guide.

On a piece of paper, draw and label two angles like the angles shown below. Then, construct angles with each of the following degree measures.

9. $2y$ **10.** $x - 2y$

11. $\frac{1}{2}x$ **12.** $\frac{1}{2}y$

13. $\frac{1}{2}(x + y)$ **14.** $\frac{1}{2}x + y$

15. $\frac{3}{4}x$ **16.** $x + \frac{1}{2}y$

Perform the following constructions.

17. Draw a segment. Then, construct an equilateral triangle with the segment as one of its sides.

18. Draw a segment. Then, construct a segment whose measure is three times the measure of the given segment.

19. Draw an acute triangle. Then, construct the angle bisector of each of the angles.

20. Draw an obtuse triangle. Then, construct a triangle congruent to the triangle drawn.

21. Construct a 30° angle.

22. Construct a 15° angle.

23. Construct a 75° angle.

24. Construct a 45° angle.

25. Construct a 120° angle.

26. Construct a 135° angle.

27. Draw an angle and two segments. Then, construct a triangle whose sides and an included angle are congruent to the figures drawn.

28. Draw two angles and a segment. Then, construct a triangle whose angles and included side are congruent to the figures drawn.

Challenge Exercise

29. Inscribe in a circle, a triangle with angles constructed that are congruent to ∠1, ∠2, and ∠3 as shown at the right.

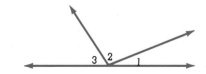

13-2 Perpendiculars and Parallels

Constructing perpendicular lines involves three different cases. Notice how these constructions are alike.

Construction

Construction 4: Construct a line perpendicular to a given line and through a given point *not* on the line.

Given: P is *not* on ℓ.

Construct: $\overleftrightarrow{PQ}$ so that $\overleftrightarrow{PQ} \perp \ell$

Method:

1. Using P as the center, draw two arcs that intersect ℓ. Call the intersection points V and W.

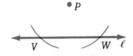

2. Keep the same compass setting. Using V as the center and then W as the center, draw arcs that intersect at a point other than P. Call the intersection Q.

   Note that in this example Q is on the opposite side of ℓ from P.

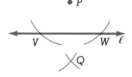

3. Draw $\overleftrightarrow{PQ}$. Then, $\overleftrightarrow{PQ} \perp \ell$.

This construction is vital to later constructions such as finding the incenter of a triangle.

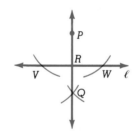

Justification: Draw $\overline{PV}$, $\overline{PW}$, $\overline{VQ}$, and $\overline{WQ}$. By construction, $\overline{PV} \cong \overline{PW}$ and $\overline{VQ} \cong \overline{WQ}$. Also, $\overline{PQ} \cong \overline{PQ}$. Thus, $\triangle PVQ \cong \triangle PWQ$. By the definition of congruent triangles, $\angle VPR \cong \angle WPR$. Also, $\overline{PR} \cong \overline{PR}$, so $\triangle VPR \cong \triangle WPR$ by SAS. The linear pair, $\angle PRV$ and $\angle PRW$, are right angles because they are congruent, supplementary angles. Thus, $\overleftrightarrow{PQ} \perp \ell$.

$$\triangle PVQ \cong \triangle PWQ \quad SSS$$
$$\angle VPR \cong \angle WPR \quad CPCTC$$
$$\triangle VPR \cong \triangle WPR \quad SAS$$
$$\angle PRV \cong \angle PRW \quad CPCTC$$

Constructions

Construction 5: **Construct the perpendicular bisector of a given segment.**

Given: $\overline{AB}$

Construct: $\overleftrightarrow{PQ}$ so that $\overleftrightarrow{PQ} \perp \overline{AB}$ and $\overleftrightarrow{PQ}$ bisects $\overline{AB}$

Method:

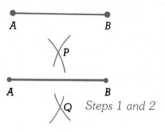

1. Set the compass with measure greater than $\frac{1}{2}AB$.

   Using A as a center, draw arcs on both sides of $\overline{AB}$.

   What happens if the compass is set with measure less than $\frac{1}{2}$ AB? The arcs do not intersect.

2. Keep the same compass setting. Using B as a center, draw arcs intersecting the arcs in Step 1. Label the points P and Q.

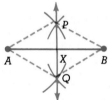

Steps 1 and 2

3. Draw $\overleftrightarrow{PQ}$. Then $\overleftrightarrow{PQ} \perp \overline{AB}$, and $\overleftrightarrow{PQ}$ bisects $\overline{AB}$ at X.

Justification: Draw $\overline{PA}$, $\overline{PB}$, $\overline{QA}$, and $\overline{QB}$. By construction, $\overline{PA} \cong \overline{PB}$ and $\overline{QA} \cong \overline{QB}$. Also, $\overline{PQ} \cong \overline{PQ}$. Thus, $\triangle PAQ \cong \triangle PBQ$. By the definition of congruent triangles, $\angle APX \cong \angle BPX$. Also, $\overline{PX} \cong \overline{PX}$, so $\triangle APX \cong \triangle BPX$ by SAS. It follows that $\overline{AX} \cong \overline{XB}$ and $\angle PXA \cong \angle PXB$. Thus, it is possible to conclude that $\overleftrightarrow{PQ} \perp \overline{AB}$ and $\overleftrightarrow{PQ}$ bisects $\overline{AB}$.

Construction 6: **Construct a line perpendicular to a given line through a given point on the line.**

Given: A is on ℓ.

Construct: $\overleftrightarrow{AB}$ so that $\overleftrightarrow{AB} \perp \ell$

Method:

1. Using A as the center, draw two arcs with the same radius that intersect ℓ. Call the intersection points X and Y.

2. Increase the compass radius. Using X as the center, draw an arc on one side of the line.

3. Keep the same compass radius. Using Y as the center, draw an arc that intersects the arc in Step 2. Call the intersection B.

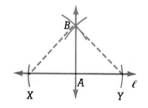

4. Draw $\overleftrightarrow{AB}$. Then $\overleftrightarrow{AB} \perp \ell$.

Justification: Draw $\overline{XB}$ and $\overline{YB}$. By construction, $\overline{XB} \cong \overline{YB}$ and $\overline{AX} \cong \overline{AY}$. Also, $\overline{AB} \cong \overline{AB}$. Thus, $\triangle AXB \cong \triangle AYB$ by SSS. By the definition of congruent triangles, $\angle BAX \cong \angle BAY$. Since $\angle BAX$ and $\angle BAY$ form a linear pair, by the Supplement Postulate they are supplementary. Congruent, supplementary angles are right angles. Thus, $\overleftrightarrow{AB} \perp \ell$.

One method used to construct parallel lines is to apply the constructions for perpendicular lines. By constructing two lines perpendicular to the same line, according to Theorem 6-8, the two lines are parallel.

Another method used to construct parallel lines is shown below.

Construction

Construction 7: **Construct a line parallel to a given line through a point *not* on the line.**

• *P*

> **Given:** *P* is *not* on ℓ.

> **Construct:** *n* so that $n \parallel \ell$ and *n* contains *P*.

> **Method:**

> 1. Draw a line through ℓ that intersects *P*. Call it $\overleftrightarrow{PX}$.

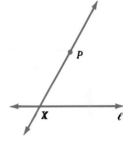

> *$\overleftrightarrow{PX}$ will be the transversal for n and ℓ.*

> 2. Copy one of the angles formed at *X* using *P* as a vertex and one side on $\overleftrightarrow{PX}$. Draw a line through *P* to form an angle congruent to the angle at *X*. Call it *n*. Then, $n \parallel \ell$ and *n* contains *P*.

> Students may experience some uncertainty as to where the arcs originate for this construction. Mention that this construction uses Construction 2 on page 476.

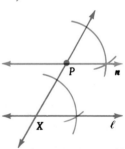

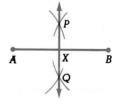

Justification: By construction, *n* contains *P*. Also, by construction, corresponding angles are congruent. Thus, $n \parallel \ell$.

EN: 1–10, 1, 2, 4–6, 10, 12, 15, 17, 18; **AV:** 1–10, 1, 2–18 even; **FD:** 1–10, 1–10, 12, p. 478, 26, 28;

Exploratory Exercises   **ALL LEVELS:** Algebra Review

The figure at the right shows the construction of the perpendicular bisector of $\overline{AB}$. Supply reasons for each statement in the justification for the construction.

1. Draw $\overline{PA}, \overline{PB}, \overline{QA}$, and $\overline{QB}$. Postulate 1-1

2. $\overline{PA} \cong \overline{PB}$ and $\overline{QA} \cong \overline{QB}$ by construction

3. $\overline{PQ} \cong \overline{PQ}$ Theorem 2-2

4. $\triangle PAQ \cong \triangle PBQ$ SSS

5. $\angle APX \cong \angle BPX$ CPCTC

6. $\overline{PX} \cong \overline{PX}$ Theorem 2-2

7. $\triangle APX \cong \triangle BPX$ SAS

8. $\overline{AX} \cong \overline{BX}$ and $\angle PXA \cong \angle PXB$ CPCTC

9. $\overleftrightarrow{PQ}$ bisects $\overline{AB}$.

9. Definition of Congruent Segments, Definition of Midpoint, Definition of Segment Bisector

10. $\overleftrightarrow{PQ} \perp \overline{AB}$ Theorem 3-14

Written Exercises

Complete each of the following constructions. For Exercises 1–18, see the Teacher Guide.

1. Draw a line and a point on the line. Label them q and T. Construct a line perpendicular to q and containing T.

2. Draw a line and a point *not* on the line. Label them ℓ and B. Construct a line perpendicular to ℓ and containing B.

3. Draw a segment. Label it $\overline{PQ}$. Construct a line perpendicular to $\overline{PQ}$.

4. Draw a segment. Label it $\overline{JK}$. Construct a bisector of $\overline{JK}$.

5. Draw a line and a point *not* on the line. Label them m and X. Construct a line parallel to m and containing X.

6. Describe a method based on perpendicular lines for constructing a line parallel to a given line and through a point *not* on the line.

7. Draw a segment. Construct a square with sides congruent to the given segment.

8. Draw an acute triangle. Construct the medians of the triangle. The medians of a triangle intersect at a point that is called the centroid of the triangle.

9. Copy $\triangle ABC$. Then construct the altitudes of the triangle. The altitudes of a triangle intersect at a point that is called the orthocenter of the triangle.

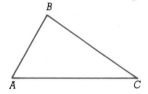

10. Copy $\triangle RST$. Then construct the altitudes of the obtuse triangle.

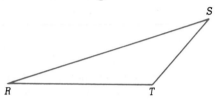

11. Draw a segment. Construct an isosceles triangle whose congruent sides are congruent to the given segment.

12. Draw an acute angle and a segment. Construct an isosceles triangle with base angles congruent to the given angle, and congruent sides congruent to the given segment.

13. Construct an isosceles right triangle.

14. Construct a 30°–60°–90° triangle.

15. Draw two segments and an angle. Construct a parallelogram with adjacent sides congruent to the given segments, and included angle congruent to the given angle.

Draw two segments of different lengths. Label the shorter segment $\overline{AB}$ and the other $\overline{CD}$. Draw an acute angle. Label it $x°$. Use the figures to complete each of the following constructions.

16. Construct a rectangle with sides measuring AB and CD.

17. Construct a rhombus with diagonals measuring AB and CD.

18. Construct a right triangle with hypotenuse measuring AB and an $x°$ angle.

13-3 Circles

The properties of a tangent can be used to construct a line tangent to a circle as shown in the following constructions.

Constructions

Construction 8: Construct a line tangent to a given circle at a given point on the circle.

Given: ⊙P with point A on the circle

Construct: ℓ so that ℓ is tangent to ⊙P at A

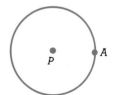

Method:

1. Draw $\overrightarrow{PA}$.
2. Construct ℓ through A and perpendicular to $\overrightarrow{PA}$.
   Line ℓ is tangent to ⊙P at A.
   Which of the constructions for perpendicular lines was used? Constructing a line perpendicular to a given line through a given point on the line.

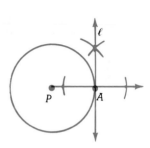

Justification: In a plane, if a line is perpendicular to a radius at a point on the circle, then the line is tangent to the circle. Therefore, ℓ is tangent to ⊙P at A.

Construction 9: Construct a line tangent to a given circle through a given point outside the circle.

Given: Point A outside ⊙C

Construct: $\overleftrightarrow{AD}$ so that $\overleftrightarrow{AD}$ is tangent to ⊙C

Method:

1. Draw $\overline{AC}$.
2. Construct the perpendicular bisector of $\overline{AC}$. Call it ℓ. Call X the intersection of ℓ and $\overline{AC}$.
3. Using X as the center, draw a circle with radius measuring XC. Call D and E the intersection points of the two circles.
4. Draw $\overleftrightarrow{AD}$. Then, $\overleftrightarrow{AD}$ is tangent to ⊙C.
   Point out that $\overleftrightarrow{AE}$ is also tangent to ⊙C.

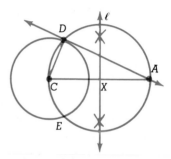

Justification: $\overline{AC}$ is a diameter of ⊙X. Thus, $\overparen{CDA}$ is a semicircle and $\angle CDA$ is a right angle. $\overline{CD} \perp \overleftrightarrow{AD}$ implies that $\overleftrightarrow{AD}$ is tangent to ⊙C at D.

Recall that in a circle, a chord that is the perpendicular bisector of another chord is a diameter. The justifications for each of the following constructions are based on that relationship.

Constructions

Construction 10: Locate the center of a given circle.

Given: a circle

Construct: point C so that C is the center of the circle

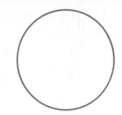

Method:

1. Draw two nonparallel chords. Call them $\overline{PQ}$ and $\overline{RS}$.
2. Construct the perpendicular bisectors for each chord. Call them ℓ and m. Call C the intersection of ℓ and m. Then, C is the center of the circle.

Justification: The perpendicular bisector of a chord contains the center of the circle. Also, two lines intersect in exactly one point. Thus, ℓ and m must intersect at the center of the circle.

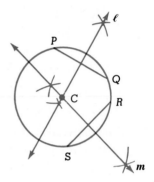

Construction 11: Construct a circle circumscribed about a given triangle.

Given: $\triangle ABC$

Construct: $\odot Q$ so that $\odot Q$ is circumscribed about $\triangle ABC$

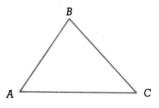

Any two sides can be used.

Method:

1. Construct perpendicular bisectors for two sides, $\overline{AB}$ and $\overline{BC}$. Call their intersection Q.
2. Using Q as a center, and QA as the measure of the radius, draw $\odot Q$. Then, $\odot Q$ is circumscribed about $\triangle ABC$.

$$QA = QB = QC$$

Justification: The perpendicular bisector of a chord contains the center of a circle. Also, each side of a triangle is a chord of a circle circumscribed about the triangle. Thus, Q must be the center of the circle circumscribed about $\triangle ABC$. Point Q is called the **circumcenter**.

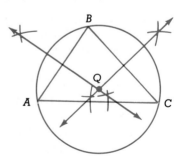

The following tells how to inscribe a circle in any triangle ABC.

Method:

1. Bisect $\angle A$. Bisect $\angle C$. Call X the intersection of the bisectors.
2. Construct a line through X and perpendicular to $\overline{AC}$. Call the intersection of the perpendicular with $\overline{AC}$, the point Y.
3. Using X as the center, draw a circle with radius measuring XY. Then, $\odot X$ is inscribed with $\triangle ABC$. Point X is called the **incenter.**

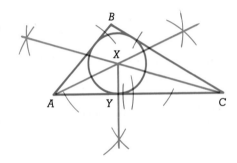

EN: 1–6, 1, 2, 4, 7, 8, 10; AV: 1–8, 1, 2, 4, 6, 7, 9, 10; FD: 1–8, 1–6, 8, p. 482, 13–15

Exploratory Exercises

The figure at the right shows the construction of a line tangent to $\odot C$ through A. Supply reasons for each of the following statements in the justification for the construction.

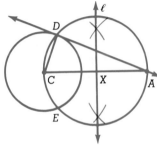

1. $\overline{AC}$ is a diameter of $\odot X$. Definition of Diameter
2. Draw $\overline{CD}$. Postulate 1-1
3. $\overset{\frown}{CDA}$ is a semicircle. Definition of Semicircle
4. $\angle CDA$ is a right angle. Theorem 10-8
5. $\overline{CD} \perp \overleftrightarrow{AD}$ Definition of Perpendicular Lines
6. $\overleftrightarrow{AD}$ is tangent to $\odot C$ at D. Theorem 10-11

State *yes* or *no* for each of the following exercises.

7. Suppose a circle is circumscribed about an acute triangle. Can the center of the circle be in the interior of the triangle? Must it be in the interior of the triangle? yes; yes

8. Suppose a circle is circumscribed about an obtuse triangle. Can the center of the circle be in the interior of the triangle? Must it be in the interior of the triangle?
   no; no

Written Exercises

Complete each of the following exercises. For Exercises 1–10, see the Teacher Guide.

1. Draw a circle. Label the center P. Locate a point on the circle. Label it A. Construct a tangent to $\odot P$ at A.

2. Draw a circle. Label the center Q. Draw a point exterior to the circle. Label it B. Construct a tangent to $\odot Q$ containing B.

3. Draw an acute triangle. Circumscribe a circle about the triangle.

4. Draw an obtuse triangle. Circumscribe a circle about the triangle.

5. Construct a right triangle. Circumscribe a circle about the triangle.

6. Construct a square. Circumscribe a circle about the square.

7. Construct a rectangle. Circumscribe a circle about the rectangle.

8. Construct an equilateral triangle. Inscribe a circle within the triangle.

9. Inscribe a circle within a right triangle.

10. Construct four circles within a square that are tangent to each other and to the sides of the square.

13-4 Proportions

It is possible to separate a segment into two congruent parts by constructing the perpendicular bisector of a segment. However, a segment cannot be separated into three congruent parts by constructing perpendicular bisectors. To do this, the method illustrated in the following construction is used.

Construction

Construction 12: Separate a segment into three congruent parts.

A similar method can be used for any given number of congruent parts.

> **Given:** $\overline{AB}$
>
> **Construct:** Points P and Q on $\overline{AB}$ so that $\overline{AP} \cong \overline{PQ} \cong \overline{QB}$

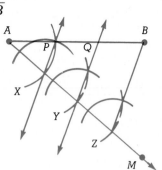

> **Method:**
>
> 1. Draw $\overrightarrow{AM}$.
> 2. With the compass point at A, mark off an arc on $\overline{AM}$ at X. Then construct $\overline{XY}$ and $\overline{YZ}$ so that $\overline{AX} \cong \overline{XY} \cong \overline{YZ}$.
> 3. Draw $\overline{ZB}$. Then, construct lines through Y and X that are parallel to $\overline{ZB}$. Call P and Q the intersection points on $\overline{AB}$. Then $\overline{AP} \cong \overline{PQ} \cong \overline{QB}$.

Justification: Since $\overleftrightarrow{PX} \parallel \overleftrightarrow{QY} \parallel \overline{BZ}$ and the lines cut off congruent segments on transversal $\overrightarrow{AZ}$, they cut off congruent segments on transversal $\overline{AB}$. Theorem 8-13

Encourage students to justify their constructions as shown in the examples.

The construction of parallel lines is used in the following construction of proportional segments.

Construction

Construction 13: Given three segments, construct a fourth segment so the measures are proportional.

> **Given:** segments with measures x, y, and z
>
> **Construct:** a segment with measure a so that $\dfrac{x}{y} = \dfrac{z}{a}$

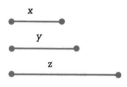

> **Method:**
>
> 1. Draw an angle. Call it $\angle P$.
> 2. With compass setting of x and compass point at P, mark an arc on one side of the angle. Call the intersection point Q.
> 3. With compass setting of y and point at Q, mark an arc on $\overrightarrow{PQ}$, labeling this intersection point R.

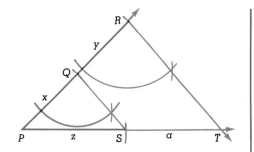

4. With compass setting of z and point at P, mark an arc on the other side of the angle at S.
5. Draw $\overline{QS}$. Then, construct a ray parallel to $\overleftrightarrow{QS}$ with endpoint R. The parallel ray intersects $\overrightarrow{PS}$ in a point. Call it T and say $ST = a$. Then, $\frac{x}{y} = \frac{z}{a}$ and $\overline{ST}$ is the required segment.

Justification: In $\triangle PRT$, $\overline{QS} \parallel \overline{RT}$. By Theorem 8-10, if a line is parallel to one side of a triangle and intersects the other two sides, then it separates the sides into segments of proportional lengths.

Recall that the measure of the altitude drawn to the hypotenuse of a right triangle is the geometric mean between the measures of the two segments of the hypotenuse. Applying this concept will help in the construction of the geometric mean for two given segments.

Construction

Construction 14: Construct the geometric mean of two given segments.

Given: $AB = x$ and $CD = y$

Construct: $\overline{PQ}$ so that PQ is the geometric mean of AB and CD

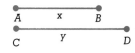

Method:

1. Draw a line. From a point P on the line, mark off segments measuring x and y. Label the endpoints L and M.
   Note that x and y are on opposite sides of P.
2. Construct the perpendicular bisector of $\overline{LM}$. Label the point of intersection S.
3. Using S as a center and LS as a radius, construct a semicircle with endpoints L and M.
4. Construct a line perpendicular to $\overline{LM}$ and containing P. Label the intersection of the line with the semicircle, Q. Then, PQ is the geometric mean of AB and CD.

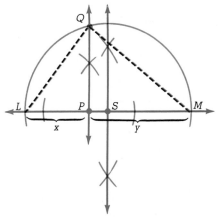

Justification: Draw $\overline{LQ}$ and $\overline{MQ}$. Since $\triangle LMQ$ is inscribed in a semicircle, $\angle LQM$ is a right angle and the triangle is a right triangle. By construction $\overline{PQ}$ is an altitude of $\triangle LQM$. Therefore, PQ is the geometric mean between LP and PM. But, $\overline{LP} \cong \overline{AB}$ and $\overline{PM} \cong \overline{CD}$, so PQ is the geometric mean between AB and CD.

Exploratory Exercises   ALL LEVELS: Mini Review

The figure at the right shows the construction of the geometric mean of *PL* and *PM*. Supply reasons for each statement in the justification for the construction.

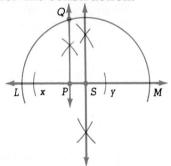

1. Draw $\overline{LQ}$ and $\overline{MQ}$. Postulate 1-1
2. $\widehat{LQM}$ is a semicircle. Definition of Semicircle
3. $\angle LQM$ is a right angle. Theorem 10-8
4. $\overline{PQ}$ is an altitude of $\triangle LQM$. Definition of Altitude
5. PQ is the geometric mean between PL and PM. Theorem 9-2

Written Exercises

For Exercises 1–21, see the Teacher Guide.
For each of the following exercises, draw a segment that is about 10 centimeters long on a piece of paper. By construction, separate the segment into the given number of congruent parts.

1. 2   2. 3   3. 4   4. 5   5. 6   6. 7   7. 8

On a piece of paper, draw and label three segments like the segments shown below. Then, for each of the following, construct a segment with measure *x* so that the given proportion holds.

8. $\dfrac{a}{b} = \dfrac{c}{x}$ 9. $\dfrac{a}{b} = \dfrac{x}{c}$

10. $\dfrac{a}{x} = \dfrac{b}{c}$ 11. $\dfrac{x}{a} = \dfrac{c}{b}$

12. $\dfrac{a}{2b} = \dfrac{c}{x}$ 13. $\dfrac{x}{2b} = \dfrac{c}{a}$

14. $\dfrac{x}{a} = \dfrac{a}{b}$ 15. $\dfrac{x}{b} = \dfrac{b}{c}$

Exercises 8– 15 and 21

Complete each of the following.

16. Draw a segment. Then, construct an equilateral triangle whose perimeter has the same measure as the segment.
17. Draw a segment. Then, construct a square whose perimeter has the same measure as the segment.
18. Draw a segment. Then, separate the segment into segments whose measures are in the ratio 2 to 3.
19. Draw a segment. Then, separate the segment into segments whose measures are in the ratio 1 to 2.
20. Draw two segments. Then, construct the geometric mean of the two segments.
21. Use the diagram for Exercise 8 and construct the geometric mean of segments *a* and *c*.

mini-review

12-6   1. Find the center and radius of a circle whose equation is $(x - 5)^2 + (y + 2)^2 = 36$. (5, −2), 6

12-2   2. The coordinates of the endpoints of a segment are (4, 7) and (8, −11). Find the coordinates of the midpoint. (6, −2)

12-4   3. Write an equation of the line containing points (2, 5) and (−6, 4).

12-2   4. Find the distance between (7, 3) and (9, −8). $5\sqrt{5}$

12-1   5. The coordinates of three vertices of a parallelogram are (1, 1), (8, −1), and (6, −5). Graph these points to find all possible coordinates for the fourth vertex.

3. $8y - x = 38$ **5.** (−1, −3), (13, −7), (3, 5)

Topology is a branch of geometry that deals with the distortion of geometric figures and shapes. Topics of topology include networks, mazes, map coloring, and one-sided surfaces such as the Möbius strip.

The concept of inside and outside is used frequently to explore topology. The Möbius strip is a famous illustration of this concept. Study the following steps for making a Möbius strip.

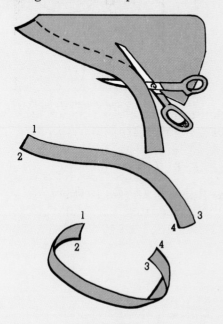

Cut a strip from a sheet of paper.

Number the ends as shown at the left.

Make a half twist on the band and join the ends, 1 to 4 and 2 to 3.

The completed band is an example of a Möbius strip (introduced by Augustus Möbius in the 19th century).

Exercises

Complete each of the following exercises.

1. Construct 2 Möbius strips using the steps shown on this page. See students' work.
2. Mark a point in the center of one strip. Then from the point, draw a line which returns to the point without removing the pencil from the paper. How many sides are there to the strip? How many edges? one, one
3. Cut the Möbius strip from Exercise 2 in half by cutting along the line that was drawn. How many sides are there? How many edges? two, two
4. Find a point on the second strip about one-third of the way from the edge. Cut the strip parallel to the edge and return to this point. Describe the result. There will be two intertwining strips; one is a two-sided band. The second is a new Möbius strip. See students' work.

13-5 Locus

Objective: Describe a locus in a plane or in space.

In geometry, a figure is a **locus** if and only if it is the set of all points and only those points that satisfy a given condition.

Circle P is the locus of all points in the plane of the page that are 2 centimeters from P. If a point is in the interior of the circle, it is less than 2 centimeters from P. If a point is in the exterior of the circle, it is more than 2 centimeters from P.

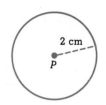

Suppose you are asked to describe a certain locus. First, you should read the problem carefully and draw the figure.

Find the locus of all points in a plane that are 15 millimeters from a given point, C.

The given figure is point C.

Draw the given figure.

After drawing the given figure, locate points that satisfy the given conditions.

Draw points that are 15 millimeters from C. Locate enough points to suggest the shape of the locus.

Locate points that satisfy given conditions.

As soon as the shape of a geometric figure begins to appear, draw a smooth curve or line that contains the points. Then, describe the locus in words.

Emphasize the importance of locating as many points as necessary to determine the shape of the locus.
Draw a smooth curve or line.

The points suggest a circle.

The locus of all points in a plane that are 15 millimeters from a given point, C, is a circle with center C and radius measuring 15 millimeters.

Describe the locus.

---

1. Draw the given figure.	
2. Locate points that satisfy the given conditions.	***Procedure for***
3. Draw a smooth curve or line.	***Determining Locus***
4. Describe the locus.	

Example

1
Determine the locus of all points in a plane that are 2 centimeters from a given line.

The figure is a line.

Draw the given figure.

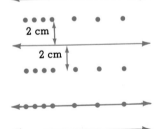

Draw enough points to determine the shape. Be sure to consider all possibilities.

Locate points that satisfy given conditions.

Draw a smooth curve or line.

The locus of all points in a plane that are 2 centimeters from a given line is a pair of lines parallel to the given line and 2 centimeters from the line.

Describe the locus.

A locus may differ depending on whether it is *in a plane* or *in space*.

The locus of all points *in a plane* that are equidistant from two parallel lines is a line that is parallel to the given lines and midway between them.

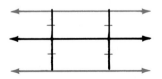

The locus of all points *in space* that are equidistant from two parallel lines is a plane that contains a line parallel to the given lines and midway between them, and is perpendicular to the plane containing the given lines.

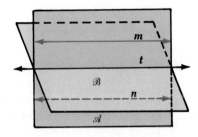

$m \parallel t \parallel n$

Plane $\mathcal{B}$ is midway between lines m and n, containing t.

Plane $\mathcal{B}$ is perpendicular to plane $\mathcal{A}$.

Exploratory Exercises   For all Exercises, see the Teacher Guide.

For each of the following exercises, describe the locus of points in a plane that are the given distance from a given point C. Then, describe the locus for all points in space.

1. 1 mm   2. 2 ft   3. 3 m   4. 4 in.

For each of the following exercises, describe the locus of points in a plane that are a given distance from a given line ℓ. Then, describe the locus for all points in space.

5. 40 m   6. 100 ft   7. 1000 cm   8. x in.

Complete the following exercises.

9. For $\angle XYZ$, describe the locus of points in the plane equidistant from $\overrightarrow{YX}$ and $\overrightarrow{YZ}$.

10. On $\overline{AB}$, describe the locus of points equidistant from both endpoints. In a plane, describe the locus of points equidistant from the endpoints of $\overline{AB}$.

11. In a plane, describe the locus of points equidistant from parallel lines p and q.

12. Describe the locus of points in a space for the given information in Exercise 11.

Written Exercises

Draw a diagram showing the locus of points for each of the following exercises. Then describe the locus.

1. all the midpoints of the radii of a circle with radius measuring 10 centimeters

2. all points in the interior of a 4-inch square that are 2 inches from two parallel sides of the square

3. all points in a plane that are equidistant from the sides of a given angle

4. all points in a plane that are equidistant from two intersecting lines in that plane

5. all the points in a plane that are equidistant from two given points

6. all the points in a plane that are equidistant from the centers of two given circles

7. all the points in a plane that are 5 centimeters from a circle with radius measuring 3 centimeters

8. all the points in a plane that are 3 centimeters from a circle with radius measuring 5 centimeters

9. all the points in a plane that are centers of circles with radii measuring 7 inches and that pass through a given point

10. all points in a plane that are centers of circles tangent to a given line at a given point on the line

11. all the points in a plane that are centers of circles that are tangent to both sides of a given angle

12. all points in a plane that are centers of circles with radii measuring 15 millimeters and tangent to a given line

13. all the points in a plane that are the third vertex of isosceles triangles with a given line segment for a base

14. all points in a plane that are the right angle vertex of right triangles with a given line segment for a hypotenuse

15. all the points in space that are a given distance from a given line

16. all the points in space that are equidistant from two given points

17. all the points in space that are the centers of spheres with radii measuring r units and tangent to a given plane

18. all the points in space that are the centers of spheres that are tangent to a given plane at a given point in the plane

Applications in Aviation   **Radar**

Because the traffic near large airports is extremely heavy, there are individuals specially trained to use radar to keep track of the continuous flow of planes arriving and departing. These individuals are called *air traffic controllers*. Air traffic controllers use *radar* to indicate the position of all aircraft within fifty miles of the airport. This airspace is called the flight information region.

The information controllers obtain through the use of radar enables them to prevent collisions of airplanes as they select the safest routes for pilots to follow to and from the airport. Controllers must depend on the use of radar as they direct landings from the ground whenever bad weather has made approach lights and runways difficult to see.

Radar is an electronic instrument that has the ability to detect and locate moving or fixed objects as small as insects or as large as mountains. It can be operated day or night and in all kinds of weather. Because of this, with the help of air traffic controllers, it contributes greatly to aviation safety.

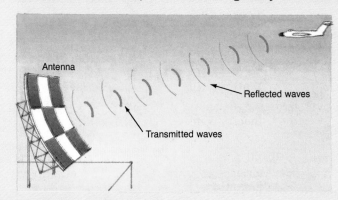

Antenna

Reflected waves

Transmitted waves

"Radar" stands for *ra*dio *d*etection *a*nd *r*anging. Most radar works by sending out radio waves that are reflected from an object and returned to the operator. The time it takes for the radio wave to return depends on the range—how far away—the object is. The direction the wave returns tells its location. Air traffic controllers see radar waves reflected from planes as bright spots on a circular display. The flight path of every plane in the area can be determined by following the movement of the spots. Through radio communication with the pilot, the controller can learn the height of the aircraft and identify its particular position shown on the radar screen.

Exercise

1. Describe the locus of points that represent the flight information region 50 miles or less from the traffic control tower. All points in the interior of or on the circle whose center is the traffic control tower and whose radius is 50 miles.

13-6 Intersection of Loci

Objective: Solve locus problems that must satisfy several conditions.

Some loci must satisfy several conditions. Such loci often can be determined by finding the intersection of loci that meet each condition.

The plural of locus is loci, pronounced low-sigh.

Example

1 **Determine the locus of all points in a plane that are equidistant from two given points and equidistant from two given parallel lines.**

Divide the problem into two separate locus problems.

The locus of all points in a plane that are equidistant from two given points is the perpendicular bisector of the segment joining the two points.

Point out that students should consider each condition separately and *then* focus on the intersection of conditions.

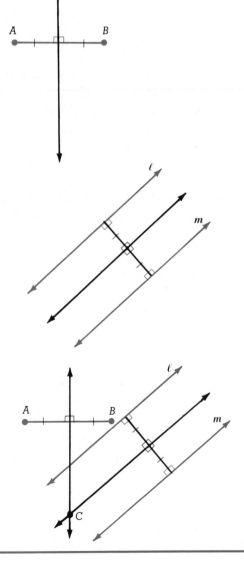

The locus of all points in a plane that are equidistant from two given parallel lines is a line parallel to the given lines and midway between them.

Consider the intersection of the separate problems.

If A and B are the given points, and ℓ and m are the given lines, then C is the only point that is equidistant from A and B, and equidistant from ℓ and m.

Some construction problems involve finding a point that satisfies several conditions.

Example

2

Given: $\overline{AB}$, $\overline{AC}$, and $\overline{CD}$

Construct: $\triangle ABC$ so that $\overline{CD}$ is an altitude of the triangle

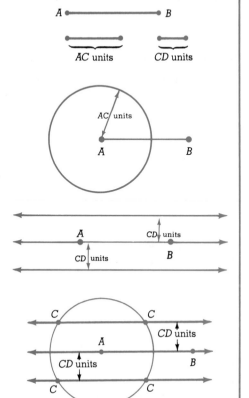

1. To determine the location of the third vertex, C, of the triangle, note that vertex C will lie AC units from A. The locus of all points AC units from A is a circle with center A and radius AC units.

   The third vertex will be somewhere on $\odot A$.

2. Endpoint D of altitude $\overline{CD}$ will lie on side $\overline{AB}$ or on the line containing $\overleftrightarrow{AB}$. Since $\overline{CD}$ is an altitude, then $\overline{CD} \perp \overleftrightarrow{AB}$. This means endpoint C will lie on a line parallel to $\overleftrightarrow{AB}$, CD units from $\overleftrightarrow{AB}$. The locus of all points meeting these conditions are two lines on either side of $\overleftrightarrow{AB}$, parallel to $\overleftrightarrow{AB}$ at a distance of CD units.

3. Point C must satisfy the conditions for being a vertex, Step 1, and the conditions for being the endpoint of an altitude, Step 2. Only four points satisfy these conditions.

   There are four possible ways to draw $\triangle ABC$.

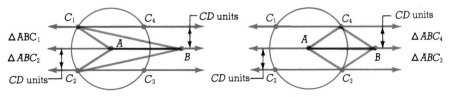

EN: 1–6, 3, 6, 9, . . . 24; AV: 1–6, 2–24 even; FD: 1–6, 2–10 even, 11–18, p. 492, 12–16 even

Exploratory Exercises

For each of the following, choose the letter of the best answer.

1. The locus of points in a plane equidistant from the endpoints of a segment is _____.

   a. a midpoint of the segment
   b. a bisector of the segment
   c. a perpendicular bisector of the segment
   d. two lines parallel to the segment

2. The locus of points in a plane equidistant from the sides of an angle is _____.

   a. a line joining the midpoints of the sides
   b. a bisector of the angle
   c. a circle about the vertex
   d. the angle vertical to the given angle

3. The locus of points in a plane equidistant from two parallel lines is _____.

(a.) a line parallel to the lines and midway between them

b. a line perpendicular to the given lines

c. a pair of lines parallel to the given lines and at a given distance from them

d. a circle between the lines and tangent to them

5. The locus of points in a plane at a given distance from a given point is _____.

a. a pair of perpendicular lines that intersect at the given point

b. a set of circles containing the point with radii of the given distance

(c.) a circle whose center is the given point and whose radius measures the given distance

d. a square whose diagonals intersect at the given point and sides measure the given distance

4. The locus of points in a plane equidistant from two intersecting lines is _____.

a. the intersection of each pair of lines and at a given distance from them

b. a circle with center at the intersection point and at a given distance from it

c. a pair of lines perpendicular to the given lines

(d.) a pair of lines that bisect the angles formed by the two intersecting lines

6. The locus of points in a plane at a given distance from a given line is _____.

(a.) a pair of lines parallel to the given line and at a given distance from it

b. a set of circles whose centers lie on the line and whose radii measure the given distance

c. a line perpendicular to the given line

d. a pair of planes parallel to each other and at the given distance from the line

Written Exercises

For each of the following exercises, describe all the possible ways the figures can intersect. For Exercises 1–24, see the Teacher Guide.

1. two parallel lines and a circle

2. two concentric circles and a line

3. two concentric circles and two parallel lines

4. a sphere and a plane

5. a sphere and two parallel lines

6. two circles

7. two spheres

8. a sphere and two parallel planes

9. a circle and a plane

10. a circle and a sphere

Draw a diagram to find the locus of points that satisfy the following conditions. Then, describe the locus.

11. all the points in a plane that are 2 centimeters from a given line and 5 centimeters from a given point on the line

12. all the points in a plane that are 3 centimeters from a given line and 1.5 centimeters from a given point on the line

13. all the points in space that are 2 inches from a given line and 5 inches from a given point on the line

14. all the points in space that are 3 inches from a given line and 2 inches from a given point on the line

15. all the points in a plane that are equidistant from three given points

16. all the points in a plane that are equidistant from a given line and equidistant from two points on the line

17. all the points in a plane that are equidistant from the sides of an angle and 4 inches from the vertex of the angle

18. all the points in a plane that are equidistant from the sides of an angle and a given distance from the vertex of the angle

19. all the points in a plane equidistant from two given parallel lines and a given distance from another line

20. all the points in a plane that are equidistant from two given parallel lines and a given distance from a point *not* on the lines

Complete each of the following.

21. Draw a line, m, and two points, C and D, on one side of the line. Then, construct the locus of points in the plane that are equidistant from C and D and on m.

22. Draw two segments, $\overline{PQ}$ and $\overline{RS}$. Choose a point between P and Q, and label it A. Then, construct a circle tangent to $\overline{PQ}$ at A and whose center lies on $\overline{RS}$.

23. Draw a line, ℓ, and a point, P, on the line. Draw Q *not* on ℓ. Then, construct the locus of the centers of all circles in the plane that contain P and Q.

24. Draw two parallel lines, ℓ and m. Choose a point between ℓ and m, and label it B. Construct a circle tangent to the two lines and containing B.

Statistics That Shape Your Life

Unemployment, the state of a person who wants to work but does not have a job, has been a problem in society. The unemployment rate varies greatly among different groups: the skilled, the unskilled, the blue-collar worker, the white-collar worker, youth, and others.

Youth unemployment

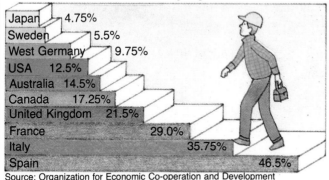

Japan — 4.75%
Sweden — 5.5%
West Germany — 9.75%
USA 12.5%
Australia 14.5%
Canada 17.25%
United Kingdom 21.5%
France 29.0%
Italy 35.75%
Spain 46.5%

Source: Organization for Economic Co-operation and Development
Copyright 1985, USA Today. Reprinted with permission.

Studies show that a large percentage of youth today do have jobs. The percentage of working teens increases through high school. Nevertheless, there are still some youth today that are seeking jobs and unable to find them.

The graph to the left indicates that this is a problem that exists worldwide. The figures shown were the projected rates of youth unemployment for 1985.

Exercises

Using the above graph, complete the following exercises.

1. Name the two countries that have the greatest difference in youth unemployment rates. What are some of the factors that could contribute to this contrast?
2. Which country has the closest rate of unemployment to the mean value? United Kingdom
3. According to the graph, which two countries have the least difference in rate?

1. Spain and Japan. Answers may vary. A possible answer is that Japan's youths have more technological expertise.
3. Sweden and Japan

Vocabulary

straightedge (475)
compass (475)
construction (475)
circumcenter (484)
incenter (485)
locus (490)

Chapter Summary

1. The parts of a construction are: *given statement, construct statement, diagram, method,* and *justification.* (475)
2. In geometry, a figure is a locus if and only if it is the set of all points and only those points that satisfy a given condition. (490)
3. Procedure for determining a locus: (490)
   1. Draw the given figure.
   2. Locate points that satisfy given conditions.
   3. Draw a smooth curve or line.
   4. Describe the locus.
4. The locus of all points *in a plane* that are equidistant from two parallel lines is a line that is parallel to the given lines and midway between them. (491)
5. The locus of all points *in space* that are equidistant from two parallel lines is a plane that contains a line parallel to the given lines and midway between them, and is perpendicular to the plane containing the given lines. (491)

Constructions:

Construction 1: Construct a segment congruent to a given segment. (475)

Construction 2: Construct an angle congruent to a given angle. (476)

Construction 3: Construct the bisector of a given angle. (477)

Construction 4: Construct a line perpendicular to a given line and through a given point *not* on the line. (479)

Construction 5: Construct the perpendicular bisector of a given segment. (480)

Construction 6: Construct a line perpendicular to a given line through a given point on the line. (480)

Construction 7: Construct a line parallel to a given line through a point *not* on the line. (481)

Construction 8: Construct a line tangent to a given circle at a given point on the circle. (483)

Construction 9: Construct a line tangent to a given circle through a point outside the circle. (483)

Construction 10: Locate the center of a given circle. (484)

Construction 11: Construct a circle circumscribed about a given triangle. (484)

Construction 12: Separate a segment into three congruent parts. (486)

Construction 13: Given three segments, construct a fourth segment so the measures are proportional. (486)

Construction 14: Construct the geometric mean of two given segments. (487)

Chapter Review

For Exercises 1–28, see the Teacher Guide.

13-1 **On a piece of paper, draw and label two segments like the segments shown at the right. Then, construct segments for each of the following measures.**

1. $XY + WZ$ **2.** $WZ - XY$

3. $4WZ$ **4.** $2XY - WZ$

On a piece of paper, draw and label two angles like the angles shown at the right. Then, construct angles with each of the following degree measures.

5. $a + b$ **6.** $2(a - b)$

7. $\frac{1}{2}a$ **8.** $a - \frac{1}{2}b$

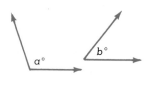

13-2 **Complete each of the following constructions.**

9. Draw a segment. Label it $\overline{AB}$. Construct a line perpendicular to $\overline{AB}$, through point B.

10. Draw a line and a point *not* on the line. Label them ℓ and Q. Construct a line parallel to ℓ and containing Q.

13-3   **Complete each of the following constructions.**

11. Draw a circle. Label the center C. Draw a point exterior to the circle. Label it A. Construct a tangent to $\odot C$ containing A.

12. Draw a triangle. Circumscribe a circle about the triangle.

13-4   **On a piece of paper, draw and label three segments like the segments shown at the right. Then, for each of the following, construct a segment with measure x so that the given proportion holds.**

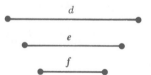

13. $\dfrac{d}{e} = \dfrac{f}{x}$

14. $\dfrac{d}{f} = \dfrac{x}{e}$

15. $\dfrac{x}{d} = \dfrac{d}{e}$

16. $\dfrac{f}{x} = \dfrac{2e}{d}$

17. Draw a segment. Then, construct an equilateral triangle whose perimeter has the same measure as the segment.

13-5   **Describe the locus for each of the following exercises.**

18. all the points in a plane that are 1 foot from a given point C

19. all the points in space that are 1 inch from a given point A

20. all the midpoints of the diameters of a circle

21. all the points in a plane that are centers of circles with radii measuring 11 centimeters and that pass through a given point

13-6   **For each of the following exercises describe all the possible ways the figures can intersect.**

22. a circle and a plane

23. a sphere and a line

24. two concentric circles and a plane

25. two parallel planes and a circle

Write a locus problem for which the following sets of points are the solutions.

26. the perpendicular bisector of a segment

27. a plane parallel to two given planes and midway between them

Complete the following construction.

28. Draw a line, ℓ, and two points, E and F, on one side of the line. Then, construct the locus of points in the plane that are equidistant from E and F.

Chapter Test

For Exercises 1–19, see the Teacher Guide.

On a piece of paper, draw and label two segments like the segments shown at the right. Then, construct segments for each of the following measures.

1. $PQ - RS$
2. $3PQ$
3. $3RS - PQ$
4. $2(RS + PQ)$

5. Draw two angles with degree measures c and d. Then, construct an angle having degree measure $c + d$.

Complete each of the following constructions.

6. Draw a line and a point *not* on the line. Label them m and T. Construct a line perpendicular to m and containing T.

7. Draw an obtuse triangle. Construct the medians of the triangle.

8. Draw a circle. Label the center H and a point on the circle T. Construct a tangent to $\odot H$ at T.

9. Construct a 30°–60°–90° triangle. Circumscribe a circle about the triangle.

10. On a piece of paper, draw and label three segments with measures r, s, and t. Then, construct a segment with measure x so that the proportion $\dfrac{r}{s} = \dfrac{x}{t}$ holds.

11. Draw a segment. Then, separate the segment into segments whose measures are in the ratio of 1 to 4.

Describe the locus for each of the following exercises.

12. all the points in a plane that are 5 inches from a given line ℓ

13. all the points in a plane that are 4 centimeters from a given point A

14. all the points in space that are 3 meters from a given point C

15. all the points in space that are 10 feet from a given line n

For each of the following, describe all the possible ways the figures can intersect.

16. two concentric spheres and a line

17. two parallel planes and a sphere

Describe the locus for each of the following exercises.

18. the intersection of two planes

19. all the points in space that are 6 millimeters from a given line and 10 millimeters from a given point on the line

CHAPTER 14

Transformations

Reflections, rotations, translations, lines of symmetry, and so on often appear in art and nature. The kaleidoscope illustrates rotations, reflections, point and line symmetry.

14-1 Mappings

Objectives: Name the image and the preimage of a mapping; recognize isometry or congruence transformations.

By moving all the points of a figure according to certain rules, new figures can be formed. Some are shown below.

A figure can be reflected.

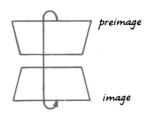

preimage

image

A figure can be rotated.

preimage

image

A figure can be slid.

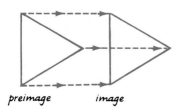

preimage   *image*

A figure can be enlarged.

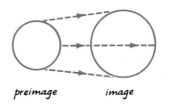

preimage   *image*

Emphasize the concept of mapping. Students may recall the use of this term with regard to the study of functions in algebra.

Notice that each point of one figure is paired with exactly one point of the corresponding figure. These mappings are called **transformations**. A transformation maps a **preimage** onto an **image**.

A transformation maps all points in a plane.

> In a plane, a mapping is a transformation if and only if each point has exactly one image point and each image point has exactly one preimage point.

Definition of Transformation

A transformation is a one-to-one mapping.

The symbol $\rightarrow$ is used to indicate mapping. For example, $\triangle ABC \rightarrow \triangle PQR$ means $\triangle ABC$ *is mapped onto* $\triangle PQR$. The order of the letters indicates the correspondence of the preimage to the image. The first vertices, A and P, are corresponding vertices. The second vertices, B and Q, are corresponding vertices. The third vertices, C and R, are corresponding vertices.

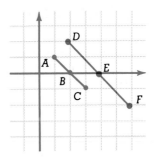

In the figure $\overline{AC} \rightarrow \overline{DF}$, A and D are corresponding points. C and F are corresponding points. B and E are corresponding points. Every point on $\overline{AC}$ corresponds to a point on $\overline{DF}$, and every point on $\overline{DF}$ corresponds to a point on $\overline{AC}$. Thus, the mapping is a transformation.

When a geometric figure and its transformation image are congruent, the mapping is called an **isometry** or a **congruence transformation**. When a figure and its transformation image are similar, the mapping is called a **similarity transformation**.

Example

1 **Suppose $\triangle ABC \rightarrow \triangle PQR$. Show that this mapping is an isometry.**

$\overline{AB} \cong \overline{PQ}, \overline{BC} \cong \overline{QR}, \overline{AC} \cong \overline{PR}$

$\triangle ABC \cong \triangle PQR$ by SSS

$\triangle ABC$ is the preimage.

$\triangle PQR$ is the image.

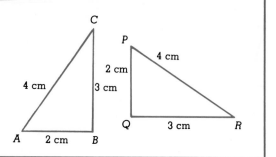

EN: 2–10 even, 2–26 even; **AV:** 1–10, 1–26; **FD:** 1–10, 1–20; ALL LEVELS: Algebra Review

Exploratory Exercises

Answer the following, if quadrilateral $RSTU \rightarrow$ quadrilateral $ABCD$.

1. Name the image of $\overline{UT}$. $\overline{DC}$
2. Name the preimage of D. U
3. Name the preimage of $\angle B$. $\angle S$
4. Name the image of $\angle T$. $\angle C$
5. Name the preimage of $\overline{AB}$. $\overline{RS}$

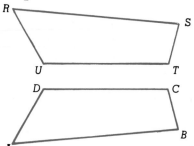

Answer each of the following, if pentagon $ABCDE \rightarrow$ pentagon $PQRST$.

6. Name the image of $\overline{CD}$. $\overline{RS}$
7. Name the image of $\angle E$. $\angle T$
8. Name the preimage of $\overline{PT}$. $\overline{AE}$
9. Name the preimage of $\angle Q$. $\angle B$
10. Name the image of $\overline{BC}$. $\overline{QR}$

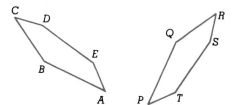

Written Exercises

In the figure, $\triangle ABC \rightarrow \triangle EBD$. Name the image of each of the following.

1. A E
2. B B
3. C D
4. $\angle CAB$ $\angle DEB$
5. $\angle BCA$ $\angle BDE$
6. $\overline{AC}$ $\overline{ED}$

Name the preimage of each of the following.

7. E A
8. B B
9. D C
10. $\overline{BE}$ $\overline{BA}$
11. $\overline{DE}$ $\overline{CA}$
12. $\angle DBE$ $\angle CBA$

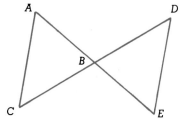

If the mapping is an isometry, use the figures below to find the image of the preimage given in Exercises 13–20.

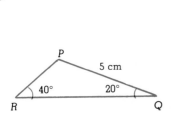

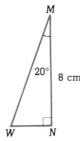

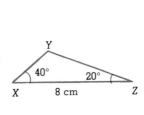

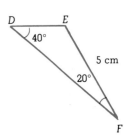

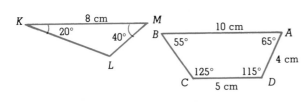

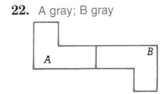

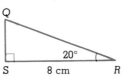

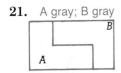

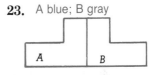

13. $\triangle MWN \triangle RQS$

14. $\triangle PQR \triangle EFD$

15. $\triangle SRQ \triangle NMW$

16. $\triangle MKL \triangle XZY$

17. $\triangle LMK \triangle YXZ$

18. quadrilateral $RSTU$ quad. $CDAB$

19. quadrilateral $BADC$ quad. $UTSR$

20. $\triangle ZYX \triangle KLM$

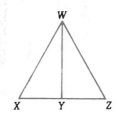

The L-shaped tile at the left is gray on top and blue underneath. Suppose two of these L-shaped tiles are used to form each of the following figures. Name the colors for figure A and figure B.

21. A gray; B gray

22. A gray; B gray

23. A blue; B gray

24. $\overline{WY}$

In the figure below, $\triangle XYW \cong \triangle ZYW$.

24. Name a segment that is its own preimage.

25. Name two points that are their own preimages. *W, Y*

26. Name a mapping that describes the congruence. $\triangle XYW \to \triangle ZYW$

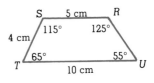

14-2 Reflections

Objectives: Name a reflection image with respect to a line; recognize line symmetry and point symmetry; draw reflection images, lines of symmetry, and points of symmetry.

One type of transformation is a **reflection.** For example, in the figure below, A is the reflection image of X with respect to ℓ. The *line of reflection, ℓ,* is a perpendicular bisector of the segment drawn from X to A. Since P is on the line of reflection, its image is P itself.

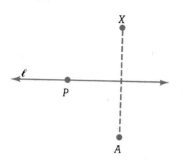

A line that is perpendicular to a segment and bisects the segment is a perpendicular bisector of the segment.

It is also possible to have a reflection image with respect to a point.

S is the reflection of R with respect to Q. The *point of reflection, Q,* is the midpoint of the segment drawn from R to S.

The reflection images of collinear points are collinear. The images of collinear points A, B, and C are the collinear points P, Q, and R. Therefore, it is said that *reflections preserve collinearity.*

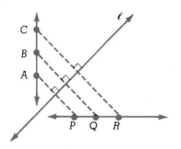

Points are collinear if and only if they lie on the same line.

The reflection image of *Y* is between the image of *X* and *Z* if and only if *Y* is between *X* and *Z*. Thus, *reflections preserve betweenness of points.*

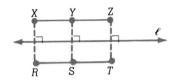

Reflections also *preserve angle measure* and *distance measure.* △*XYZ* is the reflection image of △*ABC*. By measuring the corresponding parts of △*ABC* and △*XYZ* it can be shown that △*ABC* is congruent to △*XYZ*.

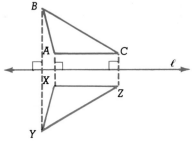

Points A, B, and C can be read in a clockwise fashion. △*ABC is said to have a clockwise orientation.*

Corresponding points X, Y, and Z are then in a counterclockwise position. △*XYZ is said to have a counterclockwise orientation.*

Emphasize that reflections preserve collinearity, betweenness of points, angle measure, and distance measure.

Point out the concept of *orientation* in terms of the corresponding parts of a figure and its image.

Suppose △*CBA* has a counterclockwise orientation, then what is the orientation of the reflection image? clockwise

Because only the orientation of a geometric figure is changed, *a reflection is an isometry.*

Example

1 **Construct the reflection image of △*ABC* with respect to ℓ.**

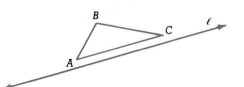

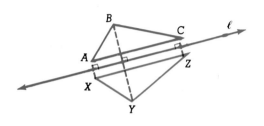

Construct perpendiculars from *A*, *B*, and *C* through ℓ. Locate *X*, *Y*, and *Z* so that ℓ is the perpendicular bisector of $\overline{AX}$, $\overline{BY}$, and $\overline{CZ}$. *X*, *Y*, and *Z* are the corresponding vertices of *A*, *B*, and *C*. The reflection image of △*ABC* is found by connecting the vertices *X*, *Y*, and *Z*.

△*ABC* → △*XYZ*

A line can be drawn through many plane figures so that the figure on one side is a reflection image of the figure on the opposite side. In such a case, the line of reflection is called a **line of symmetry.** The line of reflection is sometimes called axis of symmetry.

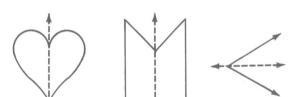

Example

2 **Test the given lines to see if they are lines of symmetry for rectangle $ABCD$.**

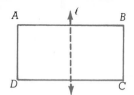

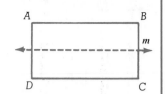

By measuring, it can be seen that ℓ is the perpendicular bisector of both $\overline{AB}$ and $\overline{CD}$. Any point to the left of ℓ has its reflection image to the right of ℓ. Likewise, by measuring, it can be seen that m is the perpendicular bisector of $\overline{AD}$ and $\overline{BC}$. Also, any point above m has its reflection image below m. Therefore, ℓ and m are lines of symmetry for rectangle $ABCD$.

A point can be found for many plane figures that is a point of reflection for all points on the figure. This point of reflection is also called a **point of symmetry.**

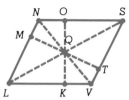

P and Q are points of symmetry.

A point of symmetry must be a midpoint for all segments with endpoints on the figure. In the figures above, P and Q are midpoints of the segments drawn. In the figure at the right, R is not a point of symmetry because R is not the midpoint of $\overline{XZ}$.

Exploratory Exercises

For each of the following figures, name the reflection image with respect to ℓ.

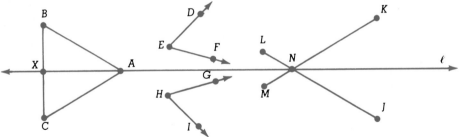

1. *A* A
2. *B* C
3. $\overline{AB}$ $\overline{AC}$
4. *F* G
5. *M* L
6. *K* J
7. $\overline{KM}$ $\overline{JL}$
8. $\angle DEF$ $\angle IHG$
9. $\overline{EF}$ $\overline{HG}$
10. $\triangle BXA$ $\triangle CXA$
11. *N* N
12. $\overline{DE}$ $\overline{IH}$

For each of the following figures, indicate if the figure has line symmetry, point symmetry, or both.

13. both
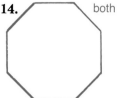

14. both
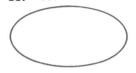

15. point

Written Exercises

Copy each figure below. Then draw the reflection image of each figure with respect to *m*.

For Exercises 1–6, see the Teacher Guide.

1.
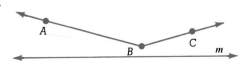

2.

3.
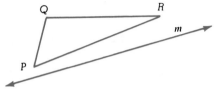

4.
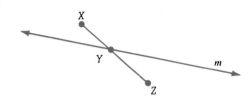

5.
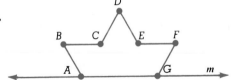

6.
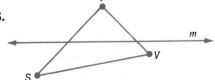

For each of the following figures, determine whether ℓ is a line of symmetry. Write *yes* or *no*. Then, explain your answer.

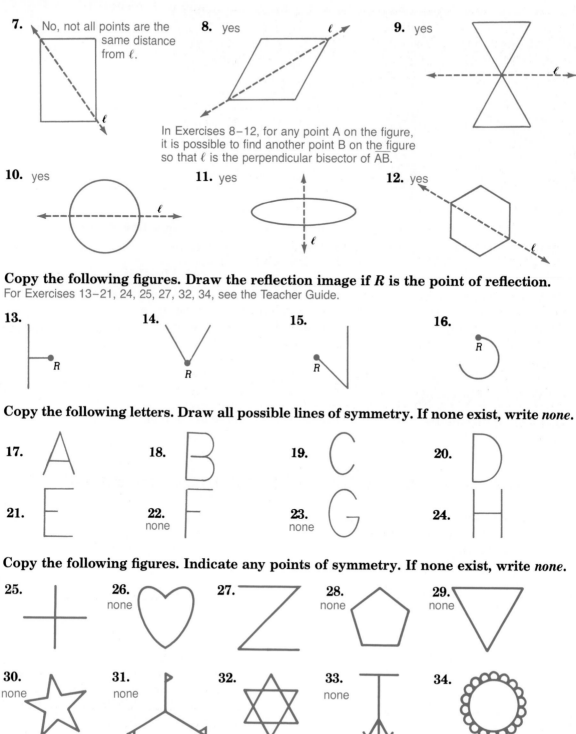

7. No, not all points are the same distance from ℓ.

8. yes

9. yes

In Exercises 8–12, for any point A on the figure, it is possible to find another point B on the figure so that ℓ is the perpendicular bisector of $\overline{AB}$.

10. yes

11. yes

12. yes

Copy the following figures. Draw the reflection image if R is the point of reflection.
For Exercises 13–21, 24, 25, 27, 32, 34, see the Teacher Guide.

13.

14.

15.

16.

Copy the following letters. Draw all possible lines of symmetry. If none exist, write *none*.

17. A

18. B

19. C

20. D

21. E

22. F
none

23. G
none

24. H

Copy the following figures. Indicate any points of symmetry. If none exist, write *none*.

25. +

26. none

27. none

28. none

29. none

30. none

31. none

32.

33. none

34.

14-3 Translations

Objective: Name and draw translation images of figures with respect to parallel lines.

A racing car speeds along a track to the finish line. The result of a movement in one direction is a transformation called a **translation.**

To find a translation image, perform two reflections in a row with respect to two parallel lines. For example, the translation image of the blue figure with respect to the parallel lines, *s* and *t*, is the red figure. First the blue figure is reflected onto the green figure with respect to *s*. Then, the green figure is reflected onto the red figure with respect to *t*. The two successive reflections are called a **composite** of reflections.

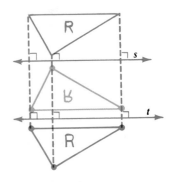

Example

1 **Draw the translation image of △*ABC* with respect to the parallel lines *s* and *t*.**

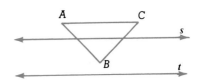

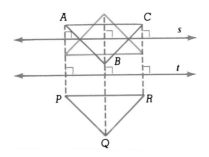

First draw the reflection image of △*ABC* with respect to *s*. Then draw the reflection image of that figure with respect to *t*. Thus, △*PQR* is the translation image of △*ABC*.

Since translations are composites of two reflections, all translations are isometries and all properties preserved by reflections are preserved by translations. The properties preserved are collinearity, angle and distance measure, and betweenness of points.

Emphasize the properties preserved by translations.

EN: 2, 7, 12, 2–18 even, 21, 24, 27, 28, 30, 31; AV: 1–12, 2–32 even;

Exploratory Exercises

FD: 1–12, 1–18, 20, 23, p. 510, 26–34 even

In the figure below, m and n are parallel. For each of the following, name the reflection image with respect to the given line.

1. A, m B
2. F, m F
3. E, m G
4. B, n C
5. H, n H
6. G, n P
7. A, n D
8. F, n Q
9. E, n R

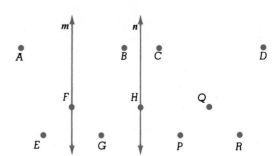

For each of the following, name the translation image with respect to m, then n.

10. A C
11. F Q
12. E P

Written Exercises

For each of the following, ℓ and m are parallel. Determine whether each red figure is a translation image of the blue figure. Write *yes* or *no*. Then, explain your answer.

1.   yes

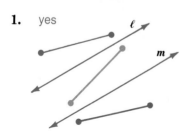

2.
No, the green reflection image is incorrect.

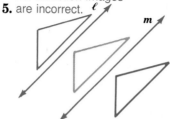

No, the green and red reflection images
5. are incorrect.

3.   yes

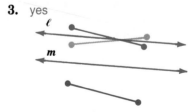

4.   yes

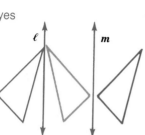

6.   yes

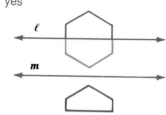

For Exercises 7–18, see the Teacher Guide.

7–12. In Exercises 1–6, name the reflections with respect to ℓ. If there are none, write *none*.

13–18. In Exercises 1–6, name the reflections with respect to m. If there are none, write *none*.

For Exercises 19–24, see the Teacher Guide.

Copy each of the following figures. Then find the translation image of each geometric figure with respect to the parallel lines s and t.

19.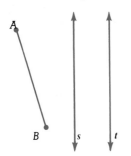

20.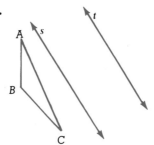

21.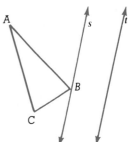

22.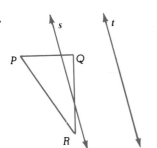

23.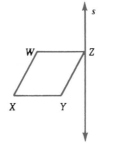

24.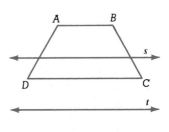

Use the figures below to name each of the following triangles. Assume s ∥ t.

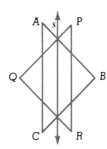

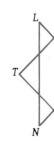

25. reflection image of △*ABC* with respect to *s* △*PQR*
26. reflection image of △*XYZ* with respect to *s* △*STU*
27. reflection image of △*PQR* with respect to *t* △*LMN*
28. translation image of △*ABC* with respect to *s* and *t* △*LMN*
29. translation image of △*PQR* with respect to *s* and *t* △*STU*

For Exercises 30–32, see the Teacher Guide.

30. Plan a proof to show that the translation image of △*ABC* with respect to the parallel lines *ℓ* and *m* preserves collinearity.

31. Plan a proof to show that the translation image of △*ABC* with respect to the parallel lines *ℓ* and *m* preserves betweenness of points.

32. Plan a proof to show that the translation image of △*ABC* with respect to the parallel lines *ℓ* and *m* preserves angle and distance measure.

14-4 Rotations

Objectives: Recognize whether a composite of two reflections is a rotation; find the measurement of the angle of rotation; find the reflection image of figures with respect to two intersecting lines.

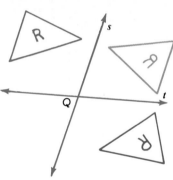

The composite of two reflections with respect to two intersecting lines is a transformation called a **rotation.** The reflection of the blue figure with respect to *s* is the green figure. The reflection of the green figure with respect to *t* is the red figure. Since *s* and *t* intersect, the red figure is the rotation image of the blue figure. *Q*, the intersection of the two lines, is called the **center of rotation.**

Point out that *Q* is a fixed point in this transformation.

Since rotations are composites of two reflections, all rotations are isometries and all properties preserved by reflections are preserved by rotations. Make note of the properties preserved.

Example

1 Suppose *t* and *s* intersect and △*ABC* is on one side of *t* and *s*. Construct the rotation image of △*ABC* with respect to *s* and then *t*.

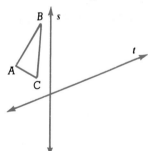 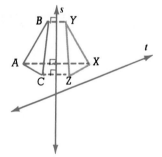 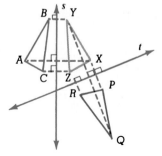

△*ABC* is on one side of *t* and *s*.

First, reflect △*ABC* with respect to *s*. The image is △*XYZ*.

Then, reflect △*XYZ* with respect to *t*. The image is △*PQR*.

The figure at the right shows how two reflections can be used to find the rotation image of $\overline{AB}$ with respect to ℓ and *m*. The image is $\overline{PQ}$.

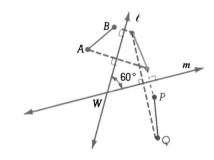

The same rotation image can be determined by using angles. Notice that ℓ and m form a 60° angle. It can be shown that $m\angle AWP = 2(60)$ or 120. Also, $\overline{AW} \cong \overline{WP}$. Likewise, it can be shown that if segments are drawn from B to W and from Q to W, then $m\angle BWQ = 120$ and $\overline{BW} \cong \overline{WQ}$.

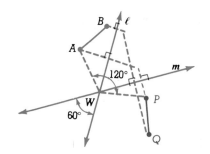

The angles, $\angle AWP$ and $\angle BWQ$, are called **angles of rotation.** In both cases, the degree measure of the angles is 2(60) or 120.

In a given rotation, if A is the preimage, P is the image, and W is the center of rotation, then the measure of the angle of rotation, $\angle AWP$, equals twice the measure of the angle between the intersecting lines of reflection.	*Postulate 14-1*

The following example shows how to find a rotation image using the angles of rotation.

Example

2 The intersection of ℓ and m at P forms a 40° angle. Use the angles of rotation to find the rotation image of $\overline{XY}$.

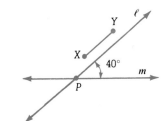

The angle of rotation has a degree measure of 2(40), or 80.

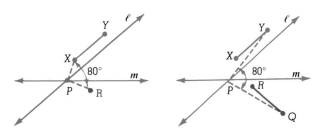

Construct $\angle XPR$ so that its degree measure is 80, and $\overline{XP} \cong \overline{PR}$. Then, construct $\angle YPQ$ so that its degree measure is 80, and $\overline{YP} \cong \overline{PQ}$. The rotation image of $\overline{XY}$ is $\overline{RQ}$.

Exploratory Exercises   ALL LEVELS: Mini Review

For each of the following figures, determine whether the indicated composition of reflections is a rotation. Explain your answer.

In both cases, there are proper successive reflections with respect to two intersecting lines.

1. yes

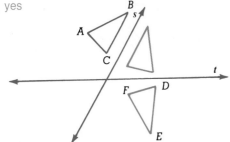

2. yes

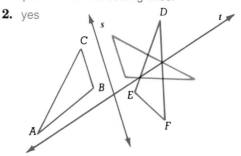

Use the figure to answer each problem.

3. Find the reflection image of quadrilateral *ABCD* with respect to *s*. quad. *EFCD*

4. Find the reflection image of quadrilateral *CDEF* with respect to *t*. quad. *JKHG*

5. Find the rotation image of quadrilateral *ABCD* with respect to *s* and *t*. quad. *HGJK*

6. Find the reflection image of quadrilateral *JKHG* with respect to *t*. quad. *CDEF*

7. Find the rotation image of quadrilateral *JKHG* with respect to *t* and *s*. quad. *CDAB*

8. Find the degree measure of ∠*APH*. 140

9. Find the degree measure of ∠*BPG*. 140

10. Find the degree measure of ∠*CPK*. 140

11. Find the degree measure of ∠*DPJ*. 140

12. Find the reflection image of *C* with respect to *s*. *C*

13. Find the rotation image of $\overline{BD}$ with respect to *s* and *t*. $\overline{GK}$

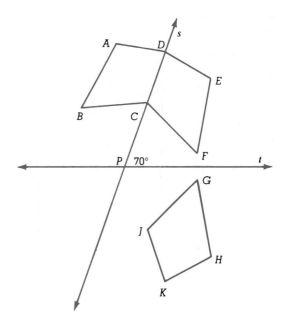

Written Exercises   For Exercises 1–2, see the Teacher Guide.

Complete each of the following.

1. Draw a segment and two intersecting lines. Find the rotation image of the segment with respect to the two intersecting lines.

2. Draw a triangle and two intersecting lines. Find the rotation image of the triangle with respect to the two intersecting lines.

Two lines intersect to form the angle with the following measurements. Find the measurement of each angle of rotation.

3. 30° 60°   **4.** 45° 90°   **5.** 60° 120°   **6.** 37° 74°

For Exercises 7–12, see the Teacher Guide.

Copy each of the following figures. Then, use the angles of rotation to find the rotation image of each geometric figure with respect to *s* and *t*.

7.

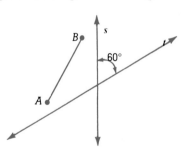

8.

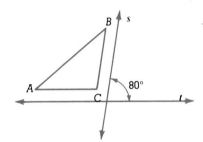

9.

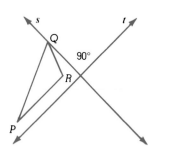

10.

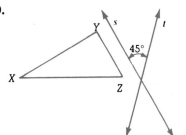

11.

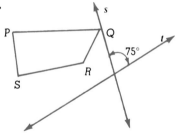

mini-review

10-6 | **1.** In the following figure, $m\widehat{BC} = 50$ and $m\widehat{AD} = 80$. Find $m \angle AED$. 65

12.

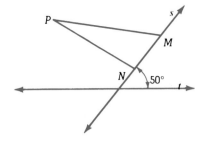

10-6 | **2.** In the following figure, $m\widehat{DE} = 100$ and $m \angle DHE = 20$. Find $m\widehat{GF}$. 60

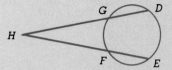

Determine whether each of the following is preserved by a rotation. Write *yes* or *no*.

13. collinearity yes

14. betweenness of points yes

15. angle measure yes

16. distance measure yes

12-3 | **3.** Write the equation of a line whose graph is parallel to the graph of $y = 4x - 5$ and passes through the origin. $y = 4x$

12-4 | **4.** Name the *y*-intercept of the line $2x - 4y + 10 = 0$. $\frac{5}{2}$

11-2 | **5.** Solve $A = \frac{1}{2}h(b_1 + b_2)$ for b_2.

5. $b_2 = \frac{2A}{h} - b_1$

14-5 Composites

Chris Yessios is an urban designer. Dr. Yessios uses a computer to generate visual models, computer graphics, of a building or of a group of buildings. The designer can study alternate points of view by using composites of geometric transformations.

Recall that composites of two reflections, rotations and translations, are isometries. Also, other composites of reflections can be described as isometries. The number of reflections and the relationship of the lines of reflections determine the kind of isometry.

Isometries is the plural of isometry.

Consider three lines intersecting at one point. The composite of three reflections with respect to these lines actually is a composite of a rotation and a reflection. But, this rotation and reflection are the same as a single reflection with respect to a line.

In the figure at the right, $\triangle ABC$ is transformed to $\triangle GHF$. This transformation can be described in the following three ways.

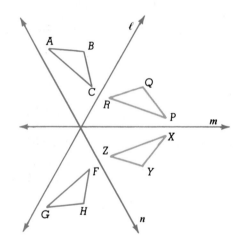

	reflection	reflection	reflection		first way
$\triangle ABC$	$\longrightarrow$	$\triangle PQR$ $\longrightarrow$	$\triangle XYZ$ $\longrightarrow$	$\triangle GHF$	

	rotation	reflection		second way
$\triangle ABC$	$\longrightarrow$	$\triangle XYZ$ $\longrightarrow$	$\triangle GHF$	

	reflection		third way
$\triangle ABC$	$\longrightarrow$	$\triangle GHF$	

$\triangle ABC$ has a clockwise orientation.   *$\triangle GHF$ has a counterclockwise orientation.*

Examples

1 Construct the composite of three reflections of $\overline{AB}$ with respect to the three parallel lines ℓ, m, and n.

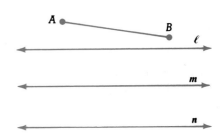

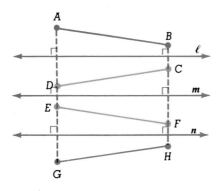

Construct perpendicular lines from A and B through ℓ, m, and n. Locate D and C so that ℓ bisects $\overline{AD}$ and $\overline{BC}$. Likewise, locate E, F, G, and H. Notice $\overline{GH}$ is the reflection image of $\overline{AB}$ with respect to the parallel lines ℓ, m, and n.

2 Describe the single isometry that can be used to map $\overline{PQ}$ onto $\overline{VW}$.

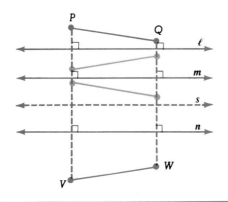

Draw $\overline{PV}$ and $\overline{QW}$ perpendicular to ℓ, m, and n. Locate s, the perpendicular bisector of $\overline{PV}$ and $\overline{QW}$. Thus, $\overline{PQ}$ maps onto $\overline{VW}$ by a single reflection of $\overline{PQ}$ with respect to s.

The figure at the right shows a composite of four reflections with respect to the parallel lines ℓ, m, n, and t. A composite of two translations with respect to ℓ, m, n, and t will also map $\triangle ABC$ onto $\triangle PQR$. But a single translation also can map $\triangle ABC$ onto $\triangle PQR$.

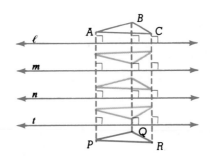

Using only ℓ, m, n, or t as the possible lines of reflection, there are two choices for finding the translation.

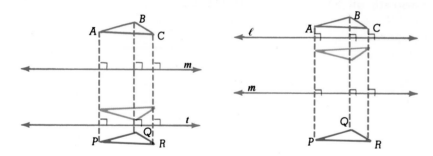

$\triangle ABC$ is mapped onto $\triangle PQR$ by a single translation with respect to either m parallel to t or ℓ parallel to n.

Example

3 **Suppose $\triangle PQR \cong \triangle ABC$. Name an isometry that maps $\triangle PQR$ onto $\triangle ABC$. Construct the necessary lines of reflection.**

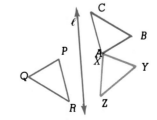

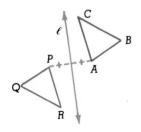

Construct ℓ, the perpendicular bisector of $\overline{PA}$.

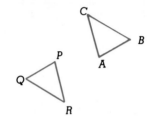

Reflect $\triangle PQR$ with respect to ℓ. Call this image $\triangle XYZ$.

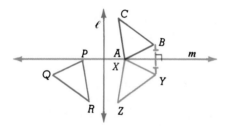

Construct m, the perpendicular bisector of $\overline{YB}$. The reflection of $\triangle XYZ$ with respect to m is $\triangle ABC$. Since ℓ intersects m, and $\triangle ABC$ is a composite of two reflections, $\triangle PQR$ maps onto $\triangle ABC$ by a rotation transformation.

Sometimes, the result of a composition of three reflections is *not* a single reflection, translation, or rotation. The result is an isometry called a **glide reflection,** which is a composition of a reflection and a translation.

In the figure, $\triangle ABC$ is reflected onto $\triangle GHK$ with respect to the parallel lines ℓ and m and the transversal n. The result is a glide reflection.

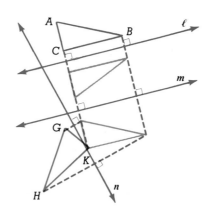

EN: 2–8, 3–5, 8, 9, 12; AV: 1–9, 1, 2, 4–10; FD: 1–9, 1, 2, 4–8, p. 517, 12–16

Exploratory Exercises

Answer each of the following for the figures labeled *A, B, C, D, E, F, G,* and *H.* Assume ℓ, m, n, p, q, r, and s are parallel.

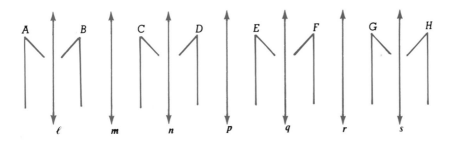

1. Name the reflection image of figure A with respect to n. F
2. Name the image of figure A as a composite of three reflections with respect to ℓ, n, and q. F
3. Name the reflection image of figure C as a composite of five reflections with respect to n, p, q, r, and s. H
4. Name the reflection image of figure G as a composite of two reflections with respect to q and m. A
5. Name the one reflection line that can be used to map figure A onto figure H. p
6. Name the two reflection lines that can be used to map figure A onto figure G.
7. Name the three reflection lines that can be used to map figure A onto figure F.
8. Name the single isometry that maps figure A onto figure E.
9. Name the single isometry that maps figure A onto figure F. reflection with respect to n
6. any of the following: m, q; ℓ, p; n, r
7. any of the following: ℓ, m, p; ℓ, n, q; m, p, q
8. translation with respect to ℓ, n or m, p

Written Exercises

For each of the following, copy the diagram. Then, complete each exercise.

1. Construct the composite of five reflections of $\overline{XY}$ with respect to the parallel lines ℓ, m, n, p, and q. See the Teacher Guide.

2. Describe the single isometry that can be used to map $\overline{XY}$ onto its image. reflection with respect to n

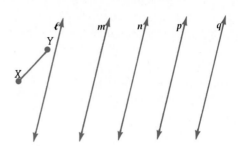

3. Construct the composite of six reflections of $\triangle ABC$ with respect to the parallel lines ℓ, m, n, p, q, and r. See the Teacher Guide.

4. Describe the single isometry that can be used to map $\triangle ABC$ onto its image with respect to n and r. translation

5. Find another pair of lines that can be used to form a single isometry that maps $\triangle ABC$ onto its image. ℓ, p or m, q

6. Name the different ways a composite of two or more reflections, with respect to parallel lines, can be described. An odd number of reflections can be called a single reflection. An even number of reflections is a translation.

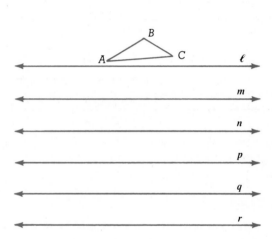

Name the kind of isometry that maps one figure onto the other. Then, copy each figure and construct the lines of reflection. For Exercises 7–12, see the Teacher Guide.

7.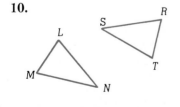

8.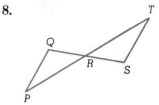

9.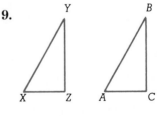

10.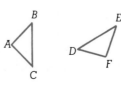

11.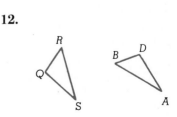

12.

Applications in Meteorology

James Seliga is a meteorologist who does research on the formation of snow and ice on the wings of airplanes at high altitudes. He knows that one of the unusual properties of water is its ability to change directly from a gas (water vapor) into a solid (ice) without going through the liquid stage. When water freezes, it may develop into sleet or hail. But when water vapor freezes, the result is snow crystals. As individual snow crystals fall through the atmosphere, they cluster together and form snowflakes.

Snow crystals generally have a hexagonal pattern. Three- and twelve-sided crystals form occasionally. The hexagonal form is a result of the arrangement of the oxygen atoms within the crystals. The exact form is directly related to the temperature and the amount of water vapor. The size of the crystal appears to depend on the amount of water vapor in the air. Because the water content of the atmosphere increases with increasing temperature, crystals formed at higher temperatures tend to grow larger and more complex than those at lower temperatures. Complicated forms of crystals will cling together with others to form snowflakes that consist of up to 100 crystals. The diameter of such a snowflake may be as large as one inch.

Photomicrography has made possible rapid documenting of the structure of snow crystals. Notice in the photograph above that the hexagonal shape is present. The geometry of the hexagon applies to the snowflake. Every snowflake has both line and point symmetry.

Exercises For Exercises 1–2, see the Teacher Guide.

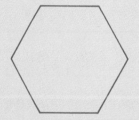

1. The figure at the right represents an ice crystal. Copy the figure, and then draw all possible lines of symmetry.

2. Copy the figure at the right, and then locate the point of symmetry.

3. Describe the result of rotating the hexagon 60° about its point of symmetry. What other degree measures produce the same result? The hexagon is mapped onto itself. Any multiple of 60° will produce this result.

14-6 Dilations

Objectives: Use scale factors to determine if a dilation is an enlargement, reduction, or a congruence transformation; find the scale factor for a given dilation; find the dilation image for a given center and scale factor.

A geometric figure can be altered in size. Enlarging or reducing the figure will *not* change its shape. This type of transformation is called a **dilation** or a **similarity transformation**.

Point out that a zoom lens on a 35 mm camera functions like a dilation.

In the figure, $\triangle XYZ$ is the dilation image of $\triangle PQR$. The measure of the distance from C to a point on $\triangle XYZ$ is twice the measure of the distance from C to a point on $\triangle PQR$. For example, the following equations hold.

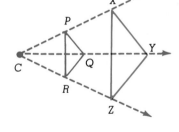

$$CX = 2(CP)$$
$$CY = 2(CQ)$$
$$CZ = 2(CR)$$

In this transformation, $\triangle PQR$, with **center** C and a **scale factor** of 2, is enlarged to $\triangle XYZ$.

The figure shows a dilation where the preimage $\overline{AB}$ is reduced to $\overline{ED}$ by a scale factor of $\frac{1}{3}$. Thus, $CE = \frac{1}{3}(CA)$. Therefore, $\frac{CE}{CA} = \frac{1}{3}$ and $\frac{CD}{CB} = \frac{1}{3}$. By proving $\triangle CAB \sim \triangle CED$, it can be shown that $ED = \frac{1}{3}(AB)$.

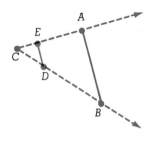

If a dilation with center C and a scale factor k maps A onto E and B onto D, then $ED = k(AB)$.	*Theorem 14-1*

Notice that when the scale factor is 3, the figure is enlarged. When the scale factor is $\frac{1}{3}$, the figure is reduced. In general, if k is the scale factor for a dilation, then the following is true.

If $k > 1$, the dilation is an *enlargement*.	*The dilation is not an isometry.*
If $0 < k < 1$, the dilation is a *reduction*.	*The dilation is not an isometry.*
If $k = 1$, the dilation is a *congruence transformation*.	*The dilation is an isometry.*

Example

1 **Given center C and a scale factor of $\frac{3}{4}$, find the dilation image of $\triangle PQR$.**

Since the scale factor is less than 1, the dilation is a reduction.

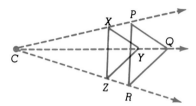

Draw $\overrightarrow{CP}$, $\overrightarrow{CQ}$, and $\overrightarrow{CR}$. Find X, Y, and Z so that $CX = \frac{3}{4}(CP)$, $CZ = \frac{3}{4}(CR)$, and $CY = \frac{3}{4}(CQ)$. $\triangle XYZ$ is the dilation image of $\triangle PQR$.

The following examples illustrate some of the basic properties of dilations.

Example

2 **Given center C, $\angle EFG$, and its dilation image $\angle QRS$, examine $\overline{EF}$ and $\overline{QR}$. Then examine $m\angle EFG$ and $m\angle QRS$. Determine whether the measures are enlarged, reduced, or congruent.**

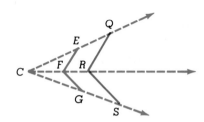

$\overline{EF}$ is enlarged to $\overline{QR}$.
$EF < QR$
$\angle EFG \cong \angle QRS$

The dilation preserves angle measure but *not* the measure of a segment unless the scale factor is 1.

Example

3 Given center C, $\triangle ABE$, and its dilation image $\triangle RFD$, describe the orientation of the two triangles.

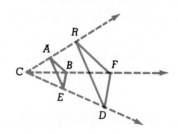

$\triangle ABE$ has a clockwise orientation and its dilation image also has a clockwise orientation. Dilation is said to preserve orientation.

EN: 1, 2, 7, 9, 6–10, 16–20, 21, 24, 27 . . . 48; AV: 1–9, 1–22, 25–47 odd;

Exploratory Exercises

FD: 1–9, 1–22, 25–45 odd, p. 522, 9, 10

For each of the following scale factors, determine whether the dilation is an enlargement, reduction, or a congruence transformation.

1. $4\frac{2}{5}$ enlargement **2.** $\frac{3}{8}$ reduction **3.** $\frac{1}{6}$ reduction **4.** $\frac{3}{2}$ enlargement

5. 0.61 reduction **6.** 7 enlargement **7.** 1 congruence **8.** 2.5 enlargement

9. Determine whether it is possible to have a scale factor of 0. Explain your answer.
No, all figures would have a single point as dilation images.

Written Exercises

A dilation with center C and a scale factor k maps A onto D, and B onto E. Find k for each of the following conditions.

1. $CD = 10$, $CA = 5$ 2 **2.** $CE = 18$, $CB = 9$ 2
3. $CD = 6$, $CA = 4$ $\frac{3}{2}$ **4.** $CA = 2$, $CD = 10$ 5
5. $AB = 3$, $DE = 1$ $\frac{1}{3}$ **6.** $AB = 3$, $DE = 4$ $\frac{4}{3}$
7. $CD = 3$, $CA = 6$ $\frac{1}{2}$ **8.** $CB = 28$, $CE = 7$ $\frac{1}{4}$
9. $DE = 12$, $AB = 4$ 3 **10.** $AB = 16$, $DE = 4$ $\frac{1}{4}$

11–20. Determine whether the dilation is an enlargement, reduction, or congruence transformation for each of the conditions in Exercises 1–10.
enlargements are: 11, 12, 13, 14, 16, 19; reductions are: 15, 17, 18, 20

Draw and label a figure like the one shown below. Then, find the dilation image of $\triangle ABC$ for the given scale factor and center. For Exercises 21–24, see the Teacher Guide.

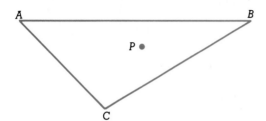

21. 3, center E **22.** $\frac{1}{3}$, center E

23. 2, center P **24.** $\frac{1}{2}$, center P

For each of the following scale factors, find the image of A with respect to a dilation with center P.

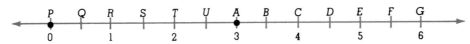

25. 1 A | **26.** 2 G | **27.** $\frac{2}{3}$ T | **28.** $1\frac{1}{3}$ C

29. $\frac{1}{2}$ S | **30.** $1\frac{1}{6}$ B | **31.** $1\frac{5}{6}$ F | **32.** $1\frac{1}{2}$ D

Graph each of the following ordered pairs. Then, connect the graphs in order. Using (0, 0) as the center of dilation and for a scale factor of 2, draw the dilation image. Then, repeat this using a scale factor of $\frac{1}{2}$. For Exercises 33–42, see the Teacher Guide.

33. (0, 2), (4, 0)
35. (−2, −1), (−2, −2)
37. (3, 4), (6, 10), (−3, 5)
39. (−1, 4), (0, 1), (2, 3)
41. (1, 2), (3, 3), (3, 5), (1, 4)

34. (3, −3), (−2, −2)
36. (3, 4), (6, 2)
38. (6, 5), (4, 5), (3, 7)
40. (1, −2), (4, −3), (6, −1)
42. (4, 2), (−4, 6), (−6, −8), (6, −10)

Find the measure of the image of $\overline{AB}$ with respect to a dilation with the given scale factor.

43. AB = 5 in., k = 6 30 in.
44. $AB = \frac{2}{3}$ cm, $k = \frac{1}{2}$ $\frac{1}{3}$ cm
45. AB = 16 ft, $k = 1\frac{1}{2}$ 24 ft

46. AB = 3.1 m, k = 5 15.5 m
47. AB = 12 cm, $k = \frac{1}{4}$ 3 cm
48. $AB = 3\frac{1}{3}$ in., k = 9 30 in.

Statistics That Shape Your Life

Presenting numerical information in a graph can be very helpful. The general relationship between two variables can be determined by glancing at the graph. However, depending on how they are constructed, graphs for the same data may lead to different conclusions. Both graphs shown here represent one student's quiz grades in geometry for one year. The only difference is that the scales on the y-axis have been altered.

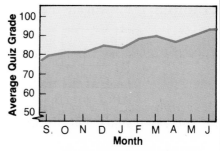

Exercises

1. Determine the range of the test scores. 12

2. The second graph appears to show a steep positive increase in quiz scores. Do you think it accurately represents the data? Answers may vary.

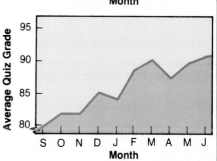

Topics in Geometry

In previous lessons you have investigated composites of various transformations. Consider the effect of four specific transformations on a rectangle.

The rectangle shown at the right has two types of symmetry: line symmetry and point symmetry. Lines ℓ and m are lines of symmetry and point O is the point of symmetry. The three symmetries are listed and illustrated in the following table. The fourth listing in the table is the identity transformation, I.

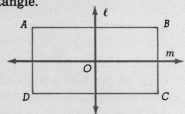

Transformation	Symbol	Original Position	Final Position
Line Reflection in ℓ	R_ℓ		
Line Reflection in m	R_m		
Rotation of 180° counterclockwise about point O.	$Rot_{180°}$		
Identity	I		

Example Investigate the effect of $Rot_{180°}$ followed by R_m. Try this with other figures.

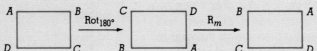

Look at the transformations above. Notice that R_ℓ takes rectangle $ABCD$ into the same position as the final one shown in the example. Therefore, R_ℓ has the same effect as $Rot_{180°}$ followed by R_m.

Exercises

1. Copy and complete the table at the right. Be sure to perform the transformation at the top first, and then the transformation at the left.

	I	R_ℓ	R_m	$Rot_{180°}$
I	I	R_ℓ	R_m	$Rot_{180°}$
R_ℓ	R_ℓ	I	$Rot_{180°}$	R_m
R_m	R_m	$Rot_{180°}$	I	R_ℓ
$Rot_{180°}$	$Rot_{180°}$	R_m	R_ℓ	I

2. A mathematical system is a group if and only if the operation in the system has the following properties: Closure, Associative, Identity, and Inverse. Show that the operation composition and the set of four transformations on the rectangle form a group. These properties may be verified. Use the completed table in Exercise 1.

Vocabulary

transformation (503)
image (503)
preimage (503)
isometry (504)
congruence transformation (504)
similarity transformation (504)
reflection (506)
line of symmetry (508)
point of symmetry (508)

translation (511)
composite (511)
rotation (514)
center of rotation (514)
angle of rotation (515)
glide reflection (521)
dilation (524)
scale factor (524)

Chapter Summary

1. Moving a geometric figure to show that it coincides with another geometric figure is called a mapping. The second figure is called the image of the first figure. The first figure is called the preimage of the second figure. (503)

2. Definition of a transformation: In a plane, a mapping is a transformation if and only if each point has exactly one image point and each image point has exactly one preimage point. (503)

3. When a geometric figure and its transformation image are congruent, the mapping is called an isometry. (504)

4. A reflection with respect to ℓ is a transformation such that if A is on ℓ then A and its image B are the same point. If A is not on ℓ, then ℓ is the perpendicular bisector of $\overline{AB}$. (506)

5. Reflections preserve collinearity, betweenness of points, angle measure, and distance measure. (507)

6. A translation is a composite of two reflections with respect to two parallel lines. (511)

7. A rotation is the composite of two reflections with respect to two intersecting lines. The point of intersection is called the center of rotation. (514)

8. Postulate 14-1: In a given rotation, if A is the preimage, P is the image, and W is the center of rotation, then the measure of the angle of rotation, $\angle AWP$, equals twice the measure of the angle between the intersecting lines of reflection. (515)

9. A composite of more than two reflections can be described as a single isometry or a congruence transformation. (518)

10. A composite of three reflections that does not result in a reflection, translation, or rotation is an isometry called a glide reflection. A glide reflection consists of a reflection and a translation. (521)

11. A dilation is a similarity transformation. (524)

12. Theorem 14-1: If a dilation with center C and a scale factor k maps A onto E and B onto D then $ED = k(AB)$. (524)

14-1 Suppose $\triangle ABE \rightarrow \triangle CBD$ and is an isometry. Name the preimage for each of the following.

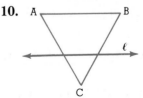

   1. *D E* **2.** $\angle CBD$ **3.** *B B* **4.** $\triangle CBD$ $\triangle ABE$
                 $\angle ABE$

Name a part congruent to the given part.

   5. $\angle A$ **6.** $\overline{BE}$ $\overline{BD}$ **7.** $\overline{AB}$ $\overline{CB}$ **8.** $\triangle BDC$ $\triangle BEA$
     $\angle C$

14-2 Copy each figure. Then draw the reflection image with respect to ℓ.
For Exercises 9–12, see the Teacher Guide.

   9.

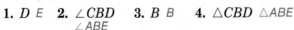

   10.

14-3 Copy each of the following. Then, draw the translation image of each figure with respect to the parallel lines s and t.

   11.   **12.**

14-4 Use the figure to complete each exercise.

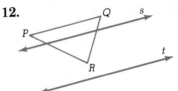

   13. Find the degree measure of the angle of rotation. 140

   14. Copy the figure at the right. Then, draw the rotation image with respect to ℓ and m. See the Teacher Guide.

14-5 Name a single isometry that can be used to map $\triangle ABC$ onto $\triangle PQR$.

   reflection with respect to m reflection with respect to m

   15.   **16.**

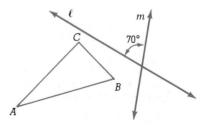

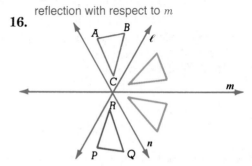

14-6 For each of the following scale factors, determine whether the dilation is an enlargement, reduction, or congruence transformation.

   17. 5 enlargement   **18.** $\frac{1}{4}$ reduction   **19.** 1 congruence transformation

Chapter Test

Determine whether each of the following is an isometry. Write *yes* or *no*.

1. reflection yes   **2.** translation yes   **3.** rotation yes   **4.** glide reflection yes

5–8. Name the properties preserved by each of the transformations in Exercises 1–4.

5. collinearity, angle measure, distance, betweenness   **6.–8.** same as reflection

Describe each of the following as a *reflection*, a *rotation*, a *translation*, or a *glide reflection*.

9. translation

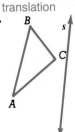

10. reflection

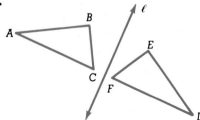

11. rotation

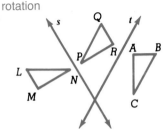

12. glide reflection

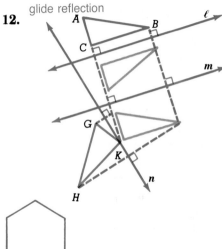

For Exercises 13–14, see the Teacher Guide.

13. Copy, then draw all possible lines of symmetry for the figure at the right.

14. Draw a triangle and four parallel lines. Reflect the triangle with respect to the four lines.

15. Name the single isometry that can be used in Exercise 14. translation

Determine whether the dilation is an enlargement, reduction, or congruence transformation for each of the following scale factors.

16. $1\frac{1}{3}$ enlargement   **17.** 1 congruence transformation   **18.** 0.3 reduction   **19.** 8 enlargement

Copy, then draw the dilation image of the figure at the right for the given conditions.

20. center C, $k = 3$

21. center C, $k = \frac{1}{3}$

22. center C, $k = 1$

For Exercises 20–22, see the Teacher Guide.

Appendix: Logo

A-1 Logo Language Commands

Refer to your Logo manual for instructions in loading the Logo language into your computer.

Logo is a unique computer language that was developed primarily to create a learning environment. It is a very powerful and complete programming language. With Logo you can examine and manipulate words, numbers, and lists. Its best known capability is turtle graphics. Logo graphics allow you to create complex figures using a simple command structure. The figure shown at the right was drawn using Logo commands.

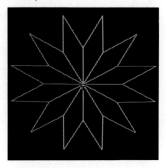

The Logo **turtle** is a small triangular shaped figure that you can use to draw shapes. Initially the turtle is located in the center of the screen. This location is called **HOME** for the turtle.

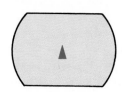

The turtle's starting point is in the center of the screen. It points upward.

The turtle will move according to the commands you give it from a computer keyboard. The turtle leaves a trail as it moves, which allows you to make a picture. Following is a list of frequently used commands for turtle movements.

*These commands are sometimes called **primitives**.*

Command	Abbreviation	Result
DRAW		Clears the screen and places the turtle in the center of the screen, pointing upward. You are now ready to draw a picture.
FORWARD	**FD**	Moves the turtle forward. A number is required to tell the turtle how many steps to move.
BACKWARD	**BK**	Moves the turtle backward. A number is required to tell the turtle how many steps to move.
RIGHT	**RT**	Turns the turtle right. A number is required to tell the turtle how many degrees to turn.
LEFT	**LT**	Turns the turtle left. A number is required to tell the turtle how many degrees to turn.
PENUP	**PU**	Allows you to move the turtle without drawing a line.
PENDOWN	**PD**	Tells the turtle to begin drawing a line again. Use this after PENUP.
HOME		Moves the turtle to the center of the screen. It is pointing upward.

Examples

1 Describe the turtle movements resulting from the following commands.

DRAW
FD 100   *Note there must be a space between the command and the number.*
RT 90
BK 75   Point out that Logo commands do not involve line numbers as in some forms of BASIC.

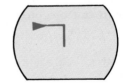

DRAW	Clears the screen and places the turtle in its HOME position.
FD 100	Moves the turtle 100 steps in the direction the turtle is facing.
RT 90	Turns the turtle 90° to the right.
BK 75	Moves the turtle back 75 steps.

Note that the turtle is facing right.

2 Write commands to draw a square.

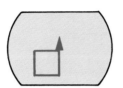

LT 90
FD 70
LT 90
FD 70
LT 90
FD 70
LT 90
FD 70

Have students draw other squares using the RT command.

How do these commands demonstrate the properties of a square?
They show four right angles and four congruent sides.

You may have noticed that all of the computer screen, except the bottom four lines, is used for graphics. These lines form a **window** for viewing the text that you type from the keyboard. Occasionally you need to use all of the screen for either graphics or text. The following commands are useful.

Command	Result
FULLSCREEN	All of the screen is used for graphics. Text can still be typed, but not viewed, in this mode.
TEXTSCREEN	All the screen is for text.
SPLITSCREEN	Returns to the split graphics/text screen.

It is often necessary to move the turtle to another position on the screen without drawing a line. The following example shows how the commands **PENUP** and **PENDOWN** can be used to accomplish this.

Example

3 **Draw a small square on the right side of the screen and a large rectangle on the left side of the screen.**

First, move the turtle to a spot on the right side of HOME.

DRAW
PU   *PENUP allows you to move the*
RT 90   *turtle without drawing a line.*
FD 60
LT 90
PD   *PENDOWN allows you to begin drawing.*

The turtle is now 60 steps right of HOME, pointing upward. The following commands will draw a square.

FD 65
RT 90
FD 65
RT 90
FD 65
RT 90
FD 65   *Notice that the turtle is pointing toward the left.*

Now, move the turtle to the left side of the screen.

PU   *PENUP*
FD 100
RT 90
PD   *PENDOWN*

The turtle is now on the left side of the screen pointing upward. Finally, draw the rectangle.

FD 115   Discuss how these
LT 90   commands demonstrate
FD 50   the properties of a
LT 90   rectangle.
FD 230
LT 90
FD 50   *Note you cannot see the bottom of the rectangle. That is*
LT 90   *because the computer is in SPLITSCREEN mode. If you type*
FD 115   *FULLSCREEN, the bottom of the rectangle will appear. What*
         happens if you type TEXTSCREEN? All the text appears.

Exploratory Exercises

1. About how many steps are there from the center of the screen to the top edge? 119

2. About how many steps are there from the center of the screen to the right edge? 139

3. About how many steps are there from the bottom left edge of the full screen to the top right edge of the screen? 366

4. Enter the following commands and describe the result. Diagonal lines
   RT 35   This is called
   FD 2000 **wraparound.**

5. Enter the following command and describe the result.
   FD −80
   The turtle moves 80 steps below HOME.

6. What other command would have the same result as Exercise 5? BK 80

Written Exercises

For Exercises 1–4, see the Teacher Guide.

Sketch the figure that would be drawn by the turtle for each set of commands. Indicate the final position of the turtle.

1. DRAW
   LT 90
   FD 100
   RT 90
   FD 100
   RT 90
   FD 100
   RT 90
   FD 100

2. DRAW
   FD 50
   RT 90
   FD 80
   RT 90
   FD 50
   RT 90
   FD 80

3. DRAW
   PU
   RT 90
   BK 100
   PD
   FD 40
   LT 90
   FD 70
   LT 90
   BK 50

4. DRAW
   FD 100
   RT 90
   FD 80
   RT 90
   FD 50
   RT 90
   FD 80
   BK 80
   LT 90
   FD 50

Write the commands to draw each figure. Answers will vary. See students' work.

5.

6.

7.

8.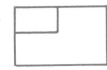

9.

10.

11.

12.

13. Write the commands to draw your initials in block letters. Answers will vary.

A-2 Polygons

In the previous section, you learned commands to draw a square. Recall that it was necessary to enter each command separately. In this section, you will learn two ways to enter commands that will save you time.

First, it is possible to put more than one command on a line. The following commands will draw a square.

FD 100 RT 90
FD 100 RT 90
FD 100 RT 90
FD 100 RT 90

Second, it is possible to combine all of the above commands on one line. This involves a new command called **REPEAT.** The format is as follows.

REPEAT *X*[COMMANDS]

X represents the number of times the commands in the brackets are to be repeated.

Emphasize that the commands are enclosed in brackets, not parentheses.

Example

1 Use the REPEAT command to draw a square.

REPEAT 4[FD 100 RT 90]

The commands in the brackets will be executed four times.
Note this square is the same as the one shown above.

The REPEAT command can be used to draw other regular polygons.

Example

2 List the steps necessary to draw an equilateral triangle like the one shown at the right.

RT 90   *Turns the turtle 90° to draw a horizontal segment.*

FD 80 LT 120   *Draws $\overline{AB}$ and turns the turtle.*

Note that the turtle must be turned 120° because the angle turned by the turtle is actually the *exterior angle*.

FD 80 LT 120   *Draws $\overline{BC}$ and turns the turtle.*

FD 80 LT 120   *Draws $\overline{CA}$ and turns the turtle.*

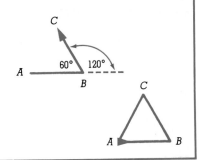

The triangle in the previous example may also be drawn using the REPEAT command. Since the turns are all exterior angle turns, it will be helpful if the segments making up the sides are extended so the angle measures of the exterior angles are more obvious. This will be the case for all polygons that are drawn in the examples for this section.

Example

3 Use the REPEAT command to draw the triangle shown below.

RT 90   *Turns the turtle to draw a horizontal segment.*

REPEAT 3[FD 100 BK 20 LT 120]

FD 100 BK 20 gives each side of the triangle a "tail."

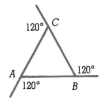

What is the sum of the exterior angles of a polygon if only one angle at each vertex is considered? You may recall from Theorem 7-2 that the answer is 360°.

You may want to review Theorem 7-2 on page 228.

This theorem from geometry leads to a rule in Logo called the **Total Turtle Trip Theorem.** If you want the turtle to draw a closed figure and end up where it started, pointing in the same direction, you must make the sum of the turns made by the turtle 360°. This will be called the **TTT Theorem.**

$$\frac{360}{\text{number of turns}} = \frac{\text{degree measure of}}{\text{each turn}}$$

TTT Theorem

The TTT Theorem is useful ·when drawing polygons. It can be used to calculate the turning angle for all regular polygons.

4   **Write the commands to draw a regular pentagon using the TTT Theorem.**

Since there are five angles, the turtle must make five turns.
Therefore, the degree measure of each turn is $\frac{360}{5}$ or 72.

RT 90

REPEAT 5[FD 90 BK 20 LT 360/5]

Note that the computer will calculate 360/5.

The figure at the right represents the
pentagon that is drawn.

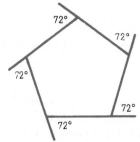

The TTT Theorem can be applied to polygons that are not regular.
The following example shows how it is possible to draw a parallelogram.

5   **Write commands to draw a parallelogram similar to the one shown below if**
$m \angle ABC = 100$, $AB = 85$, and $BC = 60$.

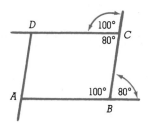

Discuss the properties of
a parallelogram.

The degree measure of an exterior angle at vertex B is 80 since $m \angle ABC$ is 100. Since
$\overline{AB} \parallel \overline{CD}$, $m \angle BCD = 80$. The turning angle is 100°, the measure of the exterior angle
at vertex C.

RT 90

REPEAT 2[FD 100 BK 15 LT 80 FD 75 BK 15 LT 100]

FD 100 BK 15 draws $\overline{AB}$ with its tail.
LT 80 turns the turtle at B so it is ready to draw $\overline{BC}$.
FD 75 BK 15 draws $\overline{BC}$ with its tail.
LT 100 turns the turtle at C so it is ready to draw $\overline{DC}$.
This sequence is executed twice.

Exploratory Exercises

Find the degree measure of the turning angle necessary to draw each regular polygon in Logo.

1. 18-gon 20

2. dodecagon 30

3. 20-gon 18

4. 24-gon 15

5. octagon 45

6. 11-gon 32.7

Written Exercises

See the Teacher Guide.

Sketch the figures that would be drawn by each of the following commands.

1. DRAW
LT 90
REPEAT 4[FD 80 BK 20 LT 90]

2. DRAW
RT 90
REPEAT 12[FD 15 BK 5 RT 360/12]

3. DRAW
REPEAT 3[FD 25 BK 10 RT 60]

4. DRAW
REPEAT 5[FD 15 BK 5 LT 30]

5. DRAW
REPEAT 2[FD 20 RT 90]
LT 90
REPEAT 3[LT 90 FD 20]

6. DRAW
RT 90
REPEAT 2[FD 50 BK 10 LT 30]
RT 260 FD 50

7. DRAW
REPEAT 5[FD 50 BK 10 RT 90]
LT 60 FD 50 BK 10
RT 120 FD 50

8. DRAW
LT 90
REPEAT 6[FD 25 BK 5 RT 60]
RT 90
REPEAT 3[FD 25 BK 5 LT 90]

Write a command using REPEAT to draw each regular figure with "tails."

9. 18-gon

10. dodecagon

11. 20-gon

12. 24-gon

13. heptagon

14. 11-gon

Write commands to draw each figure. Hint: You may have to move the turtle initially so each figure fits on the screen.

15.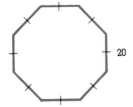

16.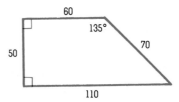

17.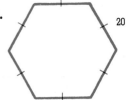

Write commands to draw each figure. Assume all polygons are equilateral.

18.

19.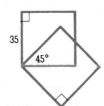

20.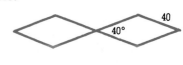

A-3 Procedures and Circles

In the previous section, you used the TTT Theorem as an aid in drawing polygons. The following commands were used to draw a regular hexagon.

> RT 90
> REPEAT 6 [FD 25 LT 360/6]

In Logo, it is possible to assign a name to these commands and store them in the temporary memory of the computer. This is called writing a **procedure.** The procedure can then be executed by simply typing its name.

It is possible to save procedures on a disk. Refer to your Logo manual for specific information.

In the following examples, you will teach the turtle how to draw a hexagon and a decagon.

Examples

1 **Write a procedure to draw a hexagon.**

The first step in writing a procedure is to choose a name. This procedure will be called HEXAGON.

TO HEXAGON

Notice that the screen has changed. The computer is now in EDIT mode.

RT 90
REPEAT 6[FD 25 LT 360/6]

Notice that the hexagon was not drawn while you entered your commands. In EDIT mode, the computer waits until you define and execute the entire procedure.

END

This command signals the end of the procedure.

The following line appears at the bottom of the screen.

> EDIT: CTRL-C TO DEFINE, CTRL-G TO ABORT

In order to define the procedure, you must hold the Control and C keys down simultaneously. The computer will respond with the message HEXAGON DEFINED.

Refer to the Logo manual for more information about the EDIT mode.

2 **Write a procedure to draw a decagon with sides of 25.**

TO DECAGON   *This step names the procedure, DECAGON.*
RT 90
REPEAT 10 [FD 25 LT 360/10]
END   *Remember to use CTRL-C to define the procedure.*

Just as typing FD 10 makes the turtle move 10 steps forward, typing the name of a procedure makes the turtle execute the commands in that procedure. If you type in the following commands, the turtle will draw the figures below.

HEXAGON
HOME
DECAGON

The "vocabulary" of the turtle can be expanded by teaching it new procedures. Previously defined procedures can be used as commands in these new procedures. HEXAGON and DECAGON are used in the following example.

Example

3 **Write a procedure to draw a decagon in the upper left part of the screen and a hexagon in the lower right part of the screen.**

First, write procedures to move the turtle to the different parts of the screen.

TO MOVEUL   *Moves the turtle to the Upper Left.*
   PU LT 90 FD 85 RT 90 FD 20 PD
END   *Remember to use CTRL-C.*

You may want to have students describe each step in these procedures.

TO MOVELR   *Moves the turtle to the Lower Right.*
   PU RT 90 FD 35 RT 90 FD 50 LT 180 PD
END

Next, write a procedure called POLYGON2 to draw both polygons in their assigned position.

TO POLYGON2
   MOVEUL
   DECAGON
   PU HOME PD   *Moves the turtle HOME before going to the next position.*
   MOVELR
   HEXAGON
END

Finally, type POLYGON2 and the figures will be drawn as shown at the right.

Have students type the command POTS (PRINTOUT TITLES) to see a list of procedures they have defined.

So far, you have only made the turtle draw polygons. You may recall that the circumference of a circle is the limit of the perimeter of the inscribed regular polygons as the number of sides increases. This suggests that circles can be created in Logo by having the turtle draw polygons with many sides.

You may want to refer to page 404 to review circumference.

Examples

4 **Using the TTT Theorem, write a procedure to draw a 20-gon.**

```
TO TWENTYGON
  RT 90
  REPEAT 20[FD 10 LT 360/20]
END
```

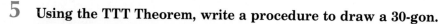

The figure at the right is a 20-gon.

5 **Using the TTT Theorem, write a procedure to draw a 30-gon.**

```
TO THIRTYGON
  RT 90
  REPEAT 30[FD 10 LT 360/30]
END
```

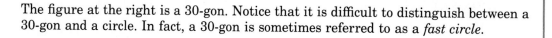

The figure at the right is a 30-gon. Notice that it is difficult to distinguish between a 30-gon and a circle. In fact, a 30-gon is sometimes referred to as a *fast circle*.

According to the TTT Theorem, the turtle must turn through 360° in order to return to its starting position when drawing polygons. The same is true when drawing circles. The above examples, and many similar examples, suggest the following rule for drawing circles.

In REPEAT X[FD Y RT Z], the product of X and Z must be 360.	*Rule for Circles*

Note that as X becomes larger, Y should become smaller so the circle will fit on the screen.

Compare the TTT Theorem with the Rule for Circles.

Example

6 **Find the value of X in the following command so that the turtle will draw a circle. Then write a procedure to draw the circle.**
REPEAT X[FD 1 LT 2]

$$2 \cdot X = 360 \quad \text{\textit{Rule for Circles, } } Z=2$$
$$X = 180$$

The following procedure will draw the required circle.

```
TO CIRCLE
   RT 90
   REPEAT 180[FD 1 LT 2]
END
```

You may want to explain that the command HIDETURTLE (HT) makes the turtle invisible and also speeds up the drawing. To make the turtle reappear use the command SHOWTURTLE (ST).

This kind of circle is sometimes called a *slow circle*.

You can use your understanding of circles to write procedures that demonstrate their properties.

Example

7 **Write procedures to draw two circles that are internally tangent and two circles that are externally tangent.**

First, write procedures to draw two different circles.

```
TO CIRCLE1
   REPEAT 36[FD 5 LT 10]
END
```

```
TO CIRCLE2
   REPEAT 36[FD 10 LT 10]
END
```

You know that the turtle begins and ends each of these circles at HOME. Therefore, let HOME be the point that is common to both circles. This procedure will draw two circles that are internally tangent.

```
TO INTANG
   CIRCLE1
   CIRCLE2
END
```

You can use basically the same procedure to draw two externally tangent circles. However, in this case the turtle must draw the circles in opposite directions. Write a procedure in which the turtle draws one circle by turning to the right.

```
TO CIRCLE3
   REPEAT 36[FD 10 RT 10]
END
```

The following procedure will draw two externally tangent circles.

```
TO EXTANG
   CIRCLE1       Turns to the left.
   CIRCLE3       Turns to the right.
END
```

Exploratory Exercises

Determine the value of X so that each command will draw a circle.

1. REPEAT X[FD 5 LT 36] $x = 10$
2. REPEAT X[FD 5 RT 18] $x = 20$
3. REPEAT 360[FD 1 RT X] $x = 1$
4. REPEAT 180[FD 1 LT X] $x = 2$
5. REPEAT 24[FD 3 LT X] $x = 15$
6. REPEAT X[FD 4 RT 14.4] $x = 25$

Indicate whether the following circles are fast or slow.

7. REPEAT 30[FD 5 RT 12] fast
8. REPEAT 60[FD 2 LT 6] slow
9. REPEAT 360[FD 1 RT 1] slow
10. REPEAT 90[FD 2 LT 4] slow

Written Exercises   See the Teacher Guide.

Locate each circle on a sketch of the computer screen. Outline its approximate position.

1. PU RT 90 FD 25 LT 90 FD 5 PD
   RT 90 REPEAT 36[FD 10 LT 10]
2. PU LT 90 FD 50 RT 90 FD 100 PD
   LT 90 REPEAT 36[FD 5 LT 10]
3. PU LT 90 FD 25 PD
   REPEAT 36[FD 3 RT 10]
4. PU FD 30 LT 90 FD 55 PD
   LT 90 REPEAT 36[FD 7 RT 10]

Write procedures to draw each figure.

5.

6.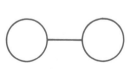

7.

8.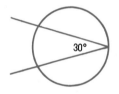

9.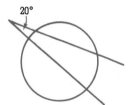

10.

11.

12.

13.

Challenge Exercises

14.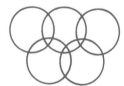

15.

16.

17. Create your own design using circles and polygons. See students' work.

A-4 Screen Coordinates

The computer screen is actually a coordinate plane in which every turtle position can be represented by an ordered pair, (x, y). The turtle's HOME position represents the origin, $(0, 0)$. The figure below shows the ordered pairs that represent the four corners of the computer screen.

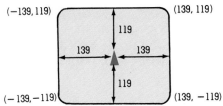

Logo has commands that will move the turtle to any of the coordinates in the screen's coordinate plane. Following is a summary of these commands.

Command	Result
SETX n	Moves the turtle horizontally to the x-coordinate specified by n.
SETY m	Moves the turtle vertically to the y-coordinate specified by m.
SETXY n m	Moves the turtle to the point specified by the ordered pair (n, m). If m is negative it should be placed in parentheses to avoid confusion with subtraction.

Note there is no comma between the n and m in the Logo command.

The above commands can be used to draw the x-axis and the y-axis.

Example

1 **Write a procedure to draw the x-axis and y-axis through $(0, 0)$. They should extend to the edges of the screen.**

```
TO XYAXES
    SETY 119         Draws from HOME to the top of the screen.
    HOME
    SETY -119        Draws from HOME to the bottom of the screen.
    HOME
    SETX 139         Draws from HOME to the right edge of the screen.
    HOME
    SETX -139        Draws from HOME to the left edge of the screen.
    HOME
    FULLSCREEN HT    Hides the turtle.
END
```

It is helpful to have the *x*-axis and *y*-axis appear on the screen when drawing figures. The procedure XYAXES should be the first part of every other procedure that is written in this section.

If you have a color monitor, you may want to have students draw the axes in a different color, using the PENCOLOR (PC) command.

The SET commands can be used to draw vertical or horizontal line segments.

Example

2 **Write a procedure to pick the pen up, move the turtle to (−50, −40), and put the pen down. Then draw a vertical segment from (−50, −40) to (−50, 40).**

TO SEGMENT
  XYAXES   *Draws the axes.*   Note −40 is in parentheses.
  PU SETXY −50 (−40)   *Picks the pen up and moves the turtle to the point represented by (−50, −40). The turtle remains pointed upward.*

  PD SETY 40   *Puts the pen down and moves the turtle vertically to (−50, 40).*

END
Note only the
y-coordinate changes.

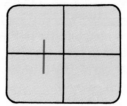

Graphing several segments will produce polygons.

Example

3 **Write a procedure to draw a triangle whose vertices have coordinates (0, 0), (−70, 100), and (−55, −75).**

TO TRI
  XYAXES
  SETXY −70 100   *Draws a segment from (0, 0) to (−70, 100).*
  SETXY −55 (−75)   *Draws a segment from (−70, 100) to (−55, −75).*
  HOME   *Draws a segment from (−55, −75) to (0, 0).*
END
HOME is a quick way to draw
a segment to the origin.

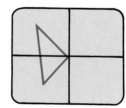

Examples

4 **Write a procedure to draw a square in the second quadrant that measures 100 steps on a side.**

TO SQUARE
  XYAXES
  PU SETXY −10 10
  PD SETY 110
  SETX −110
  SETY 10
  SETX −10
END

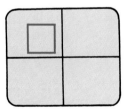

5 **The coordinates of three vertices of a parallelogram are (0, 0), (30, 40), and (100, 40). Find the coordinates of the fourth vertex and then write a procedure to draw the parallelogram.**

In a parallelogram, opposite sides are parallel and congruent. Using the sketch at the right, the point with coordinates (70, 0) satisfies both conditions.

The following procedure can be used to draw the parallelogram.

TO PARALL
  XYAXES
  SETX 70 SETXY 100 40 SETX 30 HOME
END

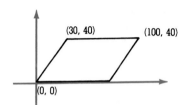

Exploratory Exercises   See the Teacher Guide

Draw the coordinate axes as they would appear on the computer screen. Sketch and then name the figure determined by the given commands.

1. SETY 50
  SETXY 50 0
  HOME

2. SETXY 100 100
  SETX 0
  HOME

3. PU SETXY 10 (−10) PD
  RT 180
  REPEAT 4[FD 100 LT 90]

4. SETY 75
  SETXY −50 0
  SETX 50
  SETXY 0 75

5. SETX −50
  SETXY −70 (−70)
  SETX −20
  HOME

6. PU SETXY −100 30 PD
  SETXY −80 (−50)
  SETXY 80 (−50)
  SETXY 100 30
  SETXY −100 30

Written Exercises

Using SETXY commands draw the coordinate axes for each exercise. Then, write procedures to draw each figure. See the Teacher Guide.

1.

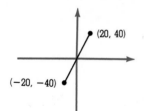

(20, 40)

(−20, −40)

2.

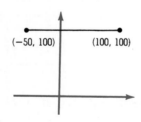

(−50, 100)   (100, 100)

3.

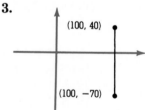

(100, 40)

(100, −70)

4.

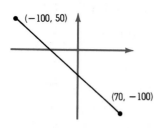

(−100, 50)

(70, −100)

5.

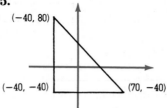

(−40, 80)

(−40, −40)   (70, −40)

6.

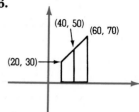

(40, 50) (60, 70)

(20, 30)

7.

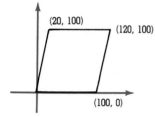

(20, 100) (120, 100)

(100, 0)

8.

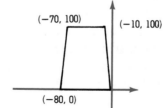

(−70, 100)   (−10, 100)

(−80, 0)

9.

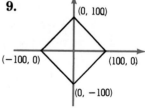

(0, 100)

(−100, 0)   (100, 0)

(0, −100)

For each of the following figures, find the missing coordinate. Then write a procedure to draw each figure.

10.

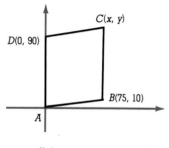

C(x, y)

D(0, 90)

B(75, 10)

A

parallelogram

11.

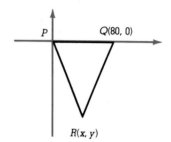

P   Q(80, 0)

R(x, y)

isosceles triangle

548 *Logo*

Diagnostic Skills Review

Integer Equations: Addition and Subtraction

Solve each equation.

1. $7 + 5 = x$ 12
2. $6 + 4 = x$ 10
3. $8 + 9 = x$ 17
4. $19 + 20 = x$ 39
5. $13 + 15 = x$ 28
6. $45 + 24 = x$ 69
7. $38 + 16 = x$ 54
8. $96 + 52 = x$ 148
9. $77 + 9 = x$ 86
10. $104 + 47 = x$ 151
11. $83 + 86 = x$ 169
12. $27 + 34 = x$ 61
13. $636 + 104 = x$ 740
14. $108 + 597 = x$ 705
15. $302 + 969 = x$ 1271
16. $47 + 38 + 76 = x$ 161
17. $29 + 62 + 35 = x$ 126
18. $51 + 89 + 96 = x$ 236
19. $20 + 63 + 57 = x$ 140
20. $34 + 49 + 72 = x$ 155
21. $66 + 28 + 92 = x$ 186
22. $-8 + (-5) = x$ -13
23. $-7 + (-9) = x$ -16
24. $-10 + (-12) = x$ -22
25. $0 + (-6) = x$ -6
26. $-4 + (-3) = x$ -7
27. $-10 + 0 = x$ -10
28. $-40 + (-30) = x$ -70
29. $-25 + (-71) = x$ -96
30. $0 + (-62) = x$ -62
31. $-66 + (-33) = x$ -99
32. $-36 + (-42) = x$ -78
33. $-86 + (-200) = x$ -286
34. $-152 + (-18) = x$ -170
35. $-206 + (-606) = x$ -812
36. $-829 + (-91) = x$ -920
37. $-709 + (-196) = x$ -905
38. $-643 + (-167) = x$ -810
39. $-229 + (-280) = x$ -509
40. $-7468 + (-4923) = x$
41. $-25,406 + (-9,329) = x$
42. $-2397 + (-4945) = x$
43. $-11 + 11 = x$ 0
44. $-1 + 12 = x$ 11
45. $5 + (-5) = x$ 0
46. $-10 + 7 = x$ -3
47. $10 + (-4) = x$ 6
48. $56 + (-10) = x$ 46
49. $-8 + 13 = x$ 5
50. $12 + (-19) = x$ -7
51. $-15 + 14 = x$ -1
52. $24 + (-36) = x$ -12
53. $52 + (-48) = x$ 4
54. $-24 + 30 = x$ 6
55. $40 + (-27) = x$ 13
56. $-54 + 46 = x$ -8
57. $38 + (-50) = x$ -12
58. $-16 + 31 = x$ 15
59. $75 + (-92) = x$ -17
60. $123 + (-106) = x$ 17
61. $-2046 + 8752 = x$ 6706
62. $-104 + 96 = x$ -8
63. $728 + (-469) = x$ 259

40. $-12,391$

41. $-34,735$

42. -7342

Solve each equation.

64. $47 - 41 = x$ ▮
65. $13 - 5 = x$ 8
66. $21 - 17 = x$ 4
67. $39 - 0 = x$ ▮
68. $85 - 72 = x$ 13
69. $65 - 0 = x$ 65
70. $165 - 141 = x$ ▮
71. $236 - 125 = x$ 111
72. $387 - 281 = x$ 106
73. $603 - 591 = x$ ▮
74. $409 - 268 = x$ 141
75. $506 - 152 = x$ 354
76. $792 - 237 = x$ ▮
77. $176 - 59 = x$ 117
78. $321 - 218 = x$ 103
79. $226 - 177 = x$ 49
80. $833 - 546 = x$ 287
81. $920 - 639 = x$ 281
82. $1072 - 295 = x$ 777
83. $2510 - 88 = x$ 2422
84. $6302 - 2567 = x$ 3735
85. $9 - 5 = x$ 4
86. $5 - 9 = x$ -4
87. $6 - 10 = x$ -4
88. $13 - 10 = x$ 3
89. $10 - 13 = x$ -3
90. $2 - 7 = x$ -5
91. $21 - 38 = x$ -17
92. $15 - 11 = x$ 4
93. $42 - 50 = x$ -8
94. $9 - (-6) = x$ 15
95. $18 - (-2) = x$ 20
96. $4 - (-5) = x$ 9
97. $22 - (-11) = x$ 33
98. $40 - (-32) = x$ 72
99. $25 - (-8) = x$ 33
100. $34 - (-6) = x$ 40
101. $75 - (-24) = x$ 99
102. $67 - (-40) = x$ 107
103. $-6 - (-2) = x$ -4
104. $-8 - (-7) = x$ -1
105. $-10 - (-6) = x$ -4
106. $-31 - (-40) = x$ 9
107. $-23 - (-28) = x$ 5
108. $-15 - (-35) = x$ 20
109. $-23 - 5 = x$ -28
110. $-31 - 18 = x$ -49
111. $-68 - 30 = x$ -98
112. $-5 - 7 = x$ -12
113. $-84 - 6 = x$ -90
114. $-92 - 7 = x$ -99

Integer Equations: Multiplication and Division

Solve each equation.

1. $20(5) = x$ 100
2. $10(100) = x$ 1000
3. $6 \cdot 40 = x$ 240
4. $100(1000) = x$ 100,000
5. $204(7) = x$ 1428
6. $505 \cdot 6 = x$ 3030
7. $32(9) = x$ 288
8. $68(8) = x$ 544
9. $43 \cdot 4 = x$ 172
10. $28(10) = x$ 280
11. $46(100) = x$ 4600
12. $1000 \cdot 97 = x$ 97,000
13. $43(36) = x$ 1548
14. $86(57) = x$ 4902
15. $62 \cdot 79 = x$ 4898
16. $709(16) = x$ 11,344
17. $32(603) = x$ 19,296
18. $204 \cdot 38 = x$ 7752
19. $840(603) = x$ 506,520
20. $958(643) = x$ 615,994
21. $657 \cdot 399 = x$ 262,143
22. $(-5)(-3) = x$ 15
23. $(-6)(-7) = x$ 42
24. $(-9)(-6) = x$ 54
25. $(-11)(-12) = x$ 132
26. $(-2)(-1000) = x$ 2000
27. $(-1)(-576) = x$ 576
28. $(-100)(-341) = x$ 34,100
29. $(-907)(-700) = x$ 634,900
30. $(-87)(-10) = x$ 870
31. $(-74)(-6) = x$ 444
32. $(-89)(-5) = x$ 445
33. $(-21)(-9) = x$ 189
34. $(-308)(-92) = x$ 28,336
35. $(-403)(-37) = x$ 14,911
36. $(-36)(-605) = x$ 21,780
37. $(-58)(-91) = x$ 5278
38. $(-26)(-19) = x$ 494
39. $(-49)(-68) = x$ 3332
40. $(-6072)(-52) = x$ 315,744
41. $(-5416)(-31) = x$ 167,896
42. $(-62)(-9557) = x$
43. $(-8)0 = x$ 0
44. $1(-17) = x$ -17
45. $0(-6) = x$ 0
46. $100(-9) = x$ -900
47. $45(-1000) = x$ $-45,000$
48. $2(-1) = x$ -2
49. $(-106)5 = x$ -530
50. $(-3)406 = x$ -1218
51. $(-309)7 = x$ -2163
52. $(-26)32 = x$ -832
53. $85(-19) = x$ -1615
54. $66(-58) = x$ -3828
55. $(-7)(-6)(4) = x$ 168
56. $(-8)(6)(-7) = x$ 336
57. $(10)(-11)(-9) = x$ 990
58. $(-5)(-3)(-2) = x$ -30
59. $(-9)(0)(-11) = x$ 0
60. $(-5)(-6)(-4) = x$ -120
61. $(-2)(-1)(5)(-4) = x$ -40
62. $(3)(4)(-7)(8) = x$ -672
63. $(-3)(-1)(-8)(-6) = x$
42. 592,534   144

Solve each equation.

64. $40 \div 5 = x$ 8
65. $24 \div 6 = x$ 4
66. $38 \div 1 = x$ 38
67. $144 \div 12 = x$ 12
68. $169 \div 13 = x$ 13
69. $56 \div 7 = x$ 8
70. $912 \div 16 = x$ 57
71. $928 \div 29 = x$ 32
72. $5644 \div 83 = x$ 68
73. $1441 \div 131 = x$ 11
74. $4080 \div 255 = x$ 16
75. $6408 \div 712 = x$ 9
76. $35,288 \div 88 = x$ 401
77. $11,495 \div 55 = x$ 209
78. $77,478 \div 37 = x$ 2094
79. $-55 \div (-11) = x$ 5
80. $-84 \div (-12) = x$ 7
81. $-51 \div (-17) = x$ 3
82. $-206 \div (-1) = x$ 206
83. $-175 \div (-25) = x$ 7
84. $-78 \div (-13) = x$ 6
85. $-720 \div (-18) = x$ 40
86. $-3600 \div (-60) = x$ 60
87. $-1950 \div (-65) = x$ 30
88. $-6570 \div (-365) = x$ 18
89. $-5280 \div (-220) = x$ 24
90. $-1728 \div (-12) = x$ 144
91. $48 \div (-6) = x$ -8
92. $-28 \div 4 = x$ -7
93. $-18 \div 9 = x$ -2
94. $63 \div (-9) = x$ -7
95. $64 \div (-16) = x$ -4
96. $-42 \div 14 = x$ -3
97. $-968 \div 8 = x$ -121
98. $-6054 \div 6 = x$ -1009
99. $5810 \div (-83) = x$ -70
100. $1950 \div (-65) = x$ -30
101. $1116 \div (-31) = x$ -36
102. $-1441 \div 131 = x$ -11
103. $-3784 \div 172 = x$ -22
104. $4500 \div (-50) = x$ -90
105. $920 \div (-23) = x$ -40

Solve each equation.

106. $8 + 5 + 6 \div 3 - 2 = x$ 13
107. $7 + 4 + 3 - 1 = x$ 13
108. $7 + 6 - 4 + 3 = x$ 12
109. $8 - 5 + 3 - 2 = x$ 4
110. $12 \cdot 8 + 12 \div 2 = x$ 102
111. $8 \div 2 + 5 \cdot 6 = x$ 34

Fraction Equations: Addition and Subtraction

Solve each equation and express answers in simplest form.

1. $\frac{1}{3} + \frac{1}{3} = x$ $\frac{2}{3}$

2. $\frac{2}{9} + \frac{5}{9} = x$ $\frac{7}{9}$

3. $\frac{4}{11} + \frac{6}{11} = x$ $\frac{10}{11}$

4. $\frac{8}{15} + \frac{11}{15} = x$ $1\frac{4}{15}$

5. $\frac{2}{3} + \frac{2}{3} = x$ $1\frac{1}{3}$

6. $\frac{11}{18} + \frac{17}{18} = x$ $1\frac{5}{9}$

7. $1\frac{1}{5} + \frac{2}{5} = x$ $1\frac{3}{5}$

8. $4\frac{1}{4} + 3\frac{3}{4} = x$ 8

9. $5\frac{1}{12} + 11\frac{7}{12} = x$ $16\frac{2}{3}$

10. $\frac{1}{2} + \frac{3}{4} = x$ $1\frac{1}{4}$

11. $\frac{1}{3} + \frac{2}{9} = x$ $\frac{5}{9}$

12. $\frac{5}{12} + \frac{1}{6} = x$ $\frac{7}{12}$

13. $7\frac{5}{6} + 4\frac{5}{9} = x$ $12\frac{7}{18}$

14. $2\frac{9}{10} + 1\frac{11}{12} = x$ $4\frac{49}{60}$

15. $3\frac{7}{20} + 1\frac{11}{12} = x$ $5\frac{4}{15}$

16. $-\frac{1}{6} + \left(-\frac{2}{6}\right) = x$ $-\frac{1}{2}$

17. $-\frac{3}{4} + \left(-\frac{1}{4}\right) = x$ -1

18. $-\frac{5}{7} + \left(-\frac{1}{7}\right) = x$ $-\frac{6}{7}$

19. $-\frac{5}{6} + \left(-\frac{5}{6}\right) = x$ $-1\frac{2}{3}$

20. $-\frac{3}{5} + \left(-\frac{4}{5}\right) = x$ $-1\frac{2}{5}$

21. $-\frac{2}{13} + \left(-\frac{12}{13}\right) = x$ $-1\frac{1}{13}$

22. $-1\frac{1}{4} + \left(-3\frac{1}{4}\right) = x$ $-4\frac{1}{2}$

23. $-2\frac{10}{21} + \left(-8\frac{17}{21}\right) = x$ $-11\frac{2}{7}$

24. $-5\frac{7}{10} + \left(-3\frac{3}{10}\right) = x$ -9

25. $-6\frac{5}{8} + \left(-\frac{1}{4}\right) = x$ $-6\frac{7}{8}$

26. $-3\frac{1}{4} + \left(-2\frac{1}{2}\right) = x$ $-5\frac{3}{4}$

27. $-4\frac{1}{7} + \left(-2\frac{2}{21}\right) = x$ $-6\frac{5}{21}$

28. $\frac{5}{7} + \left(-\frac{1}{7}\right) = x$ $\frac{4}{7}$

29. $-\frac{14}{15} + \frac{1}{15} = x$ $-\frac{13}{15}$

30. $-\frac{4}{5} + \frac{3}{5} = x$ $-\frac{1}{5}$

31. $-\frac{2}{3} + \frac{1}{3} = x$ $-\frac{1}{3}$

32. $\frac{3}{8} + \left(-\frac{1}{8}\right) = x$ $\frac{1}{4}$

33. $-\frac{3}{7} + \frac{5}{7} = x$ $\frac{2}{7}$

34. $\frac{1}{4} + \left(-\frac{2}{3}\right) = x$ $-\frac{5}{12}$

35. $-\frac{4}{5} + \frac{5}{6} = x$ $\frac{1}{30}$

36. $-\frac{3}{8} + \frac{4}{7} = x$ $\frac{11}{56}$

Solve each equation and express answers in simplest form.

37. $\frac{3}{5} - \frac{2}{5} = x$ $\frac{1}{5}$

38. $\frac{7}{9} - \frac{2}{9} = x$ $\frac{5}{9}$

39. $\frac{9}{11} - \frac{4}{11} = x$ $\frac{5}{11}$

40. $\frac{1}{2} - \frac{3}{8} = x$ $\frac{1}{8}$

41. $\frac{8}{9} - \frac{1}{6} = x$ $\frac{13}{18}$

42. $\frac{11}{12} - \frac{2}{3} = x$ $\frac{1}{4}$

43. $4\frac{3}{5} - 3\frac{1}{5} = x$ $1\frac{2}{5}$

44. $1 - \frac{2}{5} = x$ $\frac{3}{5}$

45. $1\frac{1}{9} - \frac{4}{9} = x$ $\frac{2}{3}$

46. $4 - \frac{7}{8} = x$ $3\frac{1}{8}$

47. $5\frac{1}{2} - 3\frac{1}{4} = x$ $2\frac{1}{4}$

48. $3\frac{11}{12} - 1\frac{2}{3} = x$ $2\frac{1}{4}$

49. $-\frac{2}{3} - \left(-\frac{1}{3}\right) = x$ $-\frac{1}{3}$

50. $-\frac{4}{11} - \left(-\frac{3}{11}\right) = x$ $-\frac{1}{11}$

51. $-\frac{8}{15} - \left(-\frac{4}{15}\right) = x$ $-\frac{4}{15}$

52. $-\frac{15}{17} - \left(-\frac{7}{17}\right) = x$ $-\frac{8}{17}$

53. $-\frac{1}{2} - \left(-\frac{1}{4}\right) = x$ $-\frac{1}{4}$

54. $-\frac{3}{4} - \left(-\frac{3}{8}\right) = x$ $-\frac{3}{8}$

55. $-5\frac{6}{7} - \left(-2\frac{4}{7}\right) = x$ $-3\frac{2}{7}$

56. $-5\frac{3}{5} - \left(-2\frac{3}{10}\right) = x$ $-3\frac{3}{10}$

57. $-8\frac{7}{8} - \left(-4\frac{5}{12}\right) = x$ $-4\frac{11}{24}$

58. $-1\frac{7}{8} - \left(-\frac{5}{8}\right) = x$ $-1\frac{1}{4}$

59. $-2\frac{3}{10} - \left(-1\frac{1}{10}\right) = x$ $-1\frac{1}{5}$

60. $-3\frac{5}{6} - \left(-1\frac{1}{6}\right) = x$ $-2\frac{2}{3}$

61. $2 - \left(-\frac{3}{4}\right) = x$ $2\frac{3}{4}$

62. $-3 - \frac{5}{6} = x$ $-3\frac{5}{6}$

63. $1\frac{1}{5} - -\frac{3}{5} = x$ $1\frac{4}{5}$

64. $-1\frac{1}{6} - \frac{5}{6} = x$ -2

65. $-8\frac{1}{12} - 5\frac{5}{12} = x$ $-13\frac{1}{2}$

66. $2\frac{7}{15} - \left(-6\frac{13}{15}\right) = x$ $9\frac{1}{3}$

67. $-\frac{5}{6} - \frac{1}{3} = x$ $-1\frac{1}{6}$

68. $\frac{3}{5} - \left(-\frac{9}{10}\right) = x$ $1\frac{1}{2}$

69. $-\frac{5}{8} - \frac{17}{24} = x$ $-1\frac{1}{3}$

70. $\frac{3}{5} - \left(-3\frac{1}{4}\right) = x$ $3\frac{17}{20}$

71. $-4\frac{2}{3} - 8\frac{1}{5} = x$ $-12\frac{13}{15}$

72. $-5\frac{1}{2} - 2\frac{1}{3} = x$ $-7\frac{5}{6}$

Fraction Equations: Multiplication and Division

Solve each equation and express answers in simplest form.

1. $\frac{1}{3}\left(\frac{2}{3}\right) = x$ $\frac{2}{9}$

2. $\frac{3}{4}\left(\frac{4}{3}\right) = x$ 1

3. $\frac{5}{6}\left(\frac{3}{6}\right) = x$ $\frac{5}{12}$

4. $\frac{3}{5}\left(\frac{3}{7}\right) = x$ $\frac{9}{35}$

5. $\frac{5}{7}\left(\frac{2}{13}\right) = x$ $\frac{10}{91}$

6. $\frac{8}{11}\left(\frac{9}{10}\right) = x$ $\frac{36}{55}$

7. $\frac{2}{3}\left(\frac{9}{16}\right) = x$ $\frac{3}{8}$

8. $\frac{10}{9}\left(\frac{15}{8}\right) = x$ $2\frac{1}{12}$

9. $\frac{25}{24}\left(\frac{21}{10}\right) = x$ $2\frac{3}{16}$

10. $3\left(\frac{1}{2}\right) = x$ $1\frac{1}{2}$

11. $\frac{2}{3}(9) = x$ 6

12. $\frac{3}{5}\left(5\frac{1}{6}\right) = x$ $3\frac{1}{10}$

13. $4\frac{1}{11}\left(\frac{3}{5}\right) = x$ $2\frac{5}{11}$

14. $2\frac{1}{2}\left(3\frac{2}{7}\right) = x$ $8\frac{3}{14}$

15. $\left(3\frac{1}{8}\right)\left(2\frac{4}{5}\right)\left(\frac{5}{7}\right) = x$ $6\frac{1}{4}$

16. $\left(-\frac{3}{4}\right)\left(-\frac{1}{2}\right) = x$ $\frac{3}{8}$

17. $\left(-\frac{1}{4}\right)\left(-\frac{3}{5}\right) = x$ $\frac{3}{20}$

18. $\left(-\frac{1}{7}\right)\left(-\frac{5}{8}\right) = x$ $\frac{5}{56}$

19. $\left(-\frac{9}{15}\right)\left(-\frac{15}{9}\right) = x$ 1

20. $\left(-\frac{9}{16}\right)(-64) = x$ 36

21. $(-16)\left(-\frac{5}{24}\right) = x$ $3\frac{1}{3}$

22. $\left(-3\frac{2}{3}\right)\left(-\frac{1}{8}\right) = x$ $\frac{11}{24}$

23. $\left(-\frac{4}{9}\right)\left(-3\frac{1}{8}\right) = x$ $1\frac{7}{18}$

24. $\left(-3\frac{2}{3}\right)\left(-2\frac{3}{5}\right) = x$ $9\frac{8}{15}$

25. $\left(-5\frac{1}{7}\right)\left(-4\frac{4}{5}\right) = x$ $24\frac{24}{35}$

26. $\left(-1\frac{3}{8}\right)\left(-2\frac{1}{7}\right)\left(-\frac{1}{11}\right) = x$ $-\frac{15}{56}$

27. $\left(-2\frac{1}{9}\right)\left(-\frac{5}{7}\right)\left(-4\frac{2}{3}\right) = x$

28. $\left(-\frac{1}{2}\right)\frac{3}{5} = x$ $-\frac{3}{10}$

29. $\frac{6}{7}\left(-\frac{5}{8}\right) = x$ $-\frac{15}{28}$

30. $\frac{2}{3}\left(-\frac{4}{9}\right) = x$ $-\frac{8}{27}$

31. $\frac{7}{10}\left(-\frac{5}{28}\right) = x$ $-\frac{1}{8}$

32. $\left(-\frac{4}{5}\right)30 = x$ -24

33. $(-6)\frac{5}{11} = x$ $-2\frac{8}{11}$

34. $\left(-\frac{5}{9}\right)4\frac{2}{5} = x$ $-2\frac{4}{9}$

35. $\frac{3}{10}\left(-2\frac{3}{5}\right) = x$ $-\frac{39}{50}$

36. $\left(-\frac{1}{3}\right)3\frac{3}{7} = x$ $-1\frac{1}{7}$

27. $-7\frac{1}{27}$

Solve each equation and express answers in simplest form.

37. $\frac{2}{5} \div \frac{3}{7} = x$ $\frac{14}{15}$

38. $\frac{4}{9} \div \frac{5}{7} = x$ $\frac{28}{45}$

39. $\frac{6}{13} \div \frac{5}{7} = x$ $\frac{42}{65}$

40. $\frac{8}{17} \div \frac{15}{13} = x$ $\frac{104}{255}$

41. $\frac{1}{2} \div \frac{4}{5} = x$ $\frac{5}{8}$

42. $\frac{8}{15} \div \frac{4}{5} = x$ $\frac{2}{3}$

43. $3 \div 2\frac{3}{4} = x$ $1\frac{1}{11}$

44. $2\frac{3}{5} \div 2 = x$ $1\frac{3}{10}$

45. $\frac{2}{5} \div 2\frac{1}{3} = x$ $\frac{6}{35}$

46. $7 \div \frac{7}{8} = x$ 8

47. $3\frac{1}{8} \div 3\frac{3}{4} = x$ $\frac{5}{6}$

48. $5\frac{3}{5} \div 4\frac{1}{5} = x$ $1\frac{1}{3}$

49. $-\frac{5}{8} \div \left(-\frac{8}{5}\right) = x$ $\frac{25}{64}$

50. $-\frac{7}{16} \div \left(-\frac{7}{11}\right) = x$ $\frac{11}{16}$

51. $-\frac{9}{14} \div \left(-\frac{3}{7}\right) = x$ $1\frac{1}{2}$

52. $-8 \div \left(-3\frac{2}{3}\right) = x$ $2\frac{2}{11}$

53. $-1\frac{4}{7} \div (-3) = x$ $\frac{11}{21}$

54. $-3\frac{2}{5} \div \left(-\frac{3}{4}\right) = x$ $4\frac{8}{15}$

55. $-\frac{5}{2} \div \left(-2\frac{1}{3}\right) = x$ $1\frac{1}{14}$

56. $-4\frac{5}{8} \div \left(-3\frac{4}{7}\right) = x$ $1\frac{59}{200}$

57. $-4\frac{4}{7} \div \left(-\frac{8}{9}\right) = x$ $5\frac{1}{7}$

58. $-\frac{6}{7} \div \left(-5\frac{2}{5}\right) = x$ $\frac{10}{63}$

59. $-5\frac{1}{5} \div \left(-2\frac{1}{6}\right) = x$ $2\frac{2}{5}$

60. $-2\frac{4}{7} \div \left(-1\frac{1}{2}\right) = x$ $1\frac{5}{7}$

61. $\frac{3}{8} \div \left(-\frac{5}{7}\right) = x$ $-\frac{21}{40}$

62. $-\frac{2}{3} \div \frac{1}{2} = x$ $-1\frac{1}{3}$

63. $\frac{1}{9} \div \left(-\frac{1}{9}\right) = x$ -1

64. $-\frac{2}{5} \div 7 = x$ $-\frac{2}{35}$

65. $4 \div \left(-\frac{2}{3}\right) = x$ -6

66. $-7 \div 4 = x$ $-1\frac{3}{4}$

67. $2 \div \left(-2\frac{2}{3}\right) = x$ $-\frac{3}{4}$

68. $-2\frac{8}{9} \div 4 = x$ $-\frac{13}{18}$

69. $1\frac{3}{4} \div \left(-\frac{7}{12}\right) = x$ -3

70. $4\frac{2}{5} \div \left(-\frac{11}{15}\right) = x$ -6

71. $-2 \div 2\frac{1}{7} = x$ $-\frac{14}{15}$

72. $-2\frac{5}{8} \div 7\frac{1}{2} = x$ $-\frac{7}{20}$

Decimals: Addition and Subtraction

Find each sum.

1. $0.17
   0.29
   0.54
   ‾‾‾‾‾
   $1.00

2. 7
   8.49
   0.78
   ‾‾‾‾‾
   16.27

3. 4.03
   0.95
   13.98
   ‾‾‾‾‾
   18.96

4. 0.95
   4.1
   15
   ‾‾‾‾‾
   20.05

5. 1.68
   0.93
   2.75
   ‾‾‾‾‾
   5.36

6. 9.75
   0.05
   3.764
   ‾‾‾‾‾
   13.564

7. 1.5
   70.081
   68.499
   ‾‾‾‾‾
   140.080

8. 142.7
   0.02
   82.6
   1.584
   ‾‾‾‾‾
   226.904

9. 58.27
   3.1
   0.045
   ‾‾‾‾‾
   61.415

10. $18.93
    45.27
    23.84
    ‾‾‾‾‾
    $88.04

11. 752.95
    17.461
    0.3
    8.77
    ‾‾‾‾‾
    779.481

12. $1375.34
    503.19
    594.19
    65.04
    ‾‾‾‾‾
    $2537.76

13. $6 + 4.2 + 9$ 19.2

14. $0.42 + 0.06 + 1.11$ 1.59

15. $0.2 + 6.51 + 2.03$ 8.74

16. $0.006 + 2 + 10.01$ 12.016

17. $4.4 + 30.6 + 11.2$ 46.2

18. $6.501 + 1.1 + 1$ 8.601

19. $-28 + (-45.50)$ −73.50

20. $-22.49 + (-83)$ −105.49

21. $-10.04 + (-0.18)$ −10.22

22. $-5.9 + 18.1$ 12.2

23. $7.11 + (-1.02)$ 6.09

24. $-6.51 + 2.03$ −4.48

25. $3.75 + (-6.8)$ −3.05

26. $-65 + 15.64$ −49.36

27. $0.046 + (-0.567)$ −0.521

Find each difference.

28. 7.8
    − 5.3
    ‾‾‾‾‾
    2.5

29. 57.96
    − 23.71
    ‾‾‾‾‾
    34.25

30. 4.01
    − 3.92
    ‾‾‾‾‾
    0.09

31. 6.0437
    − 1.9864
    ‾‾‾‾‾
    4.0573

32. 8.00
    − 7.87
    ‾‾‾‾‾
    0.13

33. $4
    − 1.34
    ‾‾‾‾‾
    $2.66

34. 11.000
    − 9.741
    ‾‾‾‾‾
    1.259

35. 5
    − 2.896
    ‾‾‾‾‾
    2.104

36. 20.48
    − 16.8
    ‾‾‾‾‾
    3.68

37. 28.05
    − 9.95
    ‾‾‾‾‾
    18.1

38. 8
    − 3.49
    ‾‾‾‾‾
    4.51

39. 932
    − 0.003
    ‾‾‾‾‾
    931.997

40. 26.706
    − 6.897
    ‾‾‾‾‾
    19.809

41. 1.7
    − 0.846
    ‾‾‾‾‾
    0.854

42. 86.4
    − 75.92
    ‾‾‾‾‾
    10.48

43. 86.4
    − 75.92
    ‾‾‾‾‾
    10.48

44. $-8.4 - (-2.3)$ −6.1

45. $-0.41 - (-65)$ 64.59

46. $-3.1 - (-7.5)$ 4.4

47. $-11.0 - (-6.9)$ −4.1

48. $-5 - (-1.3)$ −3.7

49. $-6.8 - (-9.9)$ 3.1

50. $-7.25 - (-15.86)$ 8.61

51. $-27.2 - (-6.4)$ −20.8

52. $-6 - (-1.4)$ −4.6

53. $0.8 - (-0.76)$ 1.56

54. $-6.51 - 4.3$ −10.81

55. $4.5 - (-2.1)$ 6.6

56. $-29.3 - 14.22$ −43.52

57. $16 - (-2.9)$ 18.9

58. $-7 - 35.8$ −42.8

59. $101 - (-76.4)$ 177.4

60. $-3.2 - 18.42$ −21.62

61. $-13.0 - 6.8$ −19.8

Decimal Equations: Multiplication and Division

Solve each equation.

12. −190.665   **15.** −26.313   **18.** 2.6064   **21.** 36.176

1. $x = 68(0.7)$ 47.6

2. $406(0.9) = x$ 365.4

3. $4065(0.7) = y$ 2845.5

4. $y = 11.5(22)$ 253

5. $a = 4.68(47)$ 219.96

6. $b = 0.09(18)$ 1.62

7. $12.5(0.5) = a$ 6.25

8. $11.54(4.3) = c$ 49.622

9. $a = 32.1(2.5)$ 80.25

10. $c = (−22.6)7.4$ −167.24

11. $7.52(−1.8) = x$ −13.536

12. $20.07(−9.5) = y$

13. $(−16.8)0.55 = a$ −9.24

14. $(−4.65)1.58 = c$ −7.347

15. $x = (−25.06)1.05$

16. $(−47.5)(−3.19) = m$ 151.525

17. $y = (−24.2)(−0.25)$ 6.05

18. $(−7.24)(−0.36) = p$

19. $y = (−6.15)(−0.51)$ 3.1365

20. $(−31.24)(−8.61) = c$ 268.9764

21. $(−452.2)(−0.08) = a$

22. $9.06(−0.53) = y$ −4.8018

23. $a = (−12.08)4.25$ −51.34

24. $8.94(0.005) = y$ 0.0447

25. $m = 32.7(2.29)$ 74.883

26. $(−4.88)1.25 = r$ −6.1

27. $(−4.48)(−6.25) = m$ 28

28. $a = 216.17(9.63)$ 2081.7171

29. $m = (−0.4082)11.85$ −4.83717

30. $(−140.15)(−0.186) = t$ 26.0679

31. $q = 19.042(8.54)$ 162.61868

32. $4.007(1.95) = n$ 7.81365

33. $0.0645(0.81) = x$ 0.052245

34. $a = 8.265(−3.32)$ −27.4398

35. $x = (−2.508)(−0.975)$ 2.4453

36. $m = 43.616(2.405)$ 104.89648

37. $0.0182(0.007) = y$ 0.0001274

38. $r = 0.0615(0.13)$ 0.007995

39. $z = (−0.0036)(−0.28)$ 0.001008

40. $y = (−723)(−0.0068)$ 4.9164

41. $462.1(0.0094) = q$ 4.34374

42. $a = 87.061(0.0016)$ 0.1392976

43. $0.0074(−61.3) = a$ −0.45362

44. $0.0076(0.00821) = b$ 0.000062396

45. $0.0086(0.00909) = c$ 0.000078174

46. $x = 1249.867(0.069)$ 86.240823

47. $n = 187.411(0.0098)$ 1.8366278

48. $t = 9.16739(8.721)$ 79.94880819

49. $0.00886(0.0708) = b$ 0.000627288

50. $y = 0.007201(0.00899)$ 0.00006473699

51. $0.06121(0.000619) = x$ 0.00003788899

66. 0.041   **90.** −1.05

52. $m = 2.7 \div 3$ 0.9

53. $z = 4.8 \div 8$ 0.6

54. $11.4 \div 6 = q$ 1.9

55. $z = 68 \div 8$ 8.5

56. $41 \div 5 = n$ 8.2

57. $79 \div 5 = p$ 15.8

58. $m = (−8) \div 20$ −0.4

59. $12 \div (−30) = a$ −0.4

60. $b = 98 \div (−8)$ −12.25

61. $p = 2.92 \div (−4)$ −0.73

62. $52.8 \div (−24) = b$ −2.2

63. $−164.97 \div 47 = z$ −3.51

64. $−0.451 \div (−11) = q$ 0.041

65. $r = −1.881 \div (−19)$ 0.099

66. $−1.681 \div (−41) = h$

67. $m = −3.286 \div (−62)$ 0.053

68. $−1.953 \div (−63) = a$ 0.031

69. $−1.892 \div −43 = b$ 0.044

70. $63 \div (−0.9) = p$ −70

71. $c = 86 \div (−4.3)$ −20

72. $d = 105 \div 2.1$ 50

73. $81 \div 0.27 = q$ 300

74. $d = 54 \div 0.18$ 300

75. $m = −33 \div 0.66$ −50

76. $x = 30.1 \div 0.7$ 43

77. $82.8 \div 0.4 = m$ 207

78. $−565.6 \div −0.7 = y$ 808

79. $19.5 \div 1.5 = q$ 13

80. $−18.53 \div (−1.7) = d$ 10.9

81. $0.0418 \div 0.19 = m$ 0.22

82. $1.781 \div 0.13 = r$ 13.7

83. $0.1804 \div 4.4 = m$ 0.041

84. $0.1696 \div 3.2 = s$ 0.053

85. $b = 0.2808 \div 0.078$ 3.6

86. $x = 0.1001 \div (−0.77)$ −0.13

87. $p = 0.5805 \div 2.15$ 0.27

88. $c = 19.317 \div 0.94$ 20.55

89. $y = 9.557 \div 1.9$ 5.03

90. $m = 15.33 \div (−14.6)$

91. $2.006 \div 0.118 = p$ 17

92. $0.4484 \div 1.18 = n$ 0.38

93. $a = 29.45 \div 6.2$ 4.75

94. $x = 0.24102 \div 0.117$ 2.06

95. $q = −9.8049 \div (−0.966)$ 10.15

96. $0.1107 \div 2.25 = r$ 0.0492

97. $m = 0.32539 \div 5.006$ 0.065

98. $0.046626 \div 8.18 = z$ 0.0057

99. $n = 21.99256 \div 3.14$ 7.004

100. $8.9238 \div (−83.4) = a$ −0.107

101. $1.573 \div (−6.05) = b$ −0.26

102. $−2800 \div −625 = d$ 4.48

103. $21.5025 \div 7.05 = p$ 3.05

Forms of Real Numbers

Write each fraction as a decimal.

1. $\frac{2}{5}$ 0.4
2. $-\frac{1}{4}$ -0.25
3. $-\frac{7}{10}$ -0.7
4. $\frac{3}{20}$ 0.15

5. $-\frac{4}{5}$ -0.8
6. $-\frac{17}{20}$ -0.85
7. $\frac{1}{3}$ $0.\overline{3}$
8. $-\frac{1}{6}$ $-0.1\overline{6}$

9. $-\frac{2}{3}$ $-0.\overline{6}$
10. $\frac{1}{9}$ $0.\overline{1}$
11. $-\frac{5}{6}$ $-0.8\overline{3}$
12. $\frac{2}{9}$ $0.\overline{2}$

13. $\frac{3}{7}$ $0.\overline{428571}$
14. $-\frac{1}{12}$ $-0.08\overline{3}$
15. $\frac{5}{7}$ $0.\overline{714285}$
16. $-\frac{7}{12}$ $-0.58\overline{3}$

17. $-\frac{8}{9}$ $-0.\overline{8}$
18. $\frac{4}{25}$ 0.16
19. $\frac{3}{11}$ $0.\overline{27}$
20. $-\frac{9}{16}$ -0.5625

Write each mixed numeral as a decimal.

21. $1\frac{3}{4}$ 1.75
22. $2\frac{1}{2}$ 2.5
23. $-5\frac{9}{10}$ -5.9
24. $-6\frac{3}{5}$ -6.6

25. $4\frac{1}{3}$ $4.\overline{3}$
26. $-1\frac{5}{6}$ $-1.8\overline{3}$
27. $7\frac{3}{16}$ 7.1875
28. $2\frac{5}{7}$ $2.\overline{714285}$

29. $-2\frac{7}{11}$ $-2.\overline{63}$
30. $8\frac{2}{3}$ $8.\overline{6}$
31. $-9\frac{5}{9}$ $-9.\overline{5}$
32. $11\frac{1}{6}$ $11.1\overline{6}$

33. $75\frac{1}{4}$ 75.25
34. $-101\frac{4}{5}$ -101.8
35. $3\frac{5}{8}$ 3.625
36. $-52\frac{7}{12}$ $-52.58\overline{3}$

37. $32\frac{1}{8}$ 32.125
38. $73\frac{3}{10}$ 73.3
39. $-18\frac{11}{12}$ $-18.91\overline{6}$
40. $16\frac{6}{7}$ $16.\overline{857142}$

For each of the following, write an equivalent fraction with a denominator of 100.

41. $-\frac{1}{2}$ $-\frac{50}{100}$
42. $-\frac{1}{5}$ $-\frac{20}{100}$
43. $\frac{1}{4}$ $\frac{25}{100}$
44. $-\frac{1}{10}$ $-\frac{10}{100}$

45. $\frac{1}{20}$ $\frac{5}{100}$
46. $-\frac{3}{4}$ $-\frac{75}{100}$
47. $-\frac{4}{5}$ $-\frac{80}{100}$
48. $\frac{7}{25}$ $\frac{28}{100}$

49. $-\frac{7}{4}$ $-\frac{17}{100}$
50. $-\frac{9}{20}$ $-\frac{45}{100}$
51. $\frac{9}{50}$ $\frac{18}{100}$
52. $-\frac{67}{10}$ $-\frac{670}{100}$

53. $\frac{49}{25}$ $\frac{196}{100}$
54. $-\frac{27}{5}$ $-\frac{540}{100}$
55. $\frac{19}{4}$ $\frac{475}{100}$
56. $-\frac{25}{20}$ $-\frac{125}{100}$

57. $\frac{13}{10}$ $\frac{130}{100}$
58. $-\frac{4320}{1000}$ $-\frac{432}{100}$
59. $\frac{14}{5}$ $\frac{280}{100}$
60. $\frac{21}{20}$ $\frac{105}{100}$

Write each decimal as a fraction in simplest form.

61. 0.7 $\frac{7}{10}$
62. -0.25 $-\frac{1}{4}$
63. -0.6 $-\frac{3}{5}$
64. -0.15 $-\frac{3}{20}$
65. -0.625 $-\frac{5}{8}$
66. 0.85 $\frac{17}{20}$
67. -0.875 $-\frac{7}{8}$
68. $0.\overline{3}$ $\frac{1}{3}$
69. -9.50 $-9\frac{1}{2}$
70. -2.75 $-2\frac{3}{4}$
71. 3.125 $3\frac{1}{8}$
72. -1.34 $-1\frac{17}{50}$
73. $11.\overline{6}$ $11\frac{2}{3}$
74. $-9.\overline{3}$ $-9\frac{1}{3}$
75. 25.25 $25\frac{1}{4}$
76. -2.75 $-2\frac{3}{4}$
77. -13.125 $-13\frac{1}{8}$
78. 4.15 $4\frac{3}{20}$
79. $-8.\overline{3}$ $-8\frac{1}{3}$
80. 22.875 $22\frac{7}{8}$
81. 1.375 $1\frac{3}{8}$
82. -2.25 $-2\frac{1}{4}$
83. $9.\overline{6}$ $9\frac{2}{3}$
84. 7.24 $7\frac{6}{25}$
85. $0.\overline{4}$ $\frac{4}{9}$
86. $0.\overline{37}$ $\frac{37}{99}$
87. $0.\overline{524}$ $\frac{524}{999}$
88. $0.\overline{163}$ $\frac{163}{999}$
89. $2.\overline{3}$ $2\frac{1}{3}$
90. $-1.\overline{26}$ $-1\frac{26}{99}$
91. $-0.3\overline{27}$ $-\frac{18}{55}$
92. $5.\overline{371}$ $5\frac{371}{999}$

Scientific Notation

Express each of the following using scientific notation.

1. 40 4×10

2. 400 4×10^2

3. 4,000 4×10^3

4. 40,000 4×10^4

5. 20,691 2.0691×10^4

6. 2069.1 2.0691×10^3

7. 206.91 2.0691×10^2

8. 20.691 2.0691×10

9. -42.3 -4.23×10

10. $-8,200,000$ -8.2×10^6

11. 36.241 3.6241×10

12. 95,236 9.5236×10^4

13. 300,000 3×10^5

14. 0.00015 1.5×10^{-4}

15. 0.0015 1.5×10^{-3}

16. 0.015 1.5×10^{-2}

17. 0.15 1.5×10^{-1}

18. 0.0692 6.92×10^{-2}

19. 0.00000308 3.08×10^{-6}

20. 0.007 7×10^{-3}

21. -0.029 -2.9×10^{-2}

22. 0.0009 9×10^{-4}

23. $-325,000,000$ -3.25×10^8

24. 1,200,000 1.2×10^6

Express each of the following using decimal notation.

25. 5×10^2 500

26. 5×10^3 5000

27. 5×10^4 50,000

28. 5×10^5 500,000

29. -2.1×10^3 -2100

30. 1.05×10^5 105,000

31. -5.704×10^3 -5704

32. 3.157×10^2 315.7

33. -9.5×10^6 $-9,500,000$

34. 6.33×10^8 633,000,000

35. -7.2×10^7 $-72,000,000$

36. -5.402×10^3 -5402

37. -62.1×10^7 $-621,000,000$

38. 9×10^{-1} 0.9

39. 9×10^{-2} 0.09

40. 9×10^{-3} 0.009

41. 9×10^{-4} 0.0009

42. 4.8×10^{-1} 0.48

43. -3.6×10^{-3} -0.0036

44. -7.7×10^{-4} -0.00077

45. -8×10^{-7} -0.0000008

46. -6.4×10^{-8} -0.000000064

47. -1.002×10^{-3} -0.001002

48. -1.6×10^{-4} -0.00016

Evaluate. Express each answer in scientific notation.

49. $(4.3 \times 10^3)(2.0 \times 10^2)$ 8.6×10^5

50. $(3.6 \times 10^5)(7.5 \times 10^3)$ 2.7×10^9

51. $(1.5 \times 10)(3.4 \times 10^6)$ 5.1×10^7

52. $(7.22 \times 10^4)(5.1 \times 10^7)$ 3.6822×10^{12}

53. $(-45 \times 10^2)(-5 \times 10^4)$ 2.25×10^8

54. $(-4.8 \times 10)(-9.6 \times 10^8)$ 4.608×10^{10}

55. $(-6 \times 10^7)(-8.2 \times 10^5)$ 4.92×10^{13}

56. $(-12.1 \times 10^3)(-3.4 \times 10^2)$ 4.114×10^6

57. $(8 \times 10^3)(-5 \times 10^9)$ -4×10^{13}

58. $(-24 \times 10^6)(3 \times 10^9)$ -7.2×10^{16}

59. $(7.01 \times 10^8)(-9.1 \times 10)$ -6.3791×10^{10}

60. $(-3 \times 10^4)(7 \times 10^4)$ -2.1×10^9

61. $(5 \times 10^{-4})(6 \times 10^{-6})$ 3×10^{-9}

62. $(2 \times 10^{-3})(4 \times 10^{-2})$ 8×10^{-5}

63. $(2.3 \times 10^{-1})(9.2 \times 10^{-5})$ 2.116×10^{-5}

64. $(34.01 \times 10^{-7})(6 \times 10^{-8})$ 2.0406×10^{-13}

65. $(7 \times 10^2)(6 \times 10^{-2})$ 4.2×10

66. $(4 \times 10^{-3})(8 \times 10^5)$ 3.2×10^3

67. $(8.8 \times 10^{-7})(1.1 \times 10^4)$ 9.68×10^{-3}

68. $(12 \times 10^{10})(12 \times 10^{-6})$ 1.44×10^6

69. $(-2 \times 10^{-5})(9 \times 10^3)$ -1.8×10^{-1}

70. $(7 \times 10^{-8})(-4 \times 10^6)$ -2.8×10^{-1}

71. $\dfrac{24 \times 10^6}{3 \times 10^2}$ 8×10^4

72. $\dfrac{45 \times 10^3}{9 \times 10^5}$ 5×10^{-2}

73. $\dfrac{12 \times 10^{12}}{4 \times 10^6}$ 3×10^6

74. $\dfrac{8 \times 10^{-5}}{2 \times 10^{-3}}$ 4×10^{-2}

75. $\dfrac{33 \times 10^{-4}}{11 \times 10^{-5}}$ 3×10

76. $\dfrac{63 \times 10^{-4}}{7 \times 10^{-4}}$ 9×10^0

77. $\dfrac{10 \times 10^8}{5 \times 10^{-3}}$ 2×10^{11}

78. $\dfrac{169 \times 10^{-4}}{13 \times 10^6}$ 1.3×10^{-9}

79. $\dfrac{6 \times 10}{2 \times 10^{-2}}$ 3×10^3

80. $\dfrac{-2.5 \times 10^2}{5 \times 10^{-3}}$ -5×10^4

81. $\dfrac{-48 \times 10^5}{-2 \times 10^{-4}}$ 2.4×10^{10}

82. $\dfrac{9 \times 10^{-1}}{-3 \times 10^{-1}}$ -3×10^0

Evaluating Expressions

Evaluate.

1. $t \div 4$ if $t = -16$ -4

2. $k \div 3$ if $k = 15$ 5

3. $-96 \div q$ if $q = 12$ -8

4. $-76 \div m$ if $m = -19$ 4

5. $\frac{x}{15}$ if $x = 60$ 4

6. $\frac{y}{-9}$ if $y = 36$ -4

7. $\frac{-54}{p}$ if $p = -9$ 6

8. $\frac{8}{n}$ if $n = -40$ $-\frac{1}{5}$

9. $\frac{z}{32}$ if $z = -8$ $-\frac{1}{4}$

10. $\frac{t}{-7}$ if $t = -84$ 12

11. $\frac{2x}{-15}$ if $x = -30$ 4

12. $\frac{-112}{-4n}$ if $n = -7$ -4

13. $2y + 3$ if $y = -5$ -7

14. $3(x - 9)$ if $x = 7$ -6

15. $t(t + 4)$ if $t = -8$ 32

16. $r^2 - 2r$ if $r = -3$ 15

17. $q^2(q - 8)$ if $q = 4$ -64

18. $\frac{5a^2 + a}{2a}$ if $a = -2$ $-4\frac{1}{2}$

Evaluate if $a = 6$, $b = 4$, and $c = -3$.

19. $a + (b + c)$ 7

20. $a + (b - c)$ 13

21. $6(a + b)$ 60

22. $a - (b - c)$ -1

23. $a - b - c$ 5

24. $a(b + |c|)$ 42

25. $ab|c|$ 72

26. $ab + ac$ 6

27. $a^2 + b^2 + c^2$ 61

28. $7a - (2b + c)$ 37

29. $a^2 - c^2$ 27

30. $36 - 4c^2$ 0

31. $\frac{4(a - b)}{|c - 1|}$ 2

32. $\frac{3(4b + 5a)}{23}$ 6

33. $\frac{(a - b)(a + b)}{2c}$ $-3\frac{1}{3}$

34. $\frac{3ab}{2a + |c|}$ $4\frac{4}{5}$

35. $\frac{5a + 3c}{3b}$ $1\frac{3}{4}$

36. $\frac{3ab^2 - c^3}{a}$ $52\frac{1}{2}$

The relationship between Celsius temperature (C) and Fahrenheit temperature (F) is given by $C = \frac{5(F - 32)}{9}$. Find the Celsius temperature for the given temperatures.

37. $68°F$ $20°C$

38. $86°F$ $30°C$

39. $-22°F$ $-30°C$

40. $32°F$ $0°C$

41. $23°F$ $-5°C$

42. $-4°F$ $-20°C$

The formula for the area of a trapezoid is $A = \frac{h}{2}(b + B)$. A stands for the area, h stands for the altitude, and b and B stand for the bases. Calculate the area of the trapezoid given the following.

43. $b = 16$, $B = 30$, and $h = 18$ 414

44. $b = 7$, $B = 12$, and $h = 9$ 85.5

45. $b = 20$, $B = 25$, and $h = 22$ 495

46. $b = 5$, $B = 11$, and $h = 8$ 64

The formula for the volume of a sphere is $V = \frac{4}{3}\pi r^3$. V stands for the volume and r for the radius. Calculate the volume of the sphere given the following.

47. $\pi = \frac{22}{7}$, $r = \frac{1}{4}$ $\frac{11}{168}$

48. $\pi = \frac{22}{7}$, $r = 2\frac{1}{2}$ $65\frac{10}{21}$

49. $\pi = 3.14$, $r = 3$ 113.04

50. $\pi = 3.14$, $r = 6$ 904.32

Solving Linear Equations

Solve each equation.

1. $5 + x = 9$ $x = 4$

2. $-14 + y = 10$ $y = 24$

3. $56 + z = -3$ $z = -59$

4. $38 = t + 21$ $t = 17$

5. $72 = p + (-8)$ $p = 80$

6. $-19 = q + (-4)$

7. $-25 + h = -33$ $h = -8$

8. $m + (-14) = 6$ $m = 20$

9. $d + 40 = 27$ $d = -13$

10. $-x + 9 = 15$ $x = -6$

11. $-y + (-2) = -85$ $y = 83$

12. $-f + (-7) = 1$ $f = -8$

13. $a - 4 = 72$ $a = 76$

14. $b - 9 = -23$ $b = -14$

15. $c - 11 = 6$ $c = 17$

16. $-102 = w - 99$ $w = -3$

17. $61 = s - 71$ $s = 132$

18. $-28 = k - 80$ $k = 52$

19. $z - (-15) = 36$ $z = 21$

20. $x - (-40) = -58$ $x = -98$

21. $y - (-16) = 59$ $y = 43$

22. $-66 = a - (-1)$ $a = -67$

23. $524 = m - (-300)$ $m = 224$

24. $-75 = q - (-24)$

25. $6x = 18$ $x = 3$

26. $8y = 64$ $y = 8$

27. $10z = 5$ $z = \frac{1}{2}$

28. $-20 = -4a$ $a = 5$

29. $-8 = 8c$ $c = -1$

30. $35 = -5d$ $d = -7$

31. $\frac{1y}{2} = 12$ $y = 24$

32. $\frac{x}{7} = 9$ $x = 63$

33. $\frac{z}{-5} = 3$ $z = -15$

34. $-13 = \frac{h}{7}$ $h = -91$

35. $-32 = \frac{t}{-14}$ $t = 448$

36. $25 = \frac{n}{-11}$ $n = -275$

37. $\frac{2r}{3} = -24$ $r = -36$

38. $\frac{-5s}{7} = -20$ $s = 28$

39. $\frac{6p}{-11} = 54$ $p = -99$

40. $-21 = \frac{-7y}{10}$ $y = 30$

41. $36 = \frac{9x}{-15}$ $x = -60$

42. $-42 = \frac{-4z}{-5}$ $z = -52\frac{1}{2}$

43. $4x + 8 = 20$ $x = 3$

44. $6y - 8 = 22$ $y = 5$

45. $9z - 30 = 6$ $z = 4$

46. $3m + 4 = -11$ $m = -5$

47. $-5r + 6 = -14$ $r = 4$

48. $3 + (-4m) = 7$ $m = -1$

49. $13 = 2x - 7$ $x = 10$

50. $47 = 3k - 7$ $k = 18$

51. $-50 = 6m - 8$ $m = -7$

52. $8a - 10 = -90$ $a = -10$

53. $25 = 4g + 5$ $g = 5$

54. $-3z - 18 = 9$ $z = -9$

55. $\frac{x}{5} + 2 = 7$ $x = 25$

56. $\frac{m}{3} + 6 = 14$ $m = 24$

57. $\frac{y}{3} + 6 = -9$ $y = -45$

58. $\frac{b}{7} - 8 = -12$ $b = -28$

59. $\frac{d}{10} - 3 = -5$ $d = -20$

60. $\frac{r}{-6} - 4 = 7$ $r = -66$

61. $\frac{d + 5}{3} = -9$ $d = -32$

62. $\frac{3 + f}{7} = -5$ $f = -38$

63. $\frac{m - 5}{4} = 5$ $m = 25$

64. $\frac{4r + 8}{16} = 7$ $r = 26$

65. $\frac{3d - 4}{5} = 4$ $d = 8$

66. $\frac{7n - (-1)}{8} = 8$ $n = 9$

67. $5y + 9 = 8y$ $y = 3$

68. $6a - 10 = 4a$ $a = 5$

69. $4c + 15 = 9c$ $c = 3$

70. $7p - 12 = 4p + 6$ $p = 6$

71. $7m + 56 = 3m + 36$ $m = -5$

72. $-3x + 6 = 12 - 2x$

73. $2(x + 2) = -32$ $x = -18$

74. $-52 = 2(3z - 8)$ $z = -6$

75. $-4(x + 1) = -12$ $x = 2$

76. $2(n + 4) = n + 10$ $n = 2$

77. $7x - 2 = 3(3x + 3)$ $x = -\frac{11}{2}$

78. $4y - 3(y - 2) = 41$

Solve each equation for the variable indicated.

79. $P = 2l + 2w$, for l

80. $A = bh$, for h

81. $d = rt$, for r

82. $C = 2\pi r$, for r

83. $a = (b - c)p$, for c

84. $x(y + z) = t$, for y

85. $\frac{e}{f} = g + h$, for f

86. $A = \frac{1}{2}bh$ for b

87. $A = \frac{h}{2}(b + B)$, for B

79. $l = (1/2)P - w$ 80. $h = A/b$ 81. $r = d/t$ 82. $r = C/2\pi$
83. $c = b - (a/p)$ 84. $y = (t/x) - z$ 85. $f = e/(g + h)$
86. $b = 2A/h$ 87. $B = (2A/h) - b$

Solving Linear Inequalities

Solve each inequality.

1. $y + 3 < 6$ $y < 3$
2. $n + 2 < 5$ $n < 3$
3. $x + 6 \geq -14$ $x \geq -20$
4. $a + 4 > 2$ $a > -2$
5. $b - 3 > 8$ $b > 11$
6. $c - 5 < 3$ $c < 8$
7. $4y \leq 3y + 4$ $y \leq 4$
8. $3y < 2y + 6$ $y < 6$
9. $6a > 5a - 2$ $a > -2$
10. $5n > 4n - 3$ $n > -3$
11. $11 \geq y - 5$ $y \leq 16$
12. $16 > n - 5$ $n < 21$
13. $13 < b + 6$ $b > 7$
14. $4 < c + 16$ $c > -12$
15. $f - (-3) \leq -6$ $f \leq -9$
16. $r - (-4) \geq 12$ $r \geq 8$
17. $-20 + 5y \geq 6y$ $y \leq -20$
18. $12d - 18 < 11d$ $d < 18$
19. $-7 + 6x < 7x + 2$ $x > -9$
20. $14z - (-3) \leq 15z + 6$ $z \geq -3$
21. $9y - 4 > 10y + (-12)$ $y < 8$
22. $\frac{x}{4} < 9$ $x < 36$
23. $\frac{y}{5} < 3$ $y < 15$
24. $\frac{z}{4} > -5$ $z > -20$
25. $\frac{r}{-2} < 4$ $r > -8$
26. $\frac{s}{-8} \geq -7$ $s \leq 56$
27. $\frac{k}{-9} < -6$ $k > 54$
28. $\frac{h}{12} \leq -40$ $h \leq -480$
29. $\frac{m}{-10} > 11$ $m < -110$
30. $\frac{y}{15} < 12$ $y < 180$
31. $2 < \frac{x}{8}$ $x > 16$
32. $-3 \leq \frac{d}{7}$ $d \geq -21$
33. $20 > \frac{g}{4}$ $g < 80$
34. $38 > \frac{t}{-2}$ $t > -76$
35. $9 < \frac{z}{-6}$ $z < -54$
36. $-13 \geq \frac{s}{-12}$ $s \geq 156$
37. $5x \geq 20$ $x \geq 4$
38. $6y < -12$ $y < -2$
39. $14z > -70$ $z > -5$
40. $-21 \leq 7a$ $a \geq -3$
41. $46 > 2c$ $c < 23$
42. $-84 < 4b$ $b > -21$
43. $-2f > 26$ $f < -13$
44. $-15x > -105$ $x < 7$
45. $-3z \geq 27$ $z \leq -9$
46. $-8r \leq -48$ $r \geq 6$
47. $-9s < 63$ $s > -7$
48. $-31t < -651$ $t > 21$
49. $1600 > -50k$ $k > -32$
50. $-925 < 37p$ $p > -25$
51. $72 \geq -8y$ $y \geq -9$
52. $-85x \leq -255$ $x \geq 3$
53. $-33w > 297$ $w < -9$
54. $-18 < 3z$ $z > -6$
55. $3a + 4 > 16$ $a > 4$
56. $5t + 40 \leq 55$ $t \leq 3$
57. $7 + 6z > 19$ $z > 2$
58. $12b - 32 < -6$ $b < 2\frac{1}{6}$
59. $9y - 5 \geq -50$ $y \geq -5$
60. $8m - 13 < -37$ $m < -3$
61. $16 - 5x > 31$ $x < -3$
62. $-4c + 3 < -21$ $c > 6$
63. $-24 \leq 8 - 16q$ $q \leq 2$
64. $-7k - 12 \geq 37$ $k \leq -7$
65. $-20 - 3w > -32$ $w < 4$
66. $-13y - 11 < 54$ $y > -5$
67. $13x - 5 \leq 10x + 4$ $x \leq 3$
68. $2y + 8 > 5y - 7$ $y < 5$
69. $z - 6 > 3z + 2$ $z < -4$
70. $16s - 15 \geq 12s - 3$ $s \geq 3$
71. $9r + 3 < 6r + 3$ $r < 0$
72. $4t - 18 < t + 9$ $t < 9$
73. $2(n + 4) > n + 10$ $n > 2$
74. $3(x + 6) > 2x + 12$ $x > -6$
75. $3y + 7 \leq 4(y + 2)$ $y \geq -1$
76. $7(m + 8) \leq 3m + 36$ $m \leq -5$
77. $-7(-x + 4) > 14$ $x > 6$
78. $9 > -3b + 6(b - 4)$ $b < 11$
79. $\frac{3a - 5}{2} > 2a + 1$ $a < -7$
80. $\frac{3c}{4} - \frac{5}{8} < 0$ $c < \frac{5}{6}$
81. $\frac{5 - 2k}{3} \leq -7$ $k \geq 13$

Find the set of all integers, x, satisfying the given conditions.

82. $x > -5$ and $x < 4$ $\{-4, -3, \ldots, 2, 3\}$
83. $x \geq -2$ and $x \leq 2$ $\{-2, -1, 0, 1, 2\}$
84. $x \leq 10$ and $x < -1$ $\{-2, -3, -4, \ldots\}$
85. $x < 9$ and $x \geq -3$ $\{-3, -2, \ldots, 7, 8\}$
86. $x > 0$ or $x \geq 3$ $\{1, 2, 3, \ldots\}$
87. $x > 25$ or $x < 30$ all integers
88. $2 < 3x + 2$ and $3x + 2 < 14$ $\{1, 2, 3\}$
89. $9 - 2x > 11$ and $5x < 2x + 9$
90. $x + 4 > -2$ and $x - 5 < -1$
$\{-5, -4, \ldots, 2, 3\}$
91. $2x < 30$ or $3x > 60$ $\{\ldots 13, 14, 21, 22, \ldots\}$
89. $\{-2, -3, -4, \ldots\}$

Proportions and Percents

Cross multiply to determine whether or not the ratios are equivalent. Write *yes* or *no*.

1. $\frac{1}{2}, \frac{2}{4}$ yes

2. $\frac{1}{3}, \frac{2}{6}$ yes

3. $\frac{1}{5}, \frac{2}{11}$ no

4. $\frac{1}{10}, \frac{2}{5}$ no

5. $\frac{1}{8}, \frac{3}{24}$ yes

6. $\frac{1}{7}, \frac{4}{28}$ yes

7. $\frac{2}{5}, \frac{4}{9}$ no

8. $\frac{3}{4}, \frac{6}{8}$ yes

9. $\frac{2}{3}, \frac{3}{9}$ no

10. $\frac{2}{7}, \frac{6}{21}$ yes

11. $\frac{4}{5}, \frac{15}{20}$ no

12. $\frac{5}{6}, \frac{15}{18}$ yes

13. $\frac{4}{9}, \frac{12}{27}$ yes

14. $\frac{6}{15}, \frac{12}{45}$ no

15. $\frac{8}{21}, \frac{4}{10}$ no

16. $\frac{11}{24}, \frac{33}{72}$ yes

Solve each proportion.

17. $\frac{2}{5} = \frac{4}{c}$ $c = 10$

18. $\frac{5}{12} = \frac{10}{y}$ $y = 24$

19. $\frac{8}{12} = \frac{2}{e}$ $e = 3$

20. $\frac{18}{24} = \frac{3}{k}$ $k = 4$

21. $\frac{3}{4} = \frac{m}{12}$ $m = 9$

22. $\frac{4}{7} = \frac{x}{14}$ $x = 8$

23. $\frac{2}{9} = \frac{z}{27}$ $z = 6$

24. $\frac{3}{10} = \frac{b}{30}$ $b = 9$

25. $\frac{h}{6} = \frac{2}{12}$ $h = 1$

26. $\frac{u}{12} = \frac{3}{36}$ $u = 1$

27. $\frac{x}{22} = \frac{15}{11}$ $x = 30$

28. $\frac{h}{30} = \frac{102}{60}$ $h = 51$

29. $\frac{1}{v} = \frac{9}{27}$ $v = 3$

30. $\frac{84}{d} = \frac{28}{5}$ $d = 15$

31. $\frac{7}{r} = \frac{21}{28}$ $r = 9\frac{1}{3}$

32. $\frac{7}{q} = \frac{28}{16}$ $q = 4$

33. $\frac{p}{84} = \frac{25}{100}$ $p = 21$

34. $\frac{p}{50} = \frac{115}{100}$ $p = 57.5$

35. $\frac{11}{44} = \frac{r}{100}$ $r = 25$

36. $\frac{12}{60} = \frac{r}{100}$ $r = 20$

37. $\frac{5}{B} = \frac{10}{100}$ $B = 50$

38. $\frac{75}{B} = \frac{50}{100}$ $B = 150$

39. $\frac{135}{B} = \frac{675}{100}$ $B = 20$

40. $\frac{90}{40} = \frac{r}{100}$ $r = 225$

Solve each of the following.

41. 10% of 60 is ___6___.

42. 25% of 84 is ___21___.

43. 6% of 150 is ___9___.

44. 485% of 180 is ___873___.

45. 205% of 22 is ___45.1___.

46. 110% of 40 is ___44___.

47. ___8.2___ is 4.1% of 200.

48. ___49.5___ is 16.5% of 300.

49. ___64.2___ is 42.8% of 150.

50. ___8___ is $16\frac{2}{3}$% of 48.

51. ___603___ is $112\frac{1}{2}$% of 536.

52. ___90___ is $11\frac{1}{4}$% of 800.

53. ___32.3___ is 19% of 170.

54. 10.8% of 20 is ___2.16___.

55. 40.5% of 120 is ___48.6___.

56. $13\frac{3}{4}$% of 4000 is ___550___.

57. $83\frac{1}{3}$% of 150 is ___125___.

58. ___45.76___ is 20.8% of 220.

59. 8 is ___25___ % of 32.

60. 9 is ___20___ % of 45.

61. 11 is ___50___ % of 22.

62. 120 is ___15___ % of 800.

63. 57 is ___60___ % of 95.

64. 713 is ___23___ % of 3100.

65. ___40___ % of 40 is 16.

66. ___11___ % of 500 is 55.

67. ___24___ % of 71 is 17.04.

68. ___120___ % of 85 is 102.

69. ___360___ % of 705 is 2538.

70. ___200___ % of 45 is 90.

71. 12 is ___12 1/2___ % of 96.

72. 25 is ___62 1/2___ % of 40.

73. 56 is ___350___ % of 16.

74. 20% of ___60___ is 12.

75. 30% of ___70___ is 21.

76. 25% of ___300___ is 75.

77. 3% of ___600___ is 18.

78. 65% of ___40___ is 26.

79. 44% of ___85___ is 37.4.

80. 85 is 68% of ___125___.

81. 117 is 26% of ___450___.

82. 738 is 72% of ___1025___.

83. 770 is $87\frac{1}{2}$% of ___880___.

84. 32 is $66\frac{2}{3}$% of ___48___.

85. 135 is 675% of ___20___.

Absolute Value

Solve each equation.

1. $|-5| = x$ 5
2. $|-9| = x$ 9
3. $|-3.7| = y$ 3.7
4. $y = |105.2|$ 105.2
5. $z = |9.7|$ 9.7
6. $r = |0.18|$ 0.18
7. $t = |5 - 12|$ 7
8. $m = |-3 + (-4)|$ 7
9. $k = |51 + (-48)|$ 3
10. $|-30 - (-5)| = s$ 25
11. $|-60 - 25| = q$ 85
12. $|24 + (-16)| = x$ 8
13. $|2(3) - 7| = f$ 1
14. $|32 - 4(8)| = k$ 0
15. $|(-11)9 + (-5)10| = y$
16. $|-5| + 4 = x$ 9
17. $-8 + |12| = z$ 4
18. $7 - |-24| = l$ −17
19. $a = |11.4| - |-12|$ −0.6
20. $r = -|3| + (-29)$ −32
21. $c = |45 - 10| - 37$ −2
22. $x + |-72| = 91 - |38|$ −19
23. $-62 + |56| = b - |47|$ 41
24. $-|84| - |100| = 12 - y$
                                                                                   196

Evaluate if $a = -3$.

25. $|a|$ 3
26. $|-7a|$ 21
27. $|11a|$ 33
28. $|a - 4|$ 7
29. $|3a + 6|$ 3
30. $|3 - a|$ 6
31. $a - |a|$ −6
32. $a + |a|$ 0
33. $|-5a - 9|$ 6
34. $25 - |2a + 7|$ 24
35. $2|4a - 9|$ 42
36. $-3|a + 1| + 2|a - 6|$ 12
37. $5|a + 4| - |6a|$ −13
38. $|-8a| + -|12a + 3|$ −9
39. $-4|7a| + 3|a|$ −75
40. $|a - 8| - 10|3a + 10|$ 1
41. $|-a + 56| + 53$ 112
42. $-6|7 - a| + |20a|$ 0

Solve each of the following open sentences.

43. $|y + 3| = 2$ −1, −5
44. $|x + 10| = 6$ −4, −16
45. $|m - 7| = 8$ 15, −1
46. $|t - 2| = 5$ 7, −3
47. $|r - 6| = -3$ no solutions
48. $|k - 9| = 4$ 13, 5
49. $|2x + 1| = 7$ 3, −4
50. $|3x + 7| = -21$ no solutions
51. $|4a - 6| = 10$ 4, −1
52. $|5s - 5| = 20$ 5, −3
53. $8|p - 3| = 88$ −8, 14
54. $5|y + 4| = 45$ 5, −13
55. $2|3d + 3| = 18$ −4, 2
56. $4|2b + 6| = 32$ 1, −7
57. $-6|2x - 14| = -42$ $\frac{21}{2}, \frac{7}{2}$
58. $4|6r - 1| = 29$ $-\frac{25}{24}, \frac{11}{8}$
59. $3|p + 9| + 6 = 0$ no solutions
60. $9|3 - 2a| = 15$ $\frac{2}{3}, \frac{7}{3}$
61. $2|7 - 3f| = 3$ $\frac{11}{6}, \frac{17}{6}$
62. $3|y + 5| = y - 7$ no solutions
63. $|4r + 6| = r - 5$ no solutions
64. $|7 + 4s| = 12 - s$ 1, $-\frac{19}{3}$
65. $5|3t - 4| = t + 1$ $\frac{3}{2}, \frac{19}{16}$
66. $42 + |3z - 8| = 10$ no solutions
67. $|a| > 3$ $a > 3$ or $a < -3$
68. $|b| > 4$ $b > 4$ or $b < -4$
69. $|z| \le 9$ $z \ge -9$ and $z \le 9$
70. $|f| \ge 2$ $f \ge 2$ or $f \le -2$
71. $|r| \le 6$ $r \le 6$ and $r \ge -6$
72. $|s| \le 7$ $s \le 7$ and $s \ge -7$
73. $|m| > -5$ all reals
74. $|t| < 0$ no solutions
75. $|x + 1| \ge 3$ $x \ge 2$ or $x \le -4$
76. $|r + 2| \ge 0$ all reals
77. $|p - 5| < 0$ no solutions
78. $|c| - 5 < 0$ $c > -5$ and $c < 5$
79. $|6 - s| \le 2$ $s \ge 4$ and $s \le 8$
80. $|2 - y| \ge 1$ $y \le 1$ or $y \ge 3$
81. $|a + 4| > -2$ all reals
82. $|8 + b| < 2$ $b > -10$ and $b < -6$
83. $|7y| \ge 21$ $y \le -3$ or $y \ge 3$
84. $|5x| < 35$ $x > -7$ and $x < 7$
85. $|2m| < 26$ $m \ge -13$ and $m \le 13$
86. $|2s - 9| \le 27$ $s \ge -9$ and $s \le 18$
87. $|3x + 11| > 42$ $x > 10\frac{1}{3}$ or $x < 17\frac{2}{3}$
88. $|4x - 3| \ge 12$ $x \ge \frac{15}{4}$ or $x \le -\frac{9}{4}$

Factoring

Find the prime factorization of each integer. Write each negative integer as the product of −1 and its prime factors.

1. 21 $3 \cdot 7$
2. 18 $2 \cdot 3^2$
3. 36 $2^2 \cdot 3^2$
4. 60 $2^2 \cdot 3 \cdot 5$
5. −24 $-1 \cdot 2^3 \cdot 3$
6. −36 $-1 \cdot 2^2 \cdot 3^2$
7. −95 $-1 \cdot 5 \cdot 19$
8. −48 $-1 \cdot 2^4 \cdot 3$
9. 16 2^4
10. −27 $-1 \cdot 3^3$
11. −55 $-1 \cdot 5 \cdot 11$
12. 72 $2^3 \cdot 3^2$
13. −450 $-1 \cdot 2 \cdot 3^2 \cdot 5^2$ **14.** 200 $2^3 \cdot 5^2$
15. 372 $2^2 \cdot 3 \cdot 31$
16. −163 $-1 \cdot 163$

Factor each expression.

17. $16y - 8$ $8(2y - 1)$
18. $3z + 9$ $3(z + 3)$
19. $13a^2 + 39$ $13(a^2 + 3)$
20. $42r^2 - 6$ $6(7r^2 - 1)$
21. $-2x + 5ax$ $x(-2 + 5a)$
22. $z - 2az$ $z(1 - 2a)$
23. $qx - 5x$ $x(q - 5)$
24. $-20xy - 16xz$ $-4x(5y + 4z)$
25. $x + 7x^2$ $x(1 + 7x)$
26. $85m - 6m^2$ $m(85 - 6m)$
27. $-17y^2 + 11y^4$ $y^2(-17 + 11y^2)$
28. $5c^5 - 3c^9$ $c^5(5 - 3c^4)$
29. $2x^6 + 8x^7$ $2x^6(1 + 4x)$
30. $-7p^3 + 56p^4$ $7p^3(-1 + 8p)$
31. $y^2 - 8y + 16$ $(y - 4)^2$
32. $a^2 - 16a + 64$ $(a - 8)^2$
33. $p^2 - 2p + 1$ $(p - 1)^2$
34. $n^2 + 10n + 25$ $(n + 5)^2$
35. $9a^2 - 12ab + 4b^2$ $(3a - 2b)^2$
36. $9x^2 - 24xy + 16y^2$ $(3x - 4y)^2$
37. $x^2 - 2xy + y^2$ $(x - y)^2$
38. $49p^2 - 14p + 1$ $(7p - 1)^2$
39. $64b^2 + 48bc + 9c^2$ $(8b + 3c)^2$
40. $36 - 24x + 4x^2$ $(6 - 2x)^2$
41. $9x^2 + 48xy + 64y^2$ $(3x + 8y)^2$
42. $4m^2 + 12m + 9$ $(2m + 3)^2$
43. $4a^4 + 4a^2 + 1$ $(2a^2 + 1)^2$
44. $49 - 28x^2 + 4x^4$ $(7 - 2x^2)^2$
45. $1 - 14p^4 + 49p^8$ $(1 - 7p^4)^2$
46. $4x^6 - 12x^3y^3 + 9y^6$ $(2x^3 - 3y^3)^2$
47. $y^2 - 81$ $(y + 9)(y - 9)$
48. $m^2 - 100$ $(m + 10)(m - 10)$
49. $r^2 - 4x^2$ $(r + 2x)(r - 2x)$
50. $c^2 - 49b^2$ $(c + 7b)(c - 7b)$
51. $25a^2 - b^2$ $(5a + b)(5a - b)$
52. $4x^2 - 9$ $(2x + 3)(2x - 3)$
53. $36s^2 - 100$ $(6s + 10)(6s - 10)$
54. $1 - 64y^2$ $(1 + 8y)(1 - 8y)$
55. $-49 + 16t^2$ $(4t + 7)(4t - 7)$
56. $-121 + 9x^2$ $(3x + 11)(3x - 11)$
57. $4x^2 - 9y^2$ $(2x + 3y)(2x - 3y)$
58. $a^8 - b^{10}$ $(a^4 + b^5)(a^4 - b^5)$
59. $12c^2 - 12$ $12(c + 1)(c - 1)$
60. $81 - 9x^2$ $9(3 + x)(3 - x)$
61. $(a + b)^2 - m^2$ $(a + b + m)(a + b - m)$
62. $(x - y)^2 - z^2$ $(x - y + z)(x - y - z)$
63. $y^4 - x^4$ $(y^2 + x^2)(y + x)(y - x)$
64. $4y^6 - 9x^4$ $(2y^3 + 3x^2)(2y^3 - 3x^2)$
65. $x^2 + 9x + 18$ $(x + 3)(x + 6)$
66. $a^2 + 20a + 36$ $(a + 2)(a + 18)$
67. $r^2 + 11r + 10$ $(r + 10)(r + 1)$
68. $p^2 + 13p + 30$ $(p + 10)(p + 3)$
69. $y^2 - 10y + 16$ $(y - 8)(y - 2)$
70. $t^2 - 11t + 28$ $(t - 4)(t - 7)$
71. $k^2 - 16k + 15$ $(k - 15)(k - 1)$
72. $m^2 - 17m + 72$ $(m - 9)(m - 8)$
73. $d^2 + 4d - 21$ $(d + 7)(d - 3)$
74. $x^2 + 8x - 20$ $(x + 10)(x - 2)$
75. $a^2 + 12a - 45$ $(a + 15)(a - 3)$
76. $h^2 + 6h - 16$ $(h + 8)(h - 2)$
77. $c^2 - 5c - 36$ $(c - 9)(c + 4)$
78. $y^2 - 2y - 48$ $(y - 8)(y + 6)$
79. $2s^2 + 7s + 3$ $(2s + 1)(s + 3)$
80. $b^2 - 2b - 63$ $(b - 9)(b + 7)$
81. $3f^2 + 13f + 12$ $(3f + 4)(f + 3)$
82. $2h^3 - 8h^2 - 42h$ $2h(h - 7)(h + 3)$

Simplifying Radicals

Simplify. See bottom of page for answers to Exercises **58, 59, 61, 62, 64,** and **90.**

1. $-\sqrt{4}$ -2
2. $\sqrt{25}$ 5
3. $\pm\sqrt{9}$ ±3
4. $-\sqrt{36}$ -6

5. $\sqrt{81}$ 9
6. $\pm\sqrt{49}$ ±7
7. $-\sqrt{64}$ -8
8. $\sqrt{121}$ 11

9. $\pm\sqrt{169}$ ±13
10. $-\sqrt{225}$ -15
11. $\sqrt{144}$ 12
12. $\pm\sqrt{100}$ ±10

13. $\sqrt{0.0036}$ 0.06
14. $\sqrt{0.16}$ 0.4
15. $\sqrt{0.64}$ 0.8
16. $\sqrt{1.44}$ 1.2

17. $\sqrt{8}$ $2\sqrt{2}$
18. $\sqrt{27}$ $3\sqrt{3}$
19. $\sqrt{12}$ $2\sqrt{3}$
20. $\sqrt{32}$ $4\sqrt{2}$

21. $-\sqrt{75}$ $-5\sqrt{3}$
22. $\pm\sqrt{72}$ $\pm6\sqrt{2}$
23. $\sqrt{240}$ $4\sqrt{15}$
24. $-\sqrt{180}$ $-6\sqrt{5}$

25. $\sqrt{128}$ $8\sqrt{2}$
26. $-\sqrt{125}$ $-5\sqrt{5}$
27. $\sqrt{147}$ $7\sqrt{3}$
28. $\pm\sqrt{108}$ $\pm6\sqrt{3}$

29. $-\sqrt{112}$ $-4\sqrt{7}$
30. $-\sqrt{44}$ $-2\sqrt{11}$
31. $\pm\sqrt{45}$ $\pm3\sqrt{5}$
32. $\sqrt{162}$ $9\sqrt{2}$

33. $\sqrt{x^2}$ $|x|$
34. $\sqrt{y^4}$ y^2
35. $\sqrt{a^6}$ $|a^3|$
36. $\sqrt{t^{10}}$ $|t^5|$

37. $\sqrt{m^8}$ m^4
38. $\sqrt{a^2}$ $|a|$
39. $\sqrt{x}$ $\sqrt{x}$
40. $\sqrt{z^{12}}$ z^6

41. $\sqrt{x^{30}}$ $|x^{15}|$
42. $\sqrt{y^{64}}$ y^{32}
43. $\sqrt{a^{150}}$ $|a^{75}|$
44. $\sqrt{c^{90}}$ $|c^{45}|$

45. $\sqrt{t^5}$ $t^2\sqrt{t}$
46. $\sqrt{k^7}$ $|k^3|\sqrt{k}$
47. $\sqrt{p^{11}}$ $|p^3|\sqrt{p}$
48. $\sqrt{s^{21}}$ $s^{10}\sqrt{s}$

49. $\sqrt{ab^2}$ $|b|\sqrt{a}$
50. $\sqrt{r^2t^4z}$ $|r|t^2\sqrt{z}$
51. $\sqrt{3c^2}$ $|c|\sqrt{3}$
52. $\sqrt{5a^4}$ $a^2\sqrt{5}$

53. $\sqrt{4m^2}$ $2|m|$
54. $\sqrt{9x^2z}$ $3|x|\sqrt{z}$
55. $\sqrt{40k^8}$ $2k^4\sqrt{10}$
56. $\sqrt{11x^6}$ $|x^3|\sqrt{11}$

57. $\sqrt{1600x^3}$ $40|x|\sqrt{x}$
58. $\sqrt{4x^5y^7}$
59. $\sqrt{0.16a^{10}b^8}$
60. $\sqrt{m^4r^3t}$ $m^2|r|\sqrt{rt}$

61. $\frac{1}{5}\sqrt{54x^2y^4}$
62. $\frac{2}{3}\sqrt{24a^2b^2}$
63. $\sqrt{3ab^5}$ $b^2\sqrt{3ab}$
64. $\frac{1}{6}\sqrt{45x^2z}$

65. $-\sqrt{\frac{4}{9}}$ $-\frac{2}{3}$
66. $\pm\sqrt{\frac{25a^2}{4b^2}}$ $\pm\frac{5|a|}{2|b|}$
67. $\sqrt{\frac{49x^4}{36y^2}}$ $\frac{7x^2}{6|y|}$
68. $\sqrt{\frac{100a^2b^6}{81c^{10}}}$ $\frac{10|a|b^3}{9|c^5|}$

69. $\sqrt{\frac{27}{x^3}}$ $\frac{3\sqrt{3}}{|x|\sqrt{x}}$
70. $\sqrt{\frac{y^4}{16y^2}}$ $\frac{|y|}{4}$
71. $\sqrt{\frac{64r^2t^{14}}{25s^6}}$ $\frac{8|rt^7|}{5|s^3|}$
72. $\sqrt{\frac{9k^{12}}{25l^{10}}}$ $\frac{3k^6}{5|l^5|}$

Rationalize the denominators of the following.

73. $\frac{1}{\sqrt{5}}$ $\frac{\sqrt{5}}{5}$
74. $\frac{3}{\sqrt{7}}$ $\frac{3\sqrt{7}}{7}$
75. $\frac{-8}{\sqrt{11}}$ $-\frac{8\sqrt{11}}{11}$
76. $\frac{-8y}{\sqrt{15}}$ $-\frac{8y\sqrt{15}}{15}$

77. $\frac{3}{2\sqrt{5}}$ $\frac{3\sqrt{5}}{10}$
78. $\sqrt{\frac{a}{3}}$ $\frac{\sqrt{3a}}{3}$
79. $\frac{5\sqrt{21}}{\sqrt{5}}$ $\sqrt{105}$
80. $\sqrt{\frac{10}{7}}$ $\frac{\sqrt{70}}{7}$

81. $\sqrt{\frac{45}{2}}$ $\frac{3\sqrt{10}}{2}$
82. $-\sqrt{\frac{50}{3}}$ $-\frac{5\sqrt{6}}{3}$
83. $-\frac{\sqrt{48}}{\sqrt{3}}$ -4
84. $\sqrt{\frac{7}{8}}$ $\frac{\sqrt{14}}{4}$

85. $-\sqrt{\frac{54}{r}}$ $-\frac{3\sqrt{6r}}{r}$
86. $\frac{\sqrt{8}}{\sqrt{9x}}$ $\frac{2\sqrt{2x}}{3x}$
87. $\pm\sqrt{\frac{7x^2}{4y}}$ $\pm\frac{x\sqrt{7y}}{2y}$
88. $\frac{\sqrt{22a}}{\sqrt{8y^2}}$ $\frac{\sqrt{11a}}{2|y|}$

89. $\sqrt{\frac{20m}{3}}$ $\frac{2\sqrt{15m}}{3}$
90. $\pm\sqrt{\frac{2k}{11m}}$
91. $\frac{\sqrt{18s}}{\sqrt{3}}$ $\sqrt{6s}$
92. $-\sqrt{\frac{b}{6}}$ $-\frac{\sqrt{6b}}{6}$

93. $\frac{-5\sqrt{21}}{\sqrt{5}}$ $-\sqrt{105}$
94. $\frac{3\sqrt{7}}{\sqrt{2}}$ $\frac{3\sqrt{14}}{2}$
95. $\frac{6\sqrt{36}}{\sqrt{2}}$ $18\sqrt{2}$
96. $\frac{-2\sqrt{27}}{\sqrt{3}}$ -6

97. $\frac{11}{4\sqrt{6}}$ $\frac{11\sqrt{6}}{24}$
98. $\frac{-3}{10\sqrt{15}}$ $-\frac{\sqrt{15}}{50}$
99. $\frac{20}{-5\sqrt{2}}$ $-2\sqrt{2}$
100. $\frac{4}{7\sqrt{8}}$ $\frac{\sqrt{2}}{7}$

101. $\frac{-6\sqrt{56}}{2\sqrt{10}}$ $\frac{-6\sqrt{35}}{5}$
102. $\frac{9\sqrt{20}}{3\sqrt{11}}$ $\frac{6\sqrt{55}}{11}$
103. $\frac{-4\sqrt{24}}{12\sqrt{27}}$ $\frac{-2\sqrt{2}}{9}$
104. $\frac{16\sqrt{40}}{8\sqrt{32}}$ $\sqrt{5}$

58. $2x^2|y^3|\sqrt{xy}$ 59. $0.4|a^5|b^4$ 61. $\frac{3}{5}|x|y^2\sqrt{6}$ 62. $\frac{4}{3}|ab|\sqrt{6}$ 64. $\frac{1}{2}|x|\sqrt{5z}$ 90. $\pm\frac{\sqrt{22km}}{11m}$

Operations With Radicals

Simplify. See bottom of page for answers to Exercises **27, 30, 33, 35, 63, 65,** and **66.**

1. $3\sqrt{5} + 2\sqrt{5}$ $5\sqrt{5}$
2. $8\sqrt{3} + (-2\sqrt{3})$ $6\sqrt{3}$
3. $-6\sqrt{7} + 4\sqrt{7}$ $-2\sqrt{7}$
4. $-8\sqrt{6} + (-2\sqrt{6})$ $-10\sqrt{6}$
5. $4\sqrt{x} + (-9\sqrt{x})$ $-5\sqrt{x}$
6. $-2\sqrt{y} + 11\sqrt{y}$ $9\sqrt{y}$
7. $\frac{1}{4}\sqrt{xy} + \frac{3}{4}\sqrt{xy}$ $\sqrt{xy}$
8. $\frac{2}{3}\sqrt{11} + \left(-\frac{1}{3}\sqrt{11}\right)$ $\frac{1}{3}\sqrt{11}$
9. $-\frac{5}{8}\sqrt{3} + \left(-\frac{1}{8}\sqrt{3}\right)$ $-\frac{3}{4}\sqrt{3}$
10. $3\sqrt{21} - 11\sqrt{21}$ $-8\sqrt{21}$
11. $18\sqrt{z} - 5\sqrt{z}$ $13\sqrt{z}$
12. $4\sqrt{t} - 10\sqrt{t}$ $-6\sqrt{t}$
13. $84\sqrt{m} - 56\sqrt{m}$ $28\sqrt{m}$
14. $-7\sqrt{3} - 11\sqrt{3}$ $-18\sqrt{3}$
15. $-2\sqrt{k} - (-5\sqrt{k})$ $3\sqrt{k}$
16. $2\sqrt{3} + \sqrt{27}$ $5\sqrt{3}$
17. $\sqrt{8} + 3\sqrt{2}$ $5\sqrt{2}$
18. $5\sqrt{5} + \sqrt{20}$ $7\sqrt{5}$
19. $\sqrt{8} + \sqrt{50}$ $7\sqrt{2}$
20. $\sqrt{27} - \sqrt{12}$ $\sqrt{3}$
21. $\sqrt{32} - \sqrt{18}$ $\sqrt{2}$
22. $-\sqrt{44a} + \sqrt{99a}$ $\sqrt{11a}$
23. $-\sqrt{50c} + (-\sqrt{32c})$ $-9\sqrt{2c}$
24. $\sqrt{20} - \sqrt{80}$ $-2\sqrt{5}$
25. $\sqrt{24x} + (-\sqrt{54x})$ $-\sqrt{6x}$
26. $-\sqrt{18y} + \sqrt{50y}$ $2\sqrt{2y}$
27. $-\sqrt{45t} + (-\sqrt{125t})$
28. $\sqrt{18} + \sqrt{72} - \sqrt{50}$ $4\sqrt{2}$
29. $2\sqrt{40} - \sqrt{160} + \sqrt{72}$ $6\sqrt{2}$
30. $\sqrt{3} - 2\sqrt{12} - \sqrt{27}$
31. $3\sqrt{18} - \sqrt{8} + 2\sqrt{32}$ $15\sqrt{2}$
32. $3\sqrt{5} + 2\sqrt{20} - \sqrt{125}$ $2\sqrt{5}$
33. $2\sqrt{20} - 3\sqrt{80} + \sqrt{45}$
34. $7\sqrt{5x^2} + |x|\sqrt{20}$ $9|x|\sqrt{5}$
35. $\sqrt{a^2b} - 2|a|\sqrt{b} + 9\sqrt{a^2b}$
36. $|y|\sqrt{x^2yz} - \sqrt{x^2y^3z}$ 0
37. $\sqrt{3}\sqrt{2}$ $\sqrt{6}$
38. $\sqrt{12}\sqrt{3}$ 6
39. $\sqrt{18}\sqrt{6}$ $6\sqrt{3}$
40. $\sqrt{2}\sqrt{24}\sqrt{3}$ 12
41. $\sqrt{a}\sqrt{a^3}$ a^2
42. $\sqrt{y^5}\sqrt{y^7}$ y^6
43. $\sqrt{5x}\sqrt{8x}$ $2|x|\sqrt{10}$
44. $4\sqrt{2}\sqrt{10}$ $8\sqrt{5}$
45. $3\sqrt{5}\sqrt{18}$ $9\sqrt{10}$
46. $(\sqrt{7})^2$ 7
47. $(2\sqrt{3})^2$ 12
48. $(2\sqrt{32})^2$ 128
49. $\sqrt{8}\sqrt{\frac{1}{2}}$ 2
50. $\sqrt{\frac{1}{3}}\sqrt{9}$ $\sqrt{3}$
51. $\sqrt{\frac{10}{4}}\sqrt{\frac{8}{5}}$ 2
52. $2\sqrt{2}(4\sqrt{8})$ 32
53. $5\sqrt{3}(7\sqrt{2})$ $35\sqrt{6}$
54. $2\sqrt{5}(\sqrt{125})$ 50
55. $\sqrt{5}(\sqrt{5} + \sqrt{3})$ $5 + \sqrt{15}$
56. $\sqrt{3}(\sqrt{3} + \sqrt{5})$ $3 + \sqrt{15}$
57. $\sqrt{2}(\sqrt{2} - \sqrt{6})$ $2 - 2\sqrt{3}$
58. $(3 - \sqrt{7})(3 + \sqrt{7})$ 2
59. $(5 - \sqrt{5})(5 + \sqrt{5})$ 20
60. $(\sqrt{2} - 3)(\sqrt{2} + 3)$ -7
61. $(\sqrt{10} + \sqrt{3})(\sqrt{10} - \sqrt{3})$ 7
62. $(\sqrt{7} - \sqrt{2})(\sqrt{7} + \sqrt{2})$ 5
63. $(\sqrt{3} + 2\sqrt{5})(\sqrt{3} - 2\sqrt{5})$
64. $(\sqrt{a + b})(\sqrt{a + b})$ $a + b$
65. $(\sqrt{a} - \sqrt{b})(\sqrt{a} + \sqrt{b})$
66. $(\sqrt{x - y})(\sqrt{4x - 4y})$
67. $\frac{\sqrt{15}}{\sqrt{3}}$ $\sqrt{5}$
68. $\frac{\sqrt{21}}{\sqrt{7}}$ $\sqrt{3}$
69. $\frac{\sqrt{93}}{\sqrt{3}}$ $\sqrt{31}$
70. $\frac{\sqrt{54}}{\sqrt{6}}$ 3
71. $\frac{\sqrt{72}}{\sqrt{8}}$ 3
72. $\frac{\sqrt{144}}{\sqrt{8}}$ $3\sqrt{2}$
73. $\frac{\sqrt{100}}{\sqrt{4}}$ 5
74. $\frac{\sqrt{36}}{\sqrt{9}}$ 2
75. $\frac{\sqrt{16x^4}}{\sqrt{4x^2}}$ $2|x|$
76. $\frac{8\sqrt{x^5}}{3\sqrt{x}}$ $\frac{8}{3}x^2$
77. $\frac{\sqrt{28}}{\sqrt{7}}$ 2
78. $\frac{\sqrt{7}}{\sqrt{3}}$ $\frac{\sqrt{21}}{3}$
79. $\frac{5\sqrt{21}}{\sqrt{5}}$ $\sqrt{105}$
80. $\sqrt{\frac{3}{7}}$ $\frac{\sqrt{21}}{7}$
81. $\sqrt{\frac{b}{6}}$ $\frac{\sqrt{6b}}{6}$
82. $\sqrt{\frac{x^4}{11}}$ $\frac{x^2\sqrt{11}}{11}$
83. $\sqrt{\frac{27}{y}}$ $\frac{3\sqrt{3y}}{y}$
84. $\sqrt{\frac{54}{z}}$ $\frac{3\sqrt{6z}}{z}$
85. $\frac{\sqrt{18y^2}}{\sqrt{3}}$ $|y|\sqrt{6}$
86. $\frac{\sqrt{24x}}{8\sqrt{x^3}}$ $\frac{\sqrt{6}}{4x}$
87. $\frac{a^3\sqrt{ab^3}}{\sqrt{a^3b}}$ a^2b

27. $-8\sqrt{5t}$ 30. $-6\sqrt{3}$ 33. $-5\sqrt{5}$ 35. $8|a|\sqrt{b}$
63. -17 65. $a - b$ 66. $2x - 2y$

Solving Radical and Quadratic Equations

Solve each equation.

1. $\sqrt{x} = 2$ 4
2. $\sqrt{y} = 9$ 81
3. $-\sqrt{r} = -6$ 36
4. $-\sqrt{m} = -5$ 25
5. $\sqrt{5y} = 5$ 5
6. $\sqrt{x} - 9 = 0$ 81
7. $\sqrt{4a} = 1$ $\frac{1}{4}$
8. $3 + \sqrt{m} = 5$ 4
9. $2 + \sqrt{r} = 10$ 64
10. $\sqrt{4b + 1} = 3$ 2
11. $\sqrt{2c + 7} = 5$ 9
12. $\sqrt{8y + 1} = 5$ 3
13. $\sqrt{3b - 5} - 4 = 0$ 7
14. $\sqrt{3x + 7} - 7 = 0$ 14
15. $\sqrt{2x + 7} - 3 = 0$ 1
16. $\sqrt{r} = 3\sqrt{5}$ 45
17. $3\sqrt{7} = \sqrt{x}$ 63
18. $\sqrt{y} = 2\sqrt{8}$ 32
19. $\sqrt{m} = 4\sqrt{7}$ 112
20. $5\sqrt{10} = \sqrt{x}$ 250
21. $5\sqrt{5} = \sqrt{c}$ 125
22. $\sqrt{\dfrac{p}{3}} = 5$ 75
23. $\sqrt{\dfrac{4a}{3}} - 2 = 0$ 3
24. $\sqrt{\dfrac{2x}{3}} - 4 = 0$ 24
25. $\dfrac{8}{\sqrt{x + 3}} = 2$ 13
26. $\dfrac{\sqrt{x}}{\sqrt{2}} = \sqrt{5}$ 10
27. $\dfrac{\sqrt{2x + 1}}{3} + 2 = 5$ 40
28. $\sqrt{2x^2 - 121} = x$ 11
29. $\sqrt{x + 2} = x - 4$ 7
30. $\sqrt{1 - 2y} = 1 + y$ 0
31. $\sqrt{5a + 1} + 6 = 10$ 3
32. $n + \sqrt{n^2 + 3} = 3n$ 1
33. $\sqrt{10 + x} - \sqrt{10 - x} = 2$ 6

Solve each equation.

34. $(x - 4)(x + 5) = 0$ 4, −5
35. $y(y - 6) = 0$ 0, 6
36. $(3x + 4)(2x - 5) = 0$ $-\frac{4}{3}, \frac{5}{2}$
37. $(x - 7)^2 = 0$ 7
38. $x^2 + 2x + 1 = 0$ −1
39. $x^2 - 36 = 0$ ±6
40. $x^2 + 2x - 48 = 0$ −8, 6
41. $x^2 - 12x + 35 = 0$ 5, 7
42. $y^2 - 7y = 0$ 0, 7
43. $y^2 + 17y + 72 = 0$ −9, −8
44. $2x^2 + 12x + 16 = 0$ −4, −2
45. $3y^2 - 21y + 36 = 0$ 3, 4
46. $9a^2 - 64 = 0$ $\frac{8}{3}, -\frac{8}{3}$
47. $25b^2 - 16 = 0$ $\frac{4}{5}, -\frac{4}{5}$
48. $3y^2 - 15y = 0$ 0, 5
49. $9x^2 + 6x + 1 = 0$ $-\frac{1}{3}$
50. $4x^2 - 12x + 9 = 0$ $\frac{3}{2}$
51. $x^2 = 121$ ±11
52. $17x^2 = 68x$ 0, 4
53. $2y^2 + 24y = -40$ −10, −2
54. $y^2 + 3y = 40$ −8, 5
55. $2a^2 - 3a = 9$ $-\frac{3}{2}, 3$
56. $10b^2 + 33b = 7$ $\frac{1}{5}, -\frac{7}{2}$
57. $18y^2 - 3y = 15$ $1, -\frac{5}{6}$

Use the quadratic formula to solve each equation. The quadratic formula is $\dfrac{-b \pm \sqrt{b^2 - 4ac}}{2a}$.

58. $x^2 + 7x + 6 = 0$ −1, −6
59. $a^2 + 8a + 15 = 0$ −3, −5
60. $2a^2 + a - 15 = 0$ $-3, \frac{5}{2}$
61. $2y^2 + 7y + 3 = 0$ $-3, -\frac{1}{2}$
62. $3m^2 + 5m + 2 = 0$ $-1, -\frac{2}{3}$
63. $3x^2 + 23x + 14 = 0$ $-7, -\frac{2}{3}$
64. $3x^2 + 14x = 5$ $-5, \frac{1}{3}$
65. $m^2 - 2m = 8$ 4, −2
66. $r^2 + 9 = 10r$ 9, 1
67. $m^2 + 36 = 13m$ 4, 9
68. $4x^2 - 8x = -3$ $\frac{1}{2}, \frac{3}{2}$
69. $4b^2 = 20b$ 0, 5
70. $2x^2 = 3 + x$ $-1, \frac{3}{2}$
71. $3y^2 + 2 = 5y$ $1, \frac{2}{3}$
72. $b^2 - b - 3 = 0$ $\frac{(1 \pm \sqrt{13})}{2}$
73. $y^2 - 27 = 0$ ±3√3
74. $x^2 - 125 = 0$ ±5√5
75. $m^2 = 32$ ±4√2
76. $x^2 - 6x - 2 = 0$ $3 \pm \sqrt{11}$
77. $y^2 - 2y = 1$ $1 \pm \sqrt{2}$
78. $y^2 + 4y = 3$ $-2 \pm \sqrt{7}$
79. $2a^2 - 5a + 1 = 0$ $\frac{(5 \pm \sqrt{17})}{4}$
80. $3b^2 - 5b + 1 = 0$ $\frac{(5 \pm \sqrt{13})}{6}$
81. $x^2 + 3x = 1$ $\frac{(-3 \pm \sqrt{13})}{2}$
82. $3y^2 + y - 1 = 0$ $\frac{(-1 \pm \sqrt{13})}{6}$
83. $x^2 + 2x + 5 = 0$ no real solution

Symbols

h	altitude	mm	millimeter
$\angle$	angle	$\sqrt{}$	nonnegative square root
a	apothem	(x, y)	ordered pair
$\approx$	approximately equal to	(x, y, z)	ordered triple
$\overset{\frown}{AB}$	arc with endpoints A and B	$\parallel$	parallel, is parallel to
B	area of base of a prism cylinder, pyramid, or cone	$\square$	parallelogram
b	base	P	perimeter
cm	centimeter	$\perp$	perpendicular, is perpendicular to
$\odot P$	circle with center P	π	pi
C	circumference	n-gon	polygon with n sides
$\cong$	congruent, is congruent to	r	radius
cos	cosine	$\overrightarrow{PQ}$	ray with endpoint P passing through Q
cm^3	cubic centimeters	k	scale factor for a dilation
m^3	cubic meters	$\overline{PQ}$	segment with endpoints P and Q
$^\circ$	degree	s	side of a regular polygon
d	diagonal of a square diameter distance	$\sim$	similar, is similar to
AB	distance between points A and B	sin	sine
$=$	equals, is equal to	l	slant height
km	kilometer	m	slope
L	lateral area	cm^2	square centimeter
$\overleftrightarrow{DE}$	line containing points D and E	m^2	square meter
$\rightarrow$	mapping, is mapped onto	S	sum of the degree measure of a convex polygon
$m\angle A$	measure of angle A	tan	tangent
$m\overset{\frown}{AB}$	measure of arc AB	T	total surface area
m	meter	$\triangle$	triangle
		V	volume

Postulates and Theorems

Chapter 1:   Points, Lines, and Planes

Postulate 1-1	Through any two points there is exactly one line. (14)
Postulate 1-2	Through any three points not on the same line there is exactly one plane. (14)
Postulate 1-3	A line contains at least two points. (15)
Postulate 1-4	A plane contains at least three points not on the same line. (15)
Postulate 1-5	If two points lie in a plane, then the entire line containing those two points lies in that plane. (15)
Postulate 1-6	If two planes intersect, then their intersection is a line. (15)
Theorem 1-1	If there is a line and a point not on the line, then there is exactly one plane that contains them. (19)
Theorem 1-2	If two lines intersect, exactly one plane contains both lines. (24)

Chapter 2:   Measure

Postulate 2-1 Number Line Postulate	Each real number corresponds to exactly one point on a number line. Each point on a number line corresponds to exactly one real number. (39)
Postulate 2-2 Ruler Postulate	The points on any line can be paired with the real numbers so that, given any two points P and Q on the line, P corresponds to zero, and Q corresponds to a positive number. (41)
Postulate 2-3 Distance Postulate	For any two points on a line and a given unit of measure, there is a unique positive number called the measure of the distance between the two points. (42)

Properties of equality: (50, 51)

		For any numbers a, b, and c
Postulate 2-4	Reflexive	$a = a$
Postulate 2-5	Symmetric	If $a = b$, then $b = a$.
Postulate 2-6	Transitive	If $a = b$ and $b = c$, then $a = c$.
Postulate 2-7	Addition and Subtraction	If $a = b$, then $a + c = b + c$, and $a - c = b - c$.
Postulate 2-8	Multiplication and Division	If $a = b$, then $a \cdot c = b \cdot c$, and if c is not zero, then $\frac{a}{c} = \frac{b}{c}$.
Postulate 2-9	Substitution	If $a = b$, then a may be replaced by b.

Properties of operations: (51)

<table>
<tr><td colspan="3" align="center">For any numbers a, b, and c</td></tr>
<tr><td></td><td align="center">Addition</td><td align="center">Multiplication</td></tr>
<tr><td>Commutative</td><td align="center">$a + b = b + a$</td><td align="center">$a \cdot b = b \cdot a$</td></tr>
<tr><td>Associative</td><td align="center">$(a + b) + c = a + (b + c)$</td><td align="center">$(a \cdot b) \cdot c = a \cdot (b \cdot c)$</td></tr>
<tr><td>Identity</td><td align="center">$a + 0 = a = 0 + a$</td><td align="center">$a \cdot 1 = a = 1 \cdot a$</td></tr>
<tr><td>Inverse</td><td align="center">$a + (-a) = 0 = -a + a$</td><td>If a is not zero, then $a \cdot \dfrac{1}{a} = 1 = \dfrac{1}{a} \cdot a.$</td></tr>
<tr><td colspan="3">Distributive Property of Multiplication over Addition:
$a(b + c) = ab + ac$ and $(b + c)a = ba + ca$</td></tr>
</table>

Postulate 2-10 — Commutative
Postulate 2-11 — Associative
Postulate 2-12 — Identity
Postulate 2-13 — Inverse
Postulate 2-14 — Distributive Property of Multiplication over Addition

Properties of inequality: (61, 62)

<table>
<tr><td colspan="2" align="center">For any numbers a, b, and c</td></tr>
<tr><td>Comparison</td><td>$a < b$, or $a = b$, or $a > b$</td></tr>
<tr><td>Addition and Subtraction</td><td>1. If $a > b$, then $a + c > b + c$ and $a - c > b - c$.
2. If $a < b$, then $a + c < b + c$ and $a - c < b - c$.</td></tr>
<tr><td>Multiplication and Division</td><td>1. If $c > 0$ and $a < b$, then $ac < bc$ and $\dfrac{a}{c} < \dfrac{b}{c}$.
2. If $c > 0$ and $a > b$, then $ac > bc$ and $\dfrac{a}{c} > \dfrac{b}{c}$.
3. If $c < 0$ and $a < b$, then $ac > bc$ and $\dfrac{a}{c} > \dfrac{b}{c}$.
4. If $c < 0$ and $a > b$, then $ac < bc$ and $\dfrac{a}{c} < \dfrac{b}{c}$.</td></tr>
<tr><td>Transitive</td><td>1. If $a < b$ and $b < c$, then $a < c$.
2. If $a > b$ and $b > c$, then $a > c$.</td></tr>
</table>

Postulate 2-15 — Comparison
Postulate 2-16 — Addition and Subtraction
Postulate 2-17 — Multiplication and Division
Postulate 2-18 — Transitive

Theorem 2-1 If a segment is given, then it has exactly one midpoint. (47)
Theorem 2-2 Congruence of segments is reflexive. (56)
Theorem 2-3 Congruence of segments is symmetric. (56)
Theorem 2-4 Congruence of segments is transitive. (56)
Theorem 2-5 If M is the midpoint of $\overline{PQ}$, then $\overline{PM} \cong \overline{MQ}$. (57)
Midpoint Theorem

Theorem 2-6 If $\overline{PQ}$ is bisected at point M, then $\overline{PM} \cong \overline{MQ}$. (58)
Bisector Theorem

Chapter 3:   Angles and Perpendiculars

Postulate 3-1
Angle Measure Postulate

For every angle there is a unique positive number between 0 and 180 called the degree measure of the angle. (77)

Postulate 3-2
Protractor Postulate

Given a ray on the edge of a half plane, for every positive number r between 0 and 180 there is exactly one ray in the half plane such that the degree measure of the angle formed by the two rays is r. (78)

Postulate 3-3 Angle Addition Postulate	If R is in the interior of $\angle PQS$, then $m \angle PQR + m \angle RQS = m \angle PQS$. (79)
Postulate 3-4 Supplement Postulate	If two angles form a linear pair, then they are supplementary angles. (83)
Theorem 3-1	Congruence of angles is reflexive, symmetric, and transitive. (79)
Theorem 3-2	If two angles are supplementary to the same angle, then they are congruent. (83)
Theorem 3-3	If two angles are supplementary to two congruent angles, then the two angles are congruent to each other. (84)
Theorem 3-4	If two angles are complementary to the same angle, then they are congruent to each other. (85)
Theorem 3-5	If two angles are complementary to two congruent angles, then the two angles are congruent to each other. (85)
Theorem 3-6	If two angles are right angles, then the angles are congruent. (88)
Theorem 3-7	If one angle in a linear pair is a right angle, then the other angle is also a right angle. (88)
Theorem 3-8	If two angles are congruent and supplementary, then each angle is a right angle. (88)
Theorem 3-9	If two intersecting lines form one right angle, then they form four right angles. (89)
Theorem 3-10	If two angles are vertical, then they are congruent. (89)
Theorem 3-11	If two lines are perpendicular, then they form four right angles. (94)
Theorem 3-12	If a point is on a line in a plane, then there is exactly one line in that plane perpendicular to the given line at the given point. (94)
Theorem 3-13	If two lines are perpendicular, then they form congruent adjacent angles. (94)
Theorem 3-14	If two intersecting lines form congruent adjacent angles, then they are perpendicular. (94)
Theorem 3-15	If a line is perpendicular to two intersecting lines at their point of intersection, then it is perpendicular to the plane that contains the two lines. (98)
Theorem 3-16	Two planes are perpendicular if and only if they intersect to form a right dihedral angle. (100)

Chapter 4: Congruent Triangles

Postulate 4-1 SSS	If each side of one triangle is congruent to the corresponding side of another triangle, then the triangles are congruent. (124)
Postulate 4-2 SAS	If two sides and the included angle of one triangle are congruent to the corresponding sides and included angle of another triangle, then the triangles are congruent. (124)
Postulate 4-3 ASA	If two angles and the included side of one triangle are congruent to the corresponding angles and included side of another triangle, then the triangles are congruent. (125)

Postulate 4-4 HL	If the hypotenuse and a leg of one right triangle are congruent to the corresponding sides of another right triangle, then the triangles are congruent. (144)
Theorem 4-1 Angle Sum Theorem	The sum of the degree measures of the angles of a triangle is 180. (116)
Theorem 4-2	If a triangle is equiangular, then the degree measure of each angle is 60. (117)
Theorem 4-3	If a triangle is a right triangle, then the acute angles are complementary. (117)
Theorem 4-4	Congruence of triangles is reflexive, symmetric, and transitive. (122)
Theorem 4-5 AAS	If two angles and a nonincluded side of one triangle are congruent to the corresponding angles and nonincluded side of another triangle, then the triangles are congruent. (130)
Theorem 4-6 Isosceles Triangle Theorem	If two sides of a triangle are congruent, then the angles opposite those sides are congruent. (138)
Theorem 4-7	If a triangle is equilateral, then the triangle is equiangular. (138)
Theorem 4-8	If a triangle is equilateral, then each angle has a degree measure of 60. (138)
Theorem 4-9	If two angles of a triangle are congruent, then the sides opposite those angles are congruent. (139)
Theorem 4-10	If a triangle is equiangular, then the triangle is equilateral. (139)
Theorem 4-11 HA	If the hypotenuse and an acute angle of one right triangle are congruent to the corresponding hypotenuse and acute angle of another right triangle, then the triangles are congruent. (142)
Theorem 4-12 LL	If the legs of one right triangle are congruent to the corresponding legs of another right triangle, then the triangles are congruent. (142)
Theorem 4-13 LA	If one leg and an acute angle of one right triangle are congruent to the corresponding leg and acute angle of another right triangle, then the triangles are congruent. (143)

Chapter 5: Triangle Inequalities

Theorem 5-1 Exterior Angle Theorem	If an angle is an exterior angle of a triangle, then its measure is equal to the sum of the measures of the two remote interior angles. (152)
Theorem 5-2 Inequality Theorem	For any numbers a and b, $a > b$ if and only if there is a positive number c such that $a = b + c$. (152)
Theorem 5-3	If an angle is an exterior angle of a triangle, then its measure is greater than the measure of either remote interior angle. (152)
Theorem 5-4	If the measures of two sides of a triangle are unequal, then the measures of the angles opposite those sides are unequal in the same order. (162)

Theorem 5-5	If the measures of two angles of a triangle are unequal, then the measures of the sides opposite those angles are unequal in the same order. (163)
Theorem 5-6	A segment is the shortest segment from a point to a line if and only if it is the segment perpendicular to the line. (164)
Theorem 5-7	A segment is the shortest segment from a point to a plane if and only if it is the segment perpendicular to the plane. (164)
Theorem 5-8 Triangle Inequality	The sum of the measures of any two sides of a triangle is greater than the measure of the third side. (167)
Theorem 5-9 Hinge Theorem	If two sides of one triangle are congruent to two sides of another triangle and the measures of the included angles are unequal, then the measures of the third sides are unequal in the same order. (173)
Theorem 5-10 Converse of the Hinge Theorem	If two sides of one triangle are congruent to two sides of another triangle and the measures of the third sides are unequal, then the measures of the angles included between the pairs of congruent sides are unequal in the same order. (173)

Chapter 6: Parallels

Postulate 6-1 Parallel Postulate	If there is a line and a point not on the line, then there is exactly one line through the point that is parallel to the given line. (201)
Theorem 6-1	If two lines are cut by a transversal and one pair of alternate interior angles are congruent, then the other pair of alternate interior angles also are congruent. (187)
Theorem 6-2	If two lines are cut by a transversal and one pair of corresponding angles are congruent, then all pairs of corresponding angles are congruent. (187)
Theorem 6-3	If a triangle is a right triangle, then it has no more than one right angle. (191)
Theorem 6-4	In a plane, if two lines are cut by a transversal so that a pair of alternate interior angles are congruent, then the two lines are parallel. (192)
Theorem 6-5	In a plane, if two lines are cut by a transversal so that a pair of corresponding angles are congruent, then the two lines are parallel. (195)
Theorem 6-6	In a plane, if two lines are cut by a transversal so that a pair of consecutive interior angles are supplementary, then the lines are parallel. (196)
Theorem 6-7	In a plane, if two lines are cut by a transversal so that a pair of alternate exterior angles are congruent, then the lines are parallel. (196)
Theorem 6-8	In a plane, if two lines are perpendicular to the same line, then the two lines are parallel. (196)
Theorem 6-9	If two parallel lines are cut by a transversal, then each pair of corresponding angles are congruent. (201)
Theorem 6-10	If two parallel lines are cut by a transversal, then each pair of alternate interior angles are congruent. (201)

Theorem 6-11	If two parallel lines are cut by a transversal, then each pair of consecutive interior angles are supplementary. (201)
Theorem 6-12	If two parallel lines are cut by a transversal, then each pair of alternate exterior angles are congruent. (201)
Theorem 6-13	In a plane, if a line is perpendicular to one of two parallel lines, then it is perpendicular to the other. (206)
Theorem 6-14	Given a line and a point not on the line, there is exactly one line through the point that is perpendicular to the given line. (211)
Theorem 6-15	In a plane, two lines are parallel if and only if they are everywhere equidistant. (211)

Chapter 7: Polygons

Theorem 7-1	If a convex polygon has n sides, and S is the sum of the degree measures of its angles, then $S = (n - 2)180$. (227)
Theorem 7-2	If a polygon is convex, then the sum of the degree measures of the exterior angles, one at each vertex, is 360. (228)
Theorem 7-3	If a quadrilateral is a parallelogram, then a diagonal separates it into two congruent triangles. (233)
Theorem 7-4	If a quadrilateral is a parallelogram, then its opposite angles are congruent. (234)
Theorem 7-5	If a quadrilateral is a parallelogram, then its opposite sides are congruent. (234)
Theorem 7-6	If a quadrilateral is a parallelogram, then its diagonals bisect each other. (234)
Theorem 7-7	If both pairs of opposite sides of a quadrilateral are congruent, then the quadrilateral is a parallelogram. (237)
Theorem 7-8	If two sides of a quadrilateral are parallel and congruent, then the quadrilateral is a parallelogram. (238)
Theorem 7-9	If the diagonals of a quadrilateral bisect each other, then the quadrilateral is a parallelogram. (238)
Theorem 7-10	If a quadrilateral is a rectangle, then its diagonals are congruent. (241)
Theorem 7-11	If a quadrilateral is a rhombus, then each diagonal bisects a pair of opposite angles. (242)
Theorem 7-12	If a quadrilateral is a rhombus, then its diagonals are perpendicular. (243)
Theorem 7-13	If a trapezoid is isosceles, then each pair of base angles is congruent. (247)
Theorem 7-14	If a trapezoid is isosceles, then its diagonals are congruent. (248)
Theorem 7-15	If a quadrilateral is a trapezoid, then the median is parallel to the bases, and its measure is one-half the sum of the measures of the bases. (249)
Theorem 7-16 Perimeter of a Rectangle	If a rectangle has a perimeter of P units, a length of ℓ units, and a width of w units, then $P = 2(\ell + w)$. (253)

Theorem 7-17	If a regular n-gon has a perimeter of P units, and a side measures s
Perimeter of a	units, then $P = ns$. (254)
Regular Polygon	

Chapter 8:   Similarity

Postulate 8-1	If two angles of one triangle are congruent to two corresponding
AA Similarity	angles of another triangle, then the triangles are similar. (281)
Theorem 8-1	For any numbers a and c, and any nonzero numbers b and d, $\frac{a}{b} = \frac{c}{d}$
Equality of Cross	if and only if $ad = bc$. (268)
Products	

For any numbers a, b, c, and d, the following properties hold whenever all denominators are nonzero.

| **Theorem 8-2** | If $\frac{a}{b} = \frac{c}{d}$, then $\frac{a}{c} = \frac{b}{d}$ or $\frac{d}{b} = \frac{c}{a}$.   (272) |

| **Theorem 8-3** | If $\frac{a}{b} = \frac{c}{d}$, then $\frac{b}{a} = \frac{d}{c}$.   (272) |

Theorem 8-4	$\frac{a}{b} = \frac{c}{d}$ if and only if $\frac{a+b}{b} = \frac{c+d}{d}$. (272)
Addition Property of	
Proportions	

Theorem 8-5	$\frac{a}{b} = \frac{c}{d}$ if and only if $\frac{a-b}{b} = \frac{c-d}{d}$. (272)
Subtraction Property of	
Proportions	

Theorem 8-6	$\frac{a}{b} = \frac{c}{d}$ if and only if $\frac{a}{b} = \frac{a+c}{b+d}$ or $\frac{c}{d} = \frac{a+c}{b+d}$. (272)
Summation Property of	
Proportions	

Theorem 8-7	If there is a correspondence between the two triangles so that the
SSS Similarity	measures of their corresponding sides are proportional, then the two
	triangles are similar. (282)
Theorem 8-8	If the measures of two sides of a triangle are proportional to the
SAS Similarity	measures of two corresponding sides of another triangle, and the
	included angles are congruent, then the triangles are similar.
	(283)
Theorem 8-9	If a line intersects two sides of a triangle, and separates the sides
	into segments of proportional lengths, then the line is parallel to the
	third side. (285)
Theorem 8-10	If a line is parallel to one side of a triangle and intersects the other
	two sides, then it separates the sides into segments of proportional
	lengths. (286)
Theorem 8-11	If a segment has as its endpoints the midpoints of two sides of a
	triangle, then it is parallel to the third side and its length is one-half
	the length of the third side. (287)
Theorem 8-12	If three parallel lines intersect two transversals, then they divide
	the transversals proportionally. (287)

Theorem 8-13	If three parallel lines cut off congruent segments on one transversal, then they cut off congruent segments on any transversal. (287)
Theorem 8-14	If two triangles are similar, then the measures of corresponding perimeters are proportional to the measures of corresponding sides. (290)
Theorem 8-15	If two triangles are similar, then the measures of corresponding altitudes are proportional to the measures of corresponding sides. (291)
Theorem 8-16	If two triangles are similar, then the measures of corresponding angle bisectors of the triangles are proportional to the measures of corresponding sides. (291)
Theorem 8-17	If two triangles are similar, then the measures of corresponding medians are proportional to the measures of corresponding sides. (292)

Chapter 9: Right Triangles

Postulate 9-1 Product Property of Square Roots	For any nonnegative numbers a and b, $\sqrt{ab} = \sqrt{a} \cdot \sqrt{b}$. (310)
Postulate 9-2 Quotient Property of Square Roots	For any nonnegative numbers a and b with $b \neq 0$, $\sqrt{\dfrac{a}{b}} = \dfrac{\sqrt{a}}{\sqrt{b}}$. (310)
Theorem 9-1	If the altitude is drawn from the vertex of the right angle to the hypotenuse of a right triangle, then the two triangles formed are similar to the given triangle and to each other. (313)
Theorem 9-2	The measure of the altitude drawn from the right angle to the hypotenuse of a right triangle is the geometric mean between the measures of the two segments of the hypotenuse. (314)
Theorem 9-3	If the altitude is drawn to the hypotenuse of a right triangle, then the measure of a leg of the triangle is the geometric mean between the measure of the hypotenuse and the measure of the segment of the hypotenuse adjacent to that leg. (315)
Theorem 9-4 The Pythagorean Theorem	If a triangle is a right triangle, then the sum of the squares of the measures of the legs equals the square of the measure of the hypotenuse. (318)
Theorem 9-5 Converse of the Pythagorean Theorem	If the sum of the squares of the measures of two sides of a triangle equals the square of the measure of the longest side, then the triangle is a right triangle. (319)
Theorem 9-6 45°–45°–90° Theorem	If each acute angle of a right triangle has a degree measure of 45, then the hypotenuse measures $\sqrt{2}$ times the measure of a leg. (323)
Theorem 9-7 30°–60°–90° Theorem	If the acute angles of a right triangle have degree measures of 30 and 60, then the measure of the hypotenuse is 2 times the measure of the shorter leg and the measure of the longer leg is $\sqrt{3}$ times the measure of the shorter leg. (323)

Chapter 10:   Circles and Spheres

Postulate 10-1 Arc Addition Postulate	If Q is a point on $\overset{\frown}{PQR}$, then $m\overset{\frown}{PQ} + m\overset{\frown}{QR} = m\overset{\frown}{PQR}$. (352)
Theorem 10-1	In a plane, if a line contains a point in the interior of a circle, then the line intersects the circle in exactly two points. (348)
Theorem 10-2	In a circle or in congruent circles, two central angles are congruent if and only if their minor arcs are congruent. (353)
Theorem 10-3	In a circle or in congruent circles, two minor arcs are congruent if and only if their corresponding chords are congruent. (355)
Theorem 10-4	In a circle, if a diameter is perpendicular to a chord, then it bisects the chord and its arcs. (356)
Theorem 10-5	In a circle or in congruent circles, two chords are congruent if and only if they are equidistant from the center. (356)
Theorem 10-6	If an angle is inscribed in a circle, then the measure of the angle equals one-half the measure of its intercepted arc. (360)
Theorem 10-7	If two inscribed angles of a circle or congruent circles intercept congruent arcs, then the angles are congruent. (361)
Theorem 10-8	If an angle is inscribed in a semicircle, then the angle is a right angle. (361)
Theorem 10-9	If the angles of a quadrilateral are inscribed in a circle, then each pair of opposite angles are supplementary. (361)
Theorem 10-10	If a line is tangent to a circle, then it is perpendicular to the radius drawn to the point of tangency. (365)
Theorem 10-11	In a plane, if a line is perpendicular to a radius of a circle at its endpoint on the circle, then the line is a tangent. (366)
Theorem 10-12	If two segments from the same exterior point are tangent to a circle, then they are congruent. (366)
Theorem 10-13	If two secants intersect in the interior of a circle, then the measure of an angle formed is one-half the sum of the measures of the arcs intercepted by the angle and its vertical angle. (370)
Theorem 10-14	If two secants intersect in the exterior of a circle, then the measure of an angle formed is one-half the positive difference of the measures of the intercepted arcs. (370)
Theorem 10-15	If a secant and a tangent intersect at the point of tangency, then the measure of each angle formed is one-half the measure of its intercepted arc. (372)
Theorem 10-16	If a secant and a tangent, or two tangents, intersect in the exterior of a circle, then the measure of the angle formed is one-half the positive difference of the measures of the intercepted arcs. (372)
Theorem 10-17	If two chords intersect in a circle, then the product of the measures of the segments of one chord equals the product of the measures of the segments of the other chord. (374)
Theorem 10-18	If two secant segments are drawn to a circle from an exterior point, then the product of the measures of one secant segment and its external secant segment equals the product of the measures of the other secant segment and its external secant segment. (375)

| Theorem 10-19 | If a tangent segment and a secant segment are drawn to a circle from an exterior point, then the square of the measure of the tangent segment equals the product of the measures of the secant segment and its external secant segment. (375) |
| Theorem 10-20 | If a plane intersects a sphere in more than one point, then the intersection is a circle. (379) |

Chapter 11: Area and Volume

Postulate 11-1 Area Postulate	For any polygonal region and a given unit of measure, there is a unique positive real number called the measure of the area of the region. (389)
Postulate 11-2	If two polygons are congruent, then they have equal areas. (390)
Postulate 11-3 Area Addition Postulate	If a polygonal region is separated into nonoverlapping regions, then the sum of the areas of these regions equals the area of the entire region. (390)
Postulate 11-4 Area of a Rectangle	If a rectangle has an area of A square units, a length of ℓ units, and a width of w units, then $A = \ell w$. (390)
Postulate 11-5 Volume Postulate	For any solid region and a given unit of measure, there is a unique positive number called the measure of the volume of the region. (419)
Postulate 11-6	If two solid regions are congruent, then they have equal volumes. (419)
Postulate 11-7 Volume Addition Postulate	If a solid region is separated into nonoverlapping regions, then the sum of the volumes of these regions equals the volume of the given region. (419)
Postulate 11-8	If a right prism has a volume of V cubic units, a base with an area of B square units, and a height of h units, then $V = Bh$. (420)
Postulate 11-9 Cavalieri's Principle	If two solids have the same cross-sectional area at every level, and the same height, then they have the same volume. (424)
Theorem 11-1 Area of a Square	If a square has an area of A square units, and each side is s units long, then $A = s^2$. (391)
Theorem 11-2 Area of a Parallelogram	If a parallelogram has an area of A square units, a base of b units, and a corresponding altitude of h units, then $A = bh$. (394)
Theorem 11-3 Area of a Triangle	If a triangle has an area of A square units, a base of b units, and a corresponding altitude of h units, then $A = \frac{1}{2}bh$. (395)
Theorem 11-4 Area of a Trapezoid	If a trapezoid has an area of A square units, bases of b_1 units and b_2 units, and an altitude of h units, then $A = \frac{1}{2}h(b_1 + b_2)$. (395)
Theorem 11-5	A polygon is regular if and only if a circle inscribed in the polygon and a circle circumscribed about the polygon have the same center. (399)

Theorem 11-6	If a segment is an apothem of a regular polygon, then it is perpendicular to a side of the polygon at the point of tangency with the inscribed circle. (400)
Theorem 11-7 Area of a Regular Polygon	If a regular polygon has an area of A square units, a perimeter of p units, and an apothem of a units, then $A = \frac{1}{2}ap$. (400)
Theorem 11-8	If a regular polygon has n sides, then the degree measure of each central angle is $\frac{360}{n}$. (401)
Theorem 11-9 Circumference of a Circle	If a circle has a circumference of C units and a radius of r units, then $C = 2\pi r$. (405)
Theorem 11-10 Area of a Circle	If a circle has an area of A square units and a radius of r units, then $A = \pi r^2$. (405)
Theorem 11-11 Lateral Area of a Right Prism	If a right prism has a lateral area of L square units, a height of h units, and each base has a perimeter of p units, then $L = ph$. (411)
Theorem 11-12 Total Surface Area of a Right Prism	If the total surface area of a right prism is T square units, each base has an area of B square units, a perimeter of p units, and a height of h units, then $T = ph + 2B$. (411)
Theorem 11-13 Lateral Area of a Right Cylinder	If a right cylinder has a lateral area of L square units, a height of h units, and the bases have radii of r units, then $L = 2\pi rh$. (412)
Theorem 11-14 Total Surface Area of a Right Cylinder	If a right cylinder has a total surface area of T square units, a height of h units, and the bases have radii of r units, then $T = 2\pi rh + 2\pi r^2$. (412)
Theorem 11-15 Lateral Area for a Regular Pyramid	If a regular pyramid has a lateral area of L square units, a slant height of ℓ units, and its base has a perimeter of p units, then $L = \frac{1}{2}p\ell$. (415)
Theorem 11-16 Lateral and Total Surface Area of a Right Circular Cone	If a right circular cone has a lateral area of L square units, a total surface area of T square units, a slant height of ℓ units, and the radius of the base is r units, then $L = \pi r\ell$ and $T = \pi r\ell + \pi r^2$. (416)
Theorem 11-17 Surface Area of a Sphere	If a sphere has a surface area of A square units and a radius of r units, then $A = 4\pi r^2$. (417)
Theorem 11-18 Volume of a Right Cylinder	If a right cylinder has a volume of V cubic units, a height of h units, and a radius of r units, then $V = \pi r^2 h$. (420)
Theorem 11-19 Volume of a Right Pyramid	If a right pyramid has a volume of V cubic units, a height of h units, and the area of the base is B square units, then $V = \frac{1}{3}Bh$. (423)
Theorem 11-20 Volume of a Right Circular Cone	If a right circular cone has a volume of V cubic units, a height of h units, and the area of the base is B square units, then $V = \frac{1}{3}Bh$. (423)
Theorem 11-21 Volume of a Sphere	If a sphere has a volume of V cubic units and a radius of r units, then $V = \frac{4}{3}\pi r^3$. (423)

Chapter 12: Coordinates

Each point in a coordinate real plane corresponds to exactly one ordered pair of real numbers. Each ordered pair of real numbers corresponds to exactly one point in a coordinate plane. (435)

The distance between two points with coordinates (x_1, y_1) and (x_2, y_2) is given by the following formula. (440)

$$d = \sqrt{(x_2 - x_1)^2 + (y_2 - y_1)^2}$$

If the coordinates of A and B are (x_1, y_1) and (x_2, y_2) respectively, then the midpoint M of $\overline{AB}$ has coordinates $\left(\dfrac{x_1 + x_2}{2}, \dfrac{y_1 + y_2}{2}\right)$. (441)

Two lines have the same slope if and only if they are parallel and nonvertical. (445)

Two nonvertical lines are perpendicular if and only if the product of their slopes is -1. (445)

The equation of the line having a slope m and y-intercept b is $y = mx + b$. (448)

The equation of the line passing through the point whose coordinates are (x_1, y_1) and which has a slope m is $y - y_1 = m(x - x_1)$. (449)

The equation of a circle with center at (h, k) and radius measuring r units is $(x - h)^2 + (y - k)^2 = r^2$. (456)

Given two points $A(x_1, y_1, z_1)$ and $B(x_2, y_2, z_2)$ in space, the distance between A and B is given by the following equation. (464)

$$AB = \sqrt{(x_2 - x_1)^2 + (y_2 - y_1)^2 + (z_2 - z_1)^2}$$

Chapter 14: Transformations

In a given rotation, if A is the preimage, P is the image, and W is the center of rotation, then the measure of the angle of rotation, $\angle AWP$, equals twice the measure of the angle between the intersecting lines of reflection. (515)

If a dilation with center C and a scale factor k maps A onto E and B onto D, then $ED = k(AB)$. (524)

SQUARES AND APPROXIMATE SQUARE ROOTS

n	n^2	$\sqrt{n}$	n	n^2	$\sqrt{n}$
1	1	1.000	51	2601	7.141
2	4	1.414	52	2704	7.211
3	9	1.732	53	2809	7.280
4	16	2.000	54	2916	7.348
5	25	2.236	55	3025	7.416
6	36	2.449	56	3136	7.483
7	49	2.646	57	3249	7.550
8	64	2.828	58	3364	7.616
9	81	3.000	59	3481	7.681
10	100	3.162	60	3600	7.746
11	121	3.317	61	3721	7.810
12	144	3.464	62	3844	7.874
13	169	3.606	63	3969	7.937
14	196	3.742	64	4096	8.000
15	225	3.873	65	4225	8.062
16	256	4.000	66	4356	8.124
17	289	4.123	67	4489	8.185
18	324	4.243	68	4624	8.246
19	361	4.359	69	4761	8.307
20	400	4.472	70	4900	8.367
21	441	4.583	71	5041	8.426
22	484	4.690	72	5184	8.485
23	529	4.796	73	5329	8.544
24	576	4.899	74	5476	8.602
25	625	5.000	75	5625	8.660
26	676	5.099	76	5776	8.718
27	729	5.196	77	5929	8.775
28	784	5.292	78	6084	8.832
29	841	5.385	79	6241	8.888
30	900	5.477	80	6400	8.944
31	961	5.568	81	6561	9.000
32	1024	5.657	82	6724	9.055
33	1089	5.745	83	6889	9.110
34	1156	5.831	84	7056	9.165
35	1225	5.916	85	7225	9.220
36	1296	6.000	86	7396	9.274
37	1369	6.083	87	7569	9.327
38	1444	6.164	88	7744	9.381
39	1521	6.245	89	7921	9.434
40	1600	6.325	90	8100	9.487
41	1681	6.403	91	8281	9.539
42	1764	6.481	92	8464	9.592
43	1849	6.557	93	8649	9.644
44	1936	6.633	94	8836	9.695
45	2025	6.708	95	9025	9.747
46	2116	6.782	96	9216	9.798
47	2209	6.856	97	9409	9.849
48	2304	6.928	98	9604	9.899
49	2401	7.000	99	9801	9.950
50	2500	7.071	100	10000	10.000

TRIGONOMETRIC RATIOS

Angle	sin	cos	tan	Angle	sin	cos	tan
0°	0.0000	1.0000	0.0000	45°	0.7071	0.7071	1.0000
1°	0.0175	0.9998	0.0175	46°	0.7193	0.6947	1.0355
2°	0.0349	0.9994	0.0349	47°	0.7314	0.6820	1.0724
3°	0.0523	0.9986	0.0524	48°	0.7431	0.6691	1.1106
4°	0.0698	0.9976	0.0699	49°	0.7547	0.6561	1.1504
5°	0.0872	0.9962	0.0875	50°	0.7660	0.6428	1.1918
6°	0.1045	0.9945	0.1051	51°	0.7771	0.6293	1.2349
7°	0.1219	0.9925	0.1228	52°	0.7880	0.6157	1.2799
8°	0.1392	0.9903	0.1405	53°	0.7986	0.6018	1.3270
9°	0.1564	0.9877	0.1584	54°	0.8090	0.5878	1.3764
10°	0.1736	0.9848	0.1763	55°	0.8192	0.5736	1.4281
11°	0.1908	0.9816	0.1944	56°	0.8290	0.5592	1.4826
12°	0.2079	0.9781	0.2126	57°	0.8387	0.5446	1.5399
13°	0.2250	0.9744	0.2309	58°	0.8480	0.5299	1.6003
14°	0.2419	0.9703	0.2493	59°	0.8572	0.5150	1.6643
15°	0.2588	0.9659	0.2679	60°	0.8660	0.5000	1.7321
16°	0.2756	0.9613	0.2867	61°	0.8746	0.4848	1.8040
17°	0.2924	0.9563	0.3057	62°	0.8829	0.4695	1.8807
18°	0.3090	0.9511	0.3249	63°	0.8910	0.4540	1.9626
19°	0.3256	0.9455	0.3443	64°	0.8988	0.4384	2.0503
20°	0.3420	0.9397	0.3640	65°	0.9063	0.4226	2.1445
21°	0.3584	0.9336	0.3839	66°	0.9135	0.4067	2.2460
22°	0.3746	0.9272	0.4040	67°	0.9205	0.3907	2.3559
23°	0.3907	0.9205	0.4245	68°	0.9272	0.3746	2.4751
24°	0.4067	0.9135	0.4452	69°	0.9336	0.3584	2.6051
25°	0.4226	0.9063	0.4663	70°	0.9397	0.3420	2.7475
26°	0.4384	0.8988	0.4877	71°	0.9455	0.3256	2.9042
27°	0.4540	0.8910	0.5095	72°	0.9511	0.3090	3.0777
28°	0.4695	0.8829	0.5317	73°	0.9563	0.2924	3.2709
29°	0.4848	0.8746	0.5543	74°	0.9613	0.2756	3.4874
30°	0.5000	0.8660	0.5774	75°	0.9659	0.2588	3.7321
31°	0.5150	0.8572	0.6009	76°	0.9703	0.2419	4.0108
32°	0.5299	0.8480	0.6249	77°	0.9744	0.2250	4.3315
33°	0.5446	0.8387	0.6494	78°	0.9781	0.2079	4.7046
34°	0.5592	0.8290	0.6745	79°	0.9816	0.1908	5.1446
35°	0.5736	0.8192	0.7002	80°	0.9848	0.1736	5.6713
36°	0.5878	0.8090	0.7265	81°	0.9877	0.1564	6.3138
37°	0.6018	0.7986	0.7536	82°	0.9903	0.1392	7.1154
38°	0.6157	0.7880	0.7813	83°	0.9925	0.1219	8.1443
39°	0.6293	0.7771	0.8098	84°	0.9945	0.1045	9.5144
40°	0.6428	0.7660	0.8391	85°	0.9962	0.0872	11.4301
41°	0.6561	0.7547	0.8693	86°	0.9976	0.0698	14.3007
42°	0.6691	0.7431	0.9004	87°	0.9986	0.0523	19.0811
43°	0.6820	0.7314	0.9325	88°	0.9994	0.0349	28.6363
44°	0.6947	0.7193	0.9657	89°	0.9998	0.0175	57.2900
45°	0.7071	0.7071	1.0000	90°	1.0000	0.0000	∞

Glossary

acute angle An acute angle is one whose degree measure is less than 90. (88)

acute triangle An acute triangle is a triangle with all acute angles. (112)

adjacent angles Two angles in the same plane are adjacent if and only if they have a common side and a common vertex, but no interior points in common. (79)

alternate exterior angles In the figure, transversal t intersects lines ℓ and m. $\angle 5$ and $\angle 3$, and $\angle 6$ and $\angle 4$ are alternate exterior angles. (186)

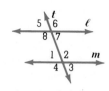

alternate interior angles In the figure, transversal t intersects lines ℓ and m. $\angle 1$ and $\angle 7$, and $\angle 2$ and $\angle 8$ are alternate interior angles. (186)

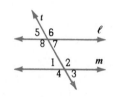

altitude of a prism An altitude of a prism is a segment perpendicular to the base planes with an endpoint in each plane. The length of an altitude is called the *height* of the prism. (410)

altitude of a triangle A segment is an altitude of a triangle if and only if the following conditions hold:
1. Its endpoints are a vertex of a triangle and a point on the line containing the opposite side.
2. It is perpendicular to the line containing the opposite side. (134)

angle A figure is an angle if and only if it consists of two non-collinear rays with a common endpoint. The rays are the *sides*

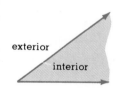

of the angle. The endpoint is the *vertex* of the angle. An angle separates a plane into three parts, the *interior* of the angle, the *exterior* of the angle, and the angle itself. (74)

angle bisector A ray, $\overrightarrow{QS}$, is a bisector of $\angle PQR$ if and only if S is in the interior of the angle and $\angle PQS \cong \angle RQS$. (135)

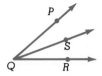

angle of rotation The angle of rotation, $\angle ABC$, is determined by A, the preimage; B, the center of rotation; and C, the rotation image. (515)

apothem of a regular polygon A segment is an apothem of a regular polygon if and only if it is a radius of a circle inscribed in the polygon. (399)

arc See major arc and minor arc. (327)

arc measure The degree measure of a minor arc is the degree measure of its central angle. The degree measure of a major arc is 360 minus the degree measure of its central angle. The degree measure of a semicircle is 180. (351)

arc of a chord A minor arc that has the same endpoints as a chord is called an arc of the chord. (355)

area The area of a polygonal region is the measure of the region formed by the polygon and its interior. (389)

area of a circle The area of a circle is the limit of the area of the inscribed polygons as the number of sides increases. (405)

area of a sector of a circle If a sector of a circle has an area of A square units, a central angle measurement of N degrees, and a radius of r units, then $A = \frac{N}{360}\pi r^2$. (406)

auxiliary figure An auxiliary figure is included on a geometric figure in order to prove a given theorem. (138)

axis In a coordinate plane, the *x-axis* is the horizontal number line and the *y-axis* is the vertical number line. (435)

axis of a cylinder See cylinder. (412)

base of a prism See prism. (410)

between A point Q is between points P and R if and only if each of the following conditions hold:
1. P, Q, and R are collinear.
2. $PQ + QR = PR$. (46)

biconditional statement A biconditional statement is a statement that can be written in *if and only if* form. All definitions are biconditional statements because they are reversible. (11)

center of a regular polygon A point is a center of a regular polygon if and only if it is the common center of its inscribed and circumscribed circles. (399)

center of rotation See rotation. (514)

central angle A central angle of a circle is an angle formed by two rays coplanar with the circle. The vertex of the angle is the center of the circle. (351)

chord A chord of a circle is a segment whose endpoints are points on the circle. (347)

circle A figure is a circle if and only if it is the set of all points in a plane that are a given distance from a given point in the plane, called the *center*. A circle separates a plane into three parts, the *interior*, the *exterior*, and the circle itself. (347)

circumcenter The center of the circle circumscribed about a given triangle is called the circumcenter of the triangle. (484)

circumference The circumference of a circle is the limit of the perimeter of the inscribed regular polygons as the number of sides increases. (404)

circumscribed polygon A polygon is circumscribed about a circle if and only if each side of the polygon is tangent to the circle. (367)

collinear points Points are collinear if and only if they lie on the same line. (5)

common tangent A line that is tangent to two circles that are in the same plane is called a common tangent of the two circles. A common tangent that does not intersect the segment whose endpoints are the centers of the circles is a *common external tangent*. A common tangent that intersects the segment whose endpoints are the centers of the circles is a *common internal tangent*. (349)

compass A compass is an instrument used to draw circles and arcs of circles. (475)

complementary angles Two angles are complementary if and only if the sum of their degree measures is 90. (82)

composite of reflections Two successive reflections are called a composite of reflections. (511)

concave polygon A polygon is concave if and only if it is not a convex polygon. (224)

concentric circles Concentric circles are circles that lie in the same plane and have the same center. (352)

conclusion See conditional statement. (10)

conditional statement A conditional statement is a statement that can be written in *if-then* form. The part following *if* is called the *hypothesis*. The part following *then* is called the *conclusion*. Conditional statements may be true or false. (9)

congruence transformation See isometry. (504)

congruent angles Two angles are congruent if and only if they have the same measurement. (78)

congruent circles Two circles are congruent if and only if their radii are congruent. (352)

congruent segments Two segments are congruent if and only if they have exactly the same length. (56)

congruent triangles Two triangles are congruent if and only if there is a correspondence such that their corresponding parts are congruent. (120)

consecutive interior angles In the figure, transversal t intersects lines ℓ and m. $\angle 7$ and $\angle 2$, and $\angle 8$ and $\angle 1$ are consecutive interior angles. (186)

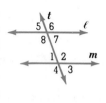

construction The process of drawing a figure that will satisfy certain given conditions, using only a compass and a straightedge, is a construction. (475)

contrapositive The contrapositive of a conditional statement is formed by interchanging the hypothesis and conclusion, and negating both. The contrapositive of a true statement is always a true statement. The contrapositive of a false statement is always a false statement. (29)

converse The converse of a conditional statement is formed by interchanging the hypothesis and conclusion. (10)

convex polygon A polygon is convex if and only if any line containing a side of the polygon does not contain a point in the interior of the polygon. (224)

coordinate 1. A number associated with a point on a number line is called the coordinate of the point. (39) 2. In an ordered pair, the first component is called the x-coordinate and the second component is called the y-coordinate. (435)

coplanar points Points are coplanar if and only if they lie in the same plane. (5)

corresponding angles In the figure, transversal t intersects lines ℓ and m. $\angle 5$ and $\angle 1$, $\angle 8$ and $\angle 4$, $\angle 6$ and $\angle 2$, and $\angle 7$ and $\angle 3$ are corresponding angles. (186)

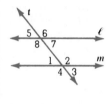

cosine A ratio is the cosine of an acute angle of a right triangle if and only if it is the ratio of the measure of the leg adjacent to the acute angle to the measure of the hypotenuse. (327)

cross products Every proportion has two cross products. In the proportion $\frac{a}{b} = \frac{c}{d}$, where $b \neq 0$ and $d \neq 0$, the cross products are ad and bc. The cross products of a proportion are equal. (268)

cross section A cross section of a solid is the intersection of the solid with a plane that is parallel to the base of the solid. (424)

cylinder A solid figure whose *bases* are formed by congruent circles in parallel planes. The segment whose endpoints are the centers of the circles is called the *axis* of the cylinder. The *altitude* is a segment perpendicular to the base planes with an endpoint in each plane. (412)

definition A definition is an explanation of how a word is to be used. (19)

degree A degree is one of the units of measure used in measuring angles. (77)

diagonal A segment joining two nonconsecutive vertices of a polygon is called a diagonal of the polygon. (227)

diameter A diameter of a circle is a chord that contains the center of the circle. (347)

dihedral angle An angle is dihedral if and only if it consists of two noncoplanar half planes with a common edge. Each half plane is called a *face*. (99)

dilation A dilation is a transformation in which size is altered based on a center, C, and a *scale factor, k*. If $k > 1$, the dilation is an *enlargement*. If $0 < k < 1$, the dilation is a *reduction*. If $k = 1$, the dilation is a *congruence transformation*. Dilations are also *similarity transformations*. (524)

distance The absolute value of the difference of the coordinates of two points on a number line represents the measure of the distance between the two points. (41)

distance between a point and a line The distance between a point and a line is the length of the segment perpendicular to the line from the point. The measure of the distance between a line and a point on the line is zero. (211)

distance formula The distance between two points with coordinates (x_1, y_1) and (x_2, y_2) is given by the following formula.
$$d = \sqrt{(x_2 - x_1)^2 + (y_2 - y_1)^2} \quad (440)$$

edge of a half plane A line that separates a plane into two half planes is called the edge of each half plane. (77)

endpoints See segment. (46)

equation of a circle The equation of a circle with center at (h, k) and radius measuring r units is $(x - h)^2 + (y - k)^2 = r^2$. (456)

equation of a sphere The equation of a sphere whose center is at (i, j, k) and that has a radius measuring r units is $(x - i)^2 + (y - j)^2 + (z - k)^2 = r^2$. (465)

equiangular triangle An equiangular triangle is a triangle with all angles congruent. (112)

equidistant Equidistant means at the same distance. (211)

equilateral triangle An equilateral triangle is a triangle with all sides congruent. (112)

exterior angle An angle is an exterior angle of a polygon if and only if it forms a linear pair with one of the angles of the polygon. In the figure, $\angle 2$ is an exterior angle. (151, 228)

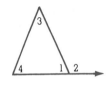

exterior angles In the figure, transversal t intersects lines ℓ and m. $\angle 3$, $\angle 4$, $\angle 5$, and $\angle 6$ are exterior angles. (186)

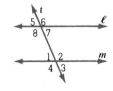

exterior of a circle See circle. (348)

exterior of an angle See angle. (75)

exterior of a triangle See triangle. (113)

formal proof A formal proof is a proof that has five main parts, namely, the theorem, the given, the prove statement, a diagram, and the proof with statements and reasons. (20)

geometric mean For any positive numbers a and b, x is the geometric mean between a and b if and only if $\frac{a}{x} = \frac{x}{b}$ and x is positive. (314)

glide reflection The composition of a translation and a line reflection is a glide reflection. (521)

golden rectangles Golden rectangles are rectangles whose measures of their adjacent sides are always in the ratio of about 1 to 1.618. (273)

great circle If a plane intersects a sphere in more than one point and contains the center of the sphere, the intersection of the plane and the sphere is called a great circle. (380)

half plane The part of a plane on one side of a line in the plane is a half plane. (77)

hypotenuse In a right triangle, the side

opposite the right angle is called the hypotenuse. (142)

hypothesis See conditional statement. (10)

if and only if form See biconditional statement. (11)

if-then form See conditional statement. (9)

image If A is mapped onto A', then A' is called the image of A. The *preimage* of A' is A. (503)

incenter The center of the circle inscribed in a given triangle is called the incenter of the triangle. (485)

indirect reasoning In indirect reasoning, you assume the opposite of what you want to prove. Then, show that this assumption leads to a contradiction. (190)

inscribed angle An angle is an inscribed angle if and only if its vertex lies on a circle and its sides contain chords of the circle. (359)

inscribed polygon A polygon is inscribed in a circle if and only if each of its vertices lie on the circle. (361)

integers The integers consist of the set of numbers $\{\ldots, -3, -2, -1, 0, 1, 2, 3, \ldots\}$. (37)

intercepted arc An angle intercepts an arc if and only if each of the following conditions hold.
1. The endpoints of the arc lie on the angle.
2. All points of the arc, except the endpoints, are in the interior of the angle.
3. Each side of the angle contains an endpoint of the arc. (359)

interior angles In the figure, transversal t intersects lines ℓ and m. $\angle 1$, $\angle 2$, $\angle 7$, and $\angle 8$ are interior angles. (186)

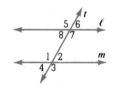

interior of a circle See circle. (348)

interior of an angle See angle. (75)

interior of a triangle See triangle. (113)

intersect Two lines, two planes, or lines and planes, intersect if they have points in common. (2)

inverse The inverse of a conditional statement is formed by negating both the hypothesis and conclusion. (29)

irrational number An irrational number is a decimal number that is nonterminating and nonrepeating. An example is π. $\pi \approx 3.1415926535897932\ldots$ (39, 311)

isometry When a geometric figure and its transformation image are congruent, the mapping is called an isometry of *congruence transformation*. (504)

isosceles trapezoid An isosceles trapezoid is a trapezoid in which the legs are congruent. (247)

isosceles triangle An isosceles triangle is a triangle with at least two sides congruent. (112)

lateral area The lateral area of a prism is the area of all the lateral faces. (411)

lateral edges See prism. (410)

lateral faces See prism. (410)

legs of a right triangle In a right triangle, the two sides that are not opposite the right angle are called the legs. (142)

length The length of a segment is the distance between the two endpoints of the segment. The length of a segment is the same as the measurement of a segment. (46)

line Line is one of the basic undefined terms of geometry. Lines extend indefinitely and have no thickness or width. Lines are represented by double arrows and named by lower case letters. A line also can be named using double arrows over capital letters representing two points on the line. (1)

linear equation An equation is linear if and only if it can be written in the form

$Ax + By = C$, where A, B, and C are any real numbers, and A and B are not both 0. (436)

line of reflection Line ℓ is a line of reflection if it is the perpendicular bisector of the segment drawn from point X to its reflection image point A. (506)

line of symmetry A line of symmetry is a line that can be drawn through a plane figure so that the figure on one side is the reflection image of the figure on the opposite side. (508)

linear pair Two angles form a linear pair if and only if they are adjacent and their noncommon sides are opposite rays. (82)

line perpendicular to a plane A line is perpendicular to a plane if and only if the given line is perpendicular to every line in the plane that intersects it. (98)

locus In geometry, a figure is a locus if and only if it is the set of all points and only those points that satisfy a given condition. (490)

major arc If $\angle APB$ is a central angle of circle P, and C is any point on the circle and in the exterior of the angle, then points A and B and all points of the circle exterior to $\angle APB$ form a major arc called $\overset{\frown}{ACB}$. Three letters are needed to name a major arc. (351)

measure See measurement. (41)

measurement A measurement consists of a number called the *measure* and a *unit of measure*. In the measurement 3 meters, 3 is the measure and meter is the unit of measure. (41)

median of a triangle A segment is a median of a triangle if and only if its endpoints are a vertex of the triangle and the midpoint of the side opposite the vertex. (134)

midpoint A point M is the midpoint of a segment, $\overline{PQ}$, if and only if M is between P and Q, and $PM = MQ$. (46)

midpoint formula If the coordinates of A and B are (x_1, y_1) and (x_2, y_2) respectively, then the midpoint M of $\overline{AB}$ has coordinates $\left(\dfrac{x_1 + x_2}{2}, \dfrac{y_1 + y_2}{2}\right)$. (441)

minor arc If $\angle APB$ is a central angle of circle P, then points A and B and all points of the circle interior to the angle form a minor arc called $\overset{\frown}{AB}$. (351)

natural numbers The natural numbers consist of the set of numbers $\{1, 2, 3, \ldots\}$. (37)

negation A negation is a statement formed by denying another statement. (28)

n-gon A polygon with n sides is called an n-gon. (224)

noncollinear points Points are noncollinear if and only if they do not lie on the same line. (6)

noncoplanar points Points are noncoplanar if and only if they do not lie in the same plane. (7)

number line A number line is a line on which each point corresponds to exactly one real number. (37)

oblique prism A prism that is not a right prism is called an oblique prism. (410)

obtuse angle An obtuse angle is one whose degree measure is greater than 90. (88)

obtuse triangle An obtuse triangle is a triangle with one obtuse angle. (112)

opposite rays $\overrightarrow{PQ}$ and $\overrightarrow{PR}$ are opposite rays if and only if P is between Q and R. (73)

ordered pair An ordered pair is a pair of numbers in which the order is specified. An ordered pair is used to locate points in a plane. (435)

origin The point of intersection of the x-axis and y-axis in a coordinate plane is called the origin and named O. (435)

parallel lines Two lines are parallel if and only if they lie in the same plane and do not intersect. (185)

parallelogram A quadrilateral is a parallelogram if and only if both pairs of opposite sides are parallel. Any side of a parallelogram may be called a *base*. For each base there is a corresponding segment called the *altitude* that is perpendicular to the base and has its endpoints on the lines containing the base and the opposite side. (233)

perimeter The sum of the measures of the sides of a polygon is the measure of the perimeter of the polygon. (253)

perpendicular bisector A segment bisector is a perpendicular bisector if and only if the bisector is perpendicular to the segment. (134)

perpendicular lines Two lines are perpendicular if and only if they intersect to form a right angle. (93)

perpendicular planes Two planes are perpendicular if and only if any line in one of them that is perpendicular to their line of intersection is also perpendicular to the other plane. (99)

plane Plane is one of the basic undefined terms of geometry. Planes extend indefinitely in all directions and have no thickness. A plane is represented by a four-sided figure and is named by a capital script letter or by three points of the plane that are not on the same line. (1)

plane angle A plane angle of a dihedral angle is the intersection of the dihedral angle and a plane perpendicular to its edge. (100)

plane perpendicular to a line A plane is perpendicular to a line if and only if every line in the plane that intersects the given line is perpendicular to it. (98)

Platonic solid A Platonic solid is any one of the five regular polyhedrons: tetrahedron, hexahedron, octahedron, dodecahedron, or icosohedron. (259)

point Point is one of the **basic undefined** terms of geometry. Points **have no** dimensions, are represented **by** dots, and are named by capital letters. (1)

point of reflection Point S is the reflection of point R with respect to point Q, the point of reflection, if Q is the midpoint of the segment drawn from R to S. (506)

point of symmetry A point of symmetry is a point that can be placed in the interior of a plane figure so that it is the midpoint of all segments that contain it and have endpoints on the figure. (508)

point of tangency See tangent. (348)

point-slope form The equation of a line passing through a point whose coordinates are (x_1, y_1) and that has a slope m is $y - y_1 = m(x - x_1)$. (449)

polygon A figure is a polygon if and only if it meets each of the following conditions.
1. It is formed by three or more coplanar segments called *sides*.
2. Sides that have a common endpoint are noncollinear.
3. Each side intersects exactly two other sides, but only at their endpoints called *vertices*. (223)

polygonal region A polygon and its interior form a polygonal region. (389)

polyhedron A solid with flat surfaces that form polygons is called a polyhedron. The flat surfaces formed by the polygons and their interiors are called *faces*. Pairs of faces intersect at *edges*. Three or more edges intersect at a *vertex*. (258)

postulate A postulate in geometry is a statement that describes a fundamental property of the basic terms. Postulates are accepted as being true. (14)

preimage See image. (503)

prism A solid with the following characteristics is a prism.
1. Two faces, called *bases*, are formed by congruent polygons that lie in parallel planes.

2. The faces that are not bases, called *lateral faces*, are formed by parallelograms.

3. The intersections of two adjacent lateral faces are called *lateral edges* and are parallel segments. (410)

proportion A proportion is an equation of the form $\frac{a}{b} = \frac{c}{d}$ that states that two ratios are equivalent. (267)

protractor A protractor is a tool used to find the degree measure of a given angle. (77)

pyramid A solid with the following characteristics is a pyramid.
1. All the faces, except one face, intersect at a point called the *vertex*.
2. The face that does not intersect at the vertex is called the *base* and forms a polygon.
3. The faces meeting at the vertex are called *lateral faces* and form triangles.

quadrant One of the four regions into which two perpendicular number lines separate the plane is a quadrant. (435)

radical sign The symbol $\sqrt{}$ is called a radical sign. It indicates a nonnegative square root. (309)

radicand The expression under a radical sign is called the radicand. (309)

radius of a circle A radius of a circle is a segment whose endpoints are the center of the circle and a point on the circle. (347)

radius of a regular polygon A segment is a radius of a regular polygon if and only if it is a radius of a circle circumscribed about the polygon. (399)

ratio A ratio is a comparison of two numbers using division. (267)

rationalizing the denominator The method used to simplify a radical fraction so that the denominator of the fraction becomes a rational number is called rationalizing the denominator. (311)

rational number A rational number is any number that can be expressed in the form $\frac{a}{b}$, where a and b denote integers and b is not zero. (37)

ray $\overrightarrow{PQ}$ is a ray if and only if it is the set of points $\overline{PQ}$ and all points S for which Q is between P and S. (73)

real numbers The rational and irrational numbers make up the real numbers. Each point on a number line can be named by a real number. (39)

rectangle A quadrilateral is a rectangle if and only if it is a parallelogram with four right angles. (241)

reflection See line of reflection or point of reflection. (506)

regular polygon A polygon is regular if and only if it is a convex polygon with all sides congruent and all angles congruent. (224)

regular polyhedron Each face of a regular polyhedron forms a regular polygon and each edge of a regular polyhedron has the same measure. (259)

regular pyramid A pyramid is a regular pyramid if and only if its base is regular and the segment is the center of the base and the vertex is perpendicular to the base. This segment is called the *altitude*. (415)

remote interior angles The angles in a triangle that are not adjacent to a given exterior angle are called remote interior angles. (151)

repeating decimal A repeating decimal is a decimal number in which a nonzero digit or group of digits repeat. A bar over the repeating digit or digits indicates a repeating decimal. Examples are $0.\overline{3}$ and $0.4\overline{21}$. (38)

rhombus A quadrilateral is a rhombus if and only if it is a parallelogram with all four sides congruent. (242)

right angle A right angle is an angle whose degree measure is 90. (88)

right circular cone A solid figure that has a circular *base* and an *axis* from the *vertex* that is perpendicular to the base is a right circular cone. The axis is also the *altitude* of the cone. (416)

right cylinder A cylinder whose axis is also an altitude of the figure is a right cylinder. Otherwise, the cylinder is an *oblique cylinder*. (412)

right dihedral angle A dihedral angle is a right dihedral angle if and only if its plane angles are right angles. (100)

right prism If the lateral edges of a prism are also altitudes, then the prism is a right prism. (410)

right triangle A right triangle is a triangle with one right angle. (112)

rotation The composite of two reflections with respect to two intersecting lines is a transformation called a rotation. The intersection of the two lines is called the *center of rotation*. (514)

scalene triangle A scalene triangle is a triangle with no two sides congruent. (112)

secant A secant is a line that intersects a circle in exactly two points. (348)

secant segment A secant segment is a segment that contains a chord of a circle. The part or parts of a secant segment that are exterior to the circle are called *external secant segments*. (375)

sector A sector of a circle is a region bounded by a central angle and the intercepted arc. (406)

segment A segment is a part of a line that consists of two points, called *endpoints*, and all the points between them. (46)

segment bisector A segment bisector is a segment, line, or plane that intersects a segment at its midpoint. (57)

semicircle A line containing the diameter of a circle separates the circle into two semicircles. (351)

sides of an angle See angle. (74)

similar figures Figures that have the same shape but that may differ in size are called similar figures. (276)

similarity transformation When a geometric figure and its transformation image are similar, the mapping is called a similarity transformation. (504)

similar polygons Two polygons are similar if and only if there is a correspondence such that their corresponding angles are congruent and the measures of their corresponding sides are proportional. (276)

sine A ratio is the sine of an acute angle of a right triangle if and only if it is the ratio of the measure of the leg opposite the acute angle to the measure of the hypotenuse. (327)

skew lines Two lines are skew if and only if they do not intersect and are not in the same plane. (185)

slant height The height of each lateral face of a regular pyramid or the length of any segment joining the vertex to the base of a right circular cone is called the slant height. (415, 416)

slope The slope of a line containing two points with coordinates (x_1, y_1) and (x_2, y_2) is given by the following formula.
$$m = \frac{y_2 - y_1}{x_2 - x_1} \quad \text{where } x_2 \neq x_1 \quad (443)$$

slope-intercept form The equation of the line having a slope m and y-intercept b is $y = mx + b$. (448)

sphere In space, a figure is a sphere if and only if it is the set of all points that are a given distance from a given point, called the *center*. (378)

square A quadrilateral is a square if and

only if it is a rectangle and all four sides are congruent.   (243)

square root   For any numbers a and b, if $a^2 = b$, then a is a square root of b. Also, a is a *principle square root* of b if a is nonnegative.   (309)

straightedge   Any instrument used as a guide to draw a line is a straightedge. (475)

supplementary angles   Two angles are supplementary if and only if the sum of their degree measures is 180.   (82)

surface area   The sum of the areas of the faces of a solid figure is the surface area. (410)

tangent   **1.** A ratio is the tangent of an acute angle of a right triangle if and only if it is the ratio of the measure of the leg opposite the acute angle to the measure of the leg adjacent to the acute angle. (327)   **2.** A tangent is a line in a plane that intersects a circle in the plane in exactly one point. The point of intersection is the *point of tangency*.   (348)

tangent segment   A tangent segment is a segment that intersects a circle in exactly one point and lies on a tangent.   (366)

terminating decimal   A terminating decimal is a decimal number in which the division process stops or terminates because a remainder of zero has been reached. An example is 0.35.   (38)

theorem   A theorem is a statement that must be proven before accepted.   (19)

transformation   In a plane, a mapping is a transformation if and only if each point has exactly one image point and each image point has exactly one preimage point.   (503)

translation   A composite of two reflections over two parallel lines is a translation. (511)

transversal   In a plane, a line is a transversal if and only if it intersects two other lines in two different points.   (186)

trapezoid   A quadrilateral is a trapezoid if and only if it has exactly one pair of parallel sides. The parallel sides of a trapezoid are called *bases*. The nonparallel sides are called *legs*. The angles formed by bases and the legs are called *base angles*. The line segment joining the midpoints of the legs of a trapezoid is called the *median*. The *altitude* is a segment perpendicular to both bases with its endpoints on the bases.   (247)

triangle   A triangle is a figure formed by three noncollinear segments called sides. Each endpoint of a side is an endpoint of exactly one other side. The endpoints are the *vertices* of the triangle. A triangle separates a plane into three parts, the triangle, its *interior*, and its *exterior*. (111)

trigonometric ratio   A ratio of the measures of two sides of a right triangle is called a trigonometric ratio. *Trigonometry* means triangle measurement.   (327)

undefined term   An undefined term is a word that has a meaning that is readily understood. The basic undefined terms of geometry are point, line, and plane.   (5)

unit of measure   See measurement.   (41)

vertex of an angle   See angle.   (74)

vertical angles   Two angles are vertical if and only if they are two nonadjacent angles formed by two intersecting lines. (89)

volume   The measure of the amount of space a figure encloses is the volume of the figure.   (419)

whole numbers   The whole numbers consist of the set {0, 1, 2, 3, . . .}.   (37)

x-axis   See axis.   (435)

y-axis   See axis.   (435)

Selected Answers

Page 3 Exploratory   1. point **3.** line
5. plane **7.** line **9.** plane **11.** point **13.** line

Page 4 Written   13. any one of $\overleftrightarrow{AF}, \overleftrightarrow{FB}, n, \overleftrightarrow{FA},$ $\overleftrightarrow{BF}, \overleftrightarrow{BA}$ **15.** none **17.** any two of A, E, D **19.** any three of $\overleftrightarrow{AF}, \overleftrightarrow{FB}, \overleftrightarrow{AB}, \overleftrightarrow{FA}, \overleftrightarrow{BF}, \overleftrightarrow{BA}$ **21.** any combination of three noncollinear points, such as plane A, F, E, plane A, B, C, plane D, E, H, etc. **23.** S **25.** R **27.** none **29.** infinitely many **31.** three

Page 7 Exploratory   1. false **3.** false **5.** true
7. false **9.** false **11.** true

Pages 7–8 Written   1. collinear
3. noncollinear **5.** collinear **7.** noncollinear
9. noncoplanar **11.** coplanar **13.** coplanar
15. $\overleftrightarrow{AE}, \overleftrightarrow{BE}, \overleftrightarrow{DE}, \overleftrightarrow{CE}, \overleftrightarrow{AB}, \overleftrightarrow{BD}, \overleftrightarrow{CD}, \overleftrightarrow{AC}, \overleftrightarrow{AD}, \overleftrightarrow{BC}$
17. A, B, C, E; A, B, D, E; B, C, D, E; A, C, D, E
19. $\overleftrightarrow{AB}$ **21.** E **23.** not good; no distinguishing properties **25.** not good; no identifying set; no distinguishing properties; not reversible **27.** not good; no identifying set **29.** good **31.** a definition is reversible provided it can be written in "if and only if" form

Page 11 Exploratory   1. it rains; the grass gets wet **3.** you live in Texas; you are an American **5.** two lines are perpendicular; two lines intersect **7.** n is even; n^2 is even **9.** an animal is a chimpanzee; it is a mammal **11.** birds; fly **13.** We will go skiing; it snows

Page 12 Written   1. If lines are parallel, then they do not intersect; if lines do not intersect, then they are parallel. **3.** If a figure is a square, then it is a rectangle; if a figure is a rectangle, then it is a square. **5.** If $x < 0$, then $5x > 6x$; if $5x > 6x$, then $x < 0$. **7.** If it rains, then it pours; if it pours, then it rains. **9.** If two lines intersect, then they are contained in exactly one plane; if two lines are contained in exactly one plane, then they intersect. **11.** If there is smoke, then there is fire; if there is fire, then there is smoke.
13. yes; true **15.** yes; neither **17.** no; neither

Page 16 Exploratory   1. Postulate 1-1
3. Postulate 1-4 **5.** Postulate 1-6 **7.** Postulate 1-3
9. Postulate 1-5

Pages 16–17 Written   1. true **3.** false
5. true **7.** false **9.** true **11.** Postulate 1-4
13. Postulate 1-5 **15.** 1 **17.** 3 **19.** 4 **21.** 15 **23.** 1
25. infinitely many if 3 collinear points taken; only one if 3 noncollinear points taken

Page 21 Exploratory   1. theorem, given, prove statement, diagram, and proof with statements and reasons **3.** information in the conclusion **5.** yes **7.** yes **9.** statements, reasons **11.** to justify statement **13.** two lines intersect **15.** a line and a plane intersect, and the plane does not contain the line **17.** there is exactly one plane that contains them **19.** their intersection is a line

Pages 21–22 Written   1. Lines ℓ and m intersect at A; Only plane $\mathcal{R}$ contains ℓ and m. **3.** Line ℓ and plane $\mathcal{M}$ intersect, and $\mathcal{M}$ does not contain ℓ; ℓ and $\mathcal{M}$ intersect at A. **15.** Point Q is not on line m. **17.** Planes $\mathcal{A}$ and $\mathcal{B}$ intersect at line ℓ. **19.** $\overleftrightarrow{PQ}$ and $\overleftrightarrow{QR}$ intersect at Q. **21.** A line intersects a plane at point P. **23.** $\overleftrightarrow{AB}$ intersects $\overleftrightarrow{CB}$ at B. Plane $\mathcal{M}$ contains $\overleftrightarrow{AB}$ but not $\overleftrightarrow{CB}$.

Page 25 Exploratory   1. Theorem 1-2
3. Postulate 1-4 **5.** Postulate 1-2 **7.** Theorem 1-2
9. none **11.** none

Pages 25–26 Written   1. Postulate 1-1
3. Postulate 1-2 **5.** Postulate 1-5 **7.** Theorem 1-1
9. definition of noncollinear points **11.** Exactly one plane contains ℓ and m. **13.** The intersection of $\mathcal{M}$ and $\mathcal{N}$ is a line. **15.** ℓ contains at least 2 points.
17. Exactly one plane contains ℓ and P. **19.** Planes $\mathcal{L}$ and $\mathcal{M}$ intersect; the intersection of $\mathcal{L}$ and $\mathcal{M}$ contains at least two points, A and B. **21.** Lines ℓ and m intersect at P; ℓ and m contain $P, A,$ and B. **23.** Postulate 1-6; Postulate 1-3

Page 30 Exploratory   1. A figure is not a triangle. **3.** Three points are noncollinear. **5.** $\mathcal{M}$ and $\mathcal{N}$ do not intersect. **7.** ℓ lies in $\mathcal{M}$. **9.** $P, Q,$ and R are coplanar. **11.** Two points lie in the same plane.

Pages 30–31 Written   1. yes **3.** no **5.** yes
7. no **9.** no **11.** no **13.** yes **15.** no **17.** yes **19.** no
21. no **23.** no **25.** If it does not rain, then the grass does not get wet; if the grass does not get wet, then it does not rain. **27.** If you do not live in Texas, then you are not an American; if you are not an American, then you do not live in Texas. **29.** If two lines are not perpendicular, then they do not intersect; if two lines do not intersect, then they are not perpendicular.
31. If n is odd, then n^2 is odd; if n^2 is odd, then n is odd.

Pages 33–34 Chapter Review   5. Points are noncoplanar points if and only if they do not lie in the same plane **7.** If an angle has a degree measure of 90, then the angle is a right angle; an angle has a degree measure of 90; the angle is a right angle **9.** If an angle is a right angle, then the angle has a degree measure of 90. **11.** Lines are skew lines if and only if they are not coplanar. **13.** 4 **19.** Postulate 1-2 **21.** If it is not green, then it is yellow; if it is yellow, then it is not green. **23.** If $2x \neq 8$, then $x \neq 4$; if $x \neq 4$, then $2x \neq 8$. **25.** If the month is not May, then it is June (false); if the month is not June, then it is May (false); if the month is June, then it is not May (true).

CHAPTER 2 MEASURE

Page 39 **Exploratory** **1.** 1 **3.** -8 **5.** 0 **7.** 5 **9.** -6 **11.** $-\frac{5}{3}$ **13.** $-\frac{4}{3}$ **15.** $-\frac{1}{3}$ **17.** $-\frac{2}{3}$ **19.** $\frac{5}{3}$ **21.** 0.7 **23.** 0.4 **25.** 0.9

Page 40 **Written** **1.** 0.3 **3.** -0.8 **5.** $0.\overline{3}$ **7.** -4.375 **9.** $5.\overline{2}$ **11.** -4.625 **13.** $\frac{7}{9}$ **15.** $\frac{5}{9}$ **17.** $\frac{524}{999}$ **19.** $\frac{11}{9}$ **21.** $\frac{26}{11}$ **23.** $\frac{125}{99}$ **29.** no, no, no, no, no, no, no, no, no, no **31.** no, yes, no, no, no, no, no, no, yes **33.** yes, no, no, no, no, yes, yes, no, no, no **35.** True **37.** False. 2 is a natural number and a whole number. **39.** True **41.** True **43.** False. π is not a natural number and is not a rational number.

Page 43 **Exploratory** **1.** 12 **3.** 30 **5.** $\frac{1}{4}$ **7.** 2.3 **9.** 7 **11.** 3 **13.** $7\frac{1}{2}$ **15.** 89 **17.** 97 **19.** 58 **21.** true **23.** true **25.** false **27.** true **29.** false **31.** true **33.** true **35.** false

Page 44 **Written** **1.** 9 **3.** -12 **5.** -18 **7.** -97 **9.** -153 **11.** 11 **13.** 6 **15.** 3 **17.** 4 **19.** 3 **21.** 9 **23.** 5.6 **25.** $4\frac{5}{6}$ **27.** $2\frac{3}{4}$ **29.** $\frac{5}{6}$ **31.** 2 **33.** $2\frac{5}{6}$ **35.** $1\frac{2}{3}$ **37.** 0 **39.** $1\frac{1}{3}$ **41.** 0 **43.** $1\frac{2}{3}$ **45.** 0.4 **47.** 2.6 **49.** 0.4 **51.** 0.8 **53.** 1.9 **55.** 1.1 **57.** 0.4 **59.** 1 **61.** 20

Page 48 **Exploratory** **1.** $|-8 - 0|$ or $|0 - (-8)|$ **3.** $|-8 - 9|$ or $|9 - (-8)|$ **5.** $|3 - 6|$ or $|6 - 3|$ **7.** $|6 - (-8)|$ or $|-8 - 6|$ **9.** $|-4 - 0|$ or $|0 - (-4)|$ **11.** -6 **13.** $4\frac{1}{2}$ **15.** $2\frac{1}{2}$ **17.** $-\frac{1}{2}$ **19.** 1

Pages 48–49 **Written** **1.** 1 **3.** 17 **5.** 4 **7.** 3 **9.** 8 **11.** 7 **13.** 14 **15.** 4 **17.** 3 **19.** 13 **43.** A = 1 or A = -11 **45.** M = -8 or M = -2 **47.** Y = 5

Page 52 **Exploratory** **1.** Reflexive Property of Equality **3.** Inverse Property of Multiplication **5.** Symmetric Property of Equality **7.** Identity Property of Multiplication **9.** Associative Property of Multiplication **11.** Identity Property of Addition

13. Commutative Property of Addition **15.** Division Property of Equality **17.** Substitution **19.** Associative Property of Addition

Pages 53–54 **Written** **1-2.** Division Property of Equality **3-2.** Subtraction Property of Equality **3-3.** Multiplication Property of Equality **5-3.** Substitution **7-2.** Multiplication Property of Equality **7-3.** Inverse Property of Multiplication, Substitution **7-4.** Identity Property of Multiplication **9-2.** Addition Property of Equality **9-3.** Definition of Between **9-4.** Substitution **11-2.** Definition of Between **11-3.** Substitution

Page 58 **Exploratory** **1.** Reflexive **3.** Symmetric **5.** Transitive **7.** Transitive

Pages 58–59 **Written** **1.** true **3.** true **5.** true **7.** true **9.** true **11.** M is the midpoint of $\overline{PQ}$ if and only if M is between P and Q, and $PM = MQ$. **13.** M is the midpoint of $\overline{PQ}$; $\overline{PM} \cong \overline{MQ}$. **15.** $\overline{PQ}$ is bisected at point M; $\overline{PM} \cong \overline{MQ}$. **17.** Given: $\overline{PQ}$ is bisected at point M. Prove: $\overline{PM} \cong \overline{MQ}$ **19.** Use definition of bisects and the Midpoint Theorem **21.** 0, 10, 5 **23.** $-2, 8, 5$ **25.** $\frac{13}{24}, \frac{5}{12}, \frac{5}{24}$ **27.** $7\frac{1}{2}$ **29.** $10\frac{1}{2}$ **31.** False. A, B, and C must be collinear.

33. Given: $\overline{AB}$

Prove: $\overline{AB} \cong \overline{AB}$

Proof:

STATEMENTS	REASONS
1. $\overline{AB}$	1. Given
2. $AB = AB$	2. Reflexive Prop. of Equality
3. $\overline{AB} \cong \overline{AB}$	3. Definition of Congruent Segments

35. Given: M is between P and Q; $\overline{PM} \cong \overline{MQ}$

Prove: M is the midpoint of $\overline{PQ}$.

Proof:

STATEMENTS	REASONS
1. M is between P and Q.	1. Given
2. $\overline{PM} \cong \overline{MQ}$	2. Given
3. $PM = MQ$	3. Definition of Congruent Segments
4. M is the midpoint of $\overline{PQ}$.	4. Definition of Midpoint

37-2. Definition of Midpoint **37-3.** Definition of Between **37-4.** Substitution **37-5.** Distributive **37-6.** Multiplication Property of Equality, Inverse Property of Multiplication, Substitution, and Identity Property of Multiplication

Page 63 **Exploratory** **1.** $<$ **3.** $>$ **5.** $>$ **7.** $=$ **9.** $<$ **11.** $<$

Pages 63–64   Written   1. $3 > 0$; $8 > 5$; $\frac{-15}{4} <$ -3; $5 > 4$ **3.** $-22 < -18$; $-7 < -3$; $\frac{5}{2} > \frac{3}{2}$; $\frac{-10}{3} < -2$, $5 > 3$ **5.** $=$ **7.** $>$ **9.** $=$ **11.** $>$ **13.** $<$ **15.** $<$ **17-2.** Subtraction Property of Equality   **19-2.** Division Property of Equality   **21-2.** Addition Property of Equality   **21-3.** Subtraction Property of Equality   **21-4.** Division Property of Equality   **23.** $x > 12$ **25.** $y > 17.6$ or $y > \frac{88}{5}$ **27.** $x < 6$ **29.** $c < 2$ **31.** $x > 20$ **33.** $QR < PQ$ or $PQ > QR$ **35.** $AB < EF$ by Transitive Property of Inequality   **37.** b

Pages 67–68   Chapter Review   1. $-1\frac{3}{4}$ **3.** 0 **5.** 0.7 **7.** $-0.\overline{6}$ **9.** $\frac{1}{3}$ **11.** $\frac{4}{33}$ **13.** $\frac{1}{2}$ **15.** $4\frac{3}{4}$ **17.** $3\frac{1}{2}$ **19.** $\frac{1}{2}$ **25.** $(8 \cdot 5)7$ **27.** $BC + AB$ **29.** $MQ = PM$ **31.** Inverse Property of Addition   **33.** Inverse Property of Multiplication   **35.** Commutative Property of Multiplication   **37-1.** Given   **37-2.** Given   **37-3.** Definition of Congruent Segments   **37-4.** Definition of Midpoint   **39.** -1 **41.** $x < 6$ **43.** $r < -6.6$

CHAPTER 3   ANGLES AND PERPENDICULARS

Page 75   Exploratory   1. true   **3.** false   **5.** true   **7.** true   **9.** false   **11.** true   **13.** false   **15.** true

Page 76   Written   1. one   **3.** their endpoint   **5.** negative   **11.** $\angle PQS$ or $\angle SQP$ **13.** Q **15.** $\overrightarrow{QS}$, $\overrightarrow{QT}$ **17.** $\angle PQV$, $\angle SQV$, $\angle 3$, $\angle 4$ **19.** V **21.** $\angle ABD$, $\angle ABC$, $\angle DBC$ **23.** $\angle ABC$

Page 80   Exploratory   1. 170   **3.** 120   **5.** 75   **7.** 25   **9.** 60   **11.** 30   **13.** 75

Pages 80–81   Written   9. $m \angle TPS$ **11.** $m \angle RPQ + m \angle TPS$ **13.** $m \angle RPQ$, $m \angle SPR$, $m \angle TPS$ **15.** 20   **17.** true   **19.** true   **21.** true   **23.** true   **25.** false   **31.** 30   **33.** 60   **35.** 90

Page 85   Exploratory   1. two sides of adjacent angles lie on a line   **3.** $\overrightarrow{BA}$, $\overrightarrow{BD}$ lie on $\overleftrightarrow{AD}$.   **5.** $\angle ABC$ and $\angle DBC$ are supplementary   **7.** Supplement Postulate (Postulate 3-4)

Page 86   Written   1. 45   **3.** 80   **5.** 45   **7.** 19   **9.** 89   **11.** 108

13. Given: $\angle A$ is the complement of $\angle B$;

$\angle C$ is the complement of $\angle B$.

Prove: $\angle A \cong \angle C$

Proof:

STATEMENTS	REASONS
1. $\angle A$ is the complement	1. Given

of $\angle B$; $\angle C$ is the complement of $\angle B$.

STATEMENTS	REASONS
2. $m \angle A + m \angle B = 90$; $m \angle C + m \angle B = 90$	2. Definition of Complementary Angles
3. $m \angle A + m \angle B = m \angle C + m \angle B$	3. Substitution
4. $m \angle A = m \angle C$	4. Subtraction Property of Equality
5. $\angle A \cong \angle C$	5. Definition of Congruent Angles

15. 45   **17.** 28; 62

Page 90   Exploratory   1. acute   **3.** acute   **5.** obtuse   **7.** right   **9.** acute   **11.** none of these   **13.** An angle with degree measure 90 and a right angle; the angles are congruent   **15.** Two angles are right angles; the angles are supplementary   **17.** One angle in a linear pair is a right angle; the other angle also is a right angle

Pages 90–92   Written   1. right   **3.** obtuse   **5-1.** Given   **5-2.** Definition of Linear Pair   **5-3.** Supplement Postulate   **5-4.** Theorem 3-2   **7.** 43   **9.** 10

11. STATEMENTS	REASONS
1. $\angle A$ and $\angle C$ are complementary.	1. Given
2. $m \angle A + m \angle C = 90$	2. Definition of Complementary Angles
3. $\angle 1 \cong \angle C$; $\angle 2 \cong \angle A$	3. Given
4. $m \angle 1 = m \angle C$; $m \angle 2 = m \angle A$	4. Definition of Congruent Angles
5. $m \angle 1 + m \angle 2 = 90$	5. Substitution
6. $m \angle 1 + m \angle 2 = m \angle ABC$	6. Angle Addition Postulate (Postulate 3-3)
7. $m \angle ABC = 90$	7. Substitution
8. $\angle ABC$ is a right angle.	8. Definition of Right Angle

Page 95   Exploratory   1. false   **3.** true   **5.** true   **7.** true   **9.** true   **11.** true   **13.** false   **15.** true   **17.** true   **19.** false

Pages 96–97   Written   1-1. Definition of Linear Pair   **1-2.** Supplement Postulate   **1-3.** Definition of Supplementary Angles   **1-4.** Given   **1-5.** Definition of Congruent Angles   **1-6.** Substitution   **1-7.** Distributive   **1-8.** Division Property of Equality   **1-9.** Definition of Right Angle   **1-10.** Definition of Perpendicular Lines

3. Given: $\overrightarrow{BA} \perp \overrightarrow{BC}$

Prove: $\angle 1$ and $\angle 2$ are complementary.

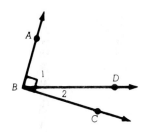

Proof:

STATEMENTS	REASONS
1. $\overrightarrow{BA} \perp \overrightarrow{BC}$	1. Given
2. $\angle ABC$ is a right angle.	2. Definition of Perpendicular Lines
3. $m \angle ABC = 90$	3. Definition of Right Angle
4. $m \angle 1 + m \angle 2 = m \angle ABC$	4. Angle Addition Postulate (Postulate 3-3)
5. $m \angle 1 + m \angle 2 = 90$	5. Substitution
6. $\angle 1$ and $\angle 2$ are complementary.	6. Definition of Complementary Angles.

7. $x = 15$, $y = 10$

Page 101   Exploratory   1. $\angle R - \overleftrightarrow{PQ} - S$
3. $\angle P - \overleftrightarrow{QR} - S$ **5.** $\angle P - \overleftrightarrow{SR} - Q$ **7.** $\angle PQR$
9. $\angle PQS$

Page 101   Written   1. $\angle S - \overleftrightarrow{RQ} - Z$; $\angle Y - \overleftrightarrow{XT} - W$ **3.** $\angle QTV$ **5.** yes **7.** no **13.** 10
15. Given: $\mathcal{P}$ intersects $\mathcal{M}$ at $\overleftrightarrow{AB}$;
$\angle V - \overleftrightarrow{AB} - R$ is a right dihedral angle.

Prove: $\mathcal{P} \perp \mathcal{M}$

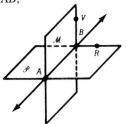

Proof:

STATEMENTS	REASONS
1. $\mathcal{P}$ intersects $\mathcal{M}$ at $\overleftrightarrow{AB}$; $\angle V - \overleftrightarrow{AB} - R$ is a right dihedral angle.	1. Given
2. $\overleftrightarrow{BR} \perp \overleftrightarrow{AB}$	2. Definition of Right Dihedral Angle
3. $\overleftrightarrow{BR} \perp \mathcal{M}$	3. Definition of a Line Perpendicular to a Plane
4. $\mathcal{P} \perp \mathcal{M}$	4. Definition of Perpendicular Planes

Pages 105–106   Chapter Review   1. Q **3.** T
5. $\overrightarrow{QP}, \overrightarrow{QR}$ **7.** $\overrightarrow{RT}$ **9.** 95 **11.** true **13.** false **15.** 94
17. 73

19.

STATEMENTS	REASONS
1. $\angle AXB$ is a right angle.	1. Given
2. $m \angle AXB = 90$	2. Definition of a Right Angle
3. $\angle AXD \cong \angle AXB$	3. Given
4. $m \angle AXD = m \angle AXB$	4. Definition of Congruent Angles
5. $m \angle AXD = 90$	5. Transitive Property of Equality
6. $\angle AXD$ is a right angle.	6. Definition of a Right Angle

21. 58 **25.** 9 **27.** $\angle ABC$ or $\angle DEF$

CHAPTER 4   CONGRUENT TRIANGLES

Pages 113–114   Exploratory   1. obtuse
3. acute **5.** obtuse **7.** isosceles **9.** scalene
11. scalene **13.** D, E, F **15.** $\angle DEF, \angle EFD, \angle EDF$
17. $\overline{DE}, \overline{DF}, \overline{EF}$ **19.** right **21.** scalene

Pages 114–115   Written   1. $\triangle PST$, $\triangle PQT$, $\triangle QRT$, $\triangle RST$, $\triangle PRS$, $\triangle PQS$, $\triangle PQR$, $\triangle QRS$ **3.** S, T, R **5.** $\overline{ST}, \overline{TR}, \overline{SR}$ **7.** $\angle STR, \angle TRS, \angle TSR$ **9.** A triangle is an equiangular triangle if and only if all its angles are congruent. **11.** A triangle is an isosceles triangle if and only if two of its sides are congruent.
15. none **21.** none **23.** obtuse **25.** scalene
27. scalene **29.** $PQ = 35, QR = 35, RP = 35$

Page 118   Exploratory   1. 64 **3.** 85 **5.** 81
7. 67 **9.** 58 **11.** 75 **13.** 32

Pages 118–119   Written   1. 150 **3.** $180 - x - y$ **5.** $145 - a$ **7.** $2x + 2$ **9.** 55 **11.** 55 **13.** $27\frac{1}{2}$
15. 24 **17.** *No; if two angles were right angles, then by Theorem 4-1, the degree measure of the third angle would have to be zero. This violates the Angle Measure Postulate.*
19. Given: Equiangular $\triangle ABC$

Prove: $m \angle A = 60$;
$m \angle B = 60$;
$m \angle C = 60$

Proof:

STATEMENTS	REASONS
1. $\triangle ABC$ is equiangular.	1. Given
2. $m \angle A = m \angle B = m \angle C$	2. Definition of Equiangular Triangle
3. $m \angle A + m \angle B + m \angle C = 180$	3. Angle Sum Theorem (Theorem 4-1)
4. $m \angle A + m \angle A + m \angle A = 180$	4. Substitution
5. $3m \angle A = 180$	5. Distributive Property
6. $m \angle A = 60$	6. Division Property of Equality
7. $m \angle B = 60$; $m \angle C = 60$	7. Substitution

Page 122   Exploratory   1. $\angle S$ **3.** $\overline{PQ}$ **5.** $\angle P$
7. $\angle Q$ **9.** $\overline{VS}$ **11.** $\overline{TV}$ **13.** $\triangle TSU$ **15.** $\triangle XYZ$
17. $\angle A$, $\angle F$; $\angle B$, $\angle G$; $\angle C$, $\angle H$; $\overline{AB}$, $\overline{FG}$; $\overline{BC}$, $\overline{GH}$; $\overline{AC}$, $\overline{FH}$

Pages 122–123   Written   1. false **3.** false
5. true **7.** true **9.** true **11.** true **13.** true
15. false **17.** true **19.** $\angle Q$ **21.** $\overline{RP}$ **23.** $\overline{TR}$ **25.** no
27. no **33.** 11

Page 126   Exploratory   1. yes; SAS **3.** no
5. yes; SAS **7.** yes; ASA **9.** yes; ASA **11.** yes; SSS
13. yes; ASA **15.** no

Pages 126–128   Written   1. $\angle W \cong \angle Z$; $\angle WXV$
$\cong \angle ZXY$ **3.** $\overline{ML} \cong \overline{JH}$; $\overline{OL} \cong \overline{KH}$ **5.** $\overline{HG} \cong \overline{JI}$; $\overline{GI} \cong \overline{IG}$ **7.** $\triangle MON$; ASA **9.** $\triangle GHF$; SSS

11.

STATEMENTS	REASONS
1. $\overline{QP} \cong \overline{ST}$; R is the midpoint of $\overline{PT}$; $\angle P$ and $\angle T$ are right angles.	1. Given
2. $\angle P \cong \angle T$	2. Theorem 3-6
3. $\overline{PR} \cong \overline{RT}$	3. Midpoint Theorem (Theorem 2-5)
4. $\triangle QPR \cong \triangle STR$	4. SAS
5. $\overline{QR} \cong \overline{SR}$	5. Definition of Congruent Triangles

13.

STATEMENTS	REASONS
1. $\angle 1 \cong \angle 6$; $\angle 3 \cong \angle 4$	1. Given
2. $\overline{AC} \cong \overline{CA}$	2. Theorem 2-2
3. $\triangle ADC \cong \triangle CBA$	3. ASA
4. $\overline{AD} \cong \overline{CB}$	4. Definition of Congruent Triangles

15.

STATEMENTS	REASONS
1. $\overline{AC} \cong \overline{EC}$; $\angle A \cong \angle E$	1. Given
2. $\angle 1$ and $\angle 2$ are vertical angles.	2. Definition of Vertical Angles
3. $\angle 1 \cong \angle 2$	3. Theorem 3-10
4. $\triangle ABC \cong \triangle EDC$	4. ASA
5. $\overline{BC} \cong \overline{DC}$	5. Definition of Congruent Triangles

17. $\angle SVT$; Theorem 3-10 **19.** $\overline{TS}$; CPCTC (Note that CPCTC will be used for Corresponding Parts of Congruent Triangles are Congruent.) **21.** $\overline{SP}$; Addition Property of Equality, Definition of Between, Substitution **23.** $\angle 1$; CPCTC or Isosceles Triangle Theorem (Theorem 4-6) **25.** $\overline{SR}$; Given **27.** $\angle 6$; Definition of Linear Pair, Supplement Postulate **29.** $\triangle SRP$; SSS or SAS **31.** $\angle PVT$; Theorem 3-10 **33.** isosceles; Definition of Isosceles Triangle

Page 132   Exploratory   1. yes; AAS **3.** not enough information **5.** yes; ASA **7.** yes; SSS **9.** yes; SAS **11.** not enough information

Pages 132–133   Written

1.

STATEMENTS	REASONS
1. $\overline{BC} \cong \overline{DC}$; $\angle A \cong \angle E$; $\angle 1 \cong \angle 2$	1. Given
2. $\triangle ABC \cong \triangle EDC$	2. AAS
3. $\overline{AC} \cong \overline{EC}$	3. CPCTC

3.

STATEMENTS	REASONS
1. $\angle A \cong \angle E$; $\overline{AC} \cong \overline{EC}$; $\angle 1 \cong \angle 2$	1. Given
2. $\triangle ABC \cong \triangle EDC$	2. ASA
3. $\angle B \cong \angle D$	3. CPCTC

5.

STATEMENTS	REASONS
1. $\angle A \cong \angle C$; $\overline{BD} \perp \overline{AC}$	1. Given
2. $\angle 3 \cong \angle 4$	2. Theorem 3-13
3. $\overline{BD} \cong \overline{BD}$	3. Theorem 2-2
4. $\triangle ABD \cong \triangle CBD$	4. AAS
5. $\overline{AB} \cong \overline{CB}$	5. CPCTC

Page 136   Exploratory   1. 90 **3.** 45 **5.** 45
7. 90 **9.** 135 **11.** 90 **13.** 90 **15.** 63 **17.** 27

Pages 136–137   Written

1.

3.

5.

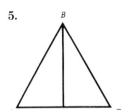

7.

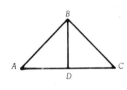

9. 24 **11.** $x = 5$; $m \angle XYZ = 34$; $m \angle XYV = m \angle VYZ = 17$

13.

STATEMENTS	REASONS
1. $\overline{AB}$ is an altitude of $\triangle ABD$; $\overline{CD}$ is an altitude of $\triangle BCD$; $\overline{BC} \cong \overline{AD}$; $\overline{CD} \cong \overline{AD}$; $\overline{AB} \cong \overline{CD}$	1. Given
2. $\overline{BD} \cong \overline{BD}$	2. Theorem 2-2
3. $\overline{BC} \cong \overline{CD}$	3. Theorem 2-4
4. $\overline{AB} \cong \overline{BC}$	4. Theorem 2-4
5. $\triangle ABD \cong \triangle CBD$	5. SSS
6. $\angle ABD \cong \angle CBD$	6. CPCTC
7. $\overline{BD}$ bisects $\angle ABC$.	7. Definition of Angle Bisector of a Triangle

15. Given: Isosceles $\triangle ABC$; $\overline{AB} \cong \overline{CB}$; $\overline{BD}$ is a median.

Prove: $\overline{BD}$ bisects $\angle ABC$.

Proof:

STATEMENTS	REASONS
1. Isosceles $\triangle ABC$; $\overline{AB} \cong \overline{CB}$; $\overline{BD}$ is a median.	1. Given
2. D is the midpoint of $\overline{AC}$.	2. Definition of Median of a Triangle
3. $\overline{AD} \cong \overline{DC}$	3. Midpoint Theorem (Theorem 2-5)
4. $\overline{BD} \cong \overline{BD}$	4. Theorem 2-2
5. $\triangle ABD \cong \triangle CBD$	5. SSS
6. $\angle ABD \cong \angle CBD$	6. CPCTC
7. $\overline{BD}$ bisects $\angle ABC$.	7. Definition of Angle Bisector of a Triangle

Page 140   Exploratory   1. yes **3.** no **5.** no
7. yes **9.** no **11.** 30

Pages 140–141   Written
1.

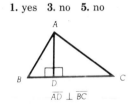

$\overline{AD} \perp \overline{BC}$

$\overline{BD} \not\cong \overline{DC}$

3. isosceles **9.** isosceles **11.** *No;* $\overline{PQ}$ has exactly one midpoint, X, but $\overline{RX}$ is not necessarily perpendicular to $\overline{PQ}$. **13.** *Yes* **15.** *No;* since $\overline{QP}$ intersects $\overline{PR}$, $\overline{XY}$ cannot be perpendicular to both. **17.** 3

19.

STATEMENTS	REASONS
1. $\overline{AB} \cong \overline{BC}$	1. Given
2. $\angle 1 \cong \angle 2$	2. Isosceles Triangle Theorem (Theorem 4-6)
3. $\angle 1$ and $\angle 3$ are a linear pair; $\angle 2$ and $\angle 4$ are a linear pair.	3. Definition of Linear Pair
4. $\angle 1$ and $\angle 3$ are supplementary; $\angle 2$ and $\angle 4$ are supplementary.	4. Supplement Postulate (Postulate 3-4)
5. $\angle 3 \cong \angle 4$	5. Theorem 3-3

Page 144   Exploratory   1. yes; HL **3.** yes; HA or AAS **5.** yes; HA or AAS

Page 144   Written

1.

STATEMENTS	REASONS
1. $\angle Q$ and $\angle S$ are right angles; $\angle 1 \cong \angle 2$	1. Given
2. $\triangle QRP$ and $\triangle SPR$ are right triangles.	2. Definition of Right Triangle
3. $\overline{PR} \cong \overline{RP}$	3. Theorem 2-2
4. $\triangle QRP \cong \triangle SPR$	4. HA
5. $\overline{QR} \cong \overline{SP}$	5. CPCTC

3.

STATEMENTS	REASONS
1. $\overline{BA} \perp \overline{AE}$; $\overline{DE} \perp \overline{AE}$; C is the midpoint of $\overline{AE}$; $\angle ABC \cong \angle EDC$	1. Given
2. $\overline{AC} \cong \overline{EC}$	2. Midpoint Theorem (Theorem 2-5)
3. $\angle A$ and $\angle E$ are right angles.	3. Theorem 3-11
4. $\triangle BAC$ and $\triangle DEC$ are right triangles.	4. Definition of Right Triangle
5. $\triangle BAC \cong \triangle DEC$	5. LA
6. $\angle 1 \cong \angle 2$	6. CPCTC

5. Given: $\triangle ABC$ and $\triangle RPQ$ are right triangles; $\angle A$ and $\angle R$ are right angles; $\overline{BC} \cong \overline{PQ}$; $\angle B \cong \angle P$

Prove: $\triangle ABC \cong \triangle RPQ$

Proof:

STATEMENTS	REASONS
1. △ABC and △RPQ are right triangles; ∠A and ∠R are right angles; $\overline{BC} \cong \overline{PQ}$; ∠B ≅ ∠P	1. Given
2. ∠A ≅ ∠R	2. Theorem 3-6
3. △ABC ≅ △RPQ	3. AAS

Pages 147–148   Chapter Review   1. △TVW
3. ∠TVW, ∠VTW, ∠TWV **5.** 28 **7.** 62 **9.** $\overline{RQ}$
11. $\overline{QS}$ **13.** $\overline{SR}$ **15.** 2

17.

STATEMENTS	REASONS
1. $\overline{PR} \perp \overline{QS}$; ∠Q ≅ ∠S	1. Given
2. ∠3 ≅ ∠4	2. Theorem 3-13
3. $\overline{PR} \cong \overline{PR}$	3. Theorem 2-2
4. △SRP ≅ △QRP	4. AAS
5. $\overline{SR} \cong \overline{QR}$	5. CPCTC
6. SR = QR	6. Definition of Congruent Segments
7. R is the midpoint of $\overline{QS}$.	7. Definition of Midpoint

19.

STATEMENTS	REASONS
1. $\overline{BC} \cong \overline{BA}$; $\overline{BP}$ is a median of △ABC.	1. Given
2. P is the midpoint of $\overline{AC}$.	2. Definition of Median of a Triangle
3. $\overline{AP} \cong \overline{CP}$	3. Midpoint Theorem (Theorem 2-5)
4. $\overline{BP} \cong \overline{BP}$	4. Theorem 2-2
5. △ABP ≅ △CBP	5. SSS
6. ∠3 ≅ ∠4	6. CPCTC
7. $\overline{BP} \perp \overline{AC}$	7. Theorem 3-14
8. $\overline{BP}$ is an altitude of △ABC.	8. Definition of Altitude of a Triangle

21.

STATEMENTS	REASONS
1. ∠A ≅ ∠D; $\overline{AB} \cong \overline{DC}$; E is the midpoint of $\overline{AD}$.	1. Given
2. $\overline{AE} \cong \overline{DE}$	2. Midpoint Theorem (Theorem 2-5)
3. △BAE ≅ △CDE	3. SAS
4. $\overline{BE} \cong \overline{CE}$	4. CPCTC
5. ∠3 ≅ ∠4	5. Isosceles Triangle Theorem (Theorem 4-6)

CHAPTER 5   TRIANGLE INEQUALITIES

Pages 153–154   Exploratory   1. $x > y$ **3.** $x > y$ **5.** $x < y$ **7.** $x < y$ **9.** $m \angle 1 > m \angle 2$ **11.** $m \angle 1 < m \angle 2$ **13.** $m \angle 1 > m \angle 2$ **15.** $m \angle 1 > m \angle 2$ **17.** 33 **19.** 30 **21.** 120 **23.** $x = 53$

Pages 154–155   Written   1. 40 **3.** 100 **5.** 20 **7.** 30 **9.** 55 **11.** 70 **13.** 125

15.

STATEMENTS	REASONS
1. ∠1 ≅ ∠2	1. Given
2. ∠1 and ∠3 are a linear pair; ∠4 and ∠2 are a linear pair.	2. Definition of Linear Pair
3. ∠1 and ∠3 are supplementary; ∠4 and ∠2 are supplementary.	3. Supplement Postulate (Postulate 3-4)
4. ∠3 ≅ ∠4	4. Theorem 3-3
5. $\overline{PQ} \cong \overline{RQ}$	5. Theorem 4-9
6. △PQR is isosceles.	6. Definition of Isosceles Triangle

17.

STATEMENTS	REASONS
1. P, Q, and N are collinear.	1. Given
2. $m \angle 1 > m \angle 2$ in △QON; $m \angle 2 > m \angle 3$ in △PQO.	2. Theorem 5-3
3. $m \angle 1 > m \angle 3$	3. Transitive Property of Inequality

Page 159   Exploratory   1. yes **3.** no **5.** no **7.** yes **9.** yes **11.** yes **13.** yes **15.** no **17.** no **19.** yes **21.** no **23.** yes **25.** yes **27.** no

Pages 159–160   Written   1. sometimes; if angles are marked **3.** yes **5.** yes **7.** yes **9.** sometimes; if angles are marked **11.** sometimes; if segments are marked **13.** ∠9, ∠8 and ∠8 and ∠7 **15.** $\overline{BE}, \overline{EC}$ **17.** no **19.** no **21.** △ABC, △ABE, △ADE, △ACE, △DEC **23.** △MNQ, △MPQ, △MNP **25.** △ADE, △BEF, △BCD, △ACF

27.

STATEMENTS	REASONS
1. $\overline{PM} \cong \overline{QO}$; ∠MPQ ≅ ∠OQP	1. Given
2. $\overline{PQ} \cong \overline{QP}$	2. Theorem 2-2
3. △MPQ ≅ △OQP	3. SAS
4. ∠1 ≅ ∠2	4. CPCTC
5. $\overline{PN} \cong \overline{QN}$	5. Theorem 4-9

29. B **31.** D **33.** C **35.** C **37.** D

Page 164 Exploratory 1. $\angle B$, $\angle A$, $\angle C$ **3.** $\angle I$, $\angle G$, $\angle H$ **5.** $\overline{LM}$, $\overline{LN}$, $\overline{MN}$ **7.** $\overline{ST}$, $\overline{TV}$, $\overline{SV}$

Page 165 Written 1. $\overline{QC}$

3. Given: $\triangle PQR$;
$\qquad PQ > QR$
Prove: $m \angle 2 > m \angle 1$

Proof:

STATEMENTS	REASONS
1. $\triangle PQR$; $PQ > QR$	1. Given
2. Extend $\overline{QR}$ to S so that $\overline{QS} \cong \overline{PQ}$.	2. Ruler Postulate (Postulate 2-2)
3. $\angle QPS \cong \angle QSP$	3. Isosceles Triangle Theorem (Theorem 4-6)
4. $m \angle QPS = m \angle 1 + m \angle 4$	4. Angle Addition Postulate (Postulate 3-3)
5. $m \angle QPS = m \angle QSP$	5. Definition of Congruent Angles
6. $m \angle QSP = m \angle 1 + m \angle 4$	6. Substitution
7. $m \angle 2 = m \angle QSP + m \angle 4$	7. Exterior Angle Theorem (Theorem 5-1)
8. $m \angle 2 = m \angle 1 + m \angle 4 + m \angle 4$	8. Substitution
9. $m \angle 2 > m \angle 1$	9. Inequality Theorem (Theorem 5-2)

5.

STATEMENTS	REASONS
1. $\triangle ABC$; $\angle A$ is a right angle.	1. Given
2. $m \angle A = 90$	2. Definition of Right Angle
3. $\angle B$ and $\angle C$ are complementary.	3. Theorem 4-3
4. $m \angle B + m \angle C = 90$	4. Definition of Complementary Angles
5. $m \angle A = m \angle B + m \angle C$	5. Substitution
6. $m \angle A > m \angle C$	6. Inequality Theorem (Theorem 5-2)
7. $BC > BA$	7. Theorem 5-5

Page 169 Exploratory 1. no **3.** yes **5.** yes
7. no **9.** no **11.** no **13.** 4, 10 **15.** 3, 27 **17.** 5.2
19. 0.2

Pages 170–171 Written 1. yes **3.** yes **5.** no

7.

STATEMENTS	REASONS
1. $\angle ABC \cong \angle ACB$	1. Given
2. $AD + AC > CD$	2. Triangle Inequality (Theorem 5-8)
3. $\overline{AB} \cong \overline{AC}$	3. Theorem 4-9
4. $AB = AC$	4. Definition of Congruent Segments
5. $AD + AB > CD$	5. Substitution

9.

STATEMENTS	REASONS
1. $\overline{ED}$ bisects $\overline{AC}$; $\overline{ED} \perp \overline{AC}$	1. Given
2. $\angle EDA$ and $\angle EDC$ are right angles.	2. Theorem 3-11
3. D is the midpoint of $\overline{AC}$.	3. Definition of Segment Bisector
4. $\overline{AD} \cong \overline{CD}$	4. Midpoint Theorem (Theorem 2-5)
5. $\overline{ED} \cong \overline{ED}$	5. Theorem 2-2
6. $\triangle AED \cong \triangle CED$	6. LL
7. $BE + AE > BA$	7. Triangle Inequality (Theorem 5-8)
8. $\overline{AE} \cong \overline{CE}$	8. CPCTC
9. $AE = CE$	9. Definition of Congruent Segments
10. $BE + CE > BA$	10. Substitution
11. $BE + CE = BC$	11. Definition of Between
12. $BC > BA$	12. Substitution

Page 175 Exploratory 1. Theorem 5-9
3. Theorem 5-10 **5.** Theorem 5-9

Pages 175–176 Written 1. AC **3.** $m \angle 1$
5. $\angle PAB$ or $\angle PCB$

7.

STATEMENTS	REASONS
1. $\overline{PQ} \cong \overline{RS}$; $QR < PS$	1. Given
2. $\overline{QS} \cong \overline{QS}$	2. Theorem 2-2
3. $m \angle 3 < m \angle 1$	3. Converse of the Hinge Theorem (Theorem 5-10)

9.

STATEMENTS	REASONS
1. $\overline{BD}$ bisects $\overline{AC}$.	1. Given
2. D is the midpoint of $\overline{AC}$.	2. Definition of Segment Bisector
3. $\overline{AD} \cong \overline{CD}$	3. Midpoint Theorem (Theorem 2-5)
4. $\overline{BD} \cong \overline{BD}$	4. Theorem 2-2
5. $AB > CB$	5. Given

6. $m \angle 1 > m \angle 2$ 6. Converse of the Hinge Theorem (Theorem 5-10)

7. $m \angle 2 > m \angle 3$ 7. Theorem 5-3

8. $m \angle 1 > m \angle 3$ 8. Transitive Property of Inequality

Pages 179–180   **Chapter Review**   **1.** $PQ < PR$
3. $PQ > PR$ **5.** 120   **7.** 30   **9.** 60   **11.** 55   **13.** yes
15. no   **17.** yes   **19.** $\triangle CDF, \triangle CDG, \triangle DFG, \triangle DEG,$
$\triangle EFG$ **21.** $\angle A, \angle C, \angle B; \overline{BC}, \overline{AB}, \overline{AC}$

23.

STATEMENTS	REASONS
1. $\overline{AK} \cong \overline{AC}$	1. Given
2. $\angle 2 \cong \angle C$	2. Isosceles Triangle Theorem (Theorem 4-6)
3. $m \angle 2 = m \angle C$	3. Definition of Congruent Angles
4. $m \angle 1 > m \angle C$	4. Theorem 5-3
5. $m \angle 1 > m \angle 2$	5. Substitution

25. no   **27.** no   **29.** yes   **31.** 2; 16

CHAPTER 6   PARALLELS

Pages 187–188   **Exploratory**   **1.** parallel
3. skew, parallel, or intersecting   **5.** parallel or
intersecting   **7.** parallel   **9.** intersecting or skew
11. parallel   **13.** parallel, skew, or intersecting
15. false   **17.** true   **19.** false   **21.** true   **23.** p **25.** q
27. p

Pages 188–189   **Written**   **1.** alternate exterior
3. alternate interior   **5.** corresponding   **7.** alternate
exterior   **9.** alternate interior   **11.** $\overleftrightarrow{WX}$ and $\overleftrightarrow{ZY}$
13. $\overleftrightarrow{XW}, \overleftrightarrow{XZ},$ and $\overleftrightarrow{YZ}$ **15.** consecutive interior
17. alternate interior   **19.** corresponding   **21.** alternate
exterior   **23.** corresponding   **25.** none of these
27. corresponding   **29.** alternate exterior   **31.** none of
these
33. Given: $\angle 3 \cong \angle 7$
    Prove: $\angle 1 \cong \angle 5;$
           $\angle 2 \cong \angle 6;$
           $\angle 4 \cong \angle 8$

Proof:

STATEMENTS	REASONS
1. $\angle 3 \cong \angle 7$	1. Given
2. $\angle 2 \cong \angle 3; \angle 7 \cong \angle 6$	2. Theorem 3-10
3. $\angle 2 \cong \angle 6$	3. Theorem 3-1
4. $\angle 1$ and $\angle 3$ are a linear pair; $\angle 5$ and $\angle 7$ are a linear pair; $\angle 2$ and $\angle 4$ are a linear pair; $\angle 6$ and $\angle 8$ are a linear pair.	4. Definition of Linear Pair
5. $\angle 1$ and $\angle 3$ are supplementary; $\angle 5$ and $\angle 7$ are supplementary; $\angle 2$ and $\angle 4$ are supplementary; $\angle 6$ and $\angle 8$ are supplementary.	5. Supplement Postulate (Postulate 3-4)
6. $\angle 1 \cong \angle 5; \angle 4 \cong \angle 8$	6. Theorem 3-3

Pages 192–193   **Exploratory**   **1.** The leaves of a
plant are in groups of three and the plant is not poison
ivy.   **3.** The radio does not play well and it is not
defective.   **5.** Two lines intersect and they intersect in
no points.   **7.** A right triangle has more than two acute
angles.   **9.** In a plane, two lines are parallel to the
same line and they are not parallel to each other.
11. The measures of two angles of a triangle are unequal, and the measures of the sides opposite those
angles are unequal in the same order.

Pages 193–194   **Written**   **1.** Two lines in the
same plane are cut by a transversal so a pair of alternate exterior angles are congruent, and the two lines
are not parallel.   **3.** A plane and a line not in the
plane intersect, and they intersect in more than one
point.   **5.** A transversal intersects two parallel lines,
and both pairs of alternate interior angles formed are
not congruent.
7. Assumption: $\triangle ABC$ is a right triangle with right
                 angle C and $\triangle ABC$ has more than
                 two acute angles.
   (a) Assumption
   (b) Definition of Acute Angle
   (c) Given
   (d) Definition of Right Angle
   (e) Comparison Property of Inequality
       (Postulate 2-15)
   (f) The prior statement, (d), contradicts the Compari-
       son Property, (e). Therefore, the initial assump-
       tion must have been false.
11. Given: $\triangle ABC$
     Prove: $\triangle ABC$ has at most one obtuse angle C.

Assumption for Indirect Proof:
△ABC has more than one obtuse angle.
Proof:

STATEMENTS	REASONS
1. ∠A and ∠C are obtuse.	1. Assumption
2. $m \angle A > 90$ and $m \angle C > 90$	2. Definition of Obtuse Angle
3. $m \angle A + m \angle C > 180$	3. Addition Property of Inequality
4. $m \angle A + m \angle B + m \angle C = 180$	4. Angle Sum Theorem (Theorem 4-1)
5. $m \angle A + m \angle C < 180$	5. Inequality Theorem (Theorem 5-2)

Step 5 contradicts Step 3. Thus, △ABC has at most one obtuse angle.

Page 197   Exploratory   1. Theorems 3-10, 6-6
3. Theorem 6-8 **5.** Theorem 6-4 **7.** Theorem 6-5
9. Theorem 6-6

Pages 198–199   Written   1. 21 **3.** 13 **5.** 20
7. $\overleftrightarrow{XA} \parallel \overleftrightarrow{FB}$, Theorem 6-6 **9.** $\overleftrightarrow{QP} \parallel \overleftrightarrow{XY}$ **11.** none
13. $\overleftrightarrow{WZ} \parallel \overleftrightarrow{QP}$

15.

STATEMENTS	REASONS
1. ∠R and ∠S are supplementary; ∠$Q \cong$ ∠S	1. Given
2. $m \angle R + m \angle S = 180$	2. Definition of Supplementary Angles
3. $m \angle Q = m \angle S$	3. Definition of Congruent Angles
4. $m \angle R + m \angle Q = 180$	4. Substitution
5. ∠R and ∠Q are supplementary.	5. Definition of Supplementary Angles
6. $\overline{QP} \parallel \overline{RS}$	6. Theorem 6-6

21. Given: ∠$ABD \cong$ ∠BEF;
$\overleftrightarrow{BC}$ bisects ∠ABD;
$\overleftrightarrow{EH}$ bisects ∠BEF.
Prove: $\overleftrightarrow{BC} \parallel \overleftrightarrow{EH}$

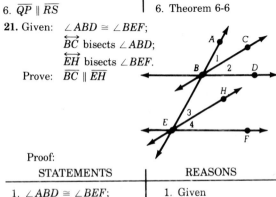

Proof:

STATEMENTS	REASONS
1. ∠$ABD \cong$ ∠BEF; $\overleftrightarrow{BC}$ bisects ∠ABD; $\overleftrightarrow{EH}$ bisects ∠BEF.	1. Given

2. $m \angle 1 + m \angle 2 = m \angle ABD$; $m \angle 3 + m \angle 4 = m \angle BEF$	2. Angle Addition Postulate (Postulate 3-3)
3. $m \angle ABD = m \angle BEF$	3. Definition of Congruent Angles
4. $m \angle 1 + m \angle 2 = m \angle 3 + m \angle 4$	4. Substitution
5. ∠$1 \cong$ ∠2; ∠$3 \cong$ ∠4	5. Definition of Angle Bisector
6. $m \angle 1 = m \angle 2$; $m \angle 3 = m \angle 4$	6. Definition of Congruent Angles
7. $m \angle 1 + m \angle 1 = m \angle 3 + m \angle 3$	7. Substitution
8. $2m \angle 1 = 2m \angle 3$	8. Distributive
9. $m \angle 1 = m \angle 3$	9. Division Property of Equality
10. ∠$1 \cong$ ∠3	10. Definition of Congruent Angles
11. $\overleftrightarrow{BC} \parallel \overleftrightarrow{EH}$	11. Theorem 6-5

Pages 203–204   Exploratory   1. any four of the following pairs: ∠4, ∠6, t; ∠2, ∠12, ℓ; ∠3, ∠5, t; ∠3, ∠9, ℓ; ∠12, ∠14, s; ∠6, ∠16, m; ∠11, ∠13, s; ∠7, ∠13, m **5.** ∠1, ∠5; ∠2, ∠4; ∠TQP, ∠6; ∠SQR, ∠7
7. 118 **9.** 62 **11.** 62 **13.** 62

Pages 204–205   Written   1. Postulate 6-1
3. Postulate 3-2 **5.** Theorem 2-1; Theorem 2-5
7. Theorem 2-6 **9.** Postulate 1-1 **11.** 33 **13.** 57
15. 123 **17.** 90 **19.** 105 **21.** 61 **23.** 75 **25.** 119
27. 105 **29.** 105 **31.** 60
33. Given: $\ell \parallel m$
Prove: ∠$4 \cong$ ∠5;
∠$3 \cong$ ∠6
Assumption for
Indirect Proof:
$\ell \parallel m$ and ∠$4 \not\cong$ ∠5

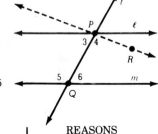

Proof:

STATEMENTS	REASONS
1. ∠$4 \not\cong$ ∠5	1. Assumption
2. Draw $\overleftrightarrow{PR}$ so that $m \angle QPR = m \angle 5$.	2. Protractor Postulate (Postulate 3-2)
3. ∠$QPR \cong$ ∠5	3. Definition of Congruent Angles
4. $\overleftrightarrow{PR} \parallel m$	4. Theorem 6-4
5. $\ell \parallel m$	5. Given

Steps 4 and 5 contradict the Parallel Postulate since $\overleftrightarrow{PR}$ and ℓ are different lines that contain P and are both parallel to m.
The original assumption is false.
Since ∠$4 \cong$ ∠5, then ∠$3 \cong$ ∠6 by Theorem 6-1.

37.

STATEMENTS	REASONS
1. $\overline{PQ} \parallel \overline{ST}$; R is the midpoint of $\overline{PT}$.	1. Given
2. $\angle Q \cong \angle S$; $\angle P \cong \angle T$	2. Theorem 6-10
3. $\overline{PR} \cong \overline{TR}$	3. Midpoint Theorem (Theorem 2-5)
4. $\triangle PQR \cong \triangle TSR$	4. AAS

Page 208   Exploratory   1. yes **3.** yes **5.** yes
7. no **9.** no **11.** yes **13.** yes **15.** no

Pages 208–209   Written

1.

STATEMENTS	REASONS
1. $\overline{AB} \parallel \overline{CD}$; $\overline{BC} \perp \overline{CD}$; $\overline{AB} \perp \overline{AD}$	1. Given
2. Draw $\overleftrightarrow{BD}$.	2. Postulate 1-1
3. $\angle A$ and $\angle C$ are right angles.	3. Definition of Perpendicular Lines
4. $\angle A \cong \angle C$	4. Theorem 3-6
5. $\angle ABD \cong \angle CDB$	5. Theorem 6-10
6. $\overline{BD} \cong \overline{BD}$	6. Theorem 2-2
7. $\triangle ABD \cong \triangle CDB$	7. AAS
8. $\angle CBD \cong \angle BDA$	8. CPCTC
9. $\overline{BC} \parallel \overline{AD}$	9. Theorem 6-4

5.

STATEMENTS	REASONS
1. $\overline{AB} \parallel \overline{CE}$; $\overline{BD} \cong \overline{AD}$	1. Given
2. $\angle 2 \cong \angle 3$	2. Isosceles Triangle Theorem (Theorem 4-6)
3. $\angle 3 \cong \angle ADE$; $\angle BDC \cong \angle 2$	3. Theorem 6-10
4. $\angle BDC \cong \angle ADE$	4. Theorem 3-1

9. Triangle: 45, 135; T-square: 75, 105 **11.** The plumb bob allows the first strip of wallpaper to be perpendicular to the floor. The following strips of wallpaper will be parallel to each other. Therefore, all other strips of wallpaper will be perpendicular to the floor. (Theorem 6-13)

Page 213   Exploratory   1. a line and a point not on the line **3.** Given: line m and point P not on m **5.** Prove: There is exactly one line through P perpendicular to m. **7.** In a plane, if two lines are parallel, then they are everywhere equidistant. In a plane, if two lines are everywhere equidistant, then they are parallel.

Pages 213–215   Written   1. Yes, alternate interior angles are congruent. **3.** No, alternate interior angles are not congruent after a transversal is drawn. **5.** direct **7.** Theorem 3-12 **9.** indirect **11.** Given: A point is on the bisector of an angle. **13.** Pick any point on the angle bisector and draw lines through that point perpendicular to the sides of the angle. Show the two

triangles formed are congruent and use CPCTC to show equidistance. **15.** If a point in the interior of an angle is equidistant from the sides of the angle, then the point is on the bisector of that angle. **19.** $\overline{PS}$ **21.** $\overline{SR}$ **23.** Down E.69 St., Definition of the distance between a point and a line

Pages 217–218   Chapter Review   1. t, n **3.** t, m **5.** t, n; ℓ is the transversal.
7. Given: $\triangle ABC$ is a right triangle.
Prove: $\triangle ABC$ has only one right angle.
Assumption for Indirect Proof:
$\triangle ABC$ is a right triangle, and $\angle A$ and $\angle C$ are right angles.
Proof:

STATEMENTS	REASONS
1. $\triangle ABC$ is a right triangle; $\angle A$ and $\angle C$ are right angles.	1. Assumption
2. $m \angle A = 90$; $m \angle C = 90$	2. Definition of Right Angle
3. $m \angle A + m \angle C = 180$	3. Addition Property of Equality
4. $m \angle A + m \angle B + m \angle C = 180$	4. Angle Sum Theorem (Theorem 4-1)

Steps 3 and 4 imply that $m \angle B = 0$.
This is a contradiction of the definition of an angle.
Thus, $\triangle ABC$ has but one right angle.

11.1. Parallel Postulate (Postulate 6-1) **11.3.** Angle Addition Postulate (Postulate 3-3) **11.4.** Substitution **11.5.** Theorem 6-10 **11.6.** Definition of Congruent Angles

CHAPTER 7   POLYGONS

Page 225   Exploratory   1. no **3.** no **5.** yes
7. no **9.** yes

Page 226   Written   1. triangle **3.** decagon
5. 24-gon **7.** n-gon **9.** pentagon; convex **11.** hexagon; convex **13.** heptagon; concave **15.** A, B, C, D, E
17. $\overline{AB}, \overline{BC}, \overline{CD}, \overline{DE}, \overline{EA}$ **19.** convex **21.** any of the following pairs: $\angle A, \angle B$; $\angle B, \angle C$; $\angle C, \angle D$; $\angle D, \angle E$; $\angle E, \angle A$ **23.** A pair of angles of a polygon is consecutive if and only if the two angles share a common side. **25.** regular; it is both equiangular and equilateral **27.** not regular; it is not equiangular

Page 230   Exploratory   1. 0; 0 **3.** 2; 3 **5.** 4; 5
7. 6; 7 **9.** 12; 13 **11.** An angle is an exterior angle of a convex polygon if and only if the angle forms a linear pair with one of the interior angles of the polygon.

Pages 230–231   Written   1. 2700 **3.** 1800
5. 10,260 **7.** $(x - 2)180$ **9.** 12 **11.** 6 **13.** 24 **15.** 10
17. 90; 90 **19.** 135; 45 **21.** 128.6; 51.4 **23.** $\frac{180(d - 2)}{d}$,
$\frac{360}{d}$ **25.** 20 **27.** 12 **29.** A triangle is the smallest
polygon with 180° as the sum of the measures of the
angles. **31.** 45, 135 **33.** 4, 1, 2 **35.** 6, 3, 9 **37.** 8, 5,
20 **39.** 35 **41.** $n - 3$ **43.** 36 **45.** 90
47. S = sum of the measures of the interior angles; n =
number of sides

$$S = \frac{180(n - 2)}{n}$$
$$S = \frac{180(4 - 2)}{4}$$
$$S = 90$$

An interior angle and exterior angle at the same
vertex are supplementary. Therefore,
1 exterior angle = 180 − 90 = 90.
4 exterior angles = 4(90) or 360
49. n = number of sides

Each interior angle = $\frac{180 - (n - 2)}{n}$

Each exterior angle = $180 - \frac{180(n - 2)}{n}$

The sum of all exterior angles, two at each vertex

$$= 2n\left(180 - \frac{180(n - 2)}{n}\right)$$
$$= 360n - 360(n - 2)$$
$$= 360n - 360n + 720$$
$$= 720$$

Page 235   Exploratory   1. yes **3.** yes **5.** yes
7. no **9.** yes **11.** yes **13.** $\overline{DC}$; Definition of
Parallelogram **15.** $\triangle CBA$; Theorem 7-3 **17.** $\overline{EB}$; Theorem 7-6

Pages 235–236   Written   1. 16 **3.** 1.2 **5.** 5
7. 8 **9.** 60 **11.** 25 **13.** $AB = 31$, $BC = 35$, $CD = 31$,
$AD = 35$
15. Given: $\square ABCD$
  Prove: $\angle BCD \cong \angle DAB$;
    $\angle ABC \cong \angle CDA$

  Proof:

STATEMENTS	REASONS
1. $\square ABCD$	1. Given
2. Draw $\overline{AC}$ and $\overline{BD}$.	2. Postulate 1-1
3. $\triangle BCD \cong \triangle DAB$;	3. Theorem 7-3
$\triangle ABC \cong \triangle CDA$	
4. $\angle BCD \cong \angle DAB$;	4. CPCTC
$\angle ABC \cong \angle CDA$	

17. Given: $\square HIJK$
  Prove: $\angle HKJ$ is supplementary to $\angle IJK$.
  Proof:

STATEMENTS	REASONS
1. $\square HIJK$	1. Given
2. $\overline{HK} \parallel \overline{IJ}$	2. Definition of
	Parallelogram

3. $\angle HKJ$ is
 supplementary to
 $\angle IJK$.

3. Theorem 6-11

19.

STATEMENTS	REASONS
1. $\square ABCD$; $\overline{DE} \perp \overline{AC}$; $\overline{BF} \perp \overline{AC}$	1. Given
2. $\triangle ABC \cong \triangle CDA$	2. Theorem 7-3
3. $\overline{BC} \cong \overline{DA}$; $\angle DAE \cong \angle BCF$	3. CPCTC
4. $\angle AED$ and $\angle CFB$ are right angles.	4. Theorem 3-11
5. $\angle AED \cong \angle CFB$	5. Theorem 3-6
6. $\triangle ADE \cong \triangle CBF$	6. AAS
7. $\overline{DE} \cong \overline{BF}$	7. CPCTC

Page 239   Exploratory   1. yes **3.** yes **5.** no
7. yes; Theorem 6-4, Theorem 7-8 **9.** no; $RT \neq 5$ Theorem 7-6 **11.** yes; Theorem 6-6, Definition of
Parallelogram **13.** yes; Theorem 7-9 **15.** yes; CPCTC,
Theorem 7-7

Pages 239–240   Written   1. 6 **3.** 8 **5.** 49
7. Given: Quadrilateral
  $ABCD$;
  $\overline{AB} \cong \overline{CD}$;
  $\overline{AB} \parallel \overline{CD}$

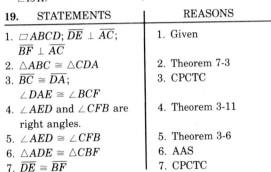

  Prove: Quadrilateral $ABCD$ is a
    parallelogram.
  Proof:

STATEMENTS	REASONS
1. $\overline{AB} \cong \overline{CD}$; $\overline{AB} \parallel \overline{CD}$	1. Given
2. Draw $\overline{AC}$.	2. Postulate 1-1
3. $\angle BAC \cong \angle DCA$	3. Theorem 6-10
4. $\overline{AC} \cong \overline{AC}$	4. Theorem 2-2
5. $\triangle ABC \cong \triangle CDA$	5. SAS
6. $\overline{BC} \cong \overline{DA}$	6. CPCTC
7. Quadrilateral $ABCD$ is a parallelogram.	7. Theorem 7-7

9. Given: Quadrilateral
  $ABCD$;
  $\angle A \cong \angle C$;
  $\overline{AB} \parallel \overline{CD}$
  Prove: Quadrilateral $ABCD$ is a
    parallelogram.

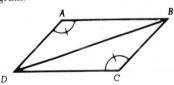

Proof:

STATEMENTS	REASONS
1. Quadrilateral $ABCD$; $\angle A \cong \angle C$; $\overline{AB} \parallel \overline{CD}$	1. Given
2. Draw $\overline{BD}$.	2. Postulate 1-1
3. $\angle ABD \cong \angle CDB$	3. Theorem 6-10
4. $\overline{BD} \cong \overline{BD}$	4. Theorem 2-2
5. $\triangle ABD \cong \triangle CDB$	5. AAS
6. $\overline{AB} \cong \overline{CD}$; $\overline{AD} \cong \overline{CB}$	6. CPCTC
7. Quadrilateral $ABCD$ is a parallelogram.	7. Theorem 7-7

11.

STATEMENTS	REASONS
1. $\overline{AE} \cong \overline{CE}$; $\angle ECD \cong \angle EAB$	1. Given
2. $\angle AEB \cong \angle CED$	2. Theorem 3-10
3. $\triangle AEB \cong \triangle CED$	3. ASA
4. $\overline{AB} \cong \overline{CD}$; $\angle BAE \cong \angle DCE$	4. CPCTC
5. $\overline{AB} \parallel \overline{CD}$	5. Theorem 6-4
6. Quadrilateral $ABCD$ is a parallelogram.	6. Theorem 7-8

13.

STATEMENTS	REASONS
1. $\triangle PQR \cong \triangle STV$; $\overline{PR} \parallel \overline{VS}$	1. Given
2. $\overline{PR} \cong \overline{SV}$	2. CPCTC
3. Quadrilateral $PRSV$ is a parallelogram.	3. Theorem 7-8

15.

STATEMENTS	REASONS
1. $\overline{AF} \cong \overline{CF}$; $\overline{BE} \cong \overline{GD}$; F is the midpoint of $\overline{EG}$.	1. Given
2. $\overline{EF} \cong \overline{FG}$	2. Midpoint Theorem (Theorem 2-5)
3. $\angle EFC \cong \angle GFA$	3. Theorem 3-10
4. $\triangle ECF = \triangle GAF$	4. SAS
5. $\angle ECF \cong \angle GAF$ $\overline{EC} \cong \overline{AG}$	5. CPCTC
6. $\overline{BC} \parallel \overline{AD}$	6. Theorem 6-4
7. $BE = GD$ $EC = AG$	7. Definition of Congruent Segments
8. $BE + EC = AG + GD$	8. Addition Property of Equality
9. $BE + EC = BC$ $AG + GD = AD$	9. Definition of Between
10. $BC = AD$	10. Substitution
11. $\overline{BC} \cong \overline{AD}$	11. Definition of Congruent Segments
12. Quadrilateral $ABCD$ is a parallelogram.	12. Theorem 7-8

17.

STATEMENTS	REASONS
1. $\angle ABF \cong \angle EDF$; $\overline{FD} \parallel \overline{AC}$	1. Given
2. $\angle ABF \cong \angle BFD$	2. Theorem 6-10
3. $\angle BFD \cong \angle EDF$	3. Theorem 3-1
4. $\overline{CD} \parallel \overline{BF}$	4. Theorem 6-4
5. Quadrilateral $FBCD$ is a parallelogram.	5. Definition of Parallelogram

19.

STATEMENTS	REASONS
1. $\square BCDG$; $\angle E \cong \angle A$; $\overline{CE} \parallel \overline{AF}$	1. Given
2. $\angle A$ is supplementary to $\angle C$.	2. Theorem 6-11
3. $m \angle A + m \angle C = 180$	3. Definition of Supplementary Angles
4. $m \angle E = m \angle A$	4. Definition of Congruent Angles
5. $m \angle E + m \angle C = 180$	5. Substitution
6. $\angle E$ is supplementary to $\angle C$.	6. Definition of Supplementary Angles
7. $\overline{AC} \parallel \overline{EF}$	7. Theorem 6-6
8. Quadrilateral $ACEF$ is a parallelogram.	8. Definition of Parallelogram

Page 243   Exploratory   1. rectangle, square
3. parallelogram, rectangle, rhombus, square
5. rhombus, square   **7.** rhombus, square

Page 244   Written   7. always   **9.** never
11. sometimes   **13.** always   **15.** $10\frac{7}{8}$ **17.** 104.2
19. $13\frac{1}{2}$ **21.** 56.3   **23.** 51.8   **25.** 90   **27.** 10
29. Given: Square $ABCD$
Prove: $\overline{AC}$ and $\overline{BD}$ bisect each other.

Proof:

STATEMENTS	REASONS
1. Square $ABCD$	1. Given
2. Quadrilateral $ABCD$ is a rectangle.	2. Definition of Square
3. Quadrilateral $ABCD$ is a parallelogram.	3. Definition of Rectangle
4. $\overline{AC}$ and $\overline{BD}$ bisect each other.	4. Theorem 7-6

31. Given: Quadrilateral $LMNO$ is a parallelogram; $\angle O$ is a right angle.
Prove: Quadrilateral $LMNO$ is a rectangle.

Proof:

STATEMENTS	REASONS
1. Quadrilateral *LMNO* is a parallelogram; ∠*O* is a right angle.	1. Given
2. $\overline{LO} \perp \overline{ON}$	2. Definition of Perpendicular Lines
3. $\overline{LM} \parallel \overline{ON}$	3. Definition of Parallelogram
4. $\overline{LO} \perp \overline{LM}$	4. Theorem 6-13
5. ∠*L* is a right angle.	5. Definition of Perpendicular Lines
6. ∠*O* ≅ ∠*M*; ∠*L* ≅ ∠*N*	6. Theorem 7-4
7. *m* ∠*O* = 90; *m* ∠*L* = 90	7. Definition of Right Angle
8. *m* ∠*M* = 90; *m* ∠*N* = 90	8. Definition of Congruent Angles
9. ∠*M* and ∠*N* are right angles.	9. Definition of Right Angle
10. Quadrilateral *LMNO* is a rectangle.	10. Definition of Rectangle

35. Given: □*EFGH*; $\overline{EG}$ bisects ∠*HEF* and ∠*FGH*.

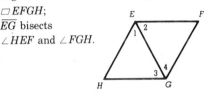

Prove: *EFGH* is a rhombus.

Proof:

STATEMENTS	REASONS
1. □*EFGH*	1. Given
2. $\overline{EF} \cong \overline{GH}$; $\overline{FG} \cong \overline{HE}$	2. Theorem 7-5
3. $\overline{EG}$ bisects ∠*HEF* and ∠*FGH*.	3. Given
4. ∠1 ≅ ∠2; ∠3 ≅ ∠4	4. Definition of Angle Bisector
5. $\overline{EG} \cong \overline{EG}$	5. Theorem 2-2
6. △*EFG* ≅ △*EHG*	6. ASA
7. $\overline{EF} \cong \overline{HE}$	7. CPCTC
8. $\overline{EF} \cong \overline{FG} \cong \overline{GH} \cong \overline{HE}$	8. Theorem 2-4
9. □*EFGH* is a rhombus.	9. Definition of Rhombus

Page 249   Exploratory   1. yes **3.** yes **5.** yes
7. no **9.** yes **11.** no

Pages 250–251   Written   1. 8.2 **3.** 11 **5.** 100
7. 12 **9.** 4 **11.** 65 **13.** 35 **15.** 90 **17.** $20\frac{3}{4}$ **19.** *a* = 170, *b* = 85, *d* = 125, *e* = 137.5
21. Given: Trapezoid *ABCD*; ∠*A* ≅ ∠*D*; ∠*ABC* ≅ ∠*C*
    Prove: Trapezoid *ABCD* is isosceles.

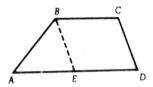

Proof:

STATEMENTS	REASONS
1. Trapezoid *ABCD*; ∠*A* ≅ ∠*D*; ∠*ABC* ≅ ∠*C*	1. Given
2. Through *B*, draw a line $\overline{BE} \parallel \overline{CD}$.	2. Postulate 6-1
3. ∠*D* ≅ ∠*AEB*	3. Theorem 6-9
4. ∠*A* ≅ ∠*AEB*	4. Theorem 3-1
5. $\overline{AB} \cong \overline{BE}$	5. Theorem 4-9
6. $\overline{BC} \parallel \overline{AD}$	6. Definition of Trapezoid
7. □*BCDE*	7. Definition of Parallelogram
8. $\overline{BE} \cong \overline{CD}$	8. Theorem 7-5
9. $\overline{AB} \cong \overline{CD}$	9. Theorem 2-4
10. Trapezoid *ABCD* is isosceles.	10. Definition of Isosceles Trapezoid

25. | STATEMENTS | REASONS |
|---|---|
| 1. $\overline{RT} \parallel \overline{PW}$; $\overline{TX} \parallel \overline{RP}$; *Q* is the midpoint of $\overline{PR}$; *V* is the midpoint of $\overline{SW}$. | 1. Given |
| 2. $\overline{SV} \cong \overline{WV}$ | 2. Midpoint Theorem (Theorem 2-5) |
| 3. ∠*T* ≅ ∠*VXW*; ∠*TSV* ≅ ∠*VWX* | 3. Theorem 6-10 |
| 4. △*STV* ≅ △*WXV* | 4. AAS |
| 5. $\overline{TV} \cong \overline{XV}$ | 5. CPCTC |
| 6. *TV* = *XV* | 6. Definition of Congruent Segments |
| 7. *V* is the midpoint of $\overline{TX}$. | 7. Definition of Midpoint |

27. | STATEMENTS | REASONS |
|---|---|
| 1. $\overline{RT} \parallel \overline{PW}$; $\overline{TX} \parallel \overline{RP}$; *Q* is the midpoint of $\overline{PR}$; *V* is the midpoint of $\overline{SW}$. | 1. Given |
| 2. $\overline{QV}$ is the median of trapezoid *PRSW*. | 2. Definition of Median |
| 3. $\overline{QV} \parallel \overline{RT}$ | 3. Theorem 7-15 |
| 4. Quadrilateral *QRTV* is a parallelogram. | 4. Definition of Parallelogram |

Pages 255–256   Exploratory   1. 46 ft **3.** 52 ft
5. 59 ft **7.** 60 m

1. 10.0 m **3.** $8\frac{3}{4}$ in.
5. 163.6 mi **7.** 55.6 cm **9.** 20 in. **11.** 3.9 mi
13. $2\frac{1}{2}$ in. **15.** $2\frac{1}{12}$ yd **17.** 72 ft **19.** 99.6 mm
21. 30 yd **23.** 2.4 m **25.** 3.1 cm **27.** 0.7 km
29. 214 ft **31.** 1500 cm **33.** 19 cm **35.** 27 m, 29 m, 31 m **37.** 20 cm

Page 260   Exploratory
1. Faces: $\triangle ABD$, $\triangle BCD$, $\triangle ADC$, $\triangle ABC$
   Edges: $\overline{AB}$, $\overline{BC}$, $\overline{AC}$, $\overline{BD}$, $\overline{CD}$, $\overline{AD}$
   Vertices: A, B, C, D
3. Faces: Quadrilaterals $ABCD$, $EFGH$, $ABFE$, $DCGH$, $ADHE$, $BCGF$
   Edges: $\overline{AD}$, $\overline{DC}$, $\overline{BC}$, $\overline{AB}$, $\overline{EH}$, $\overline{HG}$, $\overline{FG}$, $\overline{EF}$, $\overline{AE}$, $\overline{DH}$, $\overline{CG}$, $\overline{BF}$
   Vertices: A, B, C, D, E, F, G, H
5. 3 **7.** 3 **9.** 240

Page 260   Written   **1.** triangle **3.** triangle
5. 60 **7.** 60 **9.** 240 **11.** 270 **13.** 450 **15.** 360 **17.** 4 faces, 4 vertices, 6 edges **19.** 8 faces, 6 vertices, 12 edges

Pages 263–264   Chapter Review   **1.** Q, R, S, T, U **3.** $\angle Q$, $\angle R$, $\angle S$, $\angle T$, $\angle U$ **5.** convex **7.** 720
9. 1800 **11.** 108 **13.** 40 **15.** 7.2 **17.** 3 **19.** 8.2

21. STATEMENTS	REASONS
1. $\square ABCD$; $\overline{AE} \cong \overline{CF}$	1. Given
2. $\overline{BC} \parallel \overline{AD}$; $\overline{AB} \parallel \overline{CD}$	2. Definition of Parallelogram
3. $\angle BAC \cong \angle ACD$; $\angle BCA \cong \angle CAD$	3. Theorem 6-10
4. $\overline{AB} \cong \overline{DC}$; $\overline{BC} \cong \overline{AD}$	4. Theorem 7-5
5. $\triangle AEB \cong \triangle CFD$; $\triangle AED \cong \triangle CFB$	5. SAS
6. $\overline{BE} \cong \overline{DF}$; $\overline{DE} \cong \overline{BF}$	6. CPCTC
7. Quadrilateral $EBFD$ is a parallelogram.	7. Theorem 7-7

CHAPTER 8 SIMILARITY

Page 269   Exploratory   **1.** $\frac{50}{58}$ or 0.862 **3.** $\frac{63}{110}$ or 0.573 **5.** $\frac{2}{7}$ or 0.286 **7.** $\frac{8}{2}$ or 4.000 **9.** 0.50 **11.** 0.25 **13.** 0.57

Pages 269–270   Written   **1.** $\frac{3}{2}$ **3.** $\frac{1}{2}$ **5.** $\frac{5}{4}$ **7.** $\frac{1}{1}$
9. $\frac{1}{2}$ **11.** 32 **13.** 16 **15.** 16.8 **17.** 2.43 **19.** $\frac{21}{2}$
21. 2 **23.** 4 **25.** 2 **27.** $\frac{5}{2}$ **29.** $\frac{25}{9}$ **31.** $8\frac{1}{3}$% or 8.3%
33. 18.75% **35.** 87.5% **37.** 75% **39.** 60% **41.** 60%
43. 75% **45.** 96 hits **47.** $48,700

Page 274   Exploratory   **1.** Theorem 8-5
3. Theorem 8-4 **5.** Theorem 8-3 **7.** Theorem 8-6

9. Theorem 8-2 **11.** Theorem 8-3 **13.** Theorem 8-2, Symmetric Property of Equality

Pages 274–275   Written   **1.** $1\frac{1}{5}$ **3.** 16.5
5. $DA = 12\frac{1}{2}$, $AB = 7\frac{1}{2}$ **7.** $QR = 6$, $CD = 4$, $BC = 8$
9. 5, 6, 10 **11.** 2, 1, 8 **13.** $\frac{KJ}{CD}$ **15.** $\frac{QR}{PQ}$

17. STATEMENTS	REASONS
1. $\frac{a}{b} = \frac{c}{d}$	1. Given
2. $ad = bc$	2. Equality of Cross Products (Theorem 8-1)
3. $ad = cb$	3. Commutative Property of Multiplication
4. $\frac{a}{c} = \frac{b}{d}$	4. Equality of Cross Products (Theorem 8-1)

19. STATEMENTS	REASONS
1. $\frac{a}{b} = \frac{c}{d}$	1. Given
2. $\frac{a}{b} - 1 = \frac{c}{d} - 1$	2. Subtraction Property of Equality
3. $b \cdot \frac{1}{b}$ or $\frac{b}{b} = 1$; $d \cdot \frac{1}{d}$ or $\frac{d}{d} = 1$	3. Inverse Property of Multiplication
4. $\frac{a}{b} - \frac{b}{b} = \frac{c}{d} - \frac{d}{d}$	4. Substitution
5. $\frac{a-b}{b} = \frac{c-d}{d}$	5. Distributive Property

21. STATEMENTS	REASONS
1. $\frac{a}{b} = \frac{a+c}{b+d}$	1. Given
2. $a(b+d) = b(a+c)$	2. Equality of Cross Products (Theorem 8-1)
3. $ab + ad = ba + bc$	3. Distributive Property
4. $-ab + ab + ad = -ab + ba + bc$	4. Subtraction Property of Equality
5. $0 + ad = 0 + bc$	5. Inverse Property of Addition
6. $ad = bc$	6. Identity Property of Addition
7. $\frac{a}{b} = \frac{c}{d}$	7. Equality of Cross Products (Theorem 8-1)

23. 20.8 in. **25.** 118.5 km **27.** 267.9 km

Pages 278–279   Exploratory   **1.** $\angle A \cong \angle D$, $\angle B \cong \angle E$, $\angle C \cong \angle F$; $\frac{AB}{DE} = \frac{BC}{EF} = \frac{AC}{DF}$ **3.** $\angle R \cong \angle L$, $\angle S \cong \angle M$, $\angle T \cong \angle N$, $\angle V \cong \angle O$, $\angle W \cong \angle P$, $\angle X \cong \angle Q$; $\frac{RS}{LM} = \frac{ST}{MN} = \frac{TV}{NO} = \frac{VW}{OP} = \frac{WX}{PQ} = \frac{XR}{QL}$ **5.** Yes; corresponding angles are congruent, and measures of corresponding sides are proportional. **7.** Yes; corresponding angles are congruent, and measures of corresponding sides are proportional.

1. True; the angles are all 60° and the measures of corresponding sides are proportional.   **3.** False; the measures of corresponding sides may not be proportional.   **5.** False; the angles may not be congruent.   **7.** False; the corresponding angles may not be congruent or the measures of corresponding sides may not be proportional.   **9.** False; the measures of corresponding sides are proportional but the sides may not be congruent.   **11.** $1\frac{2}{3}$ ft, $1\frac{1}{3}$ ft

13. 15 cm, 35 cm   **15.** $\triangle STU \sim \triangle WVU$, $\frac{ST}{WV} = \frac{TU}{VU} = \frac{SU}{WU}$ **17.** 8, $22\frac{1}{2}$

19. Given: $\triangle ABC$
　　Prove: $\triangle ABC \sim \triangle ABC$
　　Proof:

STATEMENTS	REASONS
1. $\triangle ABC$	1. Given
2. $\angle A \cong \angle A$; $\angle B \cong \angle B$; $\angle C \cong \angle C$	2. Theorem 3-1
3. $\overline{AB} \cong \overline{AB}$; $\overline{BC} \cong \overline{BC}$; $\overline{AC} \cong \overline{AC}$	3. Theorem 2-2
4. $AB = AB$; $BC = BC$; $AC = AC$	4. Definition of Congruent Segments
5. $\frac{AB}{AB} = 1$; $\frac{BC}{BC} = 1$; $\frac{AC}{AC} = 1$	5. Division Property of Equality; Inverse Property of Multiplication
6. $\frac{AB}{AB} = \frac{BC}{BC} = \frac{AC}{AC}$	6. Substitution
7. $\triangle ABC \sim \triangle ABC$	7. Definition of Similar Polygons

21. Given: $\triangle ABC \sim \triangle RST$;
　　　　　$\triangle RST \sim \triangle PQM$
　　Prove: $\triangle ABC \sim \triangle PQM$

　　Proof:

STATEMENTS	REASONS
1. $\triangle ABC \sim \triangle RST$; $\triangle RST \sim \triangle PQM$	1. Given
2. $\angle A \cong \angle R$; $\angle B \cong \angle S$; $\angle C \cong \angle T$; $\angle R \cong \angle P$; $\angle S \cong \angle Q$; $\angle T \cong \angle M$	2. Definition of Similar Polygons
3. $\angle A \cong \angle P$; $\angle B \cong \angle Q$; $\angle C \cong \angle M$	3. Theorem 3-1
4. $\frac{AB}{RS} = \frac{BC}{ST} = \frac{CA}{TR}$; $\frac{RS}{PQ} = \frac{ST}{QM} = \frac{TR}{MP}$	4. Definition of Similar Polygons
5. $\frac{\frac{AB}{RS}}{\frac{RS}{PQ}} = \frac{\frac{BC}{ST}}{\frac{ST}{QM}} = \frac{\frac{CA}{TR}}{\frac{TR}{MP}}$	5. Division Property of Equality
6. $\frac{AB}{PQ} = \frac{BC}{QM} = \frac{CA}{MP}$	6. Simplification; Substitution
7. $\triangle ABC \sim \triangle PQM$	7. Definition of Similar Polygons

23. 27 inches

Page 283   Exploratory   1. Yes; AA Similarity **3.** No; the measures of corresponding sides are not proportional.   **5.** Yes; AA Similarity

Pages 283–284   Written   1. 11 **3.** No **5.** If $\triangle HKJ \sim \triangle HLM$, then by definition of similar polygons, $\angle HKJ \cong \angle HLM$. Therefore, $\overline{KJ} \parallel \overline{LM}$ because of Theorem 6-5.

7. Given: $\angle B \cong \angle E$;
　　　　　$\frac{AB}{DE} = \frac{BC}{EF}$
　　Prove: $\triangle ABC \sim \triangle DEF$

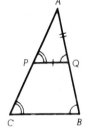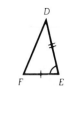

Proof:

STATEMENTS	REASONS
1. Draw $\overline{QP} \parallel \overline{BC}$ so $\overline{QP} \cong \overline{EF}$.	1. Parallel Postulate (Postulate 6-1)
2. $\angle APQ \cong \angle C$; $\angle AQP \cong \angle B$	2. Theorem 6-9
3. $\angle B \cong \angle E$	3. Given
4. $\angle AQP \cong \angle E$	4. Theorem 3-1
5. $\triangle ABC \sim \triangle AQP$	5. AA Similarity
6. $\frac{AB}{AQ} = \frac{BC}{QP}$	6. Definition of Similar Polygons
7. $\frac{AB}{DE} = \frac{BC}{EF}$	7. Given
8. $AB \cdot QP = AQ \cdot BC$; $AB \cdot EF = DE \cdot BC$	8. Equality of Cross Products (Theorem 8-1)
9. $QP = EF$	9. Definition of Congruent Segments
10. $AB \cdot EF = AQ \cdot BC$	10. Substitution
11. $AQ \cdot BC = DE \cdot BC$	11. Substitution
12. $AQ = DE$	12. Division Property of Equality
13. $\overline{AQ} \cong \overline{DE}$	13. Definition of Congruent Segments

14. $\triangle AQP \cong \triangle DEF$	14. SAS
15. $\angle APQ \cong \angle F$	15. CPCTC
16. $\angle C \cong \angle F$	16. Theorem 3-1
17. $\triangle ABC \sim \triangle DEF$	17. AA Similarity

9.

STATEMENTS	REASONS
1. $\angle D$ is a right angle; $\overline{BE} \perp \overline{AC}$	1. Given
2. $\angle ABE$ is a right angle.	2. Definition of Perpendicular Lines
3. $\angle D \cong \angle ABE$	3. Theorem 3-6
4. $\angle A \cong \angle A$	4. Theorem 3-1
5. $\triangle ADC \sim \triangle ABE$	5. AA Similarity

11.

STATEMENTS	REASONS
1. $\angle Q$ is a right angle; $\square WSTV$ is a square.	1. Given
2. $\square WSTV$ is a rectangle.	2. Definition of Square
3. $\angle SWV$ and $\angle WVT$ are right angles.	3. Definition of Rectangle
4. $\angle SWP$ and $\angle TVR$ are right angles.	4. Theorem 3-7
5. $\angle SWP \cong \angle TVR$	5. Theorem 3-6
6. $\triangle SWP$ and $\triangle PQR$ are right triangles.	6. Definition of Right Triangle
7. $\angle P$ and $\angle PSW$ are complementary angles; $\angle P$ and $\angle R$ are complementary angles.	7. Theorem 4-3
8. $\angle PSW \cong \angle R$	8. Theorem 3-4
9. $\triangle PWS \sim \triangle TVR$	9. AA Similarity

Page 288 Exploratory 1. false **3.** true **5.** false **7.** ER **9.** AR **11.** AR **13.** YO **15.** 6 **17.** 9 **19.** 114

Pages 288–289 Written 1. no **3.** yes **5.** $2\frac{1}{2}$ **7.** 3 **9.** 6.84

Page 292 Exploratory 1. true **3.** true **5.** false **7.** true **9.** false **11.** true

Pages 293–294 Written 1. $\frac{TW}{LN} = \frac{TV}{LM}; \frac{TV}{LM} = \frac{VW}{MN}, \frac{TW}{LN} = \frac{VW}{MN}, \frac{TW}{LN} = \frac{TV + VX + TX}{LM + MO + LO}, \frac{TW}{LN} = \frac{WX}{NO}; \frac{TX}{LO} = \frac{WX}{NO}, \frac{TW}{LN} = \frac{TX}{LO}, \frac{TW}{LN} = \frac{VX}{MO}$ **3.** 8 **5.** $4\frac{1}{2}$ **7.** $2\frac{1}{2}$ **9.** 12 **11.** 1.62 **13.** 9 **15.** Suppose $\triangle RST \sim \triangle EFG$ and $\overline{RV}$ bisects $\angle SRT$ while $\overline{EH}$ bisects $\angle FEG$. $\angle SRV \cong \angle FEH$ and $\angle S \cong \angle F$. By AA Similarity, $\triangle SRV \sim \triangle FEH$, which implies $\frac{RV}{EH} = \frac{RS}{EF}$.

Page 300 Exploratory 1. 4.5 cm **3.** 12.5 m

Page 300 Written 1. 48 ft **3.** 2.7 mi **5.** 0.78 cm

Pages 303–304 Chapter Review 1. $7\frac{1}{2}$ **3.** $1\frac{1}{4}$ **5.** 48 **7.** false **9.** $9\frac{1}{3}$ **11.** Yes, the corresponding angles are congruent. Also, the measures of the corresponding sides are proportional. **13.** 9, 30 **17.** yes **19.** 4 **21.** $5\frac{1}{3}$ **23.** $20\frac{1}{8}$ ft **25.** 7 ft

CHAPTER 9   RIGHT TRIANGLES

Pages 311–312 Exploratory 1. 64 **3.** 49 **5.** 0.04 **7.** $\frac{4}{25}$ **9.** 1.69 **11.** 8 **13.** -7 **15.** 0.2 **17.** ± 1.3 **19.** $\frac{2}{5}$

Page 312 Written 1. 1 **3.** 0.5 **5.** 0.3 **7.** $\frac{7}{2}$ **9.** 13 **11.** 16, rational **13.** 30, rational **15.** $4\sqrt{5}$, irrational **17.** $5\sqrt{3}$, irrational **19.** $5\sqrt{3}$, irrational **21.** $\frac{\sqrt{5}}{2}$, irrational **23.** $\frac{\sqrt{2}}{4}$, irrational **25.** $\frac{5\sqrt{3}}{3}$, irrational **27.** $\frac{\sqrt{15}}{3}$, irrational **29.** $\frac{\sqrt{6}}{2}$, irrational **31.** 8.718 **33.** 4.123 **35.** -1.015 **37.** 1.871 **39.** 14.14 **41.** ± 6.325 **43.** ± 6.928 **45.** ± 5 **47.** ± 6 **49.** ± 6.708

Page 316 Exploratory 1. 4 **3.** 6 **5.** 12 **7.** 6

Pages 316–317 Written 1. $\sqrt{15}$ **3.** $2\sqrt{10}$ **5.** $\frac{3}{2}$ **7.** 1 **9.** $\frac{\sqrt{3}}{4}$ **11.** $\frac{\sqrt{2}}{4}$ **13.** $\sqrt{30} \approx 5.477$ **15.** $\sqrt{24} \approx 4.899$ **17.** $\sqrt{28} \approx 5.292$ **19.** $x = 6, y = 6\sqrt{3}$ **21.** $x = 16\frac{2}{3}, y = 10$ **23.** $x = 4, y = 5$ **25.** $x = 8, y = 16\sqrt{5}$ **27.** $x = 5, y = 2\sqrt{5}$ **29.** $AG = 9.6, GF = 5.4, DG = 7.2, EF = 3.24, CD = 4.32, CG = 5.76, BC = 2.7648$

31. Given: $\triangle ADC$; $\angle ADC$ is a right angle; $\overline{DB}$ is an altitude of $\triangle ADC$.

Prove: $\frac{AB}{DB} = \frac{DB}{CB}$

Proof:

STATEMENTS	REASONS
1. $\triangle ADC$; $\angle ADC$ is a right angle; $\overline{DB}$ is an altitude of $\triangle ADC$.	1. Given
2. $\triangle ADB \sim \triangle DCB$	2. Theorem 9-1
3. $\frac{AB}{DB} = \frac{DB}{CB}$	3. Definition of Similar Polygons

Page 321 Exploratory 1. no **3.** yes **5.** no **7.** yes **9.** no **11.** no

Pages 321-322   **Written**   **1.** 13   **3.** 1   **5.** $x \approx$
13.6   **7.** 8   **9.** 41   **11.** 20   **13.** $\frac{41}{42}$ **15.** 17 ft   **17.** 13
units   **19.** 19.2 ft

Page 324   **Exploratory**   **1.** $\sqrt{2}$ ft   **3.** $2\sqrt{2}$ in.
5. $31.2\sqrt{2}$ m   **7.** $4\frac{2}{3}\sqrt{2}$ yd   **9.** $\frac{\sqrt{3}}{2}$ in.   **11.** $2\sqrt{3}$ cm
13. $\frac{\sqrt{3}}{3}$ yd   **15.** $\frac{11\sqrt{3}}{8}$ ft

Pages 324-325   **Written**   **1.** 7.1   **3.** 13.0   **5.** 4.9
7. 1.0   **9.** 18.0   **11.** $48 + 16\sqrt{3}$ units   **13.** $\frac{60 + 20\sqrt{3}}{3}$
units   **15.** 18.0 units   **17.** $\sqrt{2}$ **19.** 2   **21.** $\sqrt{6}$

Page 329   **Exploratory**   **1.** $\frac{21}{29}$ **3.** $\frac{21}{20}$ **5.** $\frac{21}{29}$
7. $\frac{4}{5}$ **9.** $\frac{4}{3}$ **11.** $\frac{4}{5}$ **13.** $\frac{15}{17}$ **15.** $\frac{15}{8}$ **17.** $\frac{15}{17}$

Page 329   **Written** $\sin A \approx 0.882$, $\cos A \approx 0.471$,
$\tan A \approx 1.875$; $\sin B \approx 0.471$, $\cos B \approx 0.882$, $\tan B \approx$
0.533   **3.** $\sin A \approx 0.969$, $\cos A \approx 0.246$, $\tan A \approx 3.938$;
$\sin B \approx 0.246$, $\cos B \approx 0.969$, $\tan B \approx 0.254$ **5.** $\sin A$
≈ 0.800, $\cos A \approx 0.600$, $\tan A \approx 1.333$; $\sin B \approx 0.600$,
$\cos B \approx 0.800$, $\tan B \approx 0.750$ **7.** $\frac{1}{2}$ **9.** $\frac{\sqrt{3}}{3}$ **11.** $\frac{1}{2}$
13. They are equal.   **15.** $\frac{1}{\sin W}$ **17.** $\sin T$ **19.** $\frac{1}{\cos W}$
21. $\frac{1}{\sin C}$

Page 333   **Exploratory**   **1.** 0   **3.** 1   **5.** 0   **7.** 1
9. 0   **11.** 45°

Pages 333-334   **Written**   **1.** 0   **3.** 1   **5.** 0.3584
7. 0.8480   **9.** 0.7813   **11.** 1   **13.** 0.9272   **15.** 0.8090
17. 0.2250   **19.** 1.1918   **21.** 9.5144   **23.** 0.9613
25. 1.2349   **27.** 0.9998   **29.** 6°   **31.** 26°   **33.** 64°
35. 75°   **37.** 88°   **39.** 64°   **41.** 73°   **43.** 39°   **45.** 76°
47. 17°   **49.** 49°   **51.** 14°   **53.** 56°   **55.** 88°   **57.** 37°
59. 0.3660   **61.** 1.8660   **63.** 1.0000   **65.** 0.5000
67. −0.5773   **69.** 0.4142   **71.** −0.0670   **73.** 2.7321
75. 0.6830   **77.** 0.0000   **79.** 2.0000   **81.** 0.0000
83. 2.5000

Page 337   **Exploratory**   **1.** elevation; $\angle BCA$, depression: $\angle DBC$ **3.** elevation: $\angle YXZ$, depression:
$\angle WYX$ **5.** elevation: $\angle JHK$, depression: $\angle IJH$
7. $\sin 15° = \frac{QR}{37}$ **9.** $\sin 47° = \frac{10}{PQ}$ **11.** $\cos 16° = \frac{13.4}{PQ}$

Pages 337-338   **Written**   **1.** 27   **3.** 90   **5.** 1
7. 19   **9.** 7   **11.** 71.47 m   **13.** 132.61 m   **15.** 2.80 mi
17. 19 ft   **19.** 4°   **21.** 2572 ft

Pages 341-342   **Chapter Review**   **1.** 5   **3.** $\frac{9}{4}$
5. $\frac{\sqrt{15}}{3}$ **7.** 13.23   **9.** 1.528   **11.** 8.5   **13.** 0.4   **15.** yes
17. yes   **19.** yes   **21.** 9.8   **23.** 4.2 in.   **25.** 10.0 mm
27. $\sin Q \approx 0.9$, $\cos Q \approx 0.5$, $\tan Q \approx 1.9$; $\sin R \approx 0.5$,
$\cos R \approx 0.9$, $\tan R \approx 0.5$ **29.** 0.8387   **31.** 30   **33.** 44
35. 5.91

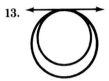

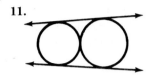

CHAPTER 10   CIRCLES AND SPHERES

Page 349   **Exploratory**   **1.** P **3.** $\overline{PD}, \overline{PB}, \overline{PC}$
5. $\overline{EA}, \overline{DB}$ **7.** $\overleftrightarrow{EA}$ **9.** F, H

Page 350   **Written**   **1.** true   **3.** false   **5.** false
7. two points   **9.** two points

11.

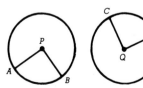

13.

15. $3n + 1$
17. Given: X is in the interior of $\odot P$.
Prove: There are points A and B on $\odot P$ such that
X is between A and B.

Proof:

STATEMENTS	REASONS
1. X is in the interior of $\odot P$.	1. Given
2. Choose any point on $\odot P$ and call it A; draw $\overleftrightarrow{AX}$.	2. Postulate 1-1
3. $\overleftrightarrow{AX}$ intersects $\odot P$ in exactly two points, A and B.	3. Theorem 10-1
4. X is between A and B.	4. Definition of Between

Page 353   **Exploratory**   **1.** minor arc
3. semicircle   **5.** major arc   **7.** major arc   **9.** minor
arc   **11.** major arc   **13.** semicircle   **15.** major arc
17. 135   **19.** 180   **21.** 315   **23.** 225   **25.** 45   **27.** 315
29. 180   **31.** 270

Pages 353-354   **Written**   **1.** 38   **3.** 28   **5.** 180
7. 180   **9.** 114   **11.** 246   **13.** 152   **15.** 218   **17.** 40
19. 45   **21.** 135   **23.** 140   **25.** 85   **27.** 320   **29.** false
31. true   **33.** false   **35.** true   **37.** 144   **39.** 112
41. 32   **43.** 216   **45.** 30   **47.** 13
49. Given: $\odot P \cong \odot Q$; $\overset{\frown}{AB} \cong \overset{\frown}{CD}$
Prove: $\angle P \cong \angle Q$

Proof:

STATEMENTS	REASONS
1. $\odot P \cong \odot Q$; $\overset{\frown}{AB} \cong \overset{\frown}{CD}$	1. Given

2. $m\overarc{AB} = m\overarc{CD}$ 2. Definition of Congruent Arcs

3. $m\overarc{AB} = m\angle P$; $m\overarc{CD} = m\angle Q$ 3. Definition of Arc Measure

4. $m\angle P = m\angle Q$ 4. Substitution

5. $\angle P \cong \angle Q$ 5. Definition of Congruent Angles

Page 357   **Exploratory**   **1.** Theorem 10-3 **3.** Theorem 10-5 **5.** Theorem 10-4 **7.** Theorem 10-4

Pages 357–358   **Written**   **1.** $\overline{QV}$ **3.** V **5.** $\overarc{YT}$ **7.** $\overline{WA}$ **9.** no **11.** 13 in. **13.** 6 cm **15.** 31

17. Given: $\odot P$; $\overline{AB} \cong \overline{CD}$
     Prove: $\overarc{AB} \cong \overarc{CD}$

Proof:

STATEMENTS	REASONS
1. $\odot P$; $\overline{AB} \cong \overline{CD}$	1. Given
2. Draw $\overline{AP}$, $\overline{BP}$, $\overline{CP}$, and $\overline{DP}$.	2. Postulate 1-1
3. $AP = DP$; $BP = CP$	3. Definition of Circle
4. $\overline{AP} \cong \overline{DP}$; $\overline{BP} \cong \overline{CP}$	4. Definition of Congruent Segments
5. $\triangle ABP \cong \triangle DCP$	5. SSS
6. $\angle APB \cong \angle DPC$	6. CPCTC
7. $\overarc{AB} \cong \overarc{CD}$	7. Theorem 10-2

19. Given: $\odot P$; $\overline{PX}$ bisects $\overarc{AB}$.
     Prove: $\overline{PX}$ bisects $\overline{AB}$.

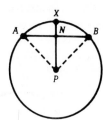

Proof:

STATEMENTS	REASONS
1. $\odot P$; $\overline{PX}$ bisects $\overarc{AB}$.	1. Given
2. $\overarc{AX} \cong \overarc{XB}$	2. Definition of Arc Bisector
3. Draw radii $\overline{AP}$ and $\overline{BP}$.	3. Postulate 1-1
4. $AP = BP$	4. Definition of Circle
5. $\overline{AP} \cong \overline{BP}$	5. Definition of Congruent Segments
6. $\overline{NP} \cong \overline{NP}$	6. Theorem 2-2
7. $\angle APX \cong \angle BPX$	7. Theorem 10-2
8. $\triangle APN \cong \triangle BPN$	8. SAS

9. $\overline{AN} \cong \overline{BN}$ 9. CPCTC
10. $AN = BN$ 10. Definition of Congruent Segments

11. $\overline{PX}$ bisects $\overline{AB}$.   11. Definition of Segment Bisector

25.

STATEMENTS	REASONS
1. $\overline{AC}$ is a diameter; $\overline{AC} \perp \overline{BC}$	1. Given
2. $\overline{AC}$ bisects $\overline{BD}$; $\overline{AC}$ bisects $\overarc{BCD}$.	2. Theorem 10-4
3. $\overline{EB} \cong \overline{ED}$	3. Bisector Theorem (Theorem 2-6)
4. $\overarc{BC} \cong \overarc{DC}$	4. Definition of Arc Bisector
5. $\overline{BC} \cong \overline{DC}$	5. Theorem 10-3
6. $\overline{EC} \cong \overline{EC}$	6. Theorem 2-2
7. $\triangle EBC \cong \triangle EDC$	7. SSS

27.

STATEMENTS	REASONS
1. $\overline{FE}$ is a diameter of $\odot A$; $\overline{UT}$ is a diameter of $\odot P$; $\overline{FE} \perp \overline{BD}$; $\overline{UT} \perp \overline{QS}$; $\odot A \cong \odot P$; $\overline{BC} \cong \overline{QR}$	1. Given
2. $\overline{FE}$ bisects $\overline{BD}$; $\overline{UT}$ bisects $\overline{QS}$.	2. Theorem 10-4
3. $\overline{BC} \cong \overline{CD}$; $\overline{QR} \cong \overline{RS}$	3. Bisector Theorem (Theorem 2-6)
4. $BC = CD$; $QR = RS$; $BC = QR$	4. Definition of Congruent Segments
5. $CD = RS$	5. Substitution
6. $BD = BC + CD$; $QS = RS + QR$	6. Definition of Between
7. $BC + CD = RS + QR$	7. Addition Property of Equality
8. $BD = QS$	8. Substitution
9. $\overline{BD} \cong \overline{QS}$	9. Definition of Congruent Segments
10. $\overarc{BD} \cong \overarc{QS}$	10. Theorem 10-3

Page 362   **Exploratory**   **1.** $\overarc{BC}$, yes **3.** $\overarc{KH}$, $\overarc{IJ}$, no **5.** $\overarc{QT}$, $\overarc{RS}$, no **7.** $\overarc{YZ}$, yes

Pages 362–363   **Written**   **1.** 104 **3.** 47 **5.** 52 **7.** 38 **9.** 47 **11.** 86 **13.** 34 **15.** 81 **17.** 94 **19.** 12 units **21.** 90 **23.** $12\sqrt{3}$ units **25.** 120 **27.** 120 **29.** 120 **31.** 90

33. Given: $\overline{BD}$ bisects inscribed $\angle ABC$.
Prove: $\overset{\frown}{AD} \cong \overset{\frown}{DC}$
Proof:

STATEMENTS	REASONS
1. $\overline{BD}$ bisects inscribed $\angle ABC$.	1. Given
2. $\angle ABD \cong \angle DBC$	2. Definition of Angle Bisector
3. $m \angle ABD = m \angle DBC$	3. Definition of Congruent Angles
4. $m \angle ABD = \frac{1}{2} m\overset{\frown}{AD}$; $m \angle DBC = \frac{1}{2} m\overset{\frown}{DC}$	4. Theorem 10-6
5. $\frac{1}{2} m\overset{\frown}{AD} = \frac{1}{2} m\overset{\frown}{DC}$	5. Substitution
6. $m\overset{\frown}{AD} = m\overset{\frown}{DC}$	6. Multiplication Property of Equality
7. $\overset{\frown}{AD} \cong \overset{\frown}{DC}$	7. Definition of Congruent Arcs

35. Given: $\odot X$ with inscribed quadrilateral $ABCD$
Prove: $\angle A$ and $\angle C$ are supplementary; $\angle B$ and $\angle D$ are supplementary.

Proof:

STATEMENTS	REASONS
1. $\odot X$ with inscribed quadrilateral $ABCD$.	1. Given
2. $m \angle A = \frac{1}{2} m\overset{\frown}{BCD}$; $m \angle C = \frac{1}{2} m\overset{\frown}{BAD}$; $m \angle B = \frac{1}{2} m\overset{\frown}{ADC}$; $m \angle D = \frac{1}{2} m\overset{\frown}{ABC}$	2. Theorem 10-6
3. $m\overset{\frown}{BCD} + m\overset{\frown}{BAD} = 360$; $m\overset{\frown}{ADC} + m\overset{\frown}{ABC} = 360$	3. Definition of Arc Measure
4. $\frac{1}{2}(m\overset{\frown}{BCD} + m\overset{\frown}{BAD}) = \frac{1}{2}(360)$; $\frac{1}{2}(m\overset{\frown}{ADC} + m\overset{\frown}{ABC}) = \frac{1}{2}(360)$	4. Multiplication Property of Equality
5. $\frac{1}{2}m\overset{\frown}{BCD} + \frac{1}{2}m\overset{\frown}{BAD} = 180$; $\frac{1}{2}m\overset{\frown}{ADC} + \frac{1}{2}m\overset{\frown}{ABC} = 180$	5. Distributive Property; Substitution
6. $m \angle A + m \angle C = 180$; $m \angle B + m \angle D = 180$	6. Substitution

| 7. $\angle A$ and $\angle C$ are supplementary; $\angle B$ and $\angle D$ are supplementary. | 7. Definition of Supplementary Angles |

Page 367 Exploratory **1.** 2 **3.** 1 **5.** inscribed
7. circumscribed

Pages 367–368 Written **1.** 12 **3.** 14 **5.** 8
7. 45 **9.** 45 **11.** 90 **13.** 45 **15.** 5 **17.** 13 **19.** $5\sqrt{2}$
21. $\sqrt{329}$
23. Given: $\odot X$ with radius $\overline{XA}$; $\overline{XA} \perp \overleftrightarrow{CA}$
Prove: $\overleftrightarrow{CA}$ is tangent to $\odot X$.
Proof:

STATEMENTS	REASONS
1. $\odot X$ with radius $\overline{XA}$.	1. Given
2. Choose point B (any point on $\overleftrightarrow{CA}$ except A) and draw $\overline{XB}$.	2. Postulate 1-1
3. $\overline{XA} \perp \overleftrightarrow{CA}$	3. Given
4. $XA < XB$	4. Theorem 5-6
5. B lies in the exterior of $\odot X$.	5. Definition of the Exterior of a Circle
6. $\overleftrightarrow{CA}$ is tangent to $\odot X$.	6. Definition of Tangent

Page 372 Exploratory **1.** 63 **3.** 35 **5.** 17.5

Pages 372–373 Written **1.** 114 **3.** 66 **5.** 138
7. 174 **9.** 49 **11.** 198 **13.** 236 **15.** 38 **17.** 44
19. 44 **21.** 200 **23.** 46 **25.** 134 **27.** 144 **29.** 160
31. 26 **33.** 144 **35.** 15
39. Given: $\overleftrightarrow{AB}$ is tangent to $\odot X$ at A; $\overleftrightarrow{BC}$ is tangent to $\odot X$ at C.
Prove: $m \angle ABC = \frac{1}{2}(m\overset{\frown}{ADC} - m\overset{\frown}{AC})$

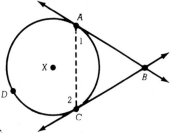

Proof:

STATEMENTS	REASONS
1. $\overleftrightarrow{AB}$ is tangent to $\odot X$ at A; $\overleftrightarrow{BC}$ is tangent to $\odot X$ at C.	1. Given
2. Draw $\overline{AC}$.	2. Postulate 1-1
3. $m \angle 1 = \frac{1}{2} m\overset{\frown}{AC}$; $m \angle 2 = \frac{1}{2} m\overset{\frown}{ADC}$	3. Theorem 10-15

4. $m \angle ABC + m \angle 1 = m \angle 2$	4. Exterior Angle Theorem (Theorem 5-1)
5. $m \angle ABC + \frac{1}{2}m\widehat{AC} = \frac{1}{2}m\widehat{ADC}$	5. Substitution
6. $m \angle ABC = \frac{1}{2}m\widehat{ADC} - \frac{1}{2}m\widehat{AC}$	6. Subtraction Property of Equality
7. $m \angle ABC = \frac{1}{2}(m\widehat{ADC} - m\widehat{AC})$	7. Distributive Property

41.

STATEMENTS	REASONS
1. $\overline{RP} \perp \overline{QT}; \overline{RT} \perp \overline{QS}$	1. Given
2. $\angle PXT$ and $\angle SVT$ are right angles.	2. Definition of Perpendicular Lines
3. $m \angle PXT = m \angle SVT$	3. Theorem 3-6
4. $m \angle PXT = \frac{1}{2}(m\widehat{PT} + m\widehat{QR});$ $m \angle SVT = \frac{1}{2}(m\widehat{ST} + m\widehat{QR})$	4. Theorem 10-13
5. $\frac{1}{2}(m\widehat{PT} + m\widehat{QR}) = \frac{1}{2}(m\widehat{ST} + m\widehat{QR})$	5. Substitution
6. $m\widehat{PT} + m\widehat{QR} = m\widehat{ST} + m\widehat{QR}$	6. Multiplication Property of Equality
7. $m\widehat{PT} = m\widehat{ST}$	7. Subtraction Property of Equality

Page 376   Exploratory   1. $3x = 4(9)$
3. $5(5 + x) = 4(12)$ **5.** $20(20) = 10(x + 10)$

Pages 376–377   Written   1. 12   **3.** 0.3   **5.** 5
7. 5   **9.** 5   **11.** 2   **13.** 4   **15.** 6.1   **17.** 19.6   **19.** 66
21. Given: Secant segments: $\overline{AC}$ and $\overline{CE}$
Prove: $AC \cdot BC = EC \cdot DC$

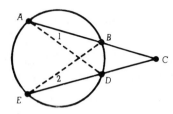

Proof:

STATEMENTS	REASONS
1. Secant segments: $\overline{AC}$ and $\overline{CE}$	1. Given
2. Draw $\overline{BE}$ and $\overline{AD}$.	2. Postulate 1-1
3. $\angle C \cong \angle C$	3. Theorem 3-1
4. $m\widehat{BD} = m\widehat{BD}$	4. Postulate 2-4
5. $\widehat{BD} \cong \widehat{BD}$	5. Definition of Congruent Arcs
6. $\angle 1 \cong \angle 2$	6. Theorem 10-7

7. $\triangle ADC \sim \triangle EBC$	7. AA Similarity
8. $\dfrac{AC}{EC} = \dfrac{DC}{BC}$	8. Definition of Similar Polygons
9. $AC \cdot BC = EC \cdot DC$	9. Equality of Cross Products (Theorem 8-1)

Page 380   Exploratory   1. sphere   **3.** sphere
5. circle   **7.** circle   **9.** circle   **11.** neither

Pages 380–381   Written   1. true   **3.** true
5. true   **7.** true   **9.** false   **11.** true   **13.** true   **15.** A segment is a radius of a sphere if and only if its endpoints are the center of the sphere and a point on the sphere.   **17.** A circle is a great circle of a sphere if and only if the center of the circle is also the center of the sphere.   **19.** A point lies in the interior of a sphere if and only if the length of the segment joining the point to the center of the sphere is less than the length of the radius of the sphere.   **21.** A line is tangent to a sphere if and only if the line intersects the sphere in exactly one point.   **23.** A line is a secant of a sphere if and only if it intersects the sphere in exactly two points.   **25.** Two spheres are congruent if and only if their radii are congruent.   **27.** one   **29.** one   **31.** one   **33.** infinitely many   **35.** 24   **37.** 5   **39.** 2

Pages 385–386   Chapter Review   1. no   **3.** A segment is a diameter of a circle if and only if its endpoints are on the circle and it contains the center of the circle.   **5.** 21   **7.** 180   **9.** 123   **11.** 57   **13.** 57
15. 24 cm

17.

STATEMENTS	REASONS
1. $\overline{AB}$ is a diameter of $\odot E$; $\overline{AB} \perp \overline{CD}$	1. Given
2. $\overline{AB}$ bisects $\widehat{CBD}$.	2. Theorem 10-4
3. $\widehat{CB} \cong \widehat{DB}$	3. Definition of Arc Bisector

19. 36   **21.** 72   **23.** 36   **25.** 72   **27.** $3\sqrt{2}$
29. tangents   **31.** 55   **33.** 125   **35.** 133   **37.** ≈ 0.806 ft
39. no   **41.** two   **43.** none

CHAPTER 11   AREA AND VOLUME

Page 391   Exploratory   1. 1 cm × 24 cm,
2 cm × 12 cm, 3 cm × 8 cm, 4 cm × 6 cm   **3.** 9 square units   **5.** 6 square units   **7.** $A = 36, p = 24$ **9.** $A = 36, p = 30$ **11.** $A = 25, p = 20$ **13.** false   **15.** true

Pages 391–393   Written   1. 20 cm²   **3.** 2269.5 cm²   **5.** $18\frac{1}{3}$ mi²   **7.** 20 ft   **9.** $(x^2 + 3x)$ft²   **11.** 448 units²   **13.** 120 units²   **15.** 54 units²   **17.** 36 units²
19. 60 units²   **21.** 12.5 units²   **23.** $\sqrt{3}$ m²   **25.** 11 in.
27. 6 in., 9 in.   **29.** $264

Page 396 **Exploratory** **1.** 96 in^2 **3.** 18 cm^2
5. 12 mm **7.** 42 cm^2 **9.** $4\frac{1}{2}$ in^2 **11.** 1.02 ft **13.** 38.5
cm^2 **15.** 34 mi **17.** 4 in.

Page 397 **Written** **1.** 150 cm^2 **3.** 135 ft^2
5. 30 m^2 **7.** 3.78 m^2 **9.** 42.42 m^2 **11.** 3.5 in
13. $72\sqrt{3}$ cm^2 **15.** $(2x + 1)$cm

17. Given: Trapezoid $ABCD$; $AB = b_1$;
$CD = b_2$; $AE = h$; $\overline{AE} \perp \overline{CD}$;
$\overline{AE} \perp \overline{AB}$; $\overline{AB} \parallel \overline{CD}$

Prove: Area of trapezoid $ABCD =$
$\frac{1}{2}h(b_1 + b_2)$

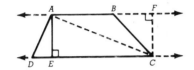

Proof:

STATEMENTS	REASONS
1. Trapezoid $ABCD$; $AB = b_1$; $CD = b_2$; $AE = h$; $\overline{AE} \perp \overline{CD}$; $\overline{AE} \perp \overline{AB}$; $\overline{AB} \parallel \overline{CD}$	1. Given
2. Draw $\overline{AC}$, $\overleftrightarrow{AB}$, and $\overleftrightarrow{CD}$.	2. Postulate 1-1
3. Draw $\overline{CF} \perp \overleftrightarrow{AB}$.	3. Theorem 6-14
4. AE is the distance between E and $\overleftrightarrow{AF}$; CF is the distance between C and $\overleftrightarrow{AF}$.	4. Definition of Distance Between a Point and a Line
5. $AE = CF$	5. Theorem 6-15
6. $h = CF$	6. Substitution
7. Area $\triangle ADC = \frac{1}{2}b_2h$; Area $\triangle ABC = \frac{1}{2}b_1h$	7. Theorem 11-3
8. Area trapezoid $ABCD$ = Area $\triangle ABC$ + Area $\triangle ADC$	8. Area Addition Postulate (Postulate 11-3)
9. Area trapezoid $ABCD$ = $\frac{1}{2}b_1h + \frac{1}{2}b_2h$	9. Substitution
10. Area trapezoid $ABCD$ = $\frac{1}{2}h(b_1 + b_2)$	10. Distributive Property

Page 401 **Exploratory** **1.** 120 **3.** 72 **5.** 45
7. 36 **9.** $25\frac{5}{7}$

Pages 402–403 **Written** **1.** $p = 12$, $a = \frac{2\sqrt{3}}{3}$,
$A = 4\sqrt{3}$ **3.** $s = 12\sqrt{3}$, $p = 36\sqrt{3}$, $A = 108\sqrt{3}$
5. $s = 3$, $a = \frac{3}{2}$, $A = 9$ **7.** $s = 10$, $p = 40$, $A = 100$

9. 174 cm^2 **11.** 289.3 mi^2 **13.** 261 m^2 **15.** $\frac{16\sqrt{3}}{3}$ cm
17. $\frac{32\sqrt{3}}{3}$ in. **19.** $36\sqrt{3}$ units^2 **21.** $288\sqrt{3}$ cm^2
23. 200 ft^2 **25.** 33 in^2 **27.** $42\sqrt{3}$ units^2
29. 88 units^2

31. Given: Regular
polygon
$ABCDE$ . . .
circumscribed
about $\odot X$;
$\overline{XN}$ is an
apothem.
Prove: $\overline{XN} \perp \overline{BA}$

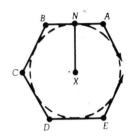

Proof:

STATEMENTS	REASONS
1. Regular polygon $ABCDE$ circumscribed about $\odot X$; $\overline{XN}$ is an apothem.	1. Given
2. $\overline{XN}$ is a radius of $\odot X$.	2. Definition of Apothem
3. $\overline{AB}$ is tangent to $\odot X$.	3. Definition of Circle Inscribed in a Polygon
4. $\overline{XN} \perp \overline{BA}$	4. Theorem 10-10

Page 407 **Exploratory** **1.** 14 cm, 14π cm,
49π cm^2 **3.** 8 ft, 16π ft, 64π ft^2 **5.** 2.4 km, 4.8 km,
5.76 π km^2 **7.** $5\sqrt{2}$ cm, $10\sqrt{2}$ π cm, 50 π cm^2
9. $4\sqrt{3}$ in., $8\sqrt{3}$ in., $8\sqrt{3}$ π in^2 **11.** $9\frac{1}{3}$ yd, $9\frac{1}{3}$ π yd,
$21\frac{7}{9}$ π yd^2

Pages 407–408 **Written** **1.** 44.0 cm **3.** 25.1 in.
5. 46.5 cm **7.** 15.1 km **9.** 3.1 ft **11.** $68\frac{4}{9}$ yd^2
13. $157\frac{1}{7}$ cm^2 **15.** $56\frac{4}{7}$ in.^{2} **17.** $\frac{1}{6}$ **19.** $\frac{1}{180}$ **21.** $\frac{1}{24}$
23. $\frac{1}{5}$ **25.** $36\frac{3}{4}$ π units^2 **27.** 120 **29.** 6 units
31. 9π m^2 **33.** $18\pi - 36$ units^2 **35.** $4\frac{1}{6}$ π units^2
37. $8\pi - 16$ units^2 **39.** 10π units^2 **41.** $196 - 49\pi$
units^2 **43.** 95.0 mi^2

Page 413 **Exploratory** **1.** heptagon $RSTVWPQ$,
heptagon $CDEFGAB$ **3.** 7 **5.** $L = 7$ sh **7.** no **9.** yes

Pages 413–414 **Written** **1.** 60 cm^2, 72 cm^2
3. 264 in^2, 312 in^2 **5.** 1024.9 ft^2 **7.** 96 in^2
9. 912 mm^2 **11.** 46.81 m^2 **13.** 22 in^2
15. 1672 mm^2 **17.** 301.4 m^2 **19.** 11,775 ft^2

Page 417 **Exploratory** **1.** pyramid **3.** prism
5. neither **7.** pyramid **9.** prism **11.** neither

Page 417–418 **Written**   **1.** 27 cm² **3.** 56.4 in²
5. 52.2 mm² **7.** 51π m² **9.** 90π ft² **11.** 50.2 in²
13. 181.4 m² **15.** 71,216.3 cm² **17.** 24 cm
19. 200,960,000 mi²

Page 421 **Exploratory**   **1.** 42 m³ **3.** 67.2 ft³
5. 337.6 cm³

Pages 421–422 **Written**   **1.** 48 m³ **3.** 14,950 ft³
5. 1508.0 m³ **7.** 290.5 cm², 140.4 cm³ **9.** It is eight
times as large as the original cube. **11.** 6 units
13. 1011.6 mm³, 863.3 mm² **15.** $1102.50
17. 107,484.1 in.

Page 425 **Exploratory**   **1.** 35 ft³ **3.** 10 ft³
5. 120.6 cm³ **7.** 418.7 ft³ **9.** 340.2 m³ **11.** 928.9 cm³

Pages 425–426 **Written**   **1.** 320 in³
3. 609.7 cm³ **5.** 512 in³ **7.** 904.3 in³ **9.** 113.0 m³
11. 814.6 cm³ **13.** 2143.6 cm³ **15.** 27:125
17. 523.3 cm³ **19.** 2:1

Pages 429–430 **Chapter Review**   **1.** 24 ft²
3. 24 m² **5.** 130 ft² **7.** 1250 cm² **9.** 2660.4 cm²
11. 60.3 m **13.** 15.7 in² **15.** 48 cm² **17.** 45 cm²
19. 14,649,984 mi² **21.** 2093.3 cm³ **23.** 2786.2 cm³
25. 1570 mm³

CHAPTER 12   COORDINATES

Page 438 **Exploratory**   **1.** $(-6, 4)$ **3.** $(-6, -5)$
5. $(1, 5)$ **7.** $(3, 3)$ **9.** $(-4, -3)$ **11.** $(4, 0)$ **13.** yes
15. yes **17.** yes

Page 438 **Written**   **13.** $(-5, 1)$ **15.** $(-3, -3)$
17. $(-2, -4)$ **19.** b, d **21.** b, d **23.** b

Page 442 **Exploratory**   **1.** 7 **3.** 4 **5.** 5
7. $(0, 2)$ **9.** $(-4, 4)$ **11.** $\left(1, \frac{3}{2}\right)$

Page 442 **Written**   **1.** $6\sqrt{2}$; $(5, 6)$ **3.** $7\sqrt{2}$;
$(4.5, 4.5)$ **5.** $\sqrt{41}$; $(2.5, 5)$ **7.** $2\sqrt{41}$; $(1, -4)$
9. $|a - c|\sqrt{2}$; $\left(\frac{a + c}{2}, \frac{c + a}{2}\right)$ **11.** $\sqrt{144 + (a - b)^2}$,
$\left(-2, \frac{a + b}{2}\right)$ **13.** 26, 36 **15.** $(-0.5, -0.5)$ **17.** $\left(\frac{5}{2}\sqrt{3}, \frac{5}{2}\right)$
or $\left(-\frac{5}{2}\sqrt{3}, \frac{5}{2}\right)$ **19.** $(-1, 3), (2, 1)$

Page 446 **Exploratory**   **1.** The slope is
undefined. **3.** The product of the two slopes is -1.
5. The slope is positive. **7.** The change in y is 2; the
change in x is 1; the slope is 2. **9.** The change in y is
4; the change in x is -3; the slope is $-\frac{4}{3}$. **11.** $-\frac{8}{3}$

13. $-\frac{1}{2}$ **15.** $\frac{2}{3}$ **17.** $-\frac{3}{11}$

Page 446 **Written**   **1.** 2 **3.** 0 **5.** $\frac{3}{2}$ **7.** -3
9. -7 **11.** 4 **13.** $-\frac{3}{4}$ **15.** $\frac{3}{7}$ **17.** -3 **19.** $-\frac{1}{2}$ **21.** Yes,
the slopes are both $-\frac{3}{4}$.

Page 450 **Exploratory**   **1.** $-\frac{3}{4}$; 2 **3.** 4; -3
5. 3; -5 **7.** 0; 6 **9.** $y = 6x - 5$ **11.** $y = 4x - 1$

Pages 450–451 **Written**   **1.** $y = 2x - 3$ **3.** $y = -4x + 7$ **5.** $y = 8$ **7.** $y = -\frac{2}{3}x - \frac{10}{3}$ **9.** $y = 3x - 2$
11. $y = -6$ **13.** $y = \frac{1}{2}x - \frac{17}{2}$ **15.** $x = -7$ **17.** 5; -3
19. 2; -4 **21.** $\frac{4}{3}$; $-\frac{5}{3}$ **23.** $y = -5x + 4$ **25.** $y = 9x + 37$ **27.** $5x - 2y = -19$ **29.** $y = 5x + 6$

Page 454 **Exploratory**   **1.** $(-10, 6)$ **3.** $(2, 0)$
5. $(-2, 4)$ **7.** $(-2, 0)$ **9.** b, c

Page 454 **Written**   **1.** $(4, 2)$ **3.** $(2, -2)$
5. $(-1, 2)$ **7.** $(10, 15)$ **9.** $(3, 1)$ **11.** $(-1, -1)$ **13.** $(14, 4)$ **15.** $(2, 2)$ **17.** $\left(\frac{12}{5}, \frac{4}{5}\right)$

Page 457 **Exploratory**   **1.** $(0, 0)$; 4 **3.** $(0, 0)$; 5
5. $(4, 6)$; 3 **7.** $(3, 12)$; 6 **9.** $(-8, 9)$; 9

Page 458 **Written**   **1.** $x^2 + y^2 = 25$
3. $(x - 3)^2 + (y - 4)^2 = 36$ **5.** $(x + 1)^2 + (y + 1)^2 = \frac{1}{16}$ **7.** $(x + 2)^2 + (y - 8)^2 = 2$ **9.** $x^2 + y^2 = 14$
11. $(x - 6)^2 + y^2 = 144$ **13.** $(x - 3)^2 + \left(y - \frac{1}{2}\right)^2 = \frac{16}{25}$
15. $\left(x + \frac{2}{5}\right)^2 + \left(y + \frac{1}{2}\right)^2 = 12$ **17.** $(0, 3)$; 2 **19.** $(-3, 4)$;
$2\sqrt{5}$ **21.** $(7, -5)$; 2 **23.** $(0, 0)$; 4 **25.** $(-7, -3)$; $\sqrt{3}$
27. $\left(-4, \frac{1}{2}\right)$; $\sqrt{6}$ **29.** $(-5, 2)$; $\frac{\sqrt{3}}{2}$ **31.** $(2, 3)$; 5
33. $(1, -3)$; 11 **35.** $(3, 4)$; $(-4, -3)$ **37.** $(5\sqrt{3}, 5)$;
$(-5\sqrt{3}, 5)$ **39.** $(0, 4)$; $(0, -4)$ **41.** $(x + 4)^2 + (y + 7)^2 = 36$ **43.** $(x - 11)^2 + (y + 8)^2 = 49$

Page 461–462 **Exploratory**   **1.** $C(r + s, t)$
3. $R(-b, 2b)$ **5.** $C(j + k, h)$

Page 462 **Written**   **1.** $A(-b, 0)$, $C(b, 2b)$,
$D(-b, 2b)$ **3.** $R(a, b)$ **5.** $A(0, 0)$, $C(a, b + c)$
7. Given: rectangle $ABCD$
    Prove: $\overline{BD} \cong \overline{AC}$

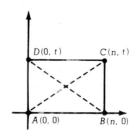

Proof:

By the distance formula,
$$BD = \sqrt{(n - 0)^2 + (0 - t)^2} = \sqrt{n^2 + t^2}$$
$$AC = \sqrt{(n - 0)^2 + (t - 0)^2} = \sqrt{n^2 + t^2}$$

By substitution, $BD = AC$. By definition of congruent segments, $\overline{BD} \cong \overline{AC}$.

9. Given: isosceles trapezoid $ABCD$
   Prove: $\overline{AC} \cong \overline{BD}$

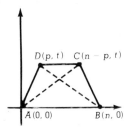

Proof:
$$AC = \sqrt{(n - p - 0)^2 + (t - 0)^2}$$
$$= \sqrt{(n - p)^2 + t^2}$$
$$BD = \sqrt{(n - p)^2 + (0 - t)^2} = \sqrt{(n - p)^2 + t^2}$$

By substitution, $AC = BD$. By definition of congruent segments, $\overline{AC} \cong \overline{BD}$.

Page 466   Exploratory   1. 4 **3.** $\sqrt{6}$ **5.** (4, 0, 0)
7. $\left(-\frac{1}{2}, 4, 8\right)$ **9.** (3, 8, 2); 7 **11.** (−4, 2, −1); 5

Page 466   Written   1. $\sqrt{13}$ **3.** 6 **5.** $\sqrt{14}$
7. $5\sqrt{3}$ **9.** $\left(\frac{3}{2}, -2, 2\right)$ **11.** $\left(\frac{5}{2}, -\frac{3}{2}, \frac{5}{2}\right)$ **13.** $\left(-\frac{1}{2}, 4, 5\right)$
15. (6, 5, −1); 9 **17.** (0, 3, 0); 2 **19.** $x^2 + y^2 + z^2 = 9$
21. $(x + 1)^2 + (y - 2)^2 + (z - 4)^2 = 16$ **23.** $(x - 2)^2 +$
$\left(y - \frac{1}{2}\right)^2 + (z - 1)^2 = \frac{1}{9}$ **25.** $10 + \sqrt{74}$ **27.** (1, 2, 6)
29. $(x - 1)^2 + (y - 2)^2 + (z - 6)^2 = 26$

Pages 468–470   Chapter Review   7. (−2, −4)
9. (−4, 2) **11.** 5 **13.** 2 **15.** $|a - b|\sqrt{2}$ **17.** $\left(-4, \frac{7}{2}\right)$
19. (−3, −5) **21.** $\left(\frac{3}{4}, \frac{1}{2}\right)$ **23.** (−12, −16) **25.** $-\frac{2}{3}$
27. undefined **29.** 2 **31.** 7 **33.** $\frac{3}{2}$ **35.** 4; 6
37. undefined slope; no y-intercept **39.** $y = 3x - 1$
41. $x = 4$ **43.** $y = \frac{6}{7}x - \frac{30}{7}$ **45.** (5, 3) **47.** (1, 1)
49. (6, 1) **51.** (−2, 0); $2\sqrt{3}$ **53.** (0, 5); $\frac{8}{11}$ **55.** $x^2 + y^2$
$= 0.09$ **57.** $\left(x + \frac{2}{3}\right)^2 + (y - 5)^2 = \frac{36}{49}$ **59.** (−a, 2a);
(a, 2a); (−a, 0) **63.** $3\sqrt{11}$ **65.** $\sqrt{74}$ **67.** $\left(\frac{1}{2}, \frac{13}{2}, \frac{1}{2}\right)$
69. (1, 3, 5) **71.** (0, 0, 0); 12 **73.** (−3, −4, 1); $\sqrt{13}$
75. $(x - 9)^2 + (y + 6)^2 + (z - 4)^2 = 64$ **77.** $(x + 2)^2 +$
$(y - 1)^2 + \left(z - \frac{2}{5}\right)^2 = \frac{4}{49}$

CHAPTER 13   LOCI AND CONSTRUCTIONS

Page 481   Exploratory   1. Postulate 1-1
3. Theorem 2-2 **5.** CPCTC **7.** SAS **9.** Definition of
Congruent Segments, Definition of Midpoint, Definition
of Segment Bisector

Page 485   Exploratory   1. Definition of
Diameter **3.** Definition of Semicircle **5.** Definition of
Perpendicular Lines **7.** yes; yes

Page 488   Exploratory   1. Postulate 1-1
3. Theorem 10-8 **5.** Theorem 9-2

Page 492   Exploratory   1. a circle with center C
and radius 1 mm; a sphere with center C and radius 1
mm **3.** a circle with center C and radius 3 m; a sphere
with center C and radius 3 m **5.** a pair of parallel
lines coplanar with ℓ and each 40 m from ℓ; a cylinder
with axis ℓ and radius 40 m **7.** a pair of parallel lines
coplanar with ℓ and each 1000 cm from ℓ; a cylinder
with axis ℓ and radius 1000 cm **9.** the bisector of
$\angle XYZ$ **11.** a line parallel to both p and q and midway
between p and q

Page 492   Written   1. a circle, concentric to the
given circle, but with radius of 5 cm **3.** the bisector of
the angle **5.** the line that is the perpendicular bisector
of the segment having the given points as endpoints
7. a circle, concentric to the given circle, with radius of
8 cm **9.** a circle in the plane with the given point as
its center and with radius of 7 in. **11.** all points on the
bisector of the angle except the vertex of the angle
13. all points on the line in the plane that is the perpendicular bisector of the given base except the midpoint of the base **15.** a cylinder with the given line as
its axis and the given distance as its radius **17.** two
planes parallel to the given plane and each r units
from the given plane.

Pages 495–496   Exploratory   1. c **3.** a **5.** c

Pages 496–497   Written   1. may have no points
of intersection; one or both lines may be tangent to the
circle; one or both lines may be secants of the circle
3. may have no points of intersection; one or both lines
may be tangent to the outer circle; one or both lines
may be tangent to the inner circle; one or both lines
may be secants of the outer circle; one or both lines
may be secants of both circles **5.** may have no points
of intersection; one or both lines may be tangent to the
sphere; one or both lines may be secants of the sphere
7. may have no points of intersection; may be tangent
at a point; may intersect in a circle; may coincide
9. may have no points of intersection; may intersect at
one or two points; the circle may lie in the plane

11. The first locus is two parallel lines both coplanar with the given line and each 2 cm from the given line. The second locus is a circle with the given point as its center and radius of 5 cm. The locus of points meeting both conditions is the four points formed by the intersection of the circle and two parallel lines. 13. The first locus is a cylinder with the given line as its axis and radius of 2 in. The second locus is a sphere with the given point as the center and radius of 5 in. The locus of points meeting both conditions is the two circles formed by the intersection of the sphere and cylinder. 15. the center of the circle determined by the three points 17. The first locus is the bisector of the given angle. The second locus is a circle with the vertex as its center and radius of 4 in. The locus of points meeting both conditions is the point 4 in. from the vertex on the bisector of the angle. 19. The first locus is a line parallel to the given lines and midway between them. The second locus is a pair of lines parallel to the given line and each the given distance from the line. The locus of points meeting both conditions can be no points, two points, or a line, depending on the given distance and whether the third line is parallel to the two parallel lines.

Page 500 **Chapter Review** **19.** a sphere with center A and radius of 1 in. **21.** a circle in the plane with the given point as center and radius of 11 cm **23.** none; tangent to sphere; intersect sphere at two points **25.** none; one or both planes tangent to circle; one or both planes intersect circle at two points; the circle lies in one of the planes **27.** Find the locus of all points in space equidistant from two parallel planes.

CHAPTER 14 TRANSFORMATIONS

Page 504 **Exploratory** **1.** $\overline{DC}$ **3.** $\angle S$ **5.** $\overline{RS}$
7. $\angle T$ **9.** $\angle B$

Pages 504–505 **Written** **1.** E **3.** D **5.** $\angle BDE$
7. A **9.** C **11.** $\overline{CA}$ **13.** $\triangle RQS$ **15.** $\triangle NMW$
17. $\triangle YXZ$ **19.** $UTSR$ **21.** A: gray; B: gray
23. A: blue; B: gray **25.** W, Y

Page 509 **Exploratory** **1.** A **3.** $\overline{AC}$ **5.** L
7. $\overline{JL}$ **9.** $\overline{HG}$ **11.** N **13.** both **15.** point

Pages 509–510 **Written** **7.** No; not all points are at the same distance from ℓ. **9.** yes **11.** yes
23. none **29.** none **31.** none **33.** none

Page 512 **Exploratory** **1.** B **3.** G **5.** H **7.** D
9. R **11.** Q

Pages 512–513 **Written** **1.** yes **3.** yes **5.** no
7. blue to green **9.** blue to green **11.** none **13.** green to red **15.** green to red **17.** none **25.** $\triangle PQR$

27. $\triangle LMN$ **29.** $\triangle STU$ **31.** Plan: A translation is composed of two consecutive reflections. The first reflection with respect to ℓ preserves betweenness of points. The second reflection with respect to m preserves betweenness of points. Therefore, by transitivity, betweenness of points is preserved from preimage to image.

Page 516 **Exploratory** **1.** yes **3.** $EFCD$
5. $HGJK$ **7.** $CDAB$ **9.** 140 **11.** $m \angle DPJ = m \angle DPK = 140$ **13.** $\overline{GK}$

Pages 516–517 **Written** **3.** $60°$ **5.** $120°$
13. yes **15.** yes

Page 521 **Exploratory** **1.** F **3.** H **5.** p **7.** ℓ, m, p; ℓ, n, q; m, p, q **9.** reflection with respect to n

Page 522 **Written** **5.** ℓ, p or m, q **7.** reflection
9. translation **11.** rotation

Page 526 **Exploratory** **1.** enlargement
3. reduction **5.** reduction **7.** congruence transformation **9.** No; all figures would have a single point as their dilation images.

Pages 526–527 **Written** **1.** 2 **3.** $\frac{3}{2}$ **5.** $\frac{1}{3}$ **7.** $\frac{1}{2}$
9. 3 **11.** enlargement **13.** enlargement
15. reduction **17.** reduction **19.** enlargement **25.** A
27. T **29.** S **31.** F **43.** 30 in. **45.** 24 ft **47.** 3 cm

Page 530 **Chapter Review** **1.** E **3.** B **5.** $\angle C$
7. $\overline{CB}$ **13.** 140 **15.** reflection with respect to m
17. enlargement **19.** congruence transformation

Index

A

Absolute values, 42–43, 439
Acute angles, 88, 90, 104
Acute triangles, 112–114
Addition properties
  of equality, 50, 52, 66
  of inequality, 61, 63, 67
  of proportions, 272, 275, 301
Adjacent angles, 79, 94, 96, 103–104
  linear pair, 82–83, 88, 103–104
Algebra Reviews, 4, 44, 86, 133, 165, 205, 231, 270, 317, 354, 393, 454, 482, 505
Alternate exterior angles, 186, 188–189, 193, 196, 201, 205
Altitudes
  of cylinders, 412
  of parallelograms, 394
  of prisms, 410
  of regular pyramids, 415
  of right circular cones, 416
  of right triangles, 313–317, 340, 487
  of similar triangles, 291–294, 302
  of triangles, 134, 136–137, 147, 291–294, 302, 313–317, 323–324, 340, 482, 487, 495
Angle addition postulate, 79–80
Angle bisectors, 363, 477–478
  of similar triangles, 291–294,
  of triangles, 291–294
Angle measure postulate, 77–78
Angles, 74–107
  acute, 88, 90, 104, 117, 119
  adjacent, 79, 82, 94, 96
  alternate exterior, 186, 188–189, 193, 196, 201
  alternate interior, 186–189, 192–193, 196, 201, 205
  bisectors, 135–137, 147, 214, 291–294, 302, 363, 477–478

central, 351–353, 383, 401
classifying, 88, 90
complementary, 82, 85–86, 103–104, 117, 119, 146
congruent, 78–79, 81, 83, 88–92, 103–104, 476, 478
consecutive interior, 186, 188–189, 196, 199, 201, 205, 216–217
constructing, 476, 478
constructing bisectors, 477–478
corresponding, 120–127, 130–131, 142–143, 146–147, 186–189, 195, 201–202, 216–217
dihedral, 99–101, 105
drawing, 78, 80
exterior, 75–76, 151–153, 155, 178, 186, 228, 261, 537
included, 124, 146
inscribed, 359–363, 384
interior, 75–76, 186
linear pair, 82–83, 88, 103–104
measure of, 77–80, 103–104, 351–352, 359–363, 370–373, 383–384
naming, 74
obtuse, 88, 90, 104
of parallelograms, 234–236, 241–244, 262
of polygons, 227–231, 261
of polyhedrons, 259–260
of rectangles, 241, 262
of rhombus, 242
of right triangles, 117, 119, 146
of rotation, 515–517, 529
of triangles, 111–112, 116–127, 130–131, 151–155, 162–165, 173–181
opposite, 234, 236, 240, 242, 244, 250, 262
plane, 100–101, 105
remote interior, 151–152, 155, 178
right, 88–94, 100, 104–105, 361, 384
supplementary, 82–88, 103–104, 361, 363, 384
vertex, 74–76, 112
vertical, 89–90, 104

Angle sum theorem, 116, 146
Apothems, 399–403, 428
Applications
  astronomy, 364
  aviation, 493
  business, 172, 455
  carpentry, 55
  chemistry, 246
  construction, 129
  laws, 13
  meteorology, 523
  physics, 102, 200
  publishing, 271
  real estate, 427
  surveying, 339
Arcs, 351–363, 383–384
  addition postulate, 352, 383
  bisectors, 363
  congruent, 353–355, 361, 363, 383
  definitions, 351
  intercepted, 359–363, 370–373, 384
  major, 351–353, 383
  minor, 351, 353, 383
  naming, 351
  of chords, 355, 383
  semicircles, 351, 361, 383–384
Area, 389–398, 400–408, 410–418, 428–429
  addition postulate, 390, 428
  cross sectional, 424, 429
  lateral, 411–418, 429
  of circles, 405–408, 428
  of parallelograms, 394–397, 428
  of rectangles, 390–394, 428
  of regular polygons, 400–403, 428
  of sectors, 406–407, 429
  of squares, 391–392, 428
  of trapezoids, 395–398, 428
  of triangles, 395–398, 428
  postulate, 389, 428
  surface, 410–418, 429
Associative properties
  of addition, 51–52, 66
  of multiplication, 51–52, 66
Axioms, 201
Axis
  of cones, 416
  of cylinders, 412
  of symmetry, 502

B

Base angles, 247–250, 262

Bases
of parallelograms, 394
of prisms, 410–411
of pyramids, 415
of trapezoids, 247, 249–251, 262

Betweenness, 46–49, 65

Biconditional statements, 11–12, 19

Bisectors
constructing, 477–478, 480–482
of angles, 135–137, 147, 214, 291–294, 302, 363, 477–478
of segments, 57–58, 66, 480–482, 494, 506, 529
perpendicular, 134, 480–482, 494, 506, 529

C

Calculators
basic functions, 31
order of operations, 31
pi key, 408
powers, 155
recall keys, 398
square root keys, 312
store keys, 398
trigonometric function keys, 334

Cavalieri's Principle, 424, 429

Centers
of circles, 347, 352, 369, 383, 456–458, 468, 484
of regular polygons, 399
of spheres, 378, 384, 465–466, 468

Central angles, 351–353, 383
of regular polygons, 401

Centroids, 482

Chapter Reviews, 33–34, 67–68, 105–106, 147–148, 179–180, 217–218, 263–264, 303–304, 341–342, 385–386, 429–430, 468–470, 499–500, 530

Chapter Summaries, 32–33, 65–67, 103–105, 146–147, 178, 216–217, 261–262,

301–302, 340–341, 383–384, 428–429, 467–468, 498–499, 529

Chapter Tests, 35, 69, 107, 149, 181, 219, 265, 305, 343, 387, 431, 471, 501, 531

Chords
arcs of, 355, 383
congruent, 355–358, 383
intersecting, 374, 376–377, 384
of circles, 347, 349–350, 355–358, 374, 376–377, 383, 384
of spheres, 378, 380

Circles, 346–387
arcs, 351–363, 383–384
area, 405–408, 428
centers, 347, 352, 369, 383, 456–458, 468, 484
central angles, 351–353, 383
chords, 347, 349–350, 355–358, 374, 376–377, 383–384
circumference, 326, 404–405, 407, 428, 542
circumscribed, 399, 428, 484–485
concentric, 352–353, 367–368, 383, 399
congruent, 352–356, 361, 363, 378, 383–384
constructing, 484–485
definition of, 347, 383
diameters, 347, 349–350, 356, 383
equations of, 456–458, 468
exterior of, 348
graphs of, 456–458
great, 380
inscribed, 367–369, 399–400, 428, 485
inscribed angles, 359–363, 384
interior of, 348
locus of points, 490–492
radius, 347–350, 352–353, 356, 365–368, 383–384, 456–458, 468
secants, 348–350, 370–373, 375–377, 384
sectors, 406–407, 429
semicircles, 351, 361, 383–384
tangents, 348–350, 364–369, 371–373, 375–377, 384, 483, 485

Circular cones, 416–418, 423–426, 429

Circumcenters, 484–485

Circumference, 326, 404–405, 407–428, 542

Circumscribed circles, 399, 428
constructing, 484–485

Circumscribed polygons, 367–368

Collinearity, 5–7, 9–10, 506, 512–513, 517, 529

Commutative properties
of addition, 51–52, 66
of multiplication, 51–52, 66

Comparison property, 61, 67

Compasses, 474

Complementary angles, 82, 85–86, 103–104

Completeness property for points in the plane, 435

Composites, 518–522
of reflections, 511–512, 514

Concave polygons, 224–226

Concentric circles, 352–353, 367–368, 383, 399

Conditional statements, 9–13, 19, 29–33

Cones
altitudes, 416
axis, 416
lateral area, 416–418, 429
oblique, 424–425
right circular, 416–418, 423–426, 429
slant heights of, 416
surface area, 416–418, 429
vertex, 416
volume, 423–426, 429

Congruence transformations, 504

Congruent angles, 78–79, 81, 83–85, 88–92, 103–104, 353–354, 383
constructing, 476, 478

Congruent circles, 352–356, 361, 363, 378, 383–384

Congruent segments, 56–59, 66, 366–368, 384
constructing, 475, 478

Congruent triangles, 110, 120–128, 130–133, 146–147
AAS, 130–133, 146
ASA, 125–128, 132, 146

Protractors, 77–80
postulate, 78, 103
Pyramids, 415–418
lateral area, 415–418, 429
lateral faces, 415
oblique, 424
regular, 415–418
right, 423, 425–426
slant height, 415–416
surface area, 416
vertex of, 415
volume, 423–426, 429
Pythagoras, 318
Pythagorean theorem,
318–323, 340, 439, 463
contrapositive of, 319
converse of, 319–321, 341
using, 320, 322

Q

Quadrants, 435
Quadrilaterals, 224, 226–227,
261–262
angles, 227, 230–231,
234–236, 241–244,
247–250, 262
diagonals, 227, 252, 262
isosceles trapezoids,
247–251, 262, 462
parallelograms, 207–208,
233–245, 261–262,
394–397, 410, 428,
460–462, 547–548
rectangles, 241–244,
253–254, 256–257, 262,
373, 390–394, 410, 428,
460–462, 528, 534–535
regular, 232
rhombus, 242–245, 262, 462
sides, 233–244, 247,
261–262
squares, 232, 243–244, 262,
277, 323–324, 391–392,
428, 459, 533–536, 547
trapezoids, 247–251, 262,
395–398, 428, 462
**Quotient property of square
roots,** 310–311, 340

R

Radians, 77
Radical sign, 309, 317, 340
Radicand, 309
Radius
of circles, 347–350,

352–353, 356, 365–368,
383–384, 456–458, 468
of regular polygons, 399
of spheres, 378, 380,
465–466, 468

Rationalizing denominators,
311

Rational numbers, 37–40,
45, 65, 311–312
absolute values, 42–43, 439

Ratios, 267–269, 301
cosine (cos), 327–329,
331–335, 341
golden, 273
sine (sin), 327–335, 341
tangent (tan), 327–339, 341
trigonometric, 327–339, 341

Rays, 73–76, 103
naming, 73
endpoints, 73–76
opposite, 73, 75–76, 82
sides of angles, 74–76

Real numbers, 39–40, 45, 65
properties of, 51–54, 61–64,
66–67

Reasoning
deductive, 145
indirect, 190–194, 216
inductive, 145

Rectangles, 241–244, 262
angles, 241, 262
area, 390–394, 428
diagonals, 241–244, 262, 462
golden, 273
midpoints of sides, 462
perimeter, 253–254,
256–257, 262

Reductions, 271, 524–526

Reflections, 502–503,
506–512, 518–522, 529
composite of, 511–512, 514,
529
glide, 521, 529
points of, 506, 508

**Reflexive property of equal-
ity,** 50, 52, 66

Regular polygons, 224–225,
229–231, 259–260, 262,
367–368, 399–404, 428
angles, 229–231
apothems, 399–403, 428
area, 400–403, 428
center, 399
central angles, 401
equilateral triangles, 229

perimeter, 254, 256, 262
radius, 399

Regular polyhedrons,
259–260, 262, 415–418,
429

Regular pyramids, 415–418,
423, 425–426

Remote interior angles,
151–152, 155, 178

Repeating decimals, 38, 40
to fractions, 38, 40

Rhombus, 242–245, 262, 462
angles, 242
diagonals, 242–244, 262, 462
sides, 242, 244, 262

Riemannian geometry, 382

Right angles, 88–94, 100,
104–105, 361, 384

Right circular cones,
416–418, 429
volume, 423–426, 429

Right cylinders, 412–414,
429
volume, 420–423, 429

Right prisms, 388, 410–411,
429
cubes, 410–413, 419–420
hexagonal, 410, 414,
420–423
triangular, 410–411, 413
volume, 420–423, 429

Right triangles, 111–114,
142–144, 146–147,
190–191, 193, 284,
313–331, 335–343
acute angles, 117, 119, 146
altitudes, 313–317, 340, 487
cosine (cos), 327–329,
331–335, 341
HA, 142, 144, 147
HL, 144, 147
hypotenuse, 142, 144, 147,
312–319, 323, 327–328,
340–341, 461, 487
isosceles, 323–326, 328, 341,
462
LA, 143–144, 147
legs, 142–144, 147,
315–319, 323, 327–328,
340–341
LL, 142, 144, 147
midpoint of hypotenuse, 461
placing on coordinate planes,
460–462
Pythagorean theorem,
318–323, 340, 439, 463

2 3 4 5 6 7 8 9 10 11 12 13 14 15—95 94 93 92 91 90 89 88 87